SCHAUM'S OUTLINE OF

THEORY AND PROBLEMS

OF

STATISTICS

Second Edition

•

MURRAY R. SPIEGEL, Ph.D.
Former Professor and Chairman
Mathematics Department
Rensselaer Polytechnic Institute
Hartford Graduate Center

SCHAUM'S OUTLINE SERIES
McGraw-Hill
New York St. Louis San Francisco Auckland Bogotá
Caracas Lisbon London Madrid Mexico City Milan
Montreal New Delhi San Juan Singapore
Sydney Tokyo Toronto

To My Mother

MURRAY R. SPIEGEL received the M.S. degree in Physics and the Ph.D. in Mathematics from Cornell University. He has had positions at Harvard University, Columbia University, Oak Ridge and Rensselaer Polytechnic Institute, and has served as a mathematical consultant at several large companies. His last position was Professor and Chairman of Mathematics at the Rensselaer Polytechnic Institute, Hartford Graduate Center. He is interested in most branches of mathematics, especially those which involve applications to physics and engineering problems. He is the author of numerous journal articles and 14 books on various topics in mathematics.

12th Printing, 1997

Schaum's Outline of Theory and Problems of
STATISTICS

12 13 14 15 16 17 18 19 20 21 22 23 24 25 26 PRS PRS 9 0 1 0 9 8 7

ISBN 0-07-060234-4

Sponsoring Editor, David Beckwith
Production Supervisor, Leroy Young
Editing Supervisor, Marthe Grice

Library of Congress Cataloging in Publication Data

Spiegel, Murray R.
Schaum's outline of theory and problems of statistics.
(Schaum's outline series)
Includes index.
1. Statistics—Problems, exercises, etc. I. Title.
QA276.2.S65 1988 519.5 88-26657
ISBN 0-07-060234-4

McGraw-Hill
A Division of The McGraw-Hill Companies

Preface

Statistics, or statistical methods as it is sometimes called, is playing an increasingly important role in nearly all phases of human endeavor. Formerly dealing only with affairs of the state, thus accounting for its name, the influence of statistics has now spread to agriculture, biology, business, chemistry, communications, economics, education, electronics, medicine, physics, political science, psychology, sociology and numerous other fields of science and engineering.

The purpose of this book is to present an introduction to the general statistical principles which will be found useful to all individuals regardless of their fields of specialization. It has been designed for use either as a supplement to all current standard texts or as a textbook for a formal course in statistics. It should also be of considerable value as a book of reference for those presently engaged in applications of statistics to their own special problems of research.

Each chapter begins with clear statements of pertinent definitions, theorems and principles together with illustrative and other descriptive material. This is followed by graded sets of solved and supplementary problems which in many instances use data drawn from actual statistical situations. The solved problems serve to illustrate and amplify the theory, bring into sharp focus those fine points without which the student continually feels himself on unsafe ground, and provide the repetition of basic principles so vital to effective teaching. Numerous derivations of formulas are included among the solved problems. The large number of supplementary problems with answers serve as a complete review of the material of each chapter.

The only mathematical background needed for an understanding of the entire book is arithmetic and the elements of algebra. A review of important mathematical concepts used in the book is presented in the first chapter which may either be read at the beginning of the course or referred to later as the need arises.

The early part of the book deals with the analysis of frequency distributions and associated measures of central tendency, dispersion, skewness and kurtosis. This leads quite naturally to a discussion of elementary probability theory and applications, which paves the way for a study of sampling theory. Techniques of large sampling theory, which involve the normal distribution, and applications to statistical estimation and tests of hypotheses and significance are treated first. Small sampling theory, involving Student's t distribution, the chi-square distribution and the F distribution together with the applications appear in a later chapter. Another chapter on curve fitting and the method of least squares leads logically to the topics of correlation and regression involving two variables. Multiple and partial correlation involving more than two variables are treated in a separate chapter. These are followed by chapters on the analysis of variance and nonparametric methods, new in this second edition. Two final chapters deal with the analysis of time series and index numbers respectively.

Considerably more material has been included here than can be covered in most first courses. This has been done to make the book more flexible, to provide a more useful book of reference and to stimulate further interest in the topics. In using the book it is possible to change the order of many later chapters or even to omit certain chapters without difficulty. For example, Chapters 13–15 and 18–19 can, for the most part, be introduced immediately after Chapter 5, if it is desired to treat correlation, regression, times series, and index numbers before sampling theory. Similarly, most of Chapter 6 may be omitted if one does not wish to devote too much time to probability. In a first course all of Chapter 15 may be omitted. The present order has been used because there is an increasing tendency in modern courses to introduce sampling theory and statistical influence as early as possible.

I wish to thank the various agencies, both governmental and private, for their cooperation in supplying data for tables. Appropriate references to such sources are given throughout the book. In particular, I am indebted to Professor Sir Ronald A. Fisher, F.R.S., Cambridge; Dr. Frank Yates, F.R.S., Rothamsted; and Messrs. Oliver and Boyd Ltd., Edinburgh, for permission to use data from Table III of their book *Statistical Tables for Biological, Agricultural, and Medical Research.* I also wish to thank Esther and Meyer Scher for their encouragement and the staff of McGraw-Hill for their cooperation.

MURRAY R. SPIEGEL

CONTENTS

Chapter 1

Variables and Graphs

STATISTICS

Statistics is concerned with scientific methods for collecting, organizing, summarizing, presenting, and analyzing data as well as with drawing valid conclusions and making reasonable decisions on the basis of such analysis.

In a narrower sense, the term *statistics* is used to denote the data themselves or numbers derived from the data, such as averages. Thus we speak of employment statistics, accident statistics, etc.

POPULATION AND SAMPLE; INDUCTIVE AND DESCRIPTIVE STATISTICS

In collecting data concerning the characteristics of a group of individuals or objects, such as the heights and weights of students in a university or the numbers of defective and nondefective bolts produced in a factory on a given day, it is often impossible or impractical to observe the entire group, especially if it is large. Instead of examining the entire group, called the *population*, or *universe*, one examines a small part of the group, called a *sample.*

A population can be *finite* or *infinite.* For example, the population consisting of all bolts produced in a factory on a given day is finite, whereas the population consisting of all possible outcomes (heads, tails) in successive tosses of a coin is infinite.

If a sample is representative of a population, important conclusions about the population can often be inferred from analysis of the sample. The phase of statistics dealing with conditions under which such inference is valid is called *inductive statistics*, or *statistical inference.* Because such inference cannot be absolutely certain, the language of *probability* is often used in stating conclusions.

The phase of statistics that seeks only to describe and analyze a given group without drawing any conclusions or inferences about a larger group is called *descriptive*, or *deductive*, *statistics.*

Before proceeding with the study of statistics, let us review some important mathematical concepts.

VARIABLES: DISCRETE AND CONTINUOUS

A *variable* is a symbol, such as X, Y, H, x, or B, that can assume any of a prescribed set of values, called the *domain* of the variable. If the variable can assume only one value, it is called a *constant.*

A variable that can theoretically assume any value between two given values is called a *continuous variable*; otherwise, it is called a *discrete variable.*

EXAMPLE 1. The number N of children in a family, which can assume any of the values 0, 1, 2, 3, ... but cannot be 2.5 or 3.842, is a discrete variable.

EXAMPLE 2. The height H of an individual, which can be 62 inches (in), 63.8 in, or 65.8341 in, depending on the accuracy of measurement, is a continuous variable.

Data that can be described by a discrete or continuous variable are called *discrete data* or *continuous data*, respectively. The number of children in each of 1000 families is an example of discrete data, while the heights of 100 university students is an example of continuous data. In general, *measurements* give rise to continuous data, while *enumerations*, or *countings*, give rise to discrete data.

It is sometimes convenient to extend the concept of variable to nonnumerical entities; for example, color C in a rainbow is a variable that can take on the "values" red, orange, yellow, green, blue, indigo, and violet. It is generally possible to replace such variables by numerical quantities; for example, denote red by 1, orange by 2, etc.

ROUNDING OF DATA

The result of rounding a number such as 72.8 to the nearest unit is 73, since 72.8 is closer to 73 than to 72. Similarly, 72.8146 rounded to the nearest hundredth (or to two decimal places) is 72.81, since 72.8146 is closer to 72.81 than to 72.82.

In rounding 72.465 to the nearest hundredth, however, we are faced with a dilemma since 72.465 is *just as far* from 72.46 as from 72.47. It has become the practice in such cases to round to the *even integer* preceding the 5. Thus 72.465 is rounded to 72.46, 183.575 is rounded to 183.58, and 116,500,000 rounded to the nearest million is 116,000,000. This practice is especially useful in minimizing *cumulative rounding errors* when a large number of operations is involved (see Problem 1.4).

SCIENTIFIC NOTATION

When writing numbers, especially those involving many zeros before or after the decimal point, it is convenient to employ the scientific notation using powers of 10.

EXAMPLE 3. $10^1 = 10$, $10^2 = 10 \times 10 = 100$, $10^5 = 10 \times 10 \times 10 \times 10 \times 10 = 100{,}000$, and $10^8 = 100{,}000{,}000$.

EXAMPLE 4. $10^0 = 1$; $10^{-1} = .1$, or 0.1; $10^{-2} = .01$, or 0.01; and $10^{-5} = .00001$, or 0.00001.

EXAMPLE 5. $864{,}000{,}000 = 8.64 \times 10^8$, and $0.00003416 = 3.416 \times 10^{-5}$.

Note that multiplying a number by 10^8, for example, has the effect of moving the decimal point of the number eight places *to the right*. Multiplying a number by 10^{-6} has the effect of moving the decimal point of the number six places *to the left*.

We often write 0.1253 rather than .1253 to emphasize the fact that a number other than zero before the decimal point has not accidentally been omitted. However, the zero before the decimal point can be omitted in cases where no confusion can result, such as in tables.

Often we use parentheses or dots to show the multiplication of two or more numbers. Thus $(5)(3) = 5 \cdot 3 = 5 \times 3 = 15$, and $(10)(10)(10) = 10 \cdot 10 \cdot 10 = 10 \times 10 \times 10 = 1000$. When letters are used to represent numbers, the parentheses or dots are often omitted; for example, $ab = (a)(b) = a \cdot b = a \times b$.

The scientific notation is often useful in computation, especially in locating decimal points. Use is then made of the rules

$$(10^p)(10^q) = 10^{p+q} \qquad \frac{10^p}{10^q} = 10^{p-q}$$

where p and q are any numbers.

In 10^p, p is called the *exponent* and 10 is called the *base*.

EXAMPLE 6.

$$(10^3)(10^2) = 1000 \times 100 = 100{,}000 = 10^5 \qquad \text{i.e., } 10^{3+2}$$

$$\frac{10^6}{10^4} = \frac{1{,}000{,}000}{10{,}000} = 100 = 10^2 \qquad \text{i.e., } 10^{6-4}$$

EXAMPLE 7.

$$(4{,}000{,}000)(0.0000000002) = (4 \times 10^6)(2 \times 10^{-10}) = (4)(2)(10^6)(10^{-10}) = 8 \times 10^{6-10}$$
$$= 8 \times 10^{-4} = 0.0008$$

EXAMPLE 8. $$\frac{(0.006)(80{,}000)}{0.04} = \frac{(6\times 10^{-3})(8\times 10^{4})}{4\times 10^{-2}} = \frac{48\times 10^{1}}{4\times 10^{-2}} = \left(\frac{48}{4}\right)\times 10^{1-(-2)}$$
$$= 12\times 10^{3} = 12{,}000$$

SIGNIFICANT FIGURES

If a height is accurately recorded as 65.4 in, it means that the true height lies between 65.35 and 65.45 in. The accurate digits, apart from zeros needed to locate the decimal point, are called the *significant digits*, or *significant figures*, of the number.

EXAMPLE 9. 65.4 has three significant figures.

EXAMPLE 10. 4.5300 has five significant figures.

EXAMPLE 11. $.0018 = 0.0018 = 1.8\times 10^{-3}$ has two significant figures.

EXAMPLE 12. $.001800 = 0.001800 = 1.800\times 10^{-3}$ has four significant figures.

Numbers associated with enumerations (or countings), as opposed to measurements, are of course exact and so have an unlimited number of significant figures. In some of these cases, however, it may be difficult to decide which figures are significant without further information. For example, the number 186,000,000 may have 3, 4, . . . , 9 significant figures. If it is known to have five significant figures, it would be better to record the number as either 186.00 million or 1.8600×10^{8}.

COMPUTATIONS

In performing calculations involving multiplication, division, and the extraction of roots of numbers, the final result can have no more significant figures than the numbers with the fewest significant figures (see Problem 1.9).

EXAMPLE 13. $73.24\times 4.52 = (73.24)(4.52) = 331$

EXAMPLE 14. $1.648/0.023 = 72$

EXAMPLE 15. $\sqrt{38.7} = 6.22$

EXAMPLE 16. $(8.416)(50) = 420.8$ (if 50 is exact)

In performing additions and subtractions of numbers, the final result can have no more significant figures after the decimal point than the numbers with the fewest significant figures after the decimal point (see Problem 1.10).

EXAMPLE 17. $3.16 + 2.7 = 5.9$

EXAMPLE 18. $83.42 - 72 = 11$

EXAMPLE 19. $47.816 - 25 = 22.816$ (if 25 is exact)

The above rule for addition and subtraction can be extended (see Problem 1.11).

FUNCTIONS

If to each value that a variable X can assume there corresponds one or more values of a variable Y, we say that Y is a *function* of X and write $Y = F(X)$ (read "Y equals F of X") to indicate this functional dependence. Other letter (G, ϕ, etc.) can be used instead of F.

The variable X is called the *independent variable*, and Y is called the *dependent variable*.

If only one value of Y corresponds to each value of X, we call Y a *single-valued function* of X; otherwise, it is called a *multiple-valued function* of X.

EXAMPLE 20. The total population P of the United States is a function of the time t, and we write $P = F(t)$.

EXAMPLE 21. The stretch S of a vertical spring is a function of the weight W placed on the end of the spring. In symbols, $S = G(W)$.

The functional dependence (or correspondence) between variables is often depicted in a table. However, it can also be indicated by an equation connecting the variables, such as $Y = 2X - 3$, from which Y can be determined corresponding to various values of X.

If $Y = F(X)$, it is customary to let $F(3)$ denote "the value of Y when $X = 3$," to let $F(10)$ denote "the value of Y when $X = 10$," etc. Thus if $Y = F(X) = X^2$, then $F(3) = 3^2 = 9$ is the value of Y when $X = 3$.

The concept of function can be extended to two or more variables (see Problem 1.17).

RECTANGULAR COORDINATES

Consider two mutually perpendicular lines $X'OX$ and $Y'OY$, called the *X and Y axes*, respectively (see Fig. 1-1), on which appropriate scales are indicated. These lines divide the plane determined by them, called the *XY plane*, into four regions denoted by I, II, III, and IV and called the first, second, third, and fourth *quadrants*, respectively.

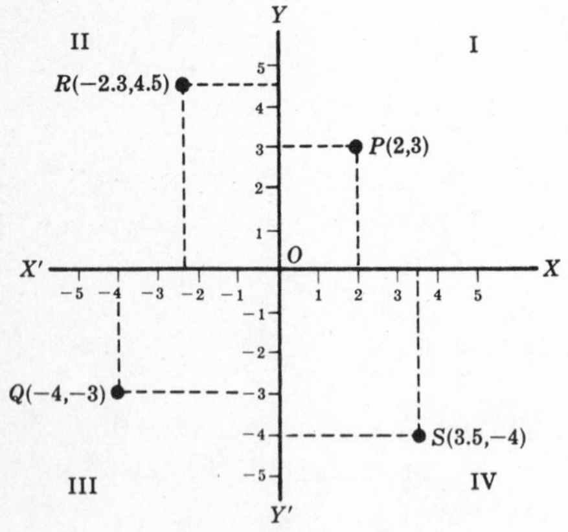

Fig. 1-1

Point O is called the *origin*, or *zero point*. Given any point P, drop perpendiculars to the X and Y axes from P. The values of X and Y at the points where the perpendiculars meet these axes are called the *rectangular coordinates*, or simply the *coordinates*, of P and are denoted by (X, Y). The coordinate X is sometimes called the *abscissa*, and Y is the *ordinate* of the point. In Fig. 1-1 the abscissa of point P is 2, the ordinate is 3, and the coordinates of P are $(2, 3)$.

Conversely, given the coordinates of a point, we can locate—or *plot*—the point. Thus the points with coordinates $(-4, -3)$, $(-2.3, 4.5)$, and $(3.5, -4)$ are represented in Fig. 1-1 by Q, R, and S, respectively.

By constructing a *Z axis* through O and perpendicular to the XY plane, we can easily extend the above ideas. In such case the coordinates of a point P would be denoted by (X, Y, Z).

GRAPHS

A *graph* is a pictorial presentation of the relationship between variables. Many types of graphs are employed in statistics, depending on the nature of the data involved and the purpose for which the graph is intended. Among these are *bar graphs, pie graphs, pictographs,* etc. These graphs are sometimes referred to as *charts* or *diagrams.* Thus we speak of bar charts, pie diagrams, etc. (see Problems 1.23, 1.24, 1.26 and 1.27).

EQUATIONS

Equations are statements of the form $A = B$, where A is called the *left-hand member* (or *side*) of the equation, and B the *right-hand member* (or *side*). So long as we apply the *same* operations to both members of an equation, we obtain *equivalent equations.* Thus we can add, subtract, multiply, or divide both members of an equation by the same value and obtain an equivalent equation, the only exception being that *division by zero is not allowed.*

EXAMPLE 22. Given the equation $2X+3=9$, subtract 3 from both members: $2X+3-3=9-3$, or $2X=6$. Divide both members by 2: $2X/2=6/2$, or $X=3$. This value of X is a *solution* of the given equation, as seen by replacing X by 3, obtaining $2(3)+3=9$, or $9=9$, which is an *identity.* The process of obtaining solutions of an equation is called *solving* the equation.

The above ideas can be extended to finding solutions of two equations in two unknowns, three equations in three unknowns, etc. Such equations are called *simultaneous equations* (see Problem 1.30).

INEQUALITIES

The symbols $<$ and $>$ mean "less than" and "greater than," respectively. The symbols $\le$ and $\ge$ mean "less than or equal to" and "greater than or equal to," respectively. They are known as *inequality symbols.*

EXAMPLE 23. $3<5$ is read "3 is less than 5."

EXAMPLE 24. $5>3$ is read "5 is greater than 3."

EXAMPLE 25. $X<8$ is read "X is less than 8."

EXAMPLE 26. $X\ge 10$ is read "X is greater than or equal to 10."

EXAMPLE 27. $4<Y\le 6$ is read "4 is less than Y, which is less than or equal to 6," or "Y is between 4 and 6, excluding 4 but including 6," or "Y is greater than 4 and less than or equal to 6."

Relations involving inequality symbols are called *inequalities.* Just as we speak of members of an equation, so we can speak of *members of an inequality.* Thus in the inequality $4<Y\le 6$, the members are 4, Y, and 6.

A valid inequality remains valid when:

1. The same number is added to or subtracted from each member.

EXAMPLE 28. Since $15>12$, $15+3>12+3$ (i.e., $18>15$) and $15-3>12-3$ (i.e., $12>9$).

2. Each member is multiplied or divided by the same *positive* number.

EXAMPLE 29. Since $15>12$, $(15)(3)>(12)(3)$ (i.e., $45>36$) and $15/3>12/3$ (i.e., $5>4$).

3. Each member is multiplied or divided by the same *negative* number, provided that the inequality symbols are reversed.

EXAMPLE 30. Since $15>12$, $(15)(-3)<(12)(-3)$ (i.e., $-45<-36$) and $15/(-3)<12/(-3)$ (i.e., $-5<-4$).

LOGARITHMS

Every positive number N can be expressed as a power of 10; that is, we can always find p such that $N=10^p$. We call p the *logarithm of N to the base 10*, or the *common logarithm of N*, and we write briefly $p=\log N$, or $p=\log_{10} N$. For example, since $1000=10^3$, $\log 1000=3$. Similarly, since $0.01=10^{-2}$, $\log 0.01=-2$.

When N is a number between 1 and 10 (i.e., 10^0 and 10^1), $p=\log N$ is a number between 0 and 1 and can be found from the table of logarithms in Appendix VII.

EXAMPLE 31. To find log 2.36 in Appendix VII, we glance down the *left* column headed N until we come to the first two digits, 23. Then we proceed *right* to the column headed 6. We find the entry 3729. Thus $\log 2.36=0.3729$ (i.e., $2.36=10^{0.3729}$).

The logarithms of *all* positive numbers can be found from the logarithms of numbers between 1 and 10.

EXAMPLE 32. From Example 31, $2.36=10^{0.3729}$. Multiplying successively by 10, we have $23.6=10^{1.3729}$, $236=10^{2.3729}$, $2360=10^{3.3729}$, and so forth. Thus $\log 2.36=0.3729$, $\log 23.6=1.3729$, $\log 236=2.3729$, and $\log 2360=3.3729$.

EXAMPLE 33. Since $2.36=10^{0.03729}$, we find on successive divisions by 10 that $0.236=10^{0.3729-1}=10^{-0.6271}$, $0.0236=10^{0.3729-2}=10^{-1.6271}$, and so forth.

Often we write $0.3729-1$ as $9.3729-10$, or $\bar{1}.3729$; and $0.3729-2$ as $8.3729-10$, or $\bar{2}.3729$; and so forth. With this notation, we have

$$\log 0.236=9.3729-10=\bar{1}.3729=-0.6271$$

$$\log 0.0236=8.3729-10=\bar{2}.3729=-1.6271$$

and so forth.

The decimal part .3729 in all these logarithms is called the *mantissa*. The remaining part, before the decimal of the mantissa [i.e., 1, 2, 3, and $\bar{1}$ and $\bar{2}$ (or $9-10$ and $8-10$, respectively)] is called the *characteristic*.

The following rules are easily demonstrated:

1. For a number greater than 1, the characteristic is positive and is one *less* than the number of digits before the decimal point.

EXAMPLE 34. The characteristics of the logarithms of 2360, 236, 23.6, and 2.36 are 3, 2, 1, and 0, and the required logarithms are 3.3729, 2.3729, 1.3729, and 0.3729.

2. For a number less than 1, the characteristic is negative and is one *more* than the number of zeros immediately following the decimal point.

EXAMPLE 35. The characteristics of the logarithms of 0.236, 0.0236, and 0.00236 are −1, −2, and −3, and the required logarithms are $\bar{1}.3729$, $\bar{2}.3729$, and $\bar{3}.3729$, or $9.3729-10$, $8.3729-10$, and $7.3729-10$, respectively.

If logarithms of four-digit numbers (such as 2.364 and 758.2) are required, the method of *interpolation* can be used (see Problem 1.36).

ANTILOGARITHMS

In the exponential form $2.36 = 10^{0.3729}$, the number 2.36 is called the *antilogarithm* of 0.3729, or antilog 0.3729. It is the number whose logarithm is 0.3729. It follows at once that antilog $1.3729 = 23.6$, antilog $2.3729 = 236$, antilog $3.3729 = 2360$, antilog $9.3729 - 10 =$ antilog $\bar{1}.3729 = 0.236$, and antilog $8.3729 - 10 =$ antilog $\bar{2}.3729 = 0.0236$. The antilog of any number can be found by reference to Appendix VII.

EXAMPLE 36. To find antilog $8.6284-10$, look up the mantissa .6284 in the body of the table. Since it appears in the row marked 42 and the column headed 5, the required digits of the number are 425. Since the characteristic is $8-10$, the required number is 0.0425.

Similarly, antilog $3.6284 = 4250$, and antilog $5.6284 = 425{,}000$.

If the mantissas are not found in Appendix VII, interpolation can be used (see Problem 1.37).

COMPUTATIONS USING LOGARITHMS

These computations employ the following properties:

$$\log MN = \log M + \log N$$

$$\log \frac{M}{N} = \log M - \log N$$

$$\log M^p = p \log M$$

By combining these results, we find, for example,

$$\log \frac{A^p B^q C^r}{D^s E^t} = p \log A + q \log B + r \log C - s \log D - t \log E$$

See Problems 1.38 to 1.45.

Solved Problems

VARIABLES

1.1 State which of the following represent discrete data and which represent continuous data:

(*a*) Numbers of shares sold each day in the stock market

(*b*) Temperatures recorded every half hour at a weather bureau

(*c*) Lifetimes of television tubes produced by a company

(*d*) Yearly incomes of college professors

(*e*) Lengths of 1000 bolts produced in a factory

SOLUTION

(*a*) Discrete; (*b*) continuous; (*c*) continuous; (*d*) discrete; (*e*) continuous.

1.2 Give the domain of each of the following variables, and state whether the variables are continuous or discrete:

(*a*) Number *G* of gallons (gal) of water in a washing machine
(*b*) Number *B* of books on a library shelf
(*c*) Sum *S* of points obtained in tossing a pair of dice
(*d*) Diameter *D* of a sphere
(*e*) Country *C* in Europe

SOLUTION

(*a*) *Domain:* Any value from 0 gal to the capacity of the machine. *Variable:* Continuous.
(*b*) *Domain:* 0, 1, 2, 3,... up to the largest number of books that can fit on a shelf. *Variable:* Discrete.
(*c*) *Domain:* Points obtained on a single die can be 1, 2, 3, 4, 5, or 6. Hence the sum of points on a pair of dice can be 2, 3, 4, 5, 6, 7, 8, 9, 10, 11, or 12, which is the domain of *S*. *Variable:* Discrete.
(*d*) *Domain:* If we consider a point as a sphere of zero diameter, the domain of *D* is all values from zero upward. *Variable:* Continuous.
(*e*) *Domain:* England, France, Germany, etc., which can be represented numerically by 1, 2, 3, etc. *Variable:* Discrete.

ROUNDING OF DATA

1.3 Round each of the following numbers to the indicated accuracy:

(*a*)	48.6	nearest unit	(*f*)	143.95	nearest tenth
(*b*)	136.5	nearest unit	(*g*)	368	nearest hundred
(*c*)	2.484	nearest hundredth	(*h*)	24,448	nearest thousand
(*d*)	0.0435	nearest thousandth	(*i*)	5.56500	nearest hundredth
(*e*)	4.50001	nearest unit	(*j*)	5.56501	nearest hundredth

SOLUTION

(*a*) 49; (*b*) 136; (*c*) 2.48; (*d*) 0.044; (*e*) 5; (*f*) 144.0; (*g*) 400; (*h*) 24,000; (*i*) 5.56; (*j*) 5.57.

1.4 Add the numbers 4.35, 8.65, 2.95, 12.45, 6.65, 7.55, and 9.75 (*a*) directly, (*b*) by rounding to the nearest tenth according to the "even integer" convention, and (*c*) by rounding so as to increase the digit before the 5.

SOLUTION

(*a*)		(*b*)		(*c*)	
	4.35		4.4		4.4
	8.65		8.6		8.7
	2.95		3.0		3.0
	12.45		12.4		12.5
	6.65		6.6		6.7
	7.55		7.6		7.6
	9.75		9.8		9.8
Total	52.35	Total	52.4	Total	52.7

Note that procedure (*b*) is superior to procedure (*c*) because *cumulative rounding errors* are minimized in procedure (*b*).

SCIENTIFIC NOTATION AND SIGNIFICANT FIGURES

1.5 Express each of the following numbers without using powers of 10:

(*a*) 4.823×10^7 (*c*) 3.80×10^{-4} (*e*) 300×10^8

(*b*) 8.4×10^{-6} (*d*) 1.86×10^5 (*f*) $70{,}000 \times 10^{-10}$

SOLUTION

(*a*) Move the decimal point seven places to the right and obtain 48,230,000; (*b*) move the decimal point six places to the left and obtain 0.0000084; (*c*) 0.000380; (*d*) 186,000; (*e*) 30,000,000,000; (*f*) 0.0000070000.

1.6 How many significant figures are in each of the following, assuming that the numbers are recorded accurately?

(*a*) 149.8 in (*d*) 0.00280 m (*g*) 9 houses

(*b*) 149.80 in (*e*) 1.00280 m (*h*) 4.0×10^3 pounds (lb)

(*c*) 0.0028 meter (m) (*f*) 9 grams (g) (*i*) 7.58400×10^{-5} dyne

SOLUTION

(*a*) Four; (*b*) five; (*c*) two; (*d*) three; (*e*) six; (*f*) one; (*g*) unlimited; (*h*) two; (*i*) six.

1.7 What is the maximum error in each of the following measurements, assuming that they are recorded accurately?

(*a*) 73.854 in (*b*) 0.09800 cubic feet (ft^3) (*c*) 3.867×10^8 kilometers (km)

SOLUTION

(*a*) The measurement can range anywhere from 73.8535 to 73.8545 in; hence the maximum error is 0.0005 in. Five significant figures are present.

(*b*) The number of cubic feet can range anywhere from 0.097995 to 0.098005 ft^3; hence the maximum error is 0.000005 ft^3. Four significant figures are present.

(*c*) The actual number of kilometers is greater than 3.8665×10^8 but less than 3.8675×10^8; hence the maximum error is 0.0005×10^8, or 50,000 km. Four significant figures are present.

1.8 Write each number using the scientific notation. Unless otherwise indicated, assume that all figures are significant.

(*a*) 24,380,000 (four significant figures) (*c*) 7,300,000,000 (five significant figures)

(*b*) 0.000009851 (*d*) 0.00018400

SOLUTION

(*a*) 2.438×10^7; (*b*) 9.851×10^{-6}; (*c*) 7.3000×10^9; (*d*) 1.8400×10^{-4}.

COMPUTATIONS

1.9 Show that the product of the numbers 5.74 and 3.8, assumed to have three and two significant figures, respectively, cannot be accurate to more than two significant figures.

SOLUTION

First method

$5.74 \times 3.8 = 21.812$, but not all figures in this product are significant. To determine how many figures are significant, observe that 5.74 stands for any number between 5.735 and 5.745, while 3.8 stands for any number between 3.75 and 3.85. Thus the smallest possible value of the product is $5.735 \times 3.75 = 21.50625$, and the largest possible value is $5.745 \times 3.85 = 21.11825$.

Since the possible range of values is 21.50625 to 22.11825, it is clear that no more than the first two figures in the product can be significant, the result being written as 22. Note that the number 22 stands for any number between 21.5 and 22.5.

Second method

With doubtful figures in italic, the product can be computed as shown here:

$$\begin{array}{r} 5.7\mathit{4} \\ 3\mathit{8} \\ \hline \mathit{4592} \\ 17\mathit{22} \\ \hline 2\mathit{1.812} \end{array}$$

We should keep no more than one doubtful figure in the answer, which is therefore 22 to two significant figures. Note that it is unnecessary to carry more significant figures than are present in the least accurate factor; thus if 5.74 is rounded to 5.7, the product is $5.7 \times 3.8 = 21.66 = 22$ to two significant figures, agreeing with the above results.

In calculating without the use of computers, labor can be saved by not keeping more than one or two figures beyond that of the least accurate factor and rounding to the proper number of significant figures in the final answer. With computers, which can supply many digits, we must be careful not to believe that all the digits are significant.

1.10 Add the numbers 4.19355, 15.28, 5.9561, 12.3, and 8.472, assuming all figures to be significant.

SOLUTION

In calculation (*a*) below, the doubtful figures in the addition are in italic type. The final answer with no more than one doubtful figure is recorded as 46.2.

$$(a)\quad \begin{array}{l} 4.1935\mathit{5} \\ 15.2\mathit{8} \\ 5.956\mathit{1} \\ 12.\mathit{3} \\ 8.47\mathit{2} \\ \hline 46.\mathit{20165} \end{array} \qquad (b)\quad \begin{array}{r} 4.19 \\ 15.28 \\ 5.96 \\ 12.3 \\ 8.47 \\ \hline 46.20 \end{array}$$

Some labor can be saved by proceeding as in calculation (*b*), where we have kept one more significant decimal place than that in the least accurate number. The final answer, rounded to 46.2, agrees with calculation (*a*).

1.11 Calculate $475{,}000{,}000 + 12{,}684{,}000 - 1{,}372{,}410$ if these numbers have three, five, and seven significant figures, respectively.

SOLUTION

In calculation (*a*) below, all figures are kept and the final answer is rounded. In calculation (*b*), a method similar to that of Problem 1.10(*b*) is used. In both cases, doubtful figures are in italic type.

$$(a)\quad \begin{array}{r} 47\mathit{5,000,000} \\ +\ 12,68\mathit{4,000} \\ \hline 48\mathit{7,684,000} \end{array} \qquad \begin{array}{r} 48\mathit{7,684,000} \\ -\ 1,372,41\mathit{0} \\ \hline 48\mathit{6,311,590} \end{array} \qquad (b)\quad \begin{array}{r} 47\mathit{5,000,000} \\ +\ 12,\mathit{700,000} \\ \hline 48\mathit{7,700,000} \end{array} \qquad \begin{array}{r} 48\mathit{7,700,000} \\ -\ 1,\mathit{400,000} \\ \hline 48\mathit{6,300,000} \end{array}$$

The final result is rounded to 486,000,000; or better yet, to show that there are three significant figures, it is written as 486 million or 4.86×10^8.

1.12 Perform each of the indicated operations.

(*a*) 48.0×943

(*b*) $8.35/98$

(*c*) $(28)(4193)(182)$

(*d*) $\dfrac{(526.7)(0.001280)}{0.000034921}$

(*e*) $\dfrac{(1.47562 - 1.47322)(4895.36)}{0.000159180}$

(*f*) If denominators 5 and 6 are exact, $\dfrac{(4.38)^2}{5} + \dfrac{(5.482)^2}{6}$

(*g*) $3.1416\sqrt{71.35}$

(*h*) $\sqrt{128.5 - 89.24}$

SOLUTION

(*a*) $48.0 \times 943 = (48.0)(943) = 45{,}300$

(*b*) $8.35/98 = 0.085$

(*c*) $(28)(4193)(182) = (2.8 \times 10^1)(4.193 \times 10^3)(1.82 \times 10^2)$

$$= (2.8)(4.193)(1.82) \times 10^{1+3+2} = 21 \times 10^6 = 2.1 \times 10^7$$

This can also be written as 21 million to show the two significant figures.

(*d*) $$\frac{(526.7)(0.001280)}{0.000034921} = \frac{(5.267 \times 10^2)(1.280 \times 10^{-3})}{3.4921 \times 10^{-5}} = \frac{(5.267)(1.280)}{3.4921} \times \frac{(10^2)(10^{-3})}{10^{-5}}$$

$$= 1.931 \times \frac{10^{2-3}}{10^{-5}} = 1.931 \times \frac{10^{-1}}{10^{-5}}$$

$$= 1.931 \times 10^{-1+5} = 1.931 \times 10^4$$

This can also be written as 19.31 thousand to show the four significant figures.

(*e*) $$\frac{(1.47562 - 1.47322)(4895.36)}{0.000159180} = \frac{(0.00240)(4895.36)}{0.000159180} = \frac{(2.40 \times 10^{-3})(4.89536 \times 10^3)}{1.59180 \times 10^{-4}}$$

$$= \frac{(2.40)(4.89536)}{1.59180} \times \frac{(10^{-3})(10^3)}{10^{-4}} = 7.38 \times \frac{10^0}{10^{-4}} = 7.38 \times 10^4$$

This can also be written as 73.8 thousand to show the three significant figures. Note that although six significant figures were originally present in all numbers, some of these were lost in subtracting 1.47322 from 1.47562.

(*f*) If denominators 5 and 6 are exact, $\dfrac{(4.38)^2}{5} + \dfrac{(5.482)^2}{6} = 3.84 + 5.009 = 8.85$

(*g*) $3.1416\sqrt{71.35} = (3.1416)(8.447) = 26.54$

(*h*) $\sqrt{128.5 - 89.24} = \sqrt{39.3} = 6.27$

1.13 Evaluate each of the following, given that $X = 3$, $Y = -5$, $A = 4$, and $B = -7$, where all numbers are assumed to be exact:

(*a*) $2X - 3Y$

(*b*) $4Y - 8X + 28$

(*c*) $\dfrac{AX + BY}{BX - AY}$

(*d*) $X^2 - 3XY - 2Y^2$

(*e*) $2(X + 3Y) - 4(3X - 2Y)$

(*f*) $\dfrac{X^2 - Y^2}{A^2 - B^2 + 1}$

(*g*) $\sqrt{2X^2 - Y^2 - 3A^2 + 4B^2 + 3}$

(*h*) $\sqrt{\dfrac{6A^2}{X} + \dfrac{2B^2}{Y}}$

SOLUTION

(*a*) $2X-3Y=2(3)-3(-5)=6+15=21$

(*b*) $4Y-8X+28=4(-5)-8(3)+28=-20-24+28=-16$

(*c*) $$\frac{AX+BY}{BX-AY}=\frac{(4)(3)+(-7)(-5)}{(-7)(3)-(4)(-5)}=\frac{12+35}{-21+20}=\frac{47}{-1}=-47$$

(*d*) $X^2-3XY-2Y^2=(3)^2-3(3)(-5)-2(-5)^2=9+45-50=4$

(*e*) $$\begin{aligned}2(X+3Y)-4(3X-2Y)&=2[(3)+3(-5)]-4[3(3)-2(-5)]\\&=2(3-15)-4(9+10)=2(-12)-4(19)=-24-76=-100\end{aligned}$$

Another method

$$\begin{aligned}2(X+3Y)-4(3X-2Y)&=2X+6Y-12X+8Y=-10X+14Y=-10(3)+14(-5)\\&=-30-70=-100\end{aligned}$$

(*f*) $$\frac{X^2-Y^2}{A^2-B^2+1}=\frac{(3)^2-(-5)^2}{(4)^2-(-7)^2+1}=\frac{9-25}{16-49+1}=\frac{-16}{-32}=\frac{1}{2}=0.5$$

(*g*) $$\begin{aligned}\sqrt{2X^2-Y^2-3A^2+4B^2+3}&=\sqrt{2(3)^2-(-5)^2-3(4)^2+4(-7)^2+3}\\&=\sqrt{18-25-48+196+3}=\sqrt{144}=12\end{aligned}$$

(*h*) $$\sqrt{\frac{6A^2}{X}+\frac{2B^2}{Y}}=\sqrt{\frac{6(4)^2}{3}+\frac{2(-7)^2}{-5}}=\sqrt{\frac{96}{3}+\frac{98}{-5}}=\sqrt{12.4}=3.52 \quad \text{approximately}$$

FUNCTIONS

Mathcad

1.14 Table 1.1 shows the number of bushels (bu) of wheat and corn produced on the PQR Farm during the years 1975–1985. With reference to this table, determine the year or years during which (*a*) the least number of bushels of wheat was produced, (*b*) the greatest number of bushels of corn was produced, (*c*) the greatest decline in wheat production occurred, (*d*) the corn production decreased while the wheat production increased over that of the preceding year, (*e*) equal amounts of wheat were produced, and (*f*) the combined production of wheat and corn was a maximum.

Table 1.1

Year	Number of Bushels of Wheat (to the nearest 5 bu)	Number of Bushels of Corn (to the nearest 5 bu)
1975	200	75
1976	185	90
1977	225	100
1978	250	85
1979	240	80
1980	195	100
1981	210	110
1982	225	105
1983	250	95
1984	230	110
1985	235	100

SOLUTION

(*a*) 1976; (*b*) 1981 and 1984; (*c*) 1980; (*d*) 1978, 1982, 1983, and 1985; (*e*) 1977 and 1982, and 1978 and 1983; (*f*) 1983.

1.15 Let W and C denote, respectively, the number of bushels of wheat and corn produced during the year t on the PQR Farm of Problem 1.14. It is clear that W and C are both functions of t; this we can indicate by $W = F(t)$ and $C = G(t)$.

(*a*) Find W when $t = 1981$.

(*b*) Find C when $t = 1978$ and 1984.

(*c*) Find t when $W = 225$.

(*d*) Find F (1979).

(*e*) Find G (1983).

(*f*) Find C when $W = 210$.

(*g*) What is the domain of the variable t?

(*h*) Is W a single-valued function of t?

(*i*) Is t a function of W? If so, is it single-valued?

(*j*) Is C a function of W?

(*k*) Which variable is independent, t or W?

SOLUTION

(*a*) 210; (*b*) 85 and 110, respectively; (*c*) 1977 and 1982; (*d*) 240; (*e*) 95; (*f*) 110; (*g*) the years 1975, 1976, . . . , 1985.

(*h*) Yes, since to each value that t can assume (i.e., in the domain of t) there corresponds one and only one value of W.

(*i*) Yes, t is a function of W since to each value that W can assume there corresponds one or more values of t that we can find from Table 1.1. Since there may be more than one value of t corresponding to a value of W (such as when $W = 225$ and $t = 1977$ or 1982), the function is multiple-valued. This functional dependence of t on W can be written $t = H(W)$.

(*j*) Yes, since to each value that W can assume there corresponds one or more values of C as determined from Table 1.1. Similarly, W is a function of C.

(*k*) Physically, it is customary to think of W as determined from t rather than of t as determined from W. Thus, physically, t is the independent variable and W is the dependent variable. Mathematically, however, either variable can be considered the independent variable and the other the dependent variable. The one that is assigned various values is the independent variable; the one that is then determined as a result is the dependent variable.

Mathcad **1.16** A variable Y is determined from a variable X according to the equation $Y = 2X - 3$, where the 2 and 3 are exact.

(*a*) Find Y when $X = 3$, -2, and 1.5.

(*b*) Construct a table showing the values of Y corresponding to $X = -2, -1, 0, 1, 2, 3$, and 4.

(*c*) If the dependence of Y on X is denoted by $Y = F(X)$, determine $F(2.4)$ and $F(0.8)$.

(*d*) What value of X corresponds to $Y = 15$?

(*e*) Can X be expressed as a function of Y?

(*f*) Is Y a single-valued function of X?

(*g*) Is X a single-valued function of Y?

SOLUTION

(*a*) When $X = 3$, $Y = 2X - 3 = 2(3) - 3 = 6 - 3 = 3$. When $X = -2$, $Y = 2X - 3 = 2(-2) - 3 = -4 - 3 = -7$. When $X = 1.5$, $Y = 2X - 3 = 2(1.5) - 3 = 3 - 3 = 0$.

(*b*) The values of Y, computed as in part (*a*), are shown in Table 1.2. Note that by using other values of X, we can construct many tables. The relation $Y = 2X - 3$ is equivalent to the collection of *all* such possible tables.

Table 1.2

X	-2	-1	0	1	2	3	4
Y	-7	-5	-3	-1	1	3	5

(*c*) $F(2.4) = 2(2.4) - 3 = 4.8 - 3 = 1.8$, and $F(0.8) = 2(0.8) - 3 = 1.6 - 3 = -1.4$.

(*d*) Substitute $Y = 15$ in $Y = 2X - 3$. This gives $15 = 2X - 3$, $2X = 18$, and $X = 9$.

(*e*) Yes. Since $Y = 2X - 3$, $Y + 3 = 2X$ and $X = \frac{1}{2}(Y + 3)$. This expresses X *explicitly* as a function of Y.

(*f*) Yes, since for each value that X can assume (and there is an indefinite number of these values) there corresponds one and only one value of Y.

(*g*) Yes, since from part (*e*), $X = \frac{1}{2}(Y + 3)$, so that corresponding to each value assumed by Y there is one and only one value of X.

1.17 If $Z = 16 + 4X - 3Y$, find the value of Z corresponding to (*a*) $X = 2$, $Y = 5$; (*b*) $X = -3$, $Y = -7$; (*c*) $X = -4$, $Y = 2$.

SOLUTION

(*a*) $Z = 16 + 4(2) - 3(5) = 16 + 8 - 15 = 9$

(*b*) $Z = 16 + 4(-3) - 3(-7) = 16 - 12 + 21 = 25$

(*c*) $Z = 16 + 4(-4) - 3(2) = 16 - 16 - 6 = -6$

Given values of X and Y, there corresponds a value of Z. We can denote this dependence of Z on X and Y by writing $Z = F(X, Y)$ (read "Z is a function of X and Y"). $F(2, 5)$ denotes the value of Z when $X = 2$ and $Y = 5$ and is 9, from part (*a*). Similarly, $F(-3, -7) = 25$ and $F(-4, 2) = -6$ from parts (*b*) and (*c*), respectively.

The variables X and Y are called *independent variables*, and Z is called a *dependent variable*.

GRAPHS

1.18 Locate on the X axis of a coordinate system the points corresponding to (*a*) $X = 4$, (*b*) $X = -3$, (*c*) $X = 2.5$, (*d*) $X = -4.3$, and (*e*) $X = 0.4$, assuming these values to be exact.

SOLUTION

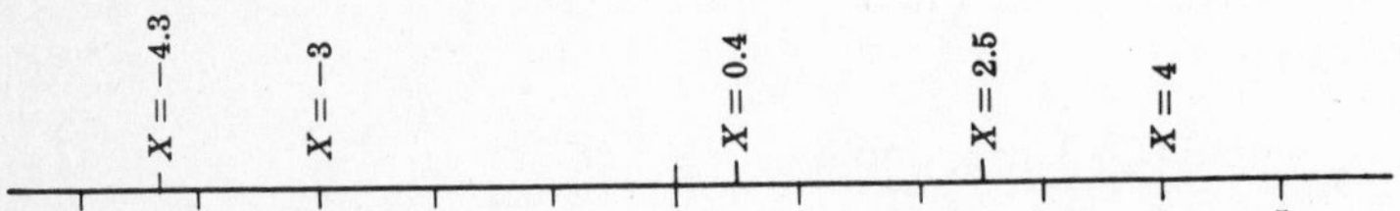

Each exact value of X corresponds to one and only one point on the axis. Conversely, it is proved in advanced mathematics that to each point on the axis there corresponds one and only one value of X.

Thus theoretically there is a point corresponding to $X = 22/7 = 3.142857142857\cdots$, or $X = \pi = 3.14159265358\cdots$. Practically, of course, we can never hope to locate a point exactly since the pencil mark that we make has a thickness and covers an infinite number of points. The X axis itself has a thickness. Thus the accompanying diagram is a physical representation of the actual mathematical situation.

1.19 Let X denote the diameter of a ball bearing in centimeters (cm). If $X = 4.58$ to three significant figures, how should this be represented on the X axis?

SOLUTION

The true measurement for 4.58 cm lies between 4.575 cm and 4.585 cm and should thus be represented by the heavy line segment shown in the diagram at the top of page 15.

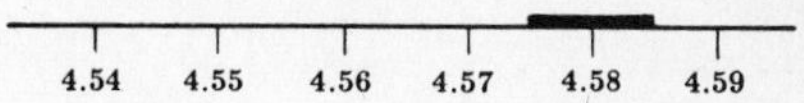

1.20 Locate on a rectangular coordinate system the points having coordinates (*a*) (5, 2), (*b*) (2, 5), (*c*) (−3, 1), (*d*) (1, −3), (*e*) (3, −4), (*f*) (−2.5, −4.8), (*g*) (0, −2.5), and (*h*) (4, 0). Assume that all given numbers are exact.

SOLUTION

See Fig. 1-2.

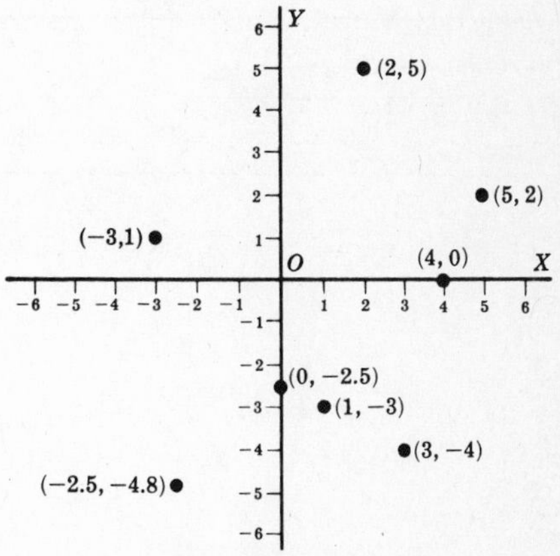

Fig. 1-2

1.21 Graph the equation $Y = 2X - 3$.

SOLUTION

Placing $X = -2, -1, 0, 1, 2, 3$, and 4, we find that $Y = -7, -5, -3, -1, 1, 3$, and 5, respectively [see Problem 1.16(*b*)]. Thus the points on the graph are given by (−2, −7), (−1, −5), (0, −3), (1, −1), (2, 1), (3, 3), and (4, 5), which are plotted on a rectangular coordinate system as shown in Fig. 1-3. All of these points, as well as points obtained by using other values of X, lie on a straight line, which is the required graph.

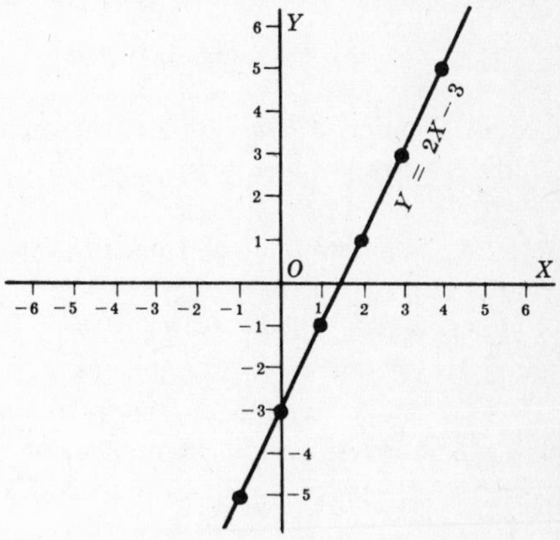

Fig. 1-3

Because the graph of $Y = 2X - 3$ is a straight line, we sometimes call $F(X) = 2X - 3$ a *linear function.* In general $F(X) = aX + b$ (where a and b are any constants) is a linear function whose graph is a straight line.

Note that only two points are actually needed to graph a linear function, since two points determine a line.

1.22 Graph the equation $Y = X^2 - 2X - 8$.

SOLUTION

The values of Y corresponding to various values of X are shown in Table 1.3; for example, when $X = -2$, $Y = (-2)^2 - 2(-2) - 8 = 4 + 4 - 8 = 0$. From the table, points on the graph are given by $(-3, 7)$, $(-2, 0)$, $(-1, -5)$, $(0, -8)$, $(1, -9)$, $(2, -8)$, $(3, -5)$, $(4, 0)$, and $(5, 7)$. These points, as well as others obtained by using different values of X, are seen to lie on the curve shown in Fig. 1-4. The curve is called a *parabola.* The function $F(X) = X^2 - 2X - 8$ is called a *quadratic function.*

Table 1.3

X	−3	−2	−1	0	1	2	3	4	5
Y	7	0	−5	−8	−9	−8	−5	0	7

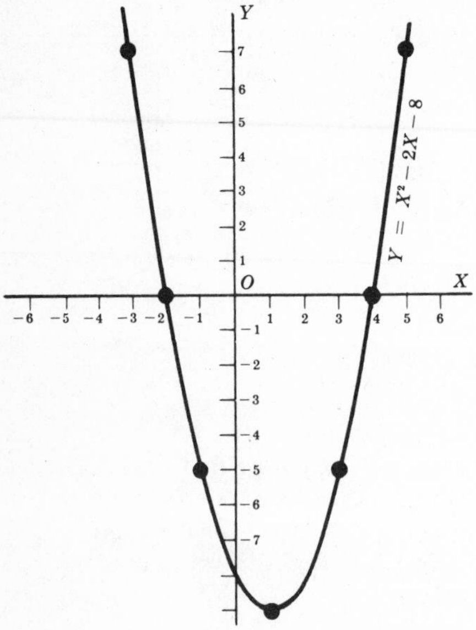

Fig. 1-4

In general the graph of an equation $Y = a + bX + cX^2$ (where a, b, and c are constants and $c \neq 0$) is a parabola. If $c = 0$, the graph is a straight line, as in Problem 1.21.

Table 1.4 Population of the United States, 1860–1980

Year	1860	1870	1880	1890	1900	1910	1920	1930	1940	1950	1960	1970	1980
Population (millions)	31.4	39.8	50.2	62.9	76.0	92.0	105.7	122.8	131.7	151.1	179.3	203.3	226.5

Source: U.S. Bureau of the Census.

1.23 Table 1.4 shows the U.S. population (in millions) for the years 1860–1980. Graph these data.

SOLUTION

First method

Refer to Fig. 1-5. In this graph, Population P is the dependent variable, and time t is the independent variable. Points are located as usual by coordinates read from the table, such as (1880, 50.2). Successive points are then connected by straight lines, since no information is given as to the population during intermediate years; for this reason, this graph is called a *line graph.*

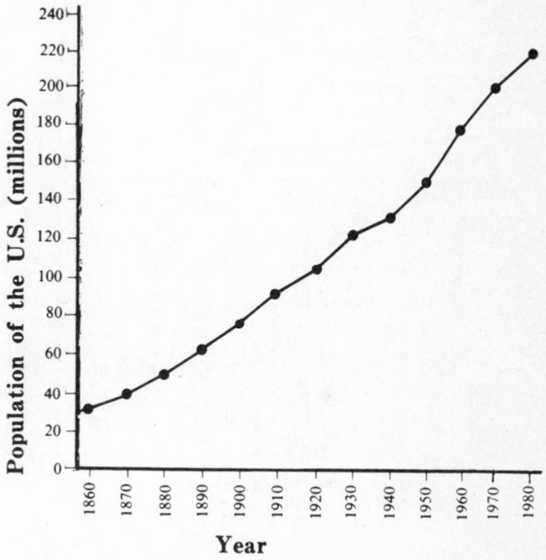

Fig. 1-5 (*Source:* U.S. Bureau of the Census).

Note that units on the axes are not equal, as they were in graphing $Y = 2X - 3$. This is perfectly justified since the two variables represent essentially different quantities.

Note also that the zero has been indicated on the vertical axis but (for obvious reasons) not on the horizontal axis. In general the zero should be indicated whenever possible, especially on the vertical axis. If it is impossible for some reason to indicate the zero and if such omission might lead to any erroneous conclusions drawn by the reader, then it is wise to call attention to the omission by some means, such as described in Problem 1.26.

A table or graph showing the distribution of a variable as a function of time is called a *time series.*

Second method

Figure 1-6 is called a *bar graph, bar chart,* or *bar diagram.* The widths of the bars, which are all equal, have no significance in this case and can be made any convenient size as long as the bars do not overlap.

The numbers at the tops of the bars may or may not be omitted. If they are kept, the vertical scale at the left is unnecessary and may be omitted.

Third method

Charts or diagrams such as shown in Fig. 1-7 are called *pictographs* or *pictograms* (short for picture diagrams) and are often used to present statistical data in a manner appealing to the general public. Many of these pictographs display a great deal of originality and ingenuity in the art of presenting the data.

The numbers to the right of the "people" figures in Fig. 1-7 may or may not be included. Even if they are not shown, the reader can still estimate the population to the nearest 5 million people.

Mathcad **1.24** Graph the data of Problem 1.14 by using (*a*) line graphs and (*b*) bar graphs.

SOLUTION

(*a*) The line graphs are shown in Fig. 1-8.

(*b*) Figures 1-9 and 1-10 show two types of bar graphs. The graph in Fig. 1-10 is called a *component bar chart.*

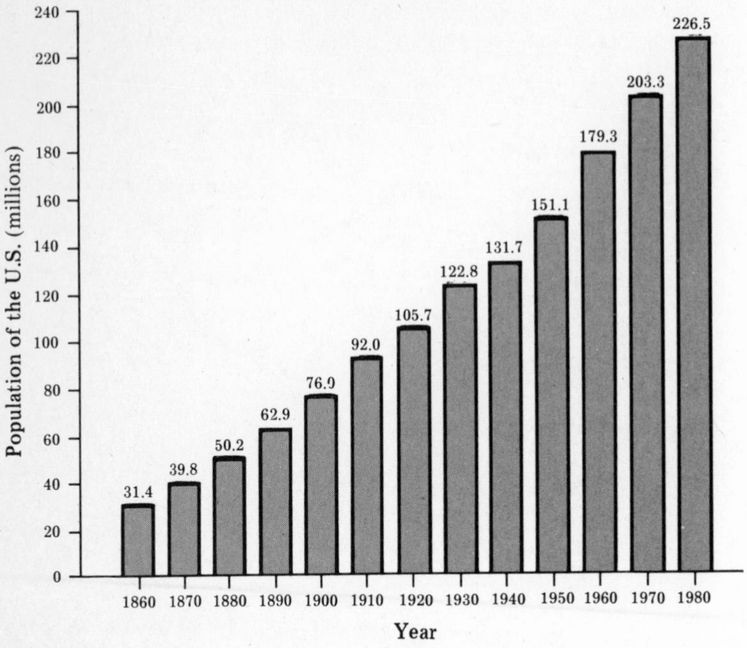

Fig. 1-6 (*Source:* U.S. Bureau of the Census).

1.25 (*a*) Express the yearly number of bushels of wheat and corn from Table 1.1 of Problem 1.14 as percentages of the total annual production.

(*b*) Graph the percentages obtained in part (*a*).

SOLUTION

(*a*) For 1975, the percentage of wheat $= 200/(200+75) = 72.7\%$, and the percentage of corn $= 100\% - 72.7\% = 27.3\%$; etc. The percentages are shown in Table 1.5.

Table 1.5

Year	1975	1976	1977	1978	1979	1980	1981	1982	1983	1984	1985
Percentage wheat	72.7	67.3	69.2	74.6	75.0	66.1	65.6	68.2	72.5	67.6	70.1
Percentage corn	27.3	32.7	30.8	25.4	25.0	33.9	34.4	31.8	27.5	32.4	29.9

(*b*) The graph of the percentages in part (*a*), shown in Fig. 1-11, is called a *percentage component graph.* A graph similar to Fig. 1-9 can also be used.

1.26 Using a line graph, represent graphically only the wheat production shown in Table 1.1.

SOLUTION

The required line graph is obtained from Fig. 1-8 by removing the lower line graph. As a result, much wasted space appears between the upper line graph and the horizontal axis. To avoid this, we could start our vertical scale at 150 bu instead of 0 bu. This may, however, lead to erroneous conclusions on the part of a reader who may not have noticed the omission of the zero. To draw attention to this omission, we can construct the graph as in Fig. 1-12.

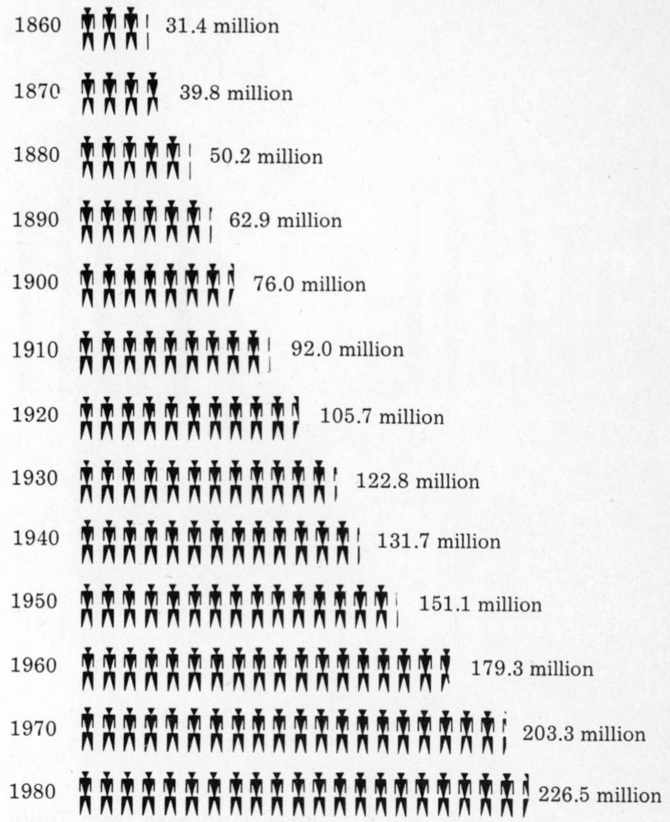

Fig. 1-7 Population of the United States during the years 1860–1980. Each figure represents 10,000,000 people. (*Source:* U.S. Bureau of the Census).

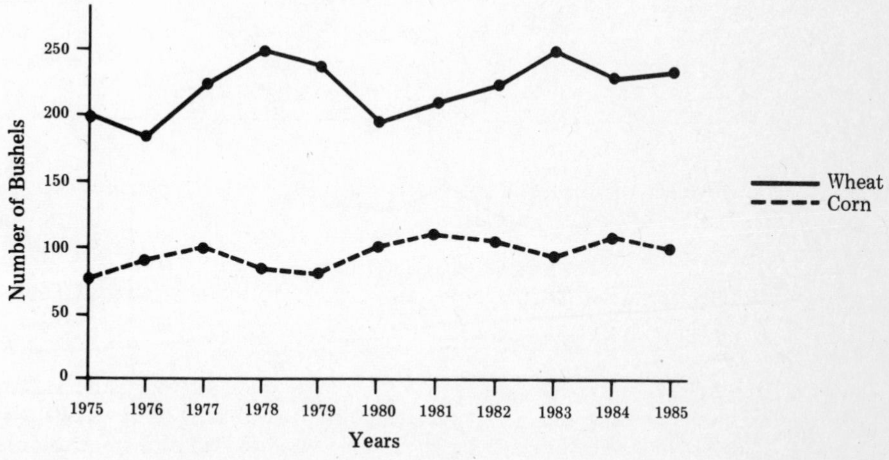

Fig. 1-8

First method:

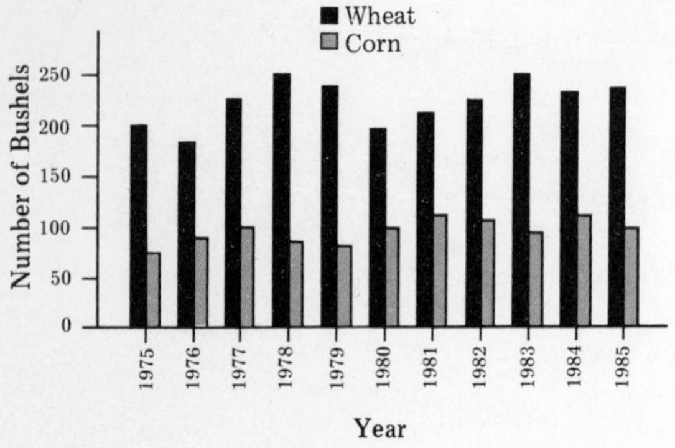

Fig. 1-9

Second method:

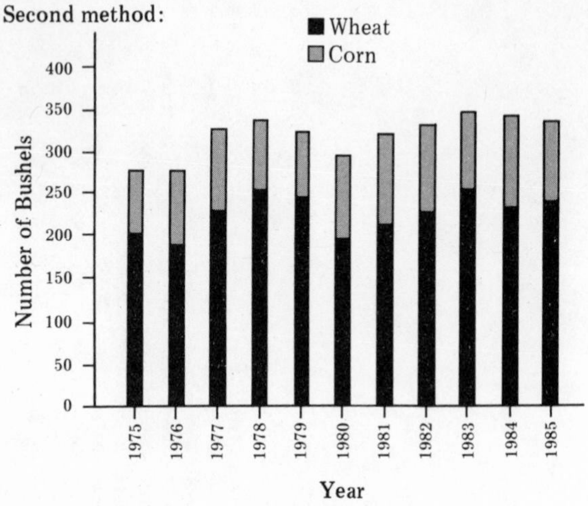

Fig. 1-10

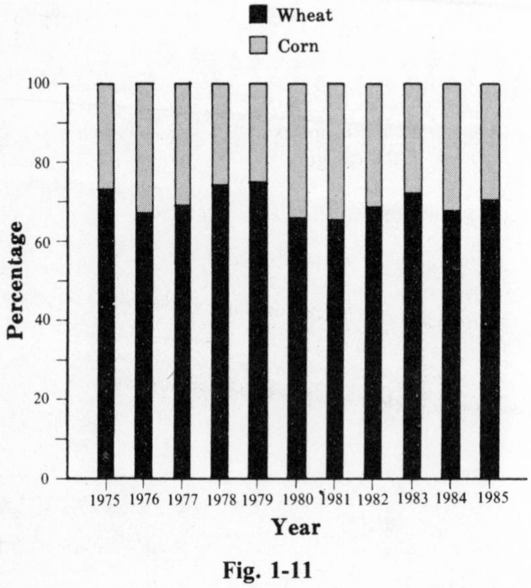

Fig. 1-11

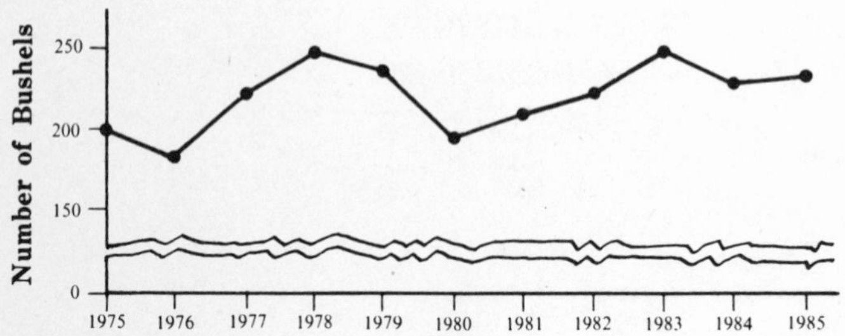

Fig. 1-12

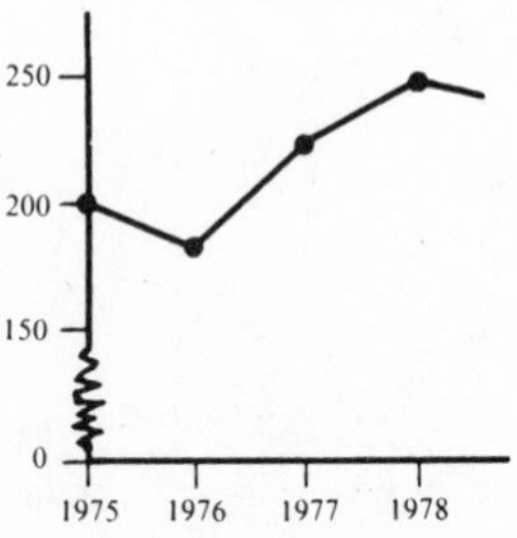

Fig. 1-13

Another device often employed to draw attention to the omission of the zero is the use of a zigzag line on one of the axes, as shown in Fig. 1-13.

Mathcad **1.27** The areas of the various continents of the world (in millions of square miles) are shown in Table 1.6. Graph the data.

Table 1.6 Areas of Continents of the World

Continent	Area (million square miles)
Africa	11.7
Asia	10.4
Europe	1.9
North America	9.4
Oceania	3.3
South America	6.9
Soviet Union	7.9
	Total 51.5

Source: United Nations.
Note: Europe excludes Turkey, which is included in the category "Asia."

SOLUTION

First method

Figure 1-14 is a bar graph in which the bars are horizontal instead of vertical. Note that the continents have been listed in alphabetical order. If desired, they could be listed in increasing or decreasing order of area.

AREAS OF CONTINENTS OF THE WORLD
(from data supplied by the United Nations)

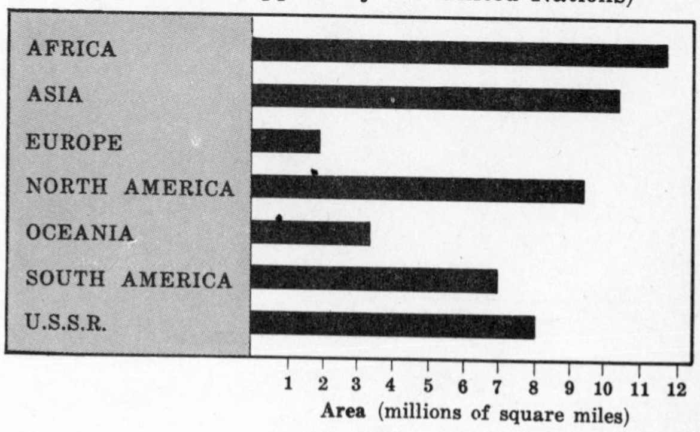

Fig. 1-14

Second method

Figure 1-15 is called a *pie graph, circular graph,* or *pie chart.* To construct it, we use the fact that the total area, 51.5 million square miles, corresponds to the total number of degrees in the circular arc, namely, 360°. Thus 1 million square miles corresponds to 360°/51.5. It follows that Africa, with 11.7 million square miles, corresponds to an arc of $11.7(360°/51.5) = 82°$, while Asia, Europe, North America, Oceania, South America, and the Soviet Union correspond to arcs of 73°, 13°, 66°, 23°, 48°, and 55°, respectively. The required dividing lines can be drawn by using a protractor.

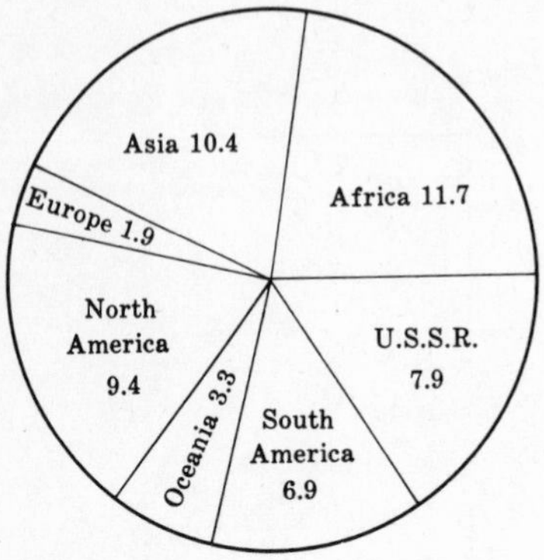

Fig. 1-15 Areas of continents of the world (millions of square miles).

1.28 The time T (in seconds) required for one complete vibration of a simple pendulum of length L (in centimeters) is shown in Table 1.7, which gives the observations obtained in a physics laboratory.

(*a*) Exhibit T graphically as a function of L.

(*b*) From the graph in part (*a*), estimate T for a pendulum whose length is 40 cm.

Table 1.7

L	10.1	16.2	22.2	33.8	42.0	53.4	66.7	74.5	86.6	100.0
T	0.64	0.81	0.95	1.17	1.30	1.47	1.65	1.74	1.87	2.01

SOLUTION

(*a*) The graph shown in Fig. 1-16 has been obtained by connecting the observation points with a smooth curve.

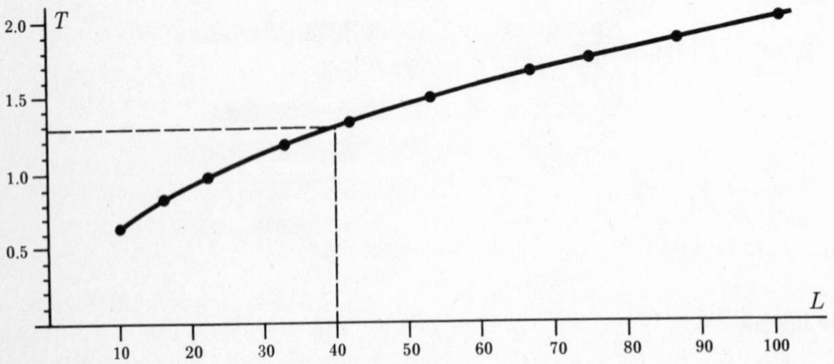

Fig. 1-16

(*b*) The estimated value of T is 1.27 seconds.

EQUATIONS

1.29 Solve each of the following equations:

(*a*) $4a - 20 = 8$ (*c*) $18 - 5b = 3(b + 8) + 10$

(*b*) $3X + 4 = 24 - 2X$ (*d*) $\dfrac{Y+2}{3} + 1 = \dfrac{Y}{2}$

SOLUTION

(*a*) Add 20 to both members: $4a - 20 + 20 = 8 + 20$, or $4a = 28$.
Divide both sides by 4: $4a/4 = 28/4$, and $a = 7$.
Check: $4(7) - 20 = 8$, $28 - 20 = 8$, and $8 = 8$.

(*b*) Subtract 4 from both members: $3X + 4 - 4 = 24 - 2X - 4$, or $3X = 20 - 2X$.
Add $2X$ to both sides: $3X + 2X = 20 - 2X + 2X$, or $5X = 20$.
Divide both sides by 5: $5X/5 = 20/5$, and $X = 4$.
Check: $3(4) + 4 = 24 - 2(4)$, $12 + 4 = 24 - 8$, and $16 = 16$.

The result can be obtained much more quickly by realizing that any term can be moved, or *transposed*, from one member of an equation to the other simply by changing its sign. Thus we can write

$$3X + 4 = 24 - 2X \qquad 3X + 2X = 24 - 4 \qquad 5X = 20 \qquad X = 4$$

(*c*) $18 - 5b = 3b + 24 + 10$, and $18 - 5b = 3b + 34$.
Transposing, $-5b - 3b = 34 - 18$, or $-8b = 16$.
Dividing by -8, $-8b/(-8) = 16/(-8)$, and $b = -2$.
Check: $18 - 5(-2) = 3(-2 + 8) + 10$, $18 + 10 = 3(6) + 10$, and $28 = 28$.

(*d*) First multiply both members by 6, the lowest common denominator.

$$6\left(\frac{Y+2}{3} + 1\right) = 6\left(\frac{Y}{2}\right) \qquad 6\left(\frac{Y+2}{3}\right) + 6(1) = \frac{6Y}{2} \qquad 2(Y+2) + 6 = 3Y$$

$$2Y + 4 + 6 = 3Y \qquad 2Y + 10 = 3Y \qquad 10 = 3Y - 2Y \qquad Y = 10$$

Check: $\dfrac{10+2}{3} + 1 = \dfrac{10}{2}$, $\dfrac{12}{3} + 1 = \dfrac{10}{2}$, $4 + 1 = 5$, and $5 = 5$.

Mathcad **1.30** Solve each of the following sets of simultaneous equations:

(*a*) $3a - 2b = 11$ (*b*) $5X + 14Y = 78$ (*c*) $3a + 2b + 5c = 15$
$5a + 7b = 39$ $7X + 3Y = -7$ $7a - 3b + 2c = 52$
$5a + b - 4c = 2$

SOLUTION

(*a*)

Multiply the first equation by 7:	$21a - 14b = 77$	(*1*)
Multiply the second equation by 2:	$10a + 14b = 78$	(*2*)
Add:	$31a = 155$	
Divide by 31:	$a = 5$	

Note that by multiplying each of the given equations by suitable numbers, we are able to write two *equivalent equations*, (*1*) and (*2*), in which the coefficients of the unknown b are numerically equal. Then by addition we are able to *eliminate* the unknown b and thus find a.

Substitute $a = 5$ in the first equation: $3(5) - 2b = 11$, $-2b = -4$, and $b = 2$. Thus $a = 5$, and $b = 2$.
Check: $3(5) - 2(2) = 11$, $15 - 4 = 11$, and $11 = 11$; $5(5) + 7(2) = 39$, $25 + 14 = 39$, and $39 = 39$.

(*b*)

Multiply the first equation by 3:	$15X + 42Y = 234$	(*3*)
Multiply the second equation by -14:	$-98X - 42Y = 98$	(*4*)
Add:	$-83X = 332$	
Divide by -83:	$X = -4$	

Substitute $X=-4$ in the first equation: $5(-4)+14Y=78$, $14Y=98$, and $Y=7$.
Thus $X=-4$, and $Y=7$.
Check: $5(-4)+14(7)=78$, $-20+98=78$, and $78=78$; $7(-4)+3(7)=-7$, $-28+21=-7$, and $-7=-7$.

(*c*) Multiply the first equation by 2: $6a+4b+10c=30$
Multiply the second equation by -5: $-35a+15b-10c=-260$
Add: $-29a+19b=-230$ (*5*)

Multiply the second equation by 2: $14a-6b+4c=104$
Repeat the third equation: $5a+b-4c=2$
Add: $19a-5b=106$ (*6*)

We have thus eliminated c and are left with two equations, (*5*) and (*6*), to be solved simultaneously for a and b.

Multiply equation (*5*) by 5: $-145a+95b=-1150$
Multiply equation (*6*) by 19: $361a-95b=2014$
Add: $216a=864$
Divide by 216: $a=4$

Substituting $a=4$ in equation (*5*) or (*6*), we find that $b=-6$.
Substituting $a=4$ and $b=-6$ in any of the given equations, we obtain $c=3$.
Thus $a=4$, $b=-6$, and $c=3$.
Check: $3(4)+2(-6)+5(3)=15$, and $15=15$; $7(4)-3(-6)+2(3)=52$, and $52=52$; $5(4)+(-6)-4(3)=2$, and $2=2$.

INEQUALITIES

1.31 Express in words the meaning of each of the following:

(*a*) $N>30$ (*b*) $X\leq 12$ (*c*) $0<p\leq 1$ (*d*) $\mu-2t<X<\mu+2t$

SOLUTION

(*a*) N is greater than 30.
(*b*) X is less than or equal to 12.
(*c*) p is greater than 0 but less than or equal to 1.
(*d*) X is greater than $\mu-2t$ but less than $\mu+2t$.

1.32 Translate the following into symbols:

(*a*) The variable X has values between 2 and 5 inclusive.
(*b*) The arithmetic mean $\bar{X}$ is greater than 28.42 but less than 31.56.
(*c*) m is a positive number less than or equal to 10.
(*d*) P is a nonnegative number.

SOLUTION

(*a*) $2\leq X\leq 5$; (*b*) $28.42<\bar{X}<31.56$; (*c*) $0<m\leq 10$; (*d*) $P\geq 0$.

1.33 Using inequality symbols, arrange the numbers 3.42, −0.6, −2.1, 1.45, and −3 in (*a*) increasing and (*b*) decreasing order of magnitude.

SOLUTION

(*a*) $-3<-2.1<-0.6<1.45<3.42$
(*b*) $3.42>1.45>-0.6>-2.1>-3$

Note that when the numbers are plotted as points on a line (see Problem 1.18), they increase from left to right.

1.34 In each of the following, find a corresponding inequality for X (i.e., solve each inequality for X):

(a) $2X < 6$

(b) $3X - 8 \geq 4$

(c) $6 - 4X < -2$

(d) $-3 < \dfrac{X-5}{2} < 3$

(e) $-1 \leq \dfrac{3-2X}{5} \leq 7$

SOLUTION

(a) Divide both sides by 2 to obtain $X < 3$.

(b) Adding 8 to both sides, $3X \geq 12$; dividing both sides by 3, $X \geq 4$.

(c) Adding -6 to both sides, $-4X < -8$; dividing both sides by -4, $X > 2$. Note that, as in equations, we can transpose a term from one side of an inequality to the other simply by changing the sign of the term; from part (b), for example, $3X \geq 8 + 4$.

(d) Multiplying by 2, $-6 < X - 5 < 6$; adding 5, $-1 < X < 11$.

(e) Multiplying by 5, $-5 \leq 3 - 2X \leq 35$; adding -3, $-8 \leq -2X \leq 32$; dividing by -2, $4 \geq X \geq -16$, or $-16 \leq X \leq 4$.

LOGARITHMS AND ANTILOGARITHMS

1.35 Determine the characteristic of the common logarithm (base 10) of each of the following numbers:

(a) 57	(d) 35.63	(g) 186,000	(j) 0.0325
(b) 57.4	(e) 982.5	(h) 0.71	(k) 0.0071
(c) 5.63	(f) 7824	(i) 0.7314	(l) 0.0003

SOLUTION

(a) 1; (b) 1; (c) 0; (d) 1; (e) 2; (f) 3; (g) 5; (h) $9-10$; (i) $9-10$; (j) $8-10$; (k) $7-10$; (l) $6-10$.

1.36 Find each of the following logarithms:

(a) log 87.2	(f) log 0.382	(k) log 4.638	(p) log 0.2548
(b) log 37,300	(g) log 0.00159	(l) log 6.753	(q) log 0.04372
(c) log 753	(h) log 0.0753	(m) log 183.2	(r) log 0.009848
(d) log 9.21	(i) log 0.000827	(n) log 43.15	(s) log 0.0001788
(e) log 54.50	(j) log 0.0503	(o) log 876,400	

SOLUTION

(a) Mantissa = .9405, and characteristic = 1; thus log 87.2 = 1.9405.

(b) 4.5717

(c) 2.8768

(d) 0.9643

(e) 1.7364

(*f*) Mantissa = .5821, and characteristic = 9 − 10; thus log 0.382 = 9.5821 − 10.

(*g*) 7.2014 − 10

(*h*) 8.8768 − 10

(*i*) 6.9175 − 10

(*j*) 8.7016 − 10

(*k*) The mantissa of log 4638 is 0.8 of the way between the mantissas of log 4630 and log 4640.

$$\begin{aligned} \text{Mantissa of log } 4640 &= .6665 \\ \text{Mantissa of log } 4630 &= \underline{.6656} \\ \text{Tabular difference} &= .0009 \end{aligned}$$

The mantissa of log 4.638 = .6656 + (0.8)(.0009) = .6663 to four digits; thus log 4.638 = .6663. This process is called *linear interpolation.* If desired, the table of proportional parts in Appendix VII can be used to give the mantissa directly (6656 + 7).

(*l*) 0.8295 (8293 + 2)

(*m*) 2.2630 (2625 + 5)

(*n*) 1.6350 (6345 + 5)

(*o*) 5.9427 (9425 + 2)

(*p*) 9.4062 − 10 (4048 + 14)

(*q*) 8.6407 − 10 (6405 + 2)

(*r*) 7.9933 − 10 (9930 + 3)

(*s*) 6.2524 − 10 (2504 + 20)

1.37 Find each of the following antilogarithms:

(*a*) antilog 1.9058

(*b*) antilog 3.8531
antilog 2.1875
antilog 0.4997
antilog 4.9360

(*c*) antilog 7.8657 − 10

(*d*) antilog 9.8267 − 10
antilog $\bar{2}.3927$
antilog 7.7443 − 10

(*e*) antilog 9.3842 − 10

(*f*) antilog 2.6715
antilog 4.1853
antilog 0.9245

(*g*) antilog $\bar{1}.6089$
antilog 8.8907 − 10
antilog 1.2000

SOLUTION

(*a*) In Appendix VII the mantissa .9058 corresponds to the number 805. Since the characteristic is 1, the number must have two digits before the decimal point; thus the required number is 80.5 (i.e., antilog 1.9058 = 80.5).

(*b*) antilog 3.8531 = 7130, antilog 2.1875 = 154, antilog 0.4997 = 3.16, and antilog 4.9360 = 86,300.

(*c*) In Appendix VII the mantissa .8657 corresponds to the number 734. Since the characteristic is 7-10, the number must have two zeros immediately following the decimal point. Thus the required number is 0.00734 (i.e., antilog 7.8657 − 10 = 0.00734). The table of proportional parts in Appendix VII can also be used.

(*d*) antilog 9.8267 − 10 = 0.671, antilog $\bar{2}.3927$ = 0.0247, and antilog 7.7443 − 10 = 0.00555.

(*e*) Since the mantissa is not found in the tables, interpolation must be used:

$$\begin{aligned} \text{Mantissa of log } 2430 &= .3856 \\ \text{Mantissa of log } 2420 &= \underline{.3838} \\ \text{Tabular difference} &= .0018 \end{aligned} \qquad \begin{aligned} \text{Given mantissa} &= .3842 \\ \text{Next smaller mantissa} &= \underline{.3838} \\ \text{Difference} &= .0004 \end{aligned}$$

Thus 2420 + (4/18)(2430 − 2420) = 2422 to four digits, and the required number is 0.2422.

(*f*) antilog 2.6715 = 469.3 (3/9 × 10 = 3 approximately), antilog 4.1853 = 15,320 (6/28 × 10 = 2 approximately), and antilog 0.9245 = 8.404 (2/5 × 10 = 4).

(*g*) antilog $\bar{1}.6089$ = 0.4064 (4/11 × 10 = 4 approximately), antilog 8.8907 − 10 = 0.07775 (3/6 × 10 = 5), and antilog 1.2000 = 15.85 (13/27 × 10 = 5 approximately).

COMPUTATIONS USING LOGARITHMS

Calculate each of the following, using logarithms.

1.38 $P = (3.81)(43.4)$

SOLUTION

$\log P = \log 3.81 + \log 43.4$:

$$\begin{aligned} \log 3.81 &= 0.5809 \\ (+)\ \log 43.4 &= \underline{1.6375} \\ \log P \quad &= 2.2184 \end{aligned}$$

Thus $P = \text{antilog } 2.2184 = 165.3$, or 165 to three significant figures. Note the exponential significance of the computation:

$$(3.81)(43.4) = (10^{0.5809})(10^{1.6375}) = 10^{0.5809+1.6375} = 10^{2.2184} = 165.3$$

1.39 $P = (73.42)(0.004620)(0.5143)$

SOLUTION

$\log P = \log 73.42 + \log 0.004620 + \log 0.5143$:

$$\begin{aligned} \log 73.42 \quad &= \ \ 1.8658 \\ (+)\ \log 0.004620 &= \ \ 7.6646 - 10 \\ (+)\ \log 0.5143 \quad &= \ \ \underline{9.7112 - 10} \\ \log P \quad &= 19.2416 - 20 = 9.2416 - 10 \end{aligned}$$

Thus $P = 0.1744$.

1.40 $P = \dfrac{(784.6)(0.0431)}{28.23}$

SOLUTION

$\log P = \log 784.6 + \log 0.0431 - \log 28.23$:

$$\begin{aligned} \log 784.6 \quad &= \ \ 2.8947 \\ (+)\ \log 0.0431 &= \ \ \underline{8.6345 - 10} \\ & \ \ \ \ 11.5292 - 10 \\ (-)\ \log 28.23 \quad &= \ \ \underline{1.4507} \\ \log P \quad &= 10.0785 - 10 = 0.0785 \end{aligned}$$

Thus $P = 1.198$, or 1.20 to three significant figures. Note the exponential significance of the computation:

$$\frac{(784.6)(0.0431)}{28.23} = \frac{(10^{2.8947})(10^{8.6345-10})}{10^{1.4507}} = 10^{2.8947+8.6345-10-1.4507} = 10^{0.0785} = 1.198$$

1.41 $P = (5.395)^8$

SOLUTION

$\log P = 8 \log 5.395 = 8(0.7320) = 5.8560$, and $P = 717{,}800$, or 7.178×10^5.

1.42 $P = \sqrt{387.2} = (387.2)^{1/2}$

SOLUTION

$\log P = \frac{1}{2} \log 387.2 = \frac{1}{2}(2.5879) = 1.2940$, and $P = 19.68$.

1.43 $P = (0.08317)^{1/5}$

SOLUTION

$\log P = \frac{1}{5} \log 0.08317 = \frac{1}{5}(8.9200 - 10) = \frac{1}{5}(48.9200 - 50) = 9.7840 - 10$, and $P = 0.6081$.

1.44 $P = \dfrac{\sqrt{0.003654}(18.37)^3}{(8.724)^4 \sqrt[4]{743.8}}$

SOLUTION

$\log P = \frac{1}{2} \log 0.003654 + 3 \log 18.37 - (4 \log 8.724 + \frac{1}{4} \log 743.8)$:

Numerator N

$$
\begin{aligned}
\tfrac{1}{2}\log 0.003654 &= \tfrac{1}{2}(7.5628 - 10) \\
&= \tfrac{1}{2}(17.5628 - 20) = 8.7814 - 10 \\
3 \log 18.37 &= 3(1.2641) = 3.7923 \\
\text{Add:} \quad \log N &= 12.5737 - 10 \\
(-) \log D &= 4.4806 \\
\log P &= 8.0931 - 10 \\
P &= 0.01239
\end{aligned}
$$

Denominator D

$$
\begin{aligned}
4 \log 8.724 &= 4(0.9407) = 3.7628 \\
\tfrac{1}{4} \log 743.6 &= \tfrac{1}{4}(2.8714) = 0.7178 \\
\text{Add:} \quad \log D &= 4.4806
\end{aligned}
$$

1.45 $P = \sqrt{\dfrac{(874.3)(0.03816)(28.53)^3}{(1.754)^4(0.007352)}}$

SOLUTION

$\log P = \frac{1}{2}[\log 874.3 + \log 0.03816 + 3 \log 28.53 - (4 \log 1.754 + \log 0.007352)]$:

$$
\begin{aligned}
\log 874.3 &= 2.9417 = 2.9417 \\
\log 0.03816 &= 8.5816 - 10 = 8.5816 - 10 \\
3 \log 28.53 &= 3(1.4553) = 4.3659 \\
\text{Add:} &\quad 15.8892 - 10 \qquad (1)
\end{aligned}
$$

$$
\begin{aligned}
4 \log 1.754 &= 4(0.2440) = 0.9760 \\
\log 0.007352 &= 7.8664 - 10 \\
\text{Add:} &\quad 8.8424 - 10 \qquad (2)
\end{aligned}
$$

From (*1*) and (*2*) we have

$$\log P = \tfrac{1}{2}[(15.8892 - 10) - (8.8424 - 10)] = \tfrac{1}{2}(7.0468) = 3.5234, \text{ and } P = 3338.$$

Supplementary Problems

VARIABLES

1.46 State which of the following represent discrete data and which represent continuous data:

(*a*) Number of inches of rainfall in a city during various months of the year
(*b*) Speed of an automobile in miles per hour
(*c*) Number of \$20 bills circulating in the United States at any time
(*d*) Total value of shares sold each day in the stock market
(*e*) Student enrollment in a university over a number of years

1.47 Give the domain of each of the following variables and state whether the variables are continuous or discrete:

(*a*) Number W of bushels of wheat produced per acre on a farm over a number of years
(*b*) Number N of individuals in a family
(*c*) Marital status of an individual
(*d*) Time T of flight of a missile
(*e*) Number P of petals on a flower

ROUNDING OF DATA, SCIENTIFIC NOTATION, AND SIGNIFICANT FIGURES

1.48 Round each of the following numbers to the indicated accuracy:

(*a*)	3256	nearest hundred	(*f*)	3,502,378	nearest million
(*b*)	5.781	nearest tenth	(*g*)	148.475	nearest unit
(*c*)	0.0045	nearest thousandth	(*h*)	0.000098501	nearest millionth
(*d*)	46.7385	nearest hundredth	(*i*)	2184.73	nearest ten
(*e*)	125.9995	two decimal places	(*j*)	43.87500	nearest hundredth

1.49 Express each number without using powers of 10.

(*a*) 132.5×10^4
(*b*) 418.72×10^{-5}
(*c*) 280×10^{-7}
(*d*) 7300×10^6
(*e*) 3.487×10^{-4}
(*f*) 0.0001850×10^5

1.50 How many significant figures are in each of the following, assuming that the numbers are accurately recorded?

(*a*) 2.54 cm
(*b*) 0.004500 yd
(*c*) 3,510,000 bu
(*d*) 3.51 million bu
(*e*) 10.000100 ft
(*f*) 378 people
(*g*) 378 oz
(*h*) 4.50×10^{-3} km
(*i*) 500.8×10^5 kg
(*j*) 100.00 mi

1.51 What is the maximum error in each of the following measurements, assumed to be accurately recorded? Give the number of significant figures in each case.

(*a*) 7.20 million bu
(*b*) 0.00004835 cm
(*c*) 5280 ft
(*d*) 3.0×10^8 m
(*e*) 186,000 mi/sec
(*f*) 186 thousand mi/sec

1.52 Write each of the following numbers using the scientific notation. Assume that all figures are significant unless otherwise indicated.

(*a*) 0.000317
(*b*) 428,000,000 (four significant figures)
(*c*) 21,600.00
(*d*) 0.000009810
(*e*) 732 thousand
(*f*) 18.0 ten-thousandths

COMPUTATIONS

1.53 Show that (*a*) the product and (*b*) the quotient of the numbers 72.48 and 5.16, assumed to have four and three significant figures, respectively, cannot be accurate to more than three significant figures. Write the accurately recorded product and quotient.

1.54 Perform each indicated operation. Unless otherwise specified, assume that the numbers are accurately recorded.

(*a*) 0.36×781.4

(*b*) $\dfrac{873.00}{4.881}$

(*c*) $5.78 \times 2700 \times 16.00$

(*d*) $\dfrac{0.00480 \times 2300}{0.2084}$

(*e*) $\sqrt{120 \times 0.5386 \times 0.4614}$ (120 exact)

(*f*) $\dfrac{(416{,}000)(0.000187)}{\sqrt{73.84}}$

(*g*) $14.8641 + 4.48 - 8.168 + 0.36125$

(*h*) $4{,}173{,}000 - 170{,}264 + 1{,}820{,}470 - 78{,}320$ (numbers are respectively accurate to four, six, six, and five significant figures)

(*i*) $\sqrt{\dfrac{7(4.386)^2 - 3(6.47)^2}{6}}$ (3, 6, and 7 are exact)

(*j*) $4.120\sqrt{\dfrac{3.1416[(9.483)^2 - (5.075)^2]}{0.0001980}}$

1.55 Evaluate each of the following, given that $U = -2$, $V = \frac{1}{2}$, $W = 3$, $X = -4$, $Y = 9$, and $Z = \frac{1}{6}$, where all numbers are assumed to be exact.

(*a*) $4U + 6V - 2W$

(*b*) $\dfrac{XYZ}{UVW}$

(*c*) $\dfrac{2X - 3Y}{UW + XV}$

(*d*) $3(U - X)^2 + Y$

(*e*) $\sqrt{U^2 - 2UV + W}$

(*f*) $3X(4Y + 3Z) - 2Y(6X - 5Z) - 25$

(*g*) $\sqrt{\dfrac{(W-2)^2}{V} + \dfrac{(Y-5)^2}{Z}}$

(*h*) $\dfrac{X - 3}{\sqrt{(Y-4)^2 + (U+5)^2}}$

(*i*) $X^3 + 5X^2 - 6X - 8$

(*j*) $\dfrac{U - V}{\sqrt{U^2 + V^2}}[U^2V(W + X)]$

FUNCTIONS, TABLES, AND GRAPHS

1.56 A variable Y is determined from a variable X according to the equation $Y = 10 - 4X$.

(*a*) Find Y when $X = -3, -2, -1, 0, 1, 2, 3, 4$, and 5, and show the results in a table.

(*b*) Find Y when $X = -2.4, -1.6, -0.8, 1.8, 2.7, 3.5$, and 4.6.

(*c*) If the dependence of Y on X is denoted by $Y = F(X)$, find $F(2.8)$, $F(-5)$, $F(\sqrt{2})$, and $F(-\pi)$.

(*d*) What value of X corresponds to $Y = -2, 6, -10, 1.6, 16, 0$, and 10?

(*e*) Express X explicitly as a function of Y.

1.57 If $Z = X^2 - Y^2$, find Z when (*a*) $X = -2$, $Y = 3$, and (*b*) $X = 1$, $Y = 5$. (*c*) If using the functional notation $Z = F(X, Y)$, find $F(-3, -1)$.

1.58 If $W = 3XZ - 4Y^2 + 2XY$, find W when (*a*) $X = 1$, $Y = -2$, $Z = 4$, and (*b*) $X = -5$, $Y = -2$, $Z = 0$. (*c*) If using the functional notation $W = F(X, Y, Z)$, find $F(3, 1, -2)$.

1.59 Locate on a rectangular coordinate system the points having coordinates (*a*) (3, 2), (*b*) (2, 3), (*c*) (−4, 4), (*d*) (4, −4), (*e*) (−3, −2), (*f*) (−2, −3), (*g*) (−4.5, 3), (*h*) (−1.2, −2.4), (*i*) (0, −3), and (*j*) (1.8, 0).

1.60 Graph the equations (*a*) $Y = 10 - 4X$ (see Problem 1.56), (*b*) $Y = 2X + 5$, (*c*) $Y = \frac{1}{3}(X - 6)$, (*d*) $2X + 3Y = 12$, and (*e*) $3X - 2Y = 6$.

1.61 Graph the equations (a) $Y=2X^2+X-10$, and (b) $Y=6-3X-X^2$.

1.62 Graph $Y=X^3-4X^2+12X-6$.

1.63 Table 1.8 shows the numbers of agricultural and nonagricultural workers in the United States for the years 1840–1980. Graph the data, using (a) line graphs, (b) bar charts, and (c) component bar charts.

Table 1.8

Year	1840	1860	1880	1900	1920	1940	1960	1980
Agricultural workers (millions)	3.72	6.20	8.59	10.90	11.46	9.22	4.19	2.33
Nonagricultural workers (millions)	1.70	4.33	8.80	18.17	30.97	43.75	65.70	103.76

Source: U.S. Bureau of the Census.

1.64 Using the data of Table 1.8, design an appropriate pictograph to show the variation in the numbers of (a) agricultural and (b) nonagricultural workers. Can you design a pictograph that will show the variation in both (a) and (b)?

1.65 Using the data of Table 1.8, construct a graph showing the percentage of all workers who are (a) agricultural and (b) nonagricultural. Can you design a graph that will show parts (a) and (b) simultaneously?

1.66 Table 1.9 shows the life expectancy in years of a child born in the United States during the period 1920–1980. Use an appropriate graph to portray the data.

Table 1.9

Year	1920	1930	1940	1950	1960	1970	1980
Male	53.6	58.1	60.8	65.6	66.6	67.1	70.0
Female	54.6	61.6	65.2	71.1	73.1	74.7	77.4

Source: National Center for Health Statistics.

1.67 Table 1.10 shows the orbital velocities of the planets in our solar system. Graph the data.

Table 1.10

Planet	Mercury	Venus	Earth	Mars	Jupiter	Saturn	Uranus	Neptune	Pluto
Velocity (mi/sec)	29.7	21.8	18.5	15.0	8.1	6.0	4.2	3.4	3.0

1.68 Table 1.11 shows the total student enrollment (in millions) for elementary schools, high schools, and colleges in the United States. Graph the data, using (a) line graphs, (b) bar charts, and (c) component bar charts.

Table 1.11

Year	1960	1965	1970	1975	1980
Elementary	32.4	35.5	37.1	33.8	30.6
High school	10.2	13.0	14.7	15.7	14.6
College	3.6	5.7	7.4	9.7	10.2

Source: U.S. Bureau of the Census.

1.69 Graph the data of Table 1.11 by using a percentage component graph.

1.70 Table 1.12 shows the marital status of males and females (18 years and older) in the United States as of the year 1983. Graph the data, using (*a*) two pie charts having the same diameter and (*b*) a graph of your own choosing.

Table 1.12

Marital Status	Male (percent of total)	Female (percent of total)
Single	25.1	18.4
Married	66.7	61.3
Widowed	2.4	12.4
Divorced	5.8	7.9

Source: U.S. Bureau of the Census.

1.71 Table 1.13 shows the total number of industrial and commercial business failures in the United States during the years 1975–1986. Graph the data, using the appropriate types of graphs.

Table 1.13

Year	1975	1976	1977	1978	1979	1980	1981	1982	1983	1984	1985	1986
Total business failures	11,432	9,628	7,919	6,619	7,564	11,742	16,794	24,908	31,334	52,078	57,252	61,183

Source: Survey of Current Business.

1.72 Table 1.14 shows the ratio of the number of divorces to marriages in the United States for the years 1900–1980. Graph the data, using two types of graphs.

Table 1.14

Year	1900	1910	1920	1930	1940	1950	1960	1970	1980
Ratio of divorces to marriages	0.079	0.088	0.134	0.174	0.165	0.231	0.258	0.328	0.491

Source: U.S. Department of Health and Human Services.

1.73 To the nearest million, Table 1.15 shows the countries of the world with the largest populations as of 1986. Graph the data, using two methods.

Table 1.15

Country	China	India	Soviet Union	United States	Indonesia	Brazil	Japan
Population (millions)	1038	768	278	239	173	135	121

Source: United Nations.

1.74 Graph the data of Table 1.15, taking into account the fact that the total world population as of 1986 was 4850 million.

1.75 Table 1.16 shows the areas of the oceans of the world in millions of square miles. Graph the data, using (*a*) a bar chart and (*b*) a pie chart.

Table 1.16

Ocean	Pacific	Atlantic	Indian	Antarctic	Arctic
Area (million square miles)	63.8	31.5	28.4	7.6	4.8

Source: United Nations.

EQUATIONS

1.76 Solve each of the following equations:

(*a*) $16-5c=36$ (*c*) $4(X-3)-11=15-2(X+4)$ (*e*) $3[2(X+1)-4]=10-5(4-2X)$

(*b*) $2Y-6=4-3Y$ (*d*) $3(2U+1)=5(3-U)+3(U-2)$ (*f*) $\frac{2}{5}(12+Y)=6-\frac{1}{4}(9-Y)$

1.77 Solve each of the following simultaneous equations:

(*a*) $2a+b=10$
$7a-3b=9$

(*b*) $3a+5b=24$
$2a+3b=14$

(*c*) $8X-3Y=2$
$3X+7Y=-9$

(*d*) $5A-9B=-10$
$3A-4B=16$

(*e*) $2a+b-c=2$
$3a-4b+2c=4$
$4a+3b-5c=-8$

(*f*) $5X+2Y+3Z=-5$
$2X-3Y-6Z=1$
$X+5Y-4Z=22$

(*g*) $3U-5V+6W=7$
$5U+3V-2W=-1$
$4U-8V+10W=11$

1.78 (*a*) Graph the equations $5X+2Y=4$ and $7X-3Y=23$, using the same set of coordinate axes.

(*b*) From the graphs determine the simultaneous solution of the two equations.

(*c*) Use the method of parts (*a*) and (*b*) to obtain the simultaneous solutions of equations (*a*) to (*d*) of Problem 1.77.

1.79 (*a*) Use the graph of Problem 1.61(*a*) to solve the equation $2X^2+X-10=0$. (*Hint:* Find the values of X where the parabola intersects the X axis: that is, where $Y=0$.)

(*b*) Use the method in part (*a*) to solve $3X^2-4X-5=0$.

1.80 The solutions of the quadratic equation $aX^2 + bX + c = 0$ are given by the *quadratic formula*:

$$X = \frac{-b \pm \sqrt{b^2 - 4ac}}{2a}$$

Use this formula to find the solutions of (*a*) $3X^2 - 4X - 5 = 0$, (*b*) $2X^2 + X - 10 = 0$, (*c*) $5X^2 + 10X = 7$, and (*d*) $X^2 + 8X + 25 = 0$.

INEQUALITIES

1.81 Using inequality symbols, arrange the numbers −4.3, −6.15, 2.37, 1.52, and −1.5 in (*a*) increasing and (*b*) decreasing order of magnitude.

1.82 Use inequality symbols to express each of the following statements:

(*a*) The number N of children is between 30 and 50 inclusive.

(*b*) The sum S of points on the pair of dice is not less than 7.

(*c*) X is greater than or equal to −4 but less than 3.

(*d*) P is at most 5.

(*e*) X exceeds Y by more than 2.

1.83 Solve each of the following inequalities:

(*a*) $3X \geq 12$

(*b*) $4X < 5X - 3$

(*c*) $2N + 15 > 10 + 3N$

(*d*) $3 + 5(Y - 2) \leq 7 - 3(4 - Y)$

(*e*) $-3 \leq \frac{1}{5}(2X + 1) \leq 3$

(*f*) $0 < \frac{1}{2}(15 - 5N) \leq 12$

(*g*) $-2 \leq 3 + \frac{1}{2}(a - 12) < 8$

LOGARITHMS AND ANTILOGARITHMS

1.84 Find the common logarithm of each of the following numbers:

(*a*) 387 (*b*) 0.387 (*c*) 0.0792 (*d*) 14,630 (*e*) 0.6042 (*f*) 0.002795 (*g*) 476.3 (*h*) 1.007 (*i*) 7.146 (*j*) 71.46 (*k*) 0.00098 (*l*) 84,620,000

1.85 Find the antilogarithm of each of the following:

(*a*) 3.5611 (*b*) 9.8293 − 10 (*c*) 1.7045 (*d*) 8.9266 − 10 (*e*) 2.4700 (*f*) 6.4700 − 10 (*g*) $\bar{2}.8003$ (*h*) 3.7072 (*i*) 0.0800 (*j*) 6.3841

1.86 Evaluate each of the following by using logarithms:

(*a*) $(783.6)(1654)$

(*b*) $\dfrac{21.7}{378.2}$

(*c*) $\dfrac{(0.04556)(624.1)}{(14.32)(0.003572)}$

(*d*) $(1.562)^{15}$

(*e*) $\dfrac{(0.3854)^4(12.48)^2}{(0.04382)^3}$

(*f*) $0.04182\sqrt{0.6758}$

(*g*) $\sqrt[3]{3728}$

(*h*) $\sqrt[5]{(21.63)(33.81)(47.53)(65.28)(87.47)}$

(*i*) $\sqrt{\dfrac{(48.79)(0.00574)^3}{(2.143)^5}}$

(*j*) $\dfrac{3.781}{0.01873}\sqrt{\dfrac{(43.25)(0.08743)}{(0.002356)(6.824)}}$

1.87 Graph (*a*) $Y = \log X$ and (*b*) $Y = 10^X$ and discuss the similarities between the two graphs.

1.88 Write the equations (*a*) $2 \log X - 3 \log Y = 2$ and (*b*) $\log Y + 2X = \log 3$ in a form free of logarithms.

1.89 If $a^p = N$, where a and p are positive numbers and $a \neq 1$, we call p the *logarithm of N to the base a* and write $p = \log_a N$. Evaluate (a) $\log_2 8$, (b) $\log_{25} 125$, (c) $\log_4 1/16$, (d) $\log_{1/2} 32$, and (e) $\log_5 1$.

1.90 Show that $\log_e N = 2.303 \log_{10} N$ approximately, where $e = 2.71828\ldots$ is called the *natural base* of logarithms and where $N > 0$.

1.91 Show that $(\log_b a)(\log_a b) = 1$, where $a > 0$, $b > 0$, $a \neq 1$, and $b \neq 1$.

Chapter 2

Frequency Distributions

RAW DATA

Raw data are collected data that have not been organized numerically. An example is the set of heights of 100 male students obtained from an alphabetical listing of university records.

ARRAYS

An *array* is an arrangement of raw numerical data in ascending or descending order of magnitude. The difference between the largest and smallest numbers is called the *range* of the data. For example, if the largest height of 100 male students is 74 inches (in) and the smallest height is 60 in, the range is $74-60=14$ in.

FREQUENCY DISTRIBUTIONS

When summarizing large masses of raw data, it is often useful to distribute the data into *classes*, or *categories*, and to determine the number of individuals belonging to each class, called the *class frequency*. A tabular arrangement of data by classes together with the corresponding class frequencies is called a *frequency distribution*, or *frequency table*. Table 2.1 is a frequency distribution of heights (recorded to the nearest inch) of 100 male students at XYZ University.

Table 2.1 Heights of 100 Male Students at XYZ University

Height (in)	Number of Students
60–62	5
63–65	18
66–68	42
69–71	27
72–74	8
	Total 100

The first class (or category), for example, consists of heights from 60 to 62 in and is indicated by the range symbol 60–62. Since five students have heights belonging to this class, the corresponding class frequency is 5.

Data organized and summarized as in the above frequency distribution are often called *grouped data*. Although the grouping process generally destroys much of the original detail of the data, an important advantage is gained in the clear "overall" picture that is obtained and in the vital relationships that are thereby made evident.

CLASS INTERVALS AND CLASS LIMITS

A symbol defining a class, such as 60–62 in Table 2.1, is called a *class interval.* The end numbers, 60 and 62, are called *class limits*; the smaller number (60) is the *lower class limit,* and the larger number (62) is the *upper class limit.* The terms *class* and *class interval* are often used interchangeably, although the class interval is actually a symbol for the class.

A class interval that, at least theoretically, has either no upper class limit or no lower class limit indicated is called an *open class interval.* For example, referring to age groups of individuals, the class interval "65 years and over" is an open class interval.

CLASS BOUNDARIES

If heights are recorded to the nearest inch, the class interval 60–62 theoretically includes all measurements from 59.5000 to 62.5000 in. These numbers, indicated briefly by the exact numbers 59.5 and 62.5, are called *class boundaries,* or *true class limits*; the smaller number (59.5) is the *lower class boundary,* and the larger number (62.5) is the *upper class boundary.*

In practice, the class boundaries are obtained by adding the upper limit of one class interval to the lower limit of the next-higher class interval and dividing by 2.

Sometimes, class boundaries are used to symbolize classes. For example, the various classes in the first column of Table 2.1 could be indicated by 59.5–62.5, 62.5–65.5, etc. To avoid ambiguity in using such notation, class boundaries should not coincide with actual observations. Thus if an observation were 62.5, it would not be possible to decide whether it belonged to the class interval 59.5–62.5 or 62.5–65.5.

THE SIZE, OR WIDTH, OF A CLASS INTERVAL

The size, or width, of a class interval is the difference between the lower and upper class boundaries and is also referred to as the *class width, class size,* or *class length.* If all class intervals of a frequency distribution have equal widths, this common width is denoted by c. In such case c is equal to the difference between two successive lower class limits or two successive upper class limits. For the data of Table 2.1, for example, the class interval is $c = 62.5 - 59.5 = 65.5 - 62.5 = 3$.

THE CLASS MARK

The *class mark* is the midpoint of the class interval and is obtained by adding the lower and upper class limits and dividing by 2. Thus the class mark of the interval 60–62 is $(60+62)/2 = 61$. The class mark is also called the *class midpoint.*

For purposes of further mathematical analysis, all observations belonging to a given class interval are assumed to coincide with the class mark. Thus all heights in the class interval 60–62 in are considered to be 61 in.

GENERAL RULES FOR FORMING FREQUENCY DISTRIBUTIONS

1. Determine the largest and smallest numbers in the raw data and thus find the range (the difference between the largest and smallest numbers).
2. Divide the range into a convenient number of class intervals having the same size. If this is not feasible, use class intervals of different sizes or open class intervals (see Problem 2.12). The number of class intervals is usually taken between 5 and 20, depending on the data. Class intervals are also chosen so that the class marks (or midpoints) coincide with the actually observed data. This tends

to lessen the so-called *grouping error* involved in further mathematical analysis. However, the class boundaries should not coincide with the actually observed data.

3. Determine the number of observations falling into each class interval; that is, find the class frequencies. This is best done by using a *tally*, or *score sheet* (see Problem 2.8).

HISTOGRAMS AND FREQUENCY POLYGONS

Histograms and frequency polygons are two graphic representations of frequency distributions.

1. A *histogram*, or *frequency histogram*, consists of a set of rectangles having (a) bases on a horizontal axis (the X axis), with centers at the class marks and lengths equal to the class interval sizes, and (b) areas proportional to the class frequencies.

   If the class intervals all have equal size, the heights of the rectangles are proportional to the class frequencies, and it is then customary to take the heights numerically equal to the class frequencies. If the class intervals do not have equal size, these heights must be adjusted (see Problem 2.13).

2. A *frequency polygon* is a line graph of the class frequency plotted against the class mark. It can be obtained by connecting the midpoints of the tops of the rectangles in the histogram.

The histogram and frequency polygon corresponding to the frequency distribution of heights in Table 2.1 are shown on the same set of axes in Fig. 2-1. It is customary to add the extensions *PQ* and *RS* to the next-lower and -higher class marks, which have a corresponding class frequency of zero. In such case the sum of the areas of the rectangles in the histogram equals the total area bounded by the frequency polygon and the X axis (see Problem 2.11).

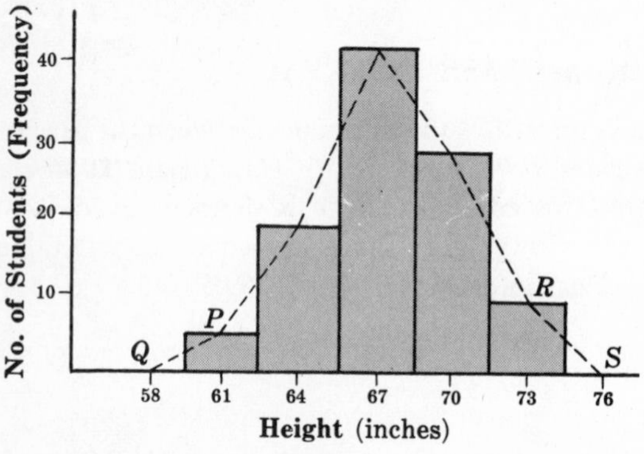

Fig. 2-1

RELATIVE-FREQUENCY DISTRIBUTIONS

The *relative frequency* of a class is the frequency of the class divided by the total frequency of all classes and is generally expressed as a percentage. For example, the relative frequency of the class 66–68 in Table 2.1 is $42/100 = 42\%$. The sum of the relative frequencies of all classes is clearly 1, or 100%.

If the frequencies in Table 2.1 are replaced with the corresponding relative frequencies, the resulting table is called a *relative-frequency distribution*, *percentage distribution*, or *relative-frequency table*.

Graphic representation of relative-frequency distributions can be obtained from the histogram or frequency polygon simply by changing the vertical scale from frequency to relative frequency, keeping exactly the same diagram. The resulting graphs are called *relative-frequency histograms* (or *percentage histograms*) and *relative-frequency polygons* (or *percentage polygons*), respectively.

CUMULATIVE-FREQUENCY DISTRIBUTIONS AND OGIVES

The total frequency of all values less than the upper class boundary of a given class interval is called the *cumulative frequency* up to and including that class interval. For example, the cumulative frequency up to and including the class interval 66–68 in Table 2.1 is $5+18+42=65$, signifying that 65 students have heights less than 68.5 in.

A table presenting such cumulative frequencies is called a *cumulative-frequency distribution, cumulative-frequency table*, or briefly a *cumulative distribution*, and is shown in Table 2.2 for the student height distribution of Table 2.1.

Table 2.2

Height (in)	Number of Students
Less than 59.5	0
Less than 62.5	5
Less than 65.5	23
Less than 68.5	65
Less than 71.5	92
Less than 74.5	100

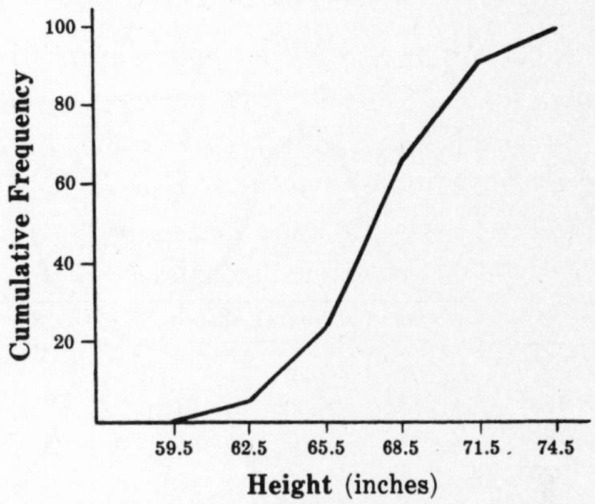

Fig. 2-2

A graph showing the cumulative frequency less than any upper class boundary plotted against the upper class boundary is called a *cumulative-frequency polygon*, or *ogive*, and is shown in Fig. 2-2 for the student height distribution of Table 2.1.

For some purposes, it is desirable to consider a cumulative-frequency distribution of all values greater than or equal to the lower class boundary of each class interval. Because in this case we consider heights of 59.5 in or more, 62.5 in or more, etc., this is sometimes called an "*or more*" *cumulative distribution*, while the one considered above is a "*less than*" *cumulative distribution*. One is easily obtained from the other (see Problem 2.15). The corresponding ogives are then called "or more" and "less than" ogives. Whenever we refer to cumulative distributions or ogives without qualification, the "less than" type is implied.

RELATIVE CUMULATIVE-FREQUENCY DISTRIBUTIONS AND PERCENTAGE OGIVES

The *relative cumulative frequency, or percentage cumulative frequency*, is the cumulative frequency divided by the total frequency. For example, the relative cumulative frequency of heights less than 68.5 in is $65/100=65\%$, signifying that 65% of the students have heights less than 68.5 in.

If relative cumulative frequencies are used in Table 2.2 and Fig. 2-2 in place of cumulative frequencies, the results are called *relative cumulative-frequency distributions* (or *percentage cumulative distributions*) and *relative cumulative-frequency polygons* (or *percentage ogives*), respectively.

FREQUENCY CURVES AND SMOOTHED OGIVES

Collected data can usually be considered as belonging to a sample drawn from a large population. Since so many observations are available in the population, it is theoretically possible (for continuous data) to choose class intervals very small and still have sizable numbers of observations falling within each class. Thus one would expect the frequency polygon or relative-frequency polygon for a large population to have so many small, broken line segments that they closely approximate curves, which we call *frequency curves* or *relative-frequency curves*, respectively.

It is reasonable to expect that such theoretical curves can be approximated by smoothing the frequency polygons or relative-frequency polygons of the sample, the approximation improving as the sample size is increased. For this reason, a frequency curve is sometimes called a *smoothed frequency polygon*.

In a similar manner, *smoothed ogives* are obtained by smoothing the cumulative-frequency polygons, or ogives. It is usually easier to smooth an ogive than a frequency polygon (see Problem 2.18).

TYPES OF FREQUENCY CURVES

Frequency curves arising in practice take on certain characteristic shapes, as shown in Fig. 2-3.

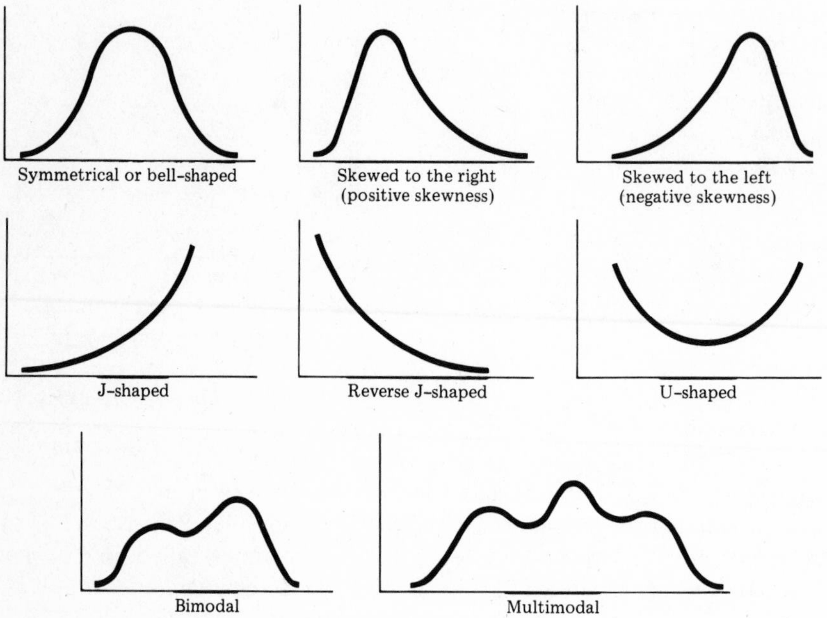

Fig. 2-3

1. The *symmetrical*, or *bell-shaped*, frequency curves are characterized by the fact that observations equidistant from the central maximum have the same frequency. An important example is the *normal curve.*
2. In the *moderately asymmetrical*, or *skewed*, frequency curves the tail of the curve to one side of the central maximum is longer than that to the other. If the longer tail occurs to the right, the curve is said to be *skewed to the right* or to have *positive skewness*, while if the reverse is true, the curve is said to be *skewed to the left* or to have *negative skewness.*
3. In a *J-shaped* or *reverse J-shaped* curve a maximum occurs at one end.
4. A *U-shaped* frequency curve has maxima at both ends.
5. A *bimodal* frequency curve has two maxima.
6. A *multimodal* frequency curve has more than two maxima.

Solved Problems

ARRAYS

2.1 (*a*) Arrange the numbers 17, 45, 38, 27, 6, 48, 11, 57, 34, and 22 in an array.
(*b*) Determine the range of these numbers.

SOLUTION

(*a*) In ascending order of magnitude, the array is: 6, 11, 17, 22, 27, 34, 38, 45, 48, 57. In descending order of magnitude, the array is: 57, 48, 45, 38, 34, 27, 22, 17, 11, 6.

(*b*) Since the smallest number is 6 and the largest number is 57, the range is $57 - 6 = 51$.

Mathcad **2.2** The final grades in mathematics of 80 students at State University are recorded in the accompanying table.

68	84	75	82	68	90	62	88	76	93
73	79	88	73	60	93	71	59	85	75
61	65	75	87	74	62	95	78	63	72
66	78	82	75	94	77	69	74	68	60
96	78	89	61	75	95	60	79	83	71
79	62	67	97	78	85	76	65	71	75
65	80	73	57	88	78	62	76	53	74
86	67	73	81	72	63	76	75	85	77

With reference to this table, find:

(*a*) The highest grade.
(*b*) The lowest grade.
(*c*) The range.
(*d*) The grades of the five highest-ranking students.
(*e*) The grades of the five lowest-ranking students.
(*f*) The grade of the student ranking tenth-highest.
(*g*) The number of students who received grades of 75 or higher.
(*h*) The number of students who received grades below 85.
(*i*) The percentage of students who received grades higher than 65 but not higher than 85.
(*j*) The grades that did not appear at all.

SOLUTION

Some of these questions are so detailed that they are best answered by first constructing an array. This can be done by subdividing the data into convenient classes and placing each number taken from the table into the appropriate class, as in Table 2.3, called an *entry table.* By then arranging the numbers of each class into an array, as in Table 2.4, the required array is obtained. From Table 2.4 it is relatively easy to answer the above questions.

(*a*) The highest grade is 97.
(*b*) The lowest grade is 53.
(*c*) The range is $97 - 53 = 44$.
(*d*) The five highest-ranking students have grades 97, 96, 95, 95, and 94.
(*e*) The five lowest-ranking students have grades 53, 57, 59, 60, and 60.
(*f*) The grade of the student ranking tenth-highest is 88.

Table 2.3

50–54	53
55–59	59, 57
60–64	62, 60, 61, 62, 63, 60, 61, 60, 62, 62, 63
65–69	68, 68, 65, 66, 69, 68, 67, 65, 65, 67
70–74	73, 73, 71, 74, 72, 74, 71, 71, 73, 74, 73, 72
75–79	75, 76, 79, 75, 75, 78, 78, 75, 77, 78, 75, 79, 79, 78, 76, 75, 78, 76, 76, 75, 77
80–84	84, 82, 82, 83, 80, 81
85–89	88, 88, 85, 87, 89, 85, 88, 86, 85
90–94	90, 93, 93, 94
95–99	95, 96, 95, 97

Table 2.4

50–54	53
55–59	57, 59
60–64	60, 60, 60, 61, 61, 62, 62, 62, 62, 63, 63
65–69	65, 65, 65, 66, 67, 67, 68, 68, 68, 69
70–74	71, 71, 71, 72, 72, 73, 73, 73, 73, 74, 74, 74
75–79	75, 75, 75, 75, 75, 75, 75, 76, 76, 76, 76, 77, 77, 78, 78, 78, 78, 78, 79, 79, 79
80–84	80, 81, 82, 82, 83, 84
85–89	85, 85, 85, 86, 87, 88, 88, 88, 89
90–94	90, 93, 93, 94
95–99	95, 95, 96, 97

(*g*) The number of students receiving grades of 75 or higher is 44.

(*h*) The number of students receiving grades below 85 is 63.

(*i*) The percentage of students receiving grades higher than 65 but not higher than 85 is $49/80 = 61.2\%$.

(*j*) The grades that did not appear are 0 through 52, 54, 55, 56, 58, 64, 70, 91, 92, 98, 99, and 100.

FREQUENCY DISTRIBUTIONS, HISTOGRAMS, AND FREQUENCY POLYGONS

2.3 Table 2.5 shows a frequency distribution of the weekly wages of 65 employees at the P&R Company. With reference to this table, determine:

(*a*) The lower limit of the sixth class.

(*b*) The upper limit of the fourth class.

(*c*) The class mark (or class midpoint) of the third class.

(*d*) The class boundaries of the fifth class.

(*e*) The size of the fifth-class interval.

(*f*) The frequency of the third class.

(*g*) The relative frequency of the third class.

(*h*) The class interval having the largest frequency. This is sometimes called the *modal class interval*; its frequency is then called the *modal class frequency.*

(*i*) The percentage of employees earning less than \$280.00 per week.

(*j*) The percentage of employees earning less than \$300.00 per week but at least \$260.00 per week.

Table 2.5

Wages	Number of Employees
\$250.00–\$259.99	8
260.00–269.99	10
270.00–279.99	16
280.00–289.99	14
290.00–299.99	10
300.00–309.99	5
310.00–319.99	2
	Total 65

SOLUTION

(*a*) \$300.00.

(*b*) \$289.99.

(*c*) The class mark of the third class $= \frac{1}{2}(\$270.00 + \$279.99) = \$274.995$. For most practical purposes, this is rounded to \$275.00.

(*d*) Lower class boundary of fifth class $= \frac{1}{2}(\$290.00 + \$289.99) = \$289.995$. Upper class boundary of fifth class $= \frac{1}{2}(\$299.99 + \$300.00) = \$299.995$.

(*e*) Size of fifth-class interval = upper boundary of fifth class − lower boundary of fifth class = $\$299.995 - \$289.985 = \$10.00$. In this case all class intervals have the same size: \$10.00.

(*f*) 16.

(*g*) $16/65 = 0.246 = 24.6\%$.

(*h*) \$270.00–\$279.99.

(*i*) Total number of employees earning less than \$280 per week $= 16 + 10 + 8 = 34$. Percentage of employees earning less than \$280 per week $= 34/65 = 52.3\%$.

(*j*) Number of employees earning less than \$300.00 per week but at least \$260 per week $= 10 + 14 + 16 + 10 = 50$. Percentage of employees earning less than \$300 per week but at least \$260 per week $= 50/65 = 76.9\%$.

2.4 If the class marks in a frequency distribution of the weights of students are 128, 137, 146, 155, 164, 173, and 182 pounds (lb), find (*a*) the class-interval size, (*b*) the class boundaries, and (*c*) the class limits, assuming that the weights were measured to the nearest pound.

SOLUTION

(*a*) Class-interval size = common difference between successive class marks $= 137 - 128 = 146 - 137 =$ etc. $= 9$ lb.

(*b*) Since the class intervals all have equal size, the class boundaries are midway between the class marks and thus have the values

$$\tfrac{1}{2}(128 + 137), \tfrac{1}{2}(137 + 146), \ldots, \tfrac{1}{2}(173 + 182) \qquad \text{or} \qquad 132.5, 141.5, 150.5, \ldots, 177.5 \text{ lb}$$

The first class boundary is $132.5 - 9 = 123.5$ and the last class boundary is $177.5 + 9 = 186.5$, since the common class-interval size is 9 lb. Thus all the class boundaries are given by

$$123.5, 132, 141.5, 150.5, 159.5, 168.5, 177.5, 186.5 \text{ lb}$$

(*c*) Since the class limits are integers, we choose them as the integers nearest to the class boundaries, namely, 123, 124, 132, 133, 141, 142, ... Thus the first class has limits 124–132, the next 133–141, etc.

2.5 Represent graphically the results of Problem 2.4.

SOLUTION

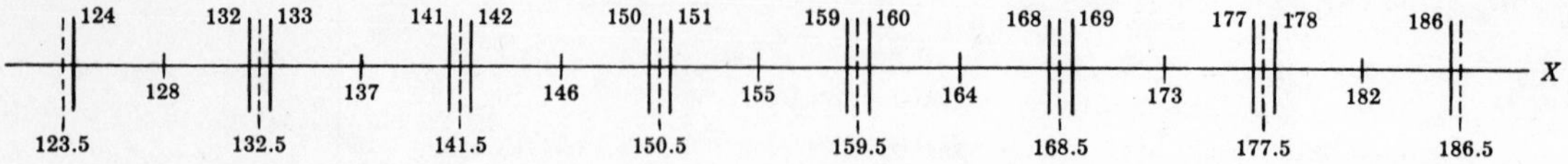

The graph is shown in the accompanying diagram. The class marks 128, 137, 146, . . . , 182 are located on the X axis. The class boundaries are indicated by the long vertical dashed lines, and the class limits are indicated by the long vertical heavy lines.

2.6 The smallest of 150 measurements is 5.18 in, and the largest is 7.44 in. Determine a suitable set of (a) class intervals, (b) class boundaries, and (c) class marks that might be used in forming a frequency distribution of these measurements.

SOLUTION

The range is $7.44 - 5.18 = 2.26$ in. For a minimum of five class intervals, the class-interval size is $2.26/5 = 0.45$ approximately; and for a maximum of 20 class intervals, the class-interval size is $2.26/20 = 0.11$ approximately. Convenient choices of class-interval sizes lying between 0.11 and 0.45 would be 0.20, 0.30, or 0.40.

(a) Columns I, II, and III of the accompanying table show suitable class intervals, having sizes 0.20, 0.30, and 0.40, respectively.

I	II	III
5.10–5.29	5.10–5.39	5.10–5.49
5.30–5.49	5.40–5.69	5.50–5.89
5.50–5.69	5.70–5.99	5.90–6.29
5.70–5.89	6.00–6.29	6.30–6.69
5.90–6.09	6.30–6.59	6.70–7.09
6.10–6.29	6.60–6.89	7.10–7.49
6.30–6.49	6.90–7.19	
6.50–6.69	7.20–7.49	
6.70–6.89		
6.90–7.09		
7.10–7.29		
7.30–7.49		

Note that the lower limit in each first class could have been different from 5.10; for example, if in column I we had started with 5.15 as the lower limit, the first class interval could have been written 5.15–5.34.

(b) The class boundaries corresponding to columns I, II, and III of part (a) are given, respectively, by

I	5.095–5.295, 5.295–5.495, 5.495–5.695, . . . , 7.295–7.495
II	5.095–5.395, 5.395–5.695, 5.695–5.995, . . . , 7.195–7.495
III	5.095–5.495, 5.495–5.895, 5.895–6.295, . . . , 7.095–7.495

Note that these class boundaries are suitable since they cannot coincide with the observed measurements.

(c) The class marks corresponding to columns I, II, and III of part (a) are given, respectively, by

I 5.195, 5.395, . . . , 7.395 II 5.245, 5.545, . . . , 7.345 III 5.295, 5.695, . . . , 7.295

These class marks have the disadvantage of not coinciding with the observed measurements.

2.7 In answering Problem 2.6(*a*), a student chose the class intervals 5.10–5.40, 5.40–5.70, ..., 6.90–7.20, and 7.20–7.50. Was there anything wrong with this choice?

SOLUTION

These class intervals overlap at 5.40, 5.70, ..., 7.20. Thus a measurement recorded as 5.40, for example, could be placed in either of the first two class intervals. Some statisticians justify this choice by agreeing to place half of such ambiguous cases in one class and half in the other.

The ambiguity is removed by writing the class intervals as 5.10 to under 5.40, 5.40 to under 5.70, etc. In this case, the class limits coincide with the class boundaries, and the class marks can coincide with the observed data.

In general it is desirable to avoid overlapping class intervals whenever possible and to choose them so that the class boundaries are values not coinciding with actual observed data. For example, the class intervals for Problem 2.6 could have been chosen as 5.095–5.395, 5.395–5.695, etc., without ambiguity. A disadvantage of this particular choice is that the class marks do not coincide with the observed data.

2.8 In the following table the weights of 40 male students at State University are recorded to the nearest pound. Construct a frequency distribution.

138	164	150	132	144	125	149	157
146	158	140	147	136	148	152	144
168	126	138	176	163	119	154	165
146	173	142	147	135	153	140	135
161	145	135	142	150	156	145	128

SOLUTION

The largest weight is 176 lb and the smallest weight is 119 lb, so that the range is $176 - 119 = 57$ lb. If five class intervals are used, the class-interval size is $57/5 = 11$ approximately; if 20 class intervals are used, the class-interval size is $57/20 = 3$ approximately.

One convenient choice for the class-interval size is 5 lb. Also, it is convenient to choose the class marks as 120, 125, 130, 135, ... lb. Thus the class intervals can be taken as 118–122, 123–127, 128–132, ... With this choice the class boundaries are 117.5, 122.5, 127.5, ..., which do not coincide with the observed data.

Table 2.6

Weight (lb)	Tally	Frequency
118–122	/	1
123–127	//	2
128–132	//	2
133–137	////	4
138–142	~~////~~ /	6
143–147	~~////~~ ///	8
148–152	~~////~~	5
153–157	////	4
158–162	//	2
163–167	///	3
168–172	/	1
173–177	//	2
		Total 40

Table 2.7

Weight (lb)	Tally	Frequency
118–126	///	3
127–135	~~////~~	5
136–144	~~////~~ ////	9
145–153	~~////~~ ~~////~~ //	12
154–162	~~////~~	5
163–171	////	4
172–180	//	2
		Total 40

The required frequency distribution is shown in Table 2.6. The center column, called a *tally*, or *score sheet*, is used to tabulate the class frequencies from the raw data and is usually omitted in the final presentation of the frequency distribution. It is unnecessary to make an array, although if it is available it can be used in tabulating the frequencies.

Another method

Of course, other possible frequency distributions exist. Table 2.7, for example, shows a frequency distribution with only seven classes in which the class interval is 9 lb.

Mathcad **2.9** Construct (a) a histogram and (b) a frequency polygon for the weight distribution in Problem 2.8.

SOLUTION

The histogram and frequency polygon for each of the cases considered in Problem 2.8 are given in Figs. 2-4(a) and 2-4(b). Note that the centers of the bases of the rectangles are located at the class marks.

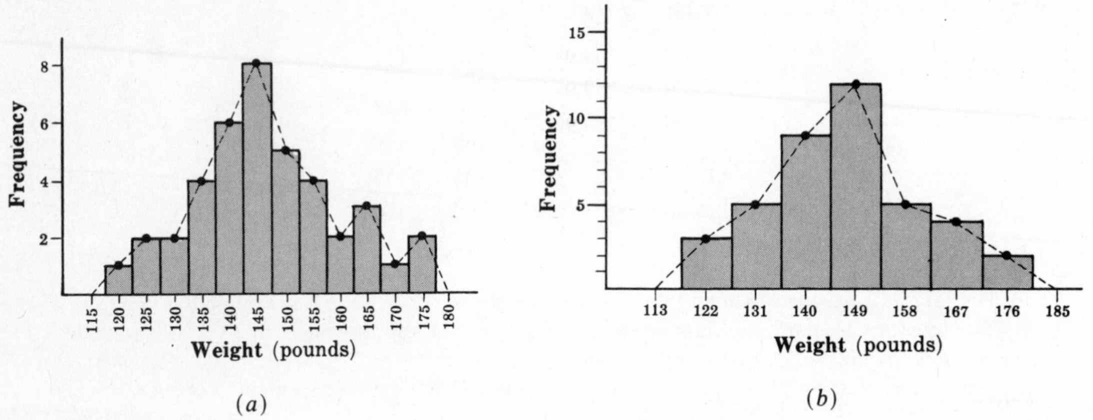

Fig. 2-4

2.10 From the data in Table 2.5 of Problem 2.3, construct (a) a relative-frequency distribution, (b) a histogram, (c) a relative-frequency histogram, (d) a frequency polygon, and (e) a relative-frequency polygon.

SOLUTION:

(a) The relative-frequency distribution shown in Table 2.8 is obtained from the frequency distribution of Table 2.5 by dividing each class frequency by the total frequency (65) and expressing the result as a percentage.

(b) and (c) The histogram and relative-frequency histogram are shown in Fig. 2-5. Note that to convert from a histogram to a relative-frequency histogram, it is only necessary to add to the histogram a vertical scale showing the relative frequencies, as shown on the right of Fig. 2-5.

(d) and (e) The frequency polygon and relative-frequency polygon are indicated by the dashed-line graph in Fig. 2-5. Thus to convert from a frequency polygon to a relative-frequency polygon, one need only add a vertical scale showing the relative frequencies.

Note that if only a relative-frequency polygon (for example) is desired, the adjoining figure would not contain the histogram, and the relative-frequency axis would be shown at the left in place of the frequency axis.

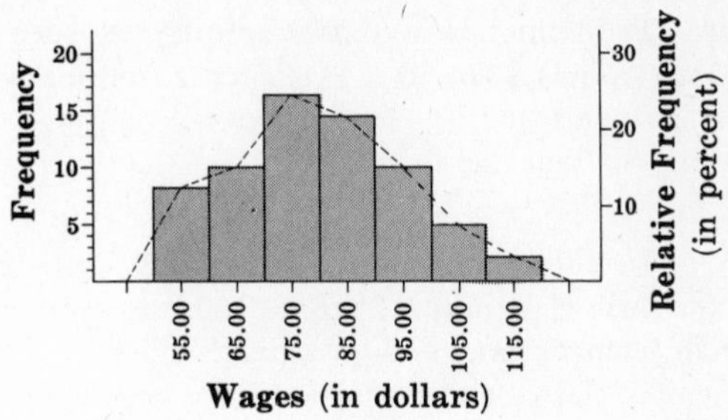

Fig. 2-5

Table 2.8

Wages	Relative Frequency (as a percentage)
\$250.00-\$259.99	12.3
260.00-269.99	15.4
270.00-279.99	24.6
280.00-289.99	21.5
290.00-299.99	15.4
300.00-309.99	7.7
310.00-319.99	3.1
	Total 100.0

2.11 Prove that the total area of the rectangles in a histogram is equal to the total area bounded by the corresponding frequency polygon and the X axis.

SOLUTION

The proof will be given for the case of a histogram consisting of three rectangles, as shown in Fig. 2-6, and the corresponding frequency polygon, shown dashed.

Total area of rectangles = shaded area + area II + area IV + area V + area VII

= shaded area + area I + area III + area VI + area VIII

= total area bounded by frequency polygon and X axis

Since area I = area II, thus area III = area IV, area V = area VI, and area VII = area VIII.

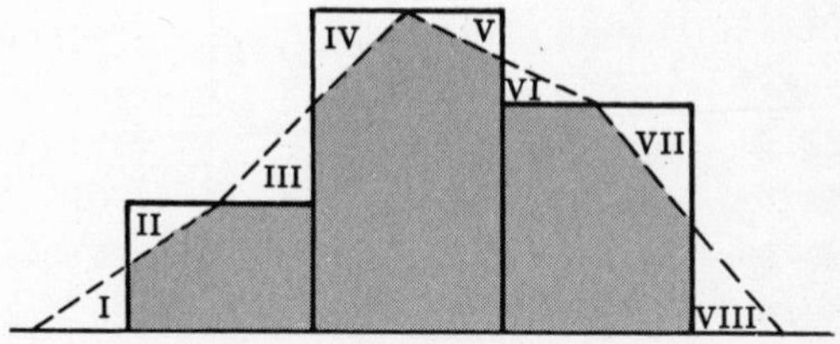

Fig. 2-6

2.12 At the P&R Company (Problem 2.3), five new employees were hired at weekly wages of \$285.34, \$316.83, \$335.78, \$356.21, and \$374.50. Construct a frequency distribution of wages for the 70 employees.

SOLUTION

Possible frequency distributions are shown in Table 2.9.

In Table 2.9(*a*), the same class-interval size, \$10.00, has been maintained throughout the table. As a result, there are too many empty classes and the detail is much too fine at the upper end of the wage scale.

In Table 2.9(*b*), empty classes and fine detail have been avoided by use of the open class interval "\$320.00 and over." A disadvantage of this is that the table becomes useless in performing certain mathematical calculations. For example, it is impossible to determine the total amount of wages paid per week, since "over \$320.00" might conceivably imply that individuals could earn as high as \$1400.00 per week.

In Table 2.9(*c*), a class-interval size of \$20.00 has been used. A disadvantage is that much information is lost at the lower end of the wage scale and the detail is still fine at the upper end of the scale.

In Table 2.9(*d*), unequal class-interval sizes have been used. A disadvantage is that certain mathematical calculations to be made later lose a simplicity that is available when class intervals have the same size. Also, the larger the class-interval size, the greater will be the grouping error.

Table 2.9(*a*)

Wages	Frequency
\$250.00–\$259.99	8
260.00–269.99	10
270.00–279.99	16
280.00–289.99	15
290.00–299.99	10
300.00–309.99	5
310.00–319.99	3
320.00–329.99	0
330.00–339.99	1
340.00–349.99	0
350.00–359.99	1
360.00–369.99	0
370.00–379.99	1
	Total 70

Table 2.9(*b*)

Wages	Frequency
\$250.00–\$259.99	8
260.00–269.99	10
270.00–279.99	16
280.00–289.99	15
290.00–299.99	10
300.00–309.99	5
310.00–319.99	3
320.00 and over	3
	Total 70

Table 2.9(*c*)

Wages	Frequency
\$250.00–\$269.99	18
270.00–289.99	31
290.00–309.99	15
310.00–329.99	3
330.00–349.99	1
350.00–369.99	1
370.00–389.99	1
	Total 70

Table 2.9(*d*)

Wages	Frequency
\$250.00–\$259.99	8
260.00–269.99	10
270.00–279.99	16
280.00–289.99	15
290.00–299.99	10
300.00–319.99	8
320.00–379.99	3
	Total 70

2.13 Construct a histogram for the frequency distribution shown in Table 2.9(*d*).

SOLUTION

The required histogram is shown in Fig. 2-7. To construct it, we use the fact that area is proportional to frequency. Suppose that rectangle *A* corresponds to the first class [see Table 2.9(*d*)] with class frequency 8. Since the sixth class of Table 2.9(*d*) also has class frequency 8, then rectangle *B*, which represents this class, should have the same area as *A*. Then since *B* is twice as wide as *A*, it must be half as high, as shown in Fig. 2-7.

Similarly, rectangle *C*, representing the last class in Table 2.9(*d*), is a half-unit high on the vertical scale.

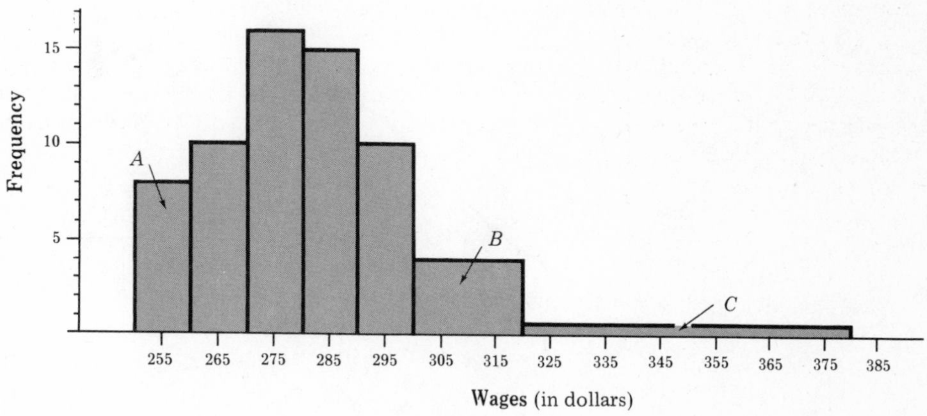

Fig. 2-7

CUMULATIVE-FREQUENCY DISTRIBUTIONS AND OGIVES

Mathcad **2.14** Construct (*a*) a cumulative-frequency distribution, (*b*) a percentage cumulative distribution, (*c*) an ogive, and (*d*) a percentage ogive from the frequency distribution in Table 2.5 of Problem 2.3.

SOLUTION

(*a*) and (*b*) The cumulative-frequency distribution and percentage cumulative distribution (or cumulative relative-frequency distribution) are shown combined in Table 2.10.

Table 2.10

Wages	Cumulative Frequency	Percentage Cumulative Distribution
Less than $250.00	0	0.0
Less than 260.00	8	12.3
Less than 270.00	18	27.7
Less than 280.00	34	52.3
Less than 290.00	48	73.8
Less than 300.00	58	89.2
Less than 310.00	63	96.9
Less than 320.00	65	100.0

Note that each entry in column 2 is obtained by adding successive entries from column 2 of Table 2.5. Thus $18 = 8 + 10$, $34 = 8 + 10 + 16$, etc.

Each entry in column 3 is obtained from the previous column by dividing by 65, the total frequency, and expressing the result as a percentage. Thus $34/65 = 52.3\%$. Entries in this column can also be obtained by adding successive entries from column 2 of Table 2.8. Thus $27.7 = 12.3 + 15.4$, $52.3 = 12.3 + 15.4 + 24.6$, etc.

(*c*) and (*d*) The ogive (or cumulative-frequency polygon) and percentage ogive (or relative cumulative-frequency polygon) are both indicated in Fig. 2-8. The vertical scale at the left enables us to read the cumulative frequency, while the vertical scale at the right indicates the percentage cumulative frequency.

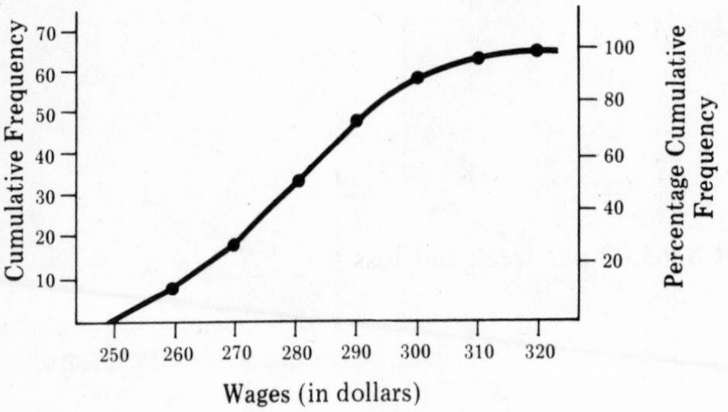

Fig. 2-8

The above are sometimes referred to as "less than" cumulative-frequency distributions and ogives because of the manner in which the frequencies have been cumulated.

Mathcad **2.15** From the frequency distribution in Table 2.5 of Problem 2.3, construct (*a*) an "or more" cumulative-frequency distribution and (*b*) an "or more" ogive.

SOLUTION

(*a*) Note that each entry in column 2 of Table 2.11 is obtained by adding successive entries from column 2 of Table 2.5, *starting at the bottom* of Table 2.5; thus $7 = 2 + 5$, $17 = 2 + 5 + 10$, etc. These entries can also be obtained by subtracting each entry in column 2 of Table 2.10 from the total frequency, 65; thus $57 = 65 - 8$, $47 = 65 - 18$, etc.

(*b*) Figure 2-9 shows the "or more" ogive.

Table 2.11

Wages	"Or More" Cumulative Frequency
\$250.00 or more	65
260.00 or more	57
270.00 or more	47
280.00 or more	31
290.00 or more	17
300.00 or more	7
310.00 or more	2
320.00 or more	0

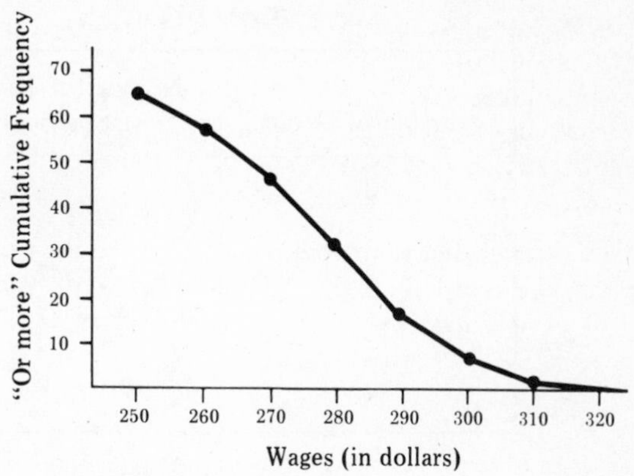

Fig. 2-9

2.16 From the ogives in Figs. 2-8 and 2-9 (of Problems 2.14 and 2.15, respectively), estimate the number of employees earning (a) less than \$288.00 per week, (b) \$296.00 or more per week, and (c) at least \$263.00 per week but less than \$275.00 per week.

SOLUTION

(a) Referring to the "less than" ogive of Fig. 2-8, construct a vertical line intersecting the "Wages" axis at \$288.00. This line meets the ogive at the point with coordinates (288, 45); hence 45 employees earn less than \$288.00 per week.

(b) In the "or more" ogive of Fig. 2-9, construct a vertical line at \$296.00. This line meets the ogive at the point (296, 11); hence 11 employees earn \$296.00 or more per week.

This can also be obtained from the "less than" ogive of Fig. 2.8. By constructing a line at \$296.00, we find that 54 employees earn less than \$296.00 per week; hence $65-54=11$ employees earn \$296.00 or more per week.

(c) Using the "less than" ogive of Fig. 2-8, we have: Required number of employees = number earning less than \$275.00 per week − number earning less than \$263.00 per week $= 26-11=15$.

Note that the above results could just as well have been obtained by the process of *interpolation* in the cumulative-frequency tables. In part (a), for example, since \$288.00 is 8/10, or 4/5, of the way between \$280.00 and \$290.00, the required number of employees should be 4/5 of the way between the corresponding values 34 and 48 (see Table 2.10). But 4/5 of the way between 34 and 48 is $\frac{4}{5}(48-34)=11$. Thus the required number of employees is $34+11=45$.

2.17 Five pennies were tossed 1000 times, and at each toss the number of heads was observed. The number of tosses during which 0, 1, 2, 3, 4, and 5 heads were obtained is shown in Table 2.12.

(a) Graph the data of Table 2.12.

(b) Construct a table showing the percentage of tosses resulting in a number of heads less than 0, 1, 2, 3, 4, 5, or 6.

(c) Graph the data of the table in part (b).

SOLUTION

(a) The data can be shown graphically either as in Fig. 2-10 or Fig. 2-11.

Figure 2-10 seems to be a more natural graph to use—since, for example, the number of heads cannot be 1.5 or 3.2. This graph is a form of bar graph where the bars have zero width and is sometimes called a *rod graph.* It is especially used when the data are discrete.

Figure 2-11 shows a histogram of the data. Note that the total area of the histogram is the total frequency 1000, as it should be. In using the histogram representation or the corresponding frequency

Table 2.12

Number of Heads	Number of Tosses (frequency)
0	38
1	144
2	342
3	287
4	164
5	25
	Total 1000

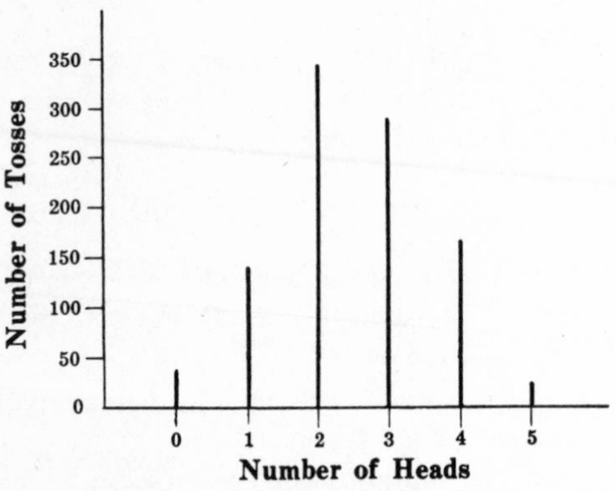

Fig. 2-10

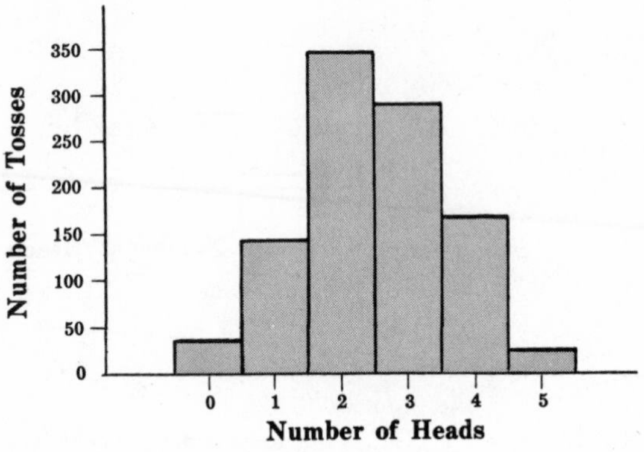

Fig. 2-11

polygon, we are essentially treating the data *as if* they were continuous. This will later be found useful. Note that we have already used the histogram and frequency polygon for discrete data in Problem 2.10.

(*b*) Referring to the required Table 2.13, note that it shows simply a cumulative-frequency distribution and percentage cumulative distribution of the number of heads. It should be observed that the entries "Less than 1," "Less than 2," etc., could just as well have been "Less than or equal to 0," "Less than or equal to 1," etc.

Table 2.13

Number of Heads	Number of Tosses (cumulative frequency)	Percentage Number of Tosses (percentage cumulative frequency)
Less than 0	0	0.0
Less than 1	38	3.8
Less than 2	182	18.2
Less than 3	524	52.4
Less than 4	811	81.1
Less than 5	975	97.5
Less than 6	1000	100.0

(*c*) The required graph can be presented either as in Fig. 2-12 or as in Fig. 2-13.

Figure 2-12 is most natural for presenting discrete data—since, for example, the percentage of tosses in which there will be less than 2 heads is equal to the percentage in which there will be less than 1.75, 1.56, or 1.23 heads, so that the same percentage (18.2%) should be shown for these values (indicated by the horizontal line).

Figure 2-13 shows the cumulative-frequency polygon, or ogive, for the data and essentially treats the data as if they were continuous.

Note that Figs. 2-12 and 2-13 correspond, respectively, to Figs. 2-10 and 2-11 of part (a).

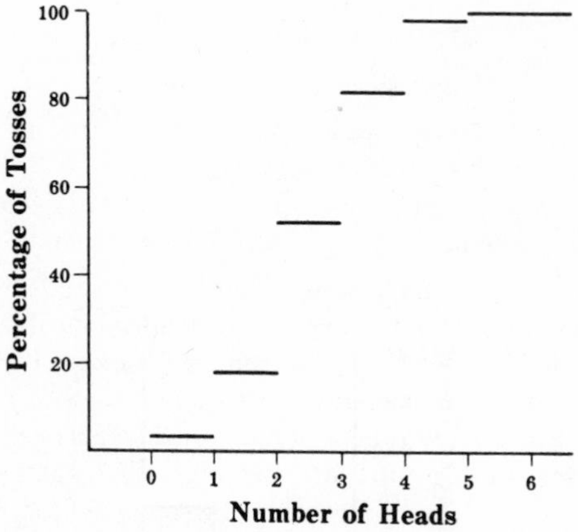

Fig. 2-12

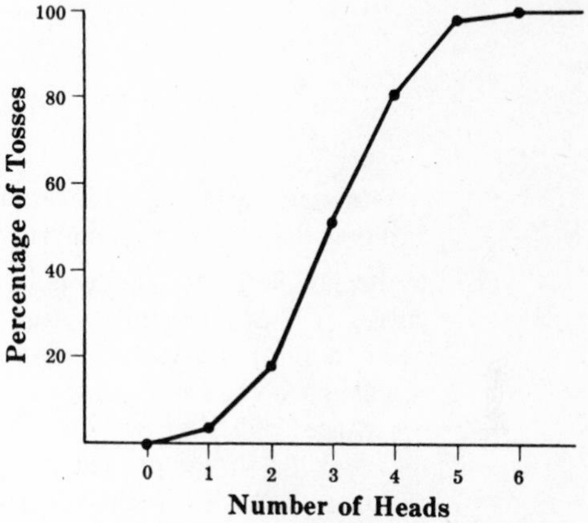

Fig. 2-13

FREQUENCY CURVES AND SMOOTHED OGIVES

2.18 The 100 male students at XYZ University (Table 2.1) actually constituted a sample of 1546 male students at the university.

(*a*) From the data provided in the sample, construct a smoothed percentage frequency polygon (frequency curve) and a smoothed "less than" percentage ogive.

(*b*) From the results of either construction in part (*a*), estimate the number of students at the university having heights between 65 and 70 in. What assumptions must you make?

(*c*) Can the results be used to estimate the proportion of males in the United States having heights between 65 and 70 in?

SOLUTION

(*a*) In Figs. 2-14 and 2-15 the dashed graphs represent the frequency polygons and ogives and are obtained from Figs. 2-1 and 2-2, respectively. The required smoothed graphs (shown heavy) are obtained by approximating these by smooth curves.

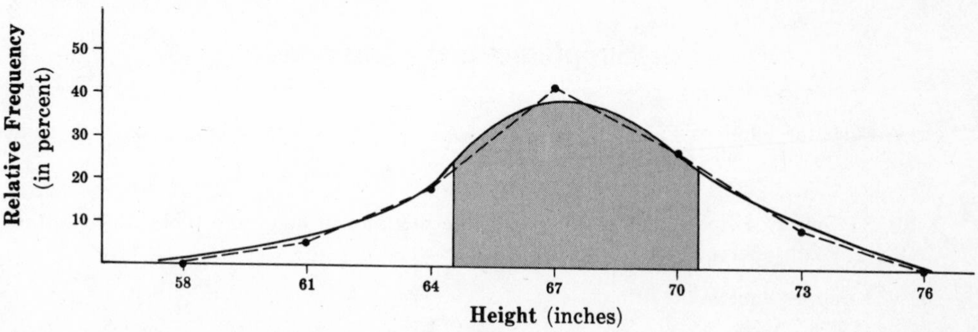

Fig. 2-14

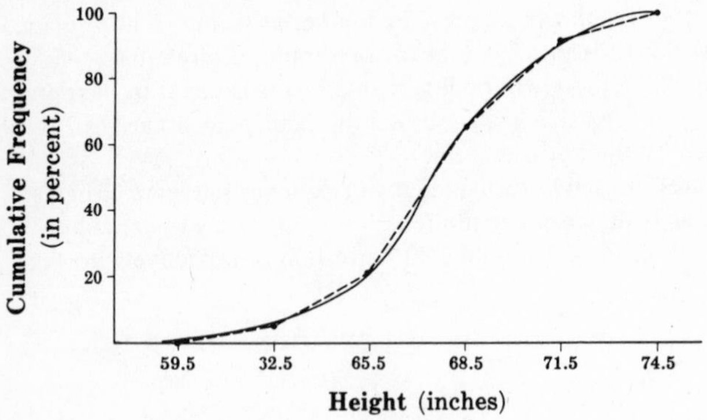

Fig. 2-15

In practice, because it is easier to smooth an ogive, very often the smoothed ogive is first obtained and then the smoothed frequency polygon is obtained by reading off values from the smoothed ogive.

(*b*) If the sample of 100 students is representative of the population of 1546 students, the smoothed curves of Figs. 2-14 and 2-15 can be assumed to be the percentage frequency curve and percentage ogive for this population. This assumption is correct only if the sample is *random* (i.e., if each student has as much chance of being selected in the sample as any other student).

Since heights between 65 and 70 in recorded to the nearest inch actually represent heights between 64.5 and 70.5 in, the percentage of students in the population having these heights can be found by dividing the shaded area in Fig. 2-14 by the total area bounded by the smoothed curve and the X axis.

It is simpler, however, to use Fig. 2-15, from which we see that

Percentage of students with heights less than 70.5 in = 82%
Percentage of students with heights less than 64.5 in = 18%

so that the percentage of students with heights between 64.5 and 70.5 in = 82% − 18% = 64%. Thus the number of students in the university having heights between 65 and 70 in to the nearest inch = 64% of 1546 = 989.

Another way of saying this is that the *probability*, or *chance*, that a person selected at random from the 1546 students has a height between 65 and 70 in is 64%, 0.64, or 64 out of 100. Because of the relationship to probability (considered in Chapter 6), relative-frequency curves are often called *probability curves*, or *probability distributions.*

(*c*) We could consider the required proportion to be 64% (with a much greater uncertainty than before) only if we were convinced that the sample of 100 students from the total male population of the United States was truly a random sample. However, this is somewhat unlikely for several reasons, such as (1) some college students may not have reached their maximum heights and (2) the younger generation may tend to be taller than their parents.

Supplementary Problems

2.19 (*a*) Arrange the numbers 12, 56, 42, 21, 5, 18, 10, 3, 61, 34, 65, and 24 in an array and (*b*) determine the range.

2.20 Table 2.14 shows a frequency distribution of the lifetimes of 400 radio tubes tested at the L&M Tube Company. With reference to this table, determine:

(*a*) The upper limit of the fifth class
(*b*) The lower limit of the eighth class
(*c*) The class mark of the seventh class
(*d*) The class boundaries of the last class

(*e*) The class-interval size

(*f*) The frequency of the fourth class

(*g*) The relative frequency of the sixth class

(*h*) The percentage of tubes whose lifetimes do not exceed 600 hours

(*i*) The percentage of tubes with lifetimes greater than or equal to 900 hours

(*j*) The percentage of tubes whose lifetimes are at least 500 hours but less than 1000 hours

Table 2.14

Lifetime (hours)	Number of Tubes
300–399	14
400–499	46
500–599	58
600–699	76
700–799	68
800–899	62
900–999	48
1000–1099	22
1100–1199	6
	Total 400

2.21 Construct (*a*) a histogram and (*b*) a frequency polygon corresponding to the frequency distribution of Table 2.14.

2.22 For the data in Table 2.14 of Problem 2.20, construct (*a*) a relative-frequency distribution, (*b*) a relative-frequency histogram, and (*c*) a relative-frequency polygon.

2.23 For the data in Table 2.14, construct (*a*) a cumulative-frequency distribution, (*b*) a percentage cumulative distribution, (*c*) an ogive, and (*d*) a percentage ogive. (Note that unless otherwise specified, a cumulative distribution refers to one made on a "less than" basis.)

2.24 Work Problem 2.23 for the case where the frequencies are cumulative on an "or more" basis.

2.25 Using the data in Table 2.14, estimate the percentage of tubes that have lifetimes of (*a*) less than 560 hours, (*b*) 970 or more hours, and (*c*) between 620 and 890 hours.

2.26 The inner diameters of washers produced by a company can be measured to the nearest thousandth of an inch. If the class marks of a frequency distribution of these diameters are given in inches by 0.321, 0.324, 0.327, 0.330, 0.333 and 0.336, find (*a*) the class-interval size, (*b*) the class boundaries, and (*c*) the class limits.

2.27 The following table shows the diameters in centimeters of a sample of 60 ball bearings manufactured by a company. Construct a frequency distribution of the diameters, using appropriate class intervals.

1.738	1.729	1.743	1.740	1.736	1.741	1.735	1.731	1.726	1.737
1.728	1.737	1.736	1.735	1.724	1.733	1.742	1.736	1.739	1.735
1.745	1.736	1.742	1.740	1.728	1.738	1.725	1.733	1.734	1.732
1.733	1.730	1.732	1.730	1.739	1.734	1.738	1.739	1.727	1.735
1.735	1.732	1.735	1.727	1.734	1.732	1.736	1.741	1.736	1.744
1.732	1.737	1.731	1.746	1.735	1.735	1.729	1.734	1.730	1.740

2.28 For the data of Problem 2.27, construct (*a*) a histogram, (*b*) a frequency polygon, (*c*) a relative-frequency distribution, (*d*) a relative-frequency histogram, (*e*) a relative-frequency polygon, (*f*) a cumulative-frequency distribution, (*g*) a percentage cumulative distribution, (*h*) an ogive, and (*i*) a percentage ogive.

2.29 From the results in Problem 2.28, determine the percentage of ball bearings having diameters (*a*) exceeding 1.732 cm, (*b*) not more than 1.736 cm, and (*c*) between 1.730 and 1.738 cm. Compare your results with those obtained directly from the raw data of Problem 2.27.

2.30 Work Problem 2.28 for the data of Problem 2.20.

2.31 Table 2.15 shows the percentage distribution of total sales for family-type farms in the United States for 1982. Using this table, answer the following questions:

(*a*) What is the width, or size, of the second class interval? The seventh class interval?

(*b*) How many different class-interval sizes are there?

(*c*) How many open class intervals are there?

(*d*) How should the first class interval be written so that its class width will equal that of the second class interval?

(*e*) What is the class mark of the second class interval? The seventh class interval?

(*f*) What are the class boundaries of the fourth class interval?

(*g*) What percentage of the farms had sales of $20,000 and over? What percentage had sales of under $10,000?

(*h*) What percentage of the farms had sales of at least $10,000 but not more than $40,000?

(*i*) What percentage of the farms had sales between $15,000 and $25,000? What assumptions are made in this calculation?

(*j*) Why do the percentages in Table 2.15 not total 100%?

Table 2.15

Sales (dollars)	Farms (percent)
Under 2,500	25.9
2,500–4,999	13.2
5,000–9,999	13.0
10,000–19,999	11.7
20,000–39,999	11.0
40,000–99,999	14.4
100,000–249,999	8.5
250,000–499,999	1.8
500,000 and over	0.6

2.32 (*a*) Why is it impossible to construct a percentage histogram or frequency polygon for the distribution in Table 2.15?

(*b*) How would you modify the distribution so that a percentage histogram and frequency polygon could be constructed?

(*c*) Perform the construction using the modification in part (*b*).

2.33 The total number of farms in the distribution of Table 2.15 is 1,945,000. From this, determine the number of farms in which sales (*a*) exceeded $40,000, (*b*) were less than $40,000, and (*c*) were between $30,000 and $50,000.

2.34 (*a*) Construct a smoothed percentage frequency polygon and smoothed percentage ogive corresponding to the data of Table 2.14.

(*b*) From the results in part (*a*), estimate the probability that a tube will burn out before 600 hours.

(*c*) Discuss the risk or chance that the manufacturer takes in guaranteeing that a tube will last 425 hours. And discuss the risk for 875 hours.

(*d*) If the manufacturer offers a 90-day money-back guarantee on a tube, what is the probability that he will have to refund the money, assuming that a tube is in use 4 hours per day? Eight hours per day?

2.35 (*a*) Toss four coins 50 times and tabulate the number of heads at each toss.

(*b*) Construct a frequency distribution showing the number of tosses in which 0, 1, 2, 3, and 4 heads appeared.

(*c*) Construct a percentage distribution corresponding to part (*b*).

(*d*) Compare the percentage obtained in part (*c*) with the theoretical ones 6.25%, 25%, 37.5%, 25%, and 6.25% (proportional to 1, 4, 6, 4, and 1) arrived at by rules of probability.

(*e*) Graph the distributions in parts (*b*) and (*c*).

(*f*) Construct a percentage ogive for the data.

2.36 Work Problem 2.35 with 50 more tosses of the four coins and see if the experiment is more in agreement with theoretical expectation. If not, give possible reasons for the differences.

Chapter 3

The Mean, Median, Mode, and Other Measures of Central Tendency

INDEX, OR SUBSCRIPT, NOTATION

Let the symbol X_j (read "X sub j") denote any of the N *values* $X_1, X_2, X_3, \ldots, X_N$ assumed by a variable X. The letter j in X_j, which can stand for any of the numbers $1, 2, 3, \ldots, N$ is called a *subscript*, or *index*. Clearly any letter other than j, such as i, k, p, q, or s, could have been used as well.

SUMMATION NOTATION

The symbol $\sum_{j=1}^{N} X_j$ is used to denote the sum of all the X_j's from $j=1$ to $j=N$; by definition,

$$\sum_{j=1}^{N} X_j = X_1 + X_2 + X_3 + \cdots + X_N$$

When no confusion can result, we often denote this sum simply by $\sum X$, $\sum X_j$, or $\sum_j X_j$. The symbol $\sum$ is the Greek capital letter *sigma*, denoting sum.

EXAMPLE 1. $\sum_{j=1}^{N} X_j Y_j = X_1 Y_1 + X_2 Y_2 + X_3 Y_3 + \cdots + X_N Y_N$

EXAMPLE 2. $\sum_{j=1}^{N} aX_j = aX_1 + aX_2 + \cdots + aX_N = a(X_1 + X_2 + \cdots + X_N) = a \sum_{j=1}^{N} X_j$

where a is a constant. More simply, $\sum aX = a \sum X$.

EXAMPLE 3. If a, b, and c are any constants, then $\sum (aX + bY - cZ) = a \sum X + b \sum Y - c \sum Z$. See Problem 3.3.

AVERAGES, OR MEASURES OF CENTRAL TENDENCY

An *average* is a value that is typical, or representative, of a set of data. Since such typical values tend to lie centrally within a set of data arranged according to magnitude, averages are also called *measures of central tendency*.

Several types of averages can be defined, the most common being the *arithmetic mean*, the *median*, the *mode*, the *geometric mean*, and the *harmonic mean*. Each has advantages and disadvantages, depending on the data and the intended purpose.

THE ARITHMETIC MEAN

The *arithmetic mean*, or briefly the *mean*, of a set of N numbers $X_1, X_2, X_3, \ldots, X_N$ is denoted by $\bar{X}$ (read "X bar") and is defined as

$$\bar{X} = \frac{X_1 + X_2 + X_3 + \cdots + X_N}{N} = \frac{\sum_{j=1}^{N} X_j}{N} = \frac{\sum X}{N} \tag{1}$$

EXAMPLE 4. The arithmetic mean of the numbers 8, 3, 5, 12, and 10 is

$$\bar{X} = \frac{8+3+5+12+10}{5} = \frac{38}{5} = 7.6$$

If the numbers $X_1, X_2, \ldots, X_K$ occur $f_1, f_2, \ldots, f_K$ times, respectively (i.e., occur with frequencies $f_1, f_2, \ldots, f_K$), the arithmetic mean is

$$\bar{X} = \frac{f_1X_1 + f_2X_2 + \cdots + f_KX_K}{f_1 + f_2 + \cdots + f_K} = \frac{\sum_{j=1}^{K} f_jX_j}{\sum_{j=1}^{K} f_j} = \frac{\sum fX}{\sum f} = \frac{\sum fX}{N} \tag{2}$$

where $N = \sum f$ is the *total frequency* (i.e., the total number of cases).

EXAMPLE 5. If 5, 8, 6, and 2 occur with frequencies 3, 2, 4, and 1, respectively, the arithmetic mean is

$$\bar{X} = \frac{(3)(5)+(2)(8)+(4)(6)+(1)(2)}{3+2+4+1} = \frac{15+16+24+2}{10} = 5.7$$

THE WEIGHTED ARITHMETIC MEAN

Sometimes we associate with the numbers $X_1, X_2, \ldots, X_K$ certain *weighting factors* (or *weights*) $w_1, w_2, \ldots, w_K$, depending on the significance or importance attached to the numbers. In this case,

$$\bar{X} = \frac{w_1X_1 + w_2X_2 + \cdots + w_KX_k}{w_1 + w_2 + \cdots + w_K} = \frac{\sum wX}{\sum w} \tag{3}$$

is called the *weighted arithmetic mean.* Note the similarity to equation (*2*), which can be considered a weighted arithmetic mean with weights $f_1, f_2, \ldots, f_K$.

EXAMPLE 6. If a final examination in a course is weighted 3 times as much as a quiz and a student has a final examination grade of 85 and quiz grades of 70 and 90, the mean grade is

$$\bar{X} = \frac{(1)(70)+(1)(90)+(3)(85)}{1+1+3} = \frac{415}{5} = 83$$

PROPERTIES OF THE ARITHMETIC MEAN

1. The algebraic sum of the deviations of a set of numbers from their arithmetic mean is zero.

EXAMPLE 7. The deviations of the numbers 8, 3, 5, 12, and 10 from their arithmetic mean 7.6 are $8-7.6$, $3-7.6$, $5-7.6$, $12-7.6$, and $10-7.6$, or 0.4, −4.6, −2.6, 4.4, and 2.4, with algebraic sum $0.4-4.6-2.6+4.4+2.4=0$.

2. The sum of the squares of the deviations of a set of numbers X_j from any number a is a minimum if and only if $a = \bar{X}$ (see Problem 4.27).
3. If f_1 numbers have mean m_1, f_2 numbers have mean $m_2, \ldots, f_K$ numbers have mean m_K, then the mean of all the numbers is

$$\bar{X} = \frac{f_1m_1 + f_2m_2 + \cdots + f_Km_K}{f_1 + f_2 + \cdots + f_K} \tag{4}$$

that is, a weighted arithmetic mean of all the means (see Problem 3.12).

4. If A is any *guessed* or *assumed arithmetic mean* (which may be any number) and if $d_j = X_j - A$ are the deviations of X_j from A, then equations (*1*) and (*2*) become, respectively,

$$\bar{X} = A + \frac{\sum_{j=1}^{N} d_j}{N} = A + \frac{\sum d}{N} \tag{5}$$

$$\bar{X} = A + \frac{\sum_{j=1}^{K} f_j d_j}{\sum_{j=1}^{K} f_j} = A + \frac{\sum fd}{N} \tag{6}$$

where $N = \sum_{j=1}^{K} f_j = \sum f$. Note that formulas (*5*) and (*6*) are summarized in the equation $\bar{X} = A + \bar{d}$ (see Problem 3.18).

THE ARITHMETIC MEAN COMPUTED FROM GROUPED DATA

When data are presented in a frequency distribution, all values falling within a given class interval are considerd to be coincident with the class mark, or midpoint, of the interval. Formulas (*2*) and (*6*) are valid for such grouped data if we interpret X_j as the class mark, f_j as its corresponding class frequency, A as any guessed or assumed class mark, and $d_j = X_j - A$ as the deviations of X_j from A.

Computations using formulas (*2*) and (*6*) are sometimes called the *long* and *short methods*, respectively (see Problems 3.15 and 3.20).

If class intervals all have equal size c, the deviations $d_j = X_j - A$ can all be expressed as cu_j, where u_j can be positive or negative integers or zero (i.e., 0, ± 1, ± 2, $\pm 3, \ldots$), and formula (*6*) becomes

$$\bar{X} = A + \left(\frac{\sum_{j=1}^{K} f_j u_j}{N} \right) = A + \left(\frac{\sum fu}{N} \right) c \tag{7}$$

which is equivalent to the equation $\bar{X} = A + c\bar{u}$ (see Problem 3.21). This is called the *coding method* for computing the mean. It is a very short method and should always be used for grouped data where the class-interval sizes are equal (see Problems 3.22 and 3.23). Note that in the coding method the values of the variable X are *transformed* into the values of the variable u according to $X = A + cu$.

THE MEDIAN

The *median* of a set of numbers arranged in order of magnitude (i.e., in an array) is either the middle value or the arithmetic mean of the two middle values.

EXAMPLE 8. The set of numbers 3, 4, 4, 5, 6, 8, 8, 8, and 10 has median 6.

EXAMPLE 9. The set of numbers 5, 5, 7, 9, 11, 12, 15, and 18 has median $\frac{1}{2}(9+11) = 10$.

For grouped data, the median, obtained by interpolation, is given by

$$\text{Median} = L_1 + \left(\frac{\frac{N}{2} - (\sum f)_1}{f_{\text{median}}} \right) c \tag{8}$$

where L_1 = lower class boundary of the median class (i.e., the class containing the median)
N = number of items in the data (i.e., total frequency)
$(\sum f)_1$ = sum of frequencies of all classes lower than the median class
f_{median} = frequency of the median class
c = size of the median class interval

Geometrically the median is the value of X (abscissa) corresponding to the vertical line which divides a histogram into two parts having equal areas. This value of X is sometimes denoted by $\tilde{X}$.

THE MODE

The *mode* of a set of numbers is that value which occurs with the greatest frequency; that is, it is the most common value. The mode may not exist, and even if it does exist it may not be unique.

EXAMPLE 10. The set 2, 2, 5, 7, 9, 9, 9, 10, 10, 11, 12, and 18 has mode 9.

EXAMPLE 11. The set 3, 5, 8, 10, 12, 15, and 16 has no mode.

EXAMPLE 12. The set 2, 3, 4, 4, 4, 5, 5, 7, 7, 7, and 9 has two modes, 4 and 7, and is called *bimodal.*

A distribution having only one mode is called *unimodal.*

In the case of grouped data where a frequency curve has been constructed to fit the data, the mode will be the value (or values) of X corresponding to the maximum point (or points) on the curve. This value of X is sometimes denoted by $\hat{X}$.

From a frequency distribution or histogram the mode can be obtained from the formula

$$\text{Mode} = L_1 + \left(\frac{\Delta_1}{\Delta_1 + \Delta_2}\right)c \tag{9}$$

where L_1 = lower class boundary of the modal class (i.e., the class containing the mode)
Δ_1 = excess of modal frequency over frequency of next-lower class
Δ_2 = excess of modal frequency over frequency of next-higher class
c = size of the modal class interval

THE EMPIRICAL RELATION BETWEEN THE MEAN, MEDIAN, AND MODE

For unimodal frequency curves that are moderately skewed (asymmetrical), we have the empirical relation

$$\text{Mean} - \text{mode} = 3(\text{mean} - \text{median}) \tag{10}$$

Figures 3-1 and 3-2 show the relative positions of the mean, median, and mode for frequency curves skewed to the right and left, respectively. For symmetrical curves, the mean, mode, and median all coincide.

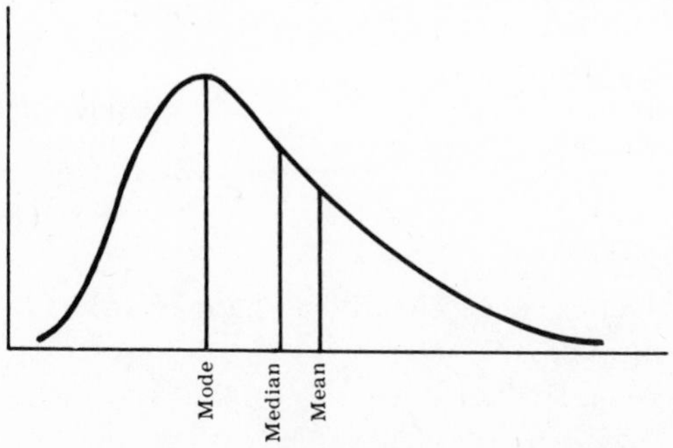

Fig. 3-1

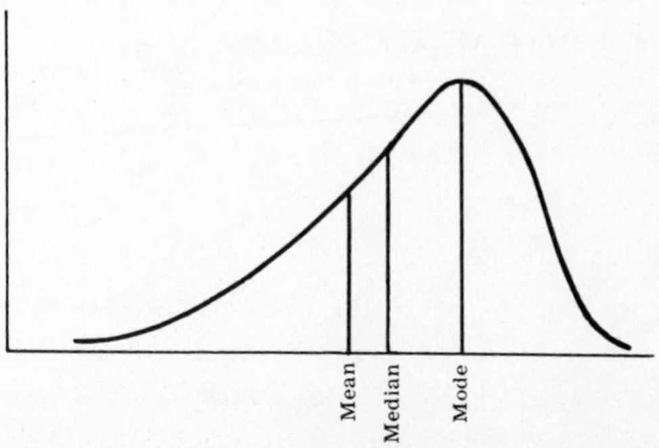

Fig. 3-2

THE GEOMETRIC MEAN G

The geometric mean G of a set of N positive numbers $X_1, X_2, X_3, \ldots, X_N$ is the Nth root of the product of the numbers:

$$G = \sqrt[N]{X_1 X_2 X_3 \cdots X_N} \tag{11}$$

EXAMPLE 13. The geometric mean of the numbers 2, 4, and 8 is $G = \sqrt[3]{(2)(4)(8)} = \sqrt[3]{64} = 4$.

We can compute G by logarithms (see Problem 3.35) or by using a calculator. For the geometric mean from grouped data, see Problems 3.36 and 3.91.

THE HARMONIC MEAN H

The harmonic mean H of a set of N numbers $X_1, X_2, X_3, \ldots, X_N$ is the reciprocal of the arithmetic mean of the reciprocals of the numbers:

$$H = \frac{1}{\dfrac{1}{N}\displaystyle\sum_{j=1}^{N} \frac{1}{X_j}} = \frac{N}{\sum \dfrac{1}{X}} \tag{12}$$

In practice it may be easier to remember that

$$\frac{1}{H} = \frac{\sum \dfrac{1}{X}}{N} = \frac{1}{N} \sum \frac{1}{X} \tag{13}$$

EXAMPLE 14. The harmonic mean of the numbers 2, 4, and 8 is

$$H = \frac{3}{\frac{1}{2} + \frac{1}{4} + \frac{1}{8}} = \frac{3}{\frac{7}{8}} = 3.43$$

For the harmonic mean from grouped data, see Problems 3.99 and 3.100.

THE RELATION BETWEEN THE ARITHMETIC, GEOMETRIC, AND HARMONIC MEANS

The geometric mean of a set of positive numbers $X_1, X_2, \ldots, X_N$ is less than or equal to their arithmetic mean but is greater than or equal to their harmonic mean. In symbols,

$$H \le G \le \bar{X} \tag{14}$$

The equality signs hold only if all the numbers $X_1, X_2, \ldots, X_N$ are identical.

EXAMPLE 15. The set 2, 4, 8 has arithmetic mean 4.67, geometric mean 4, and harmonic mean 3.43.

THE ROOT MEAN SQUARE (RMS)

The root mean square (RMS), or *quadratic mean*, of a set of numbers $X_1, X_2, \ldots, X_N$ is sometimes denoted by $\sqrt{\overline{X^2}}$ and is defined by

$$\text{RMS} = \sqrt{\overline{X^2}} = \sqrt{\frac{\displaystyle\sum_{j=1}^{N} X_j^2}{N}} = \sqrt{\frac{\sum X^2}{N}} \tag{15}$$

This type of average is frequently used in physical applications.

EXAMPLE 16. The RMS of the set 1, 3, 4, 5, and 7 is

$$\sqrt{\frac{1^2+3^2+4^2+5^2+7^2}{5}}=\sqrt{20}=4.47$$

QUARTILES, DECILES, AND PERCENTILES

If a set of data is arranged in order of magnitude, the middle value (or arithmetic mean of the two middle values) that divides the set into two equal parts is the median. By extending this idea, we can think of those values which divide the set into four equal parts. These values, denoted by Q_1, Q_2, and Q_3, are called the first, second, and third *quartiles*, respectively, the value Q_2 being equal to the median.

Similarly, the values that divide the data into 10 equal parts are called *deciles* and are denoted by $D_1, D_2, \ldots, D_9$, while the values dividing the data into 100 equal parts are called *percentiles* and are denoted by $P_1, P_2, \ldots, P_{99}$. The fifth decile and the 50th percentile correspond to the median. The 25th and 75th percentiles correspond to the first and third quartiles, respectively.

Collectively, quartiles, deciles, percentiles, and other values obtained by equal subdivisions of the data are called *quantiles.* For computations of these from grouped data, see Problems 3.44 to 3.46.

Solved Problems

SUMMATION NOTATION

3.1 Write out the terms in each of the following indicated sums:

(a) $\sum_{j=1}^{6} X_j$ (c) $\sum_{j=1}^{N} a$ (e) $\sum_{j=1}^{3} (X_j-a)$

(b) $\sum_{j=1}^{4} (Y_j-3)^2$ (d) $\sum_{k=1}^{5} f_k X_k$

SOLUTION

(a) $X_1+X_2+X_3+X_4+X_5+X_6$

(b) $(Y_1-3)^2+(Y_2-3)^2+(Y_3-3)^2+(Y_4-3)^2$

(c) $a+a+a+\cdots+a=Na$

(d) $f_1X_1+f_2X_2+f_3X_3+f_4X_4+f_5X_5$

(e) $(X_1-a)+(X_2-a)+(X_3-a)=X_1+X_2+X_3-3a$

3.2 Express each of the following by using the summation notation:

(a) $X_1^2+X_2^2+X_3^2+\cdots+X_{10}^2$

(b) $(X_1+Y_1)+(X_2+Y_2)+\cdots+(X_8+Y_8)$

(c) $f_1X_1^3+f_2X_2^3+\cdots+f_{20}X_{20}^3$

(d) $a_1b_1+a_2b_2+a_3b_3+\cdots+a_Nb_N$

(e) $f_1X_1Y_1+f_2X_2Y_2+f_3X_3Y_3+f_4X_4Y_4$

SOLUTION

(a) $\sum_{j=1}^{10} X_j^2$ (c) $\sum_{j=1}^{20} f_j X_j^3$ (e) $\sum_{j=1}^{4} f_j X_j Y_j$

(b) $\sum_{j=1}^{8} (X_j + Y_j)$ (d) $\sum_{j=1}^{N} a_j b_j$

3.3 Prove that $\sum_{j=1}^{N} (aX_j + bY_j - cZ_j) = a\sum_{j=1}^{N} X_j + b\sum_{j=1}^{N} Y_j - c\sum_{j=1}^{N} Z_j$, where a, b, and c are any constants.

SOLUTION

$$\begin{aligned}\sum_{j=1}^{N} (aX_j + bY_j - cZ_j) &= (aX_1 + bY_1 - cZ_1) + (aX_2 + bY_2 - cZ_2) + \cdots + (aX_N + bY_N - cZ_N)\\ &= (aX_1 + aX_2 + \cdots + aX_N) + (bY_1 + bY_2 + \cdots + bY_N) - (cZ_1 + cZ_2 + \cdots + cZ_N)\\ &= a(X_1 + X_2 + \cdots + X_N) + b(Y_1 + Y_2 + \cdots + Y_N) - c(Z_1 + Z_2 + \cdots + Z_N)\\ &= a\sum_{j=1}^{N} X_j + b\sum_{j=1}^{N} Y_j - c\sum_{j=1}^{N} Z_j\end{aligned}$$

or briefly, $\sum (aX + bY - cZ) = a\sum X + b\sum Y - c\sum Z$.

3.4 Two variables, X and Y, assume the values $X_1 = 2$, $X_2 = -5$, $X_3 = 4$, $X_4 = -8$ and $Y_1 = -3$, $Y_2 = -8$, $Y_3 = 10$, $Y_4 = 6$, respectively. Calculate (a) $\sum X$, (b) $\sum Y$, (c) $\sum XY$, (d) $\sum X^2$, (e) $\sum Y^2$, (f) $(\sum X)(\sum Y)$, (g) $\sum XY^2$, and (h) $\sum (X + Y)(X - Y)$.

SOLUTION

Note that in each case the subscript j on X and Y has been omitted and $\sum$ is understood as $\sum_{j=1}^{4}$. Thus $\sum X$, for example, is short for $\sum_{j=1}^{4} X_j$.

(a) $\sum X = (2) + (-5) + (4) + (-8) = 2 - 5 + 4 - 8 = -7$

(b) $\sum Y = (-3) + (-8) + (10) + (6) = -3 - 8 + 10 + 6 = 5$

(c) $\sum XY = (2)(-3) + (-5)(-8) + (4)(10) + (-8)(6) = -6 + 40 + 40 - 48 = 26$

(d) $\sum X^2 = (2)^2 + (-5)^2 + (4)^2 + (-8)^2 = 4 + 25 + 16 + 64 = 109$

(e) $\sum Y^2 = (-3)^2 + (-8)^2 + (10)^2 + (6)^2 = 9 + 64 + 100 + 36 = 209$

(f) $(\sum X)(\sum Y) = (-7)(5) = -35$, using parts (a) and (b). Note that $(\sum X)(\sum Y) \neq \sum XY$.

(g) $\sum XY^2 = (2)(-3)^2 + (-5)(-8)^2 + (4)(10)^2 + (-8)(6)^2 = -190$

(h) $\sum (X + Y)(X - Y) = \sum (X^2 - Y^2) = \sum X^2 - \sum Y^2 = 109 - 209 = -100$, using parts (d) and (e).

3.5 If $\sum_{j=1}^{6} X_j = -4$ and $\sum_{j=1}^{6} X_j^2 = 10$, calculate (a) $\sum_{j=1}^{6} (2X_j + 3)$, (b) $\sum_{j=1}^{6} X_j(X_j - 1)$, and (c) $\sum_{j=1}^{6} (X_j - 5)^2$.

SOLUTION

(a) $\sum_{j=1}^{6} (2X_j + 3) = \sum_{j=1}^{6} 2X_j + \sum_{j=1}^{6} 3 = 2\sum_{j=1}^{6} X_j + (6)(3) = 2(-4) + 18 = 10$

(b) $\sum_{j=1}^{6} X_j(X_j - 1) = \sum_{j=1}^{6} (X_j^2 - X_j) = \sum_{j=1}^{6} X_j^2 - \sum_{j=1}^{6} X_j = 10 - (-4) = 14$

(c) $\sum_{j=1}^{6} (X_j - 5)^2 = \sum_{j=1}^{6} (X_j^2 - 10X_j + 25) = \sum_{j=1}^{6} X_j^2 - 10\sum_{j=1}^{6} X_j + 25(6) = 10 - 10(-4) + 25(6) = 200$

If desired, we can omit the subscript j and use $\sum$ in place of $\sum_{j=1}^{6}$ so long as these abbreviations are understood.

THE ARITHMETIC MEAN

3.6 The grades of a student on six examinations were 84, 91, 72, 68, 87, and 78. Find the arithmetic mean of the grades.

SOLUTION

$$\bar{X} = \frac{\sum X}{N} = \frac{84+91+72+68+87+78}{6} = \frac{480}{6} = 80$$

Frequently one uses the term *average* synonymously with *arithmetic mean.* Strictly speaking, however, this is incorrect since there are averages other than the arithmetic mean.

3.7 Ten measurements of the diameter of a cylinder were recorded by a scientist as 3.88, 4.09, 3.92, 3.97, 4.02, 3.95, 4.03, 3.92, 3.98, and 4.06 centimeters (cm). Find the arithmetic mean of the measurements.

SOLUTION

$$\bar{X} = \frac{\sum X}{N} = \frac{3.88+4.09+3.92+3.97+4.02+3.95+4.03+3.92+3.98+4.06}{10} = \frac{39.82}{10} = 3.98 \text{ cm}$$

3.8 The annual salaries of four men were \$15,000, \$16,000, \$16,500, and \$40,000.

(*a*) Find the arithmetic mean of their salaries.

(*b*) Would you say that this average is *typical* of the salaries?

SOLUTION

(*a*) Assuming that all figures are significant in the reported salaries,

$$\bar{X} = \frac{\$15{,}000+\$16{,}000+\$16{,}500+\$40{,}000}{4} = \frac{\$87{,}500}{4} = \$21{,}875$$

(*b*) The mean \$21,875 is certainly not typical of the salaries, and presenting this figure as an *average* salary without further comment would be grossly misleading. A great disadvantage of the mean is that it is strongly affected by extreme values.

3.9 Find the arithmetic mean of the numbers 5, 3, 6, 5, 4, 5, 2, 8, 6, 5, 4, 8, 3, 4, 5, 4, 8, 2, 5, and 4.

SOLUTION

First method

$$\bar{X} = \frac{\sum X}{N} = \frac{5+3+6+5+4+5+2+8+6+5+4+8+3+4+5+4+8+2+5+4}{20} = \frac{96}{20} = 4.8$$

Second method

There are six 5's, two 3's, two 6's, five 4's, two 2's and three 8's. Thus

$$\bar{X} = \frac{\sum fX}{\sum f} = \frac{\sum fX}{N} = \frac{(6)(5)+(2)(3)+(2)(6)+(5)(4)+(2)(2)+(3)(8)}{6+2+2+5+2+3} = \frac{96}{20} = 4.8$$

3.10 Out of 100 numbers, 20 were 4's, 40 were 5's, 30 were 6's and the remainder were 7's. Find the arithmetic mean of the numbers.

SOLUTION

$$\bar{X} = \frac{\sum fX}{\sum f} = \frac{\sum fX}{N} = \frac{(20)(4)+(40)(5)+(30)(6)+(10)(7)}{100} = \frac{530}{100} = 5.30$$

3.11 A student's final grades in mathematics, physics, English and hygiene are, respectively, 82, 86, 90, and 70. If the respective credits received for these courses are 3, 5, 3, and 1, determine an appropriate average grade.

SOLUTION

We use a weighted arithmetic mean, the weights associated with each grade being taken as the number of credits received. Thus

$$\bar{X}=\frac{\sum wX}{\sum w}=\frac{(3)(82)+(5)(86)+(3)(90)+(1)(70)}{3+5+3+1}=85$$

3.12 In a company having 80 employees, 60 earn \$7.00 per hour and 20 earn \$4.00 per hour.

(*a*) Determine the mean earnings per hour.

(*b*) Would the answer to part (*a*) be the same if the 60 employees earn a *mean* hourly wage of \$4.00 per hour? Prove your answer.

(*c*) Do you believe the mean hourly wage to be typical?

SOLUTION

(*a*)
$$\bar{X}=\frac{\sum fX}{N}=\frac{(60)(\$7.00)+(20)(\$4.00)}{60+20}=\frac{\$500.00}{80}=\$6.25$$

(*b*) Yes, the result is the same. To prove this, suppose that f_1 numbers have mean m_1 and that f_2 numbers have mean m_2. We must show that the mean of all the numbers is

$$\bar{X}=\frac{f_1m_1+f_2m_2}{f_1+f_2}$$

Let the f_1 numbers add up to M_1 and the f_2 numbers add up to M_2. Then by definition of the arithmetic mean,

$$m_1=\frac{M_1}{f_1} \qquad m_2=\frac{M_2}{f_2}$$

or $M_1=f_1m_1$ and $M_2=f_2m_2$. Since all (f_1+f_2) numbers add up to (M_1+M_2), the arithmetic mean of all numbers is

$$\bar{X}=\frac{M_1+M_2}{f_1+f_2}=\frac{f_1m_1+f_2m_2}{f_1+f_2}$$

as required. The result is easily extended.

(*c*) We can say that \$6.25 is a "typical" hourly wage in the sense that most of the employees earn \$7.00 per hour, which is not far from \$6.25 per hour. It must be remembered that whenever we summarize numerical data into a single number (as is true in an average), we are bound to make some error. Certainly, however, the result is not as misleading as that of Problem 3.8.

Actually, to be on safe ground, some estimate of the "spread," or "variation," of the data about the mean (or other average) should be given. This is called the *dispersion* of the data. Various measures of dispersion are given in Chapter 4.

3.13 Four groups of students, consisting of 15, 20, 10, and 18 individuals, reported mean weights of 162, 148, 153, and 140 pounds (lb), respectively. Find the mean weight of all the students.

SOLUTION

$$\bar{X}=\frac{\sum fX}{\sum f}=\frac{(15)(162)+(20)(148)+(10)(153)+(18)(140)}{15+20+10+18}=150\text{ lb}$$

3.14 If the mean annual incomes of agricultural and nonagricultural workers in the United States are \$9000 and \$15,000, respectively, would the mean annual income of both groups together be $\frac{1}{2}$(\$9000 + \$15,000) = \$12,000?

SOLUTION

It would be \$12,000 only if the numbers of agricultural and nonagricultural workers were the same. To determine the true mean annual income, we would have to know the relative numbers of workers in each group. If, for example, there is 1 agricultural worker for every 11 nonagricultural workers, the mean would be

$$\bar{X} = \frac{(1)(\$9000) + (11)(\$15{,}000)}{1 + 11} = \$14{,}500$$

This is a weighted arithmetic mean.

3.15 Use the frequency distribution of heights in Table 2.1 to find the mean height of the 100 male students at XYZ university.

SOLUTION

The work is outlined in Table 3.1. Note that all students having heights 60 to 62 inches (in), 63 to 65 in, etc., are considered as having heights 61 in, 64 in, etc. The problem then reduces to finding the mean height of 100 students if 5 students have height 61 in, 18 have height 64 in, etc.

The computations involved can become tedious, especially for cases in which the numbers are large and many classes are present. Short techniques are available for lessening the labor in such cases; for example, see Problems 3.20 and 3.22.

Table 3.1

Height (in)	Class Mark (X)	Frequency (f)	fX
60–62	61	5	305
63–65	64	18	1152
66–68	67	42	2814
69–71	70	27	1890
72–74	73	8	584
		$N = \sum f = 100$	$\sum fX = 6745$

$$\bar{X} = \frac{\sum fX}{\sum f} = \frac{\sum fX}{N} = \frac{6745}{100} = 67.45 \text{ in}$$

PROPERTIES OF THE ARITHMETIC MEAN

3.16 Prove that the sum of the deviations of $X_1, X_2, \ldots, X_N$ from their mean $\bar{X}$ is equal to zero.

SOLUTION

Let $d_1 = X_1 - \bar{X}$, $d_2 = X_2 - \bar{X}, \ldots, d_N = X_N - \bar{X}$ be the deviations of $X_1, X_2, \ldots, X_N$ from their mean $\bar{X}$. Then

$$\text{Sum of deviations} = \sum d_j = \sum (X_j - \bar{X}) = \sum X_j - N\bar{X}$$
$$= \sum X_j - N\left(\frac{\sum X_j}{N}\right) = \sum X_j - \sum X_j = 0$$

where we have used $\sum$ in place of $\sum_{j=1}^{N}$. We could, if desired, have omitted the subscript j in X_j, provided that it is *understood.*

3.17 If $Z_1 = X_1 + Y_1$, $Z_2 = X_2 + Y_2, \ldots, Z_N = X_N + Y_N$, prove that $\bar{Z} = \bar{X} + \bar{Y}$.

SOLUTION

By definition,

$$\bar{X} = \frac{\sum X}{N} \qquad \bar{Y} = \frac{\sum Y}{N} \qquad \bar{Z} = \frac{\sum Z}{N}$$

Thus $$\bar{Z} = \frac{\sum Z}{N} = \frac{\sum (X+Y)}{N} = \frac{\sum X + \sum Y}{N} = \frac{\sum X}{N} + \frac{\sum Y}{N} = \bar{X} + \bar{Y}$$

where the subscripts j on X, Y, and Z have been omitted and where $\sum$ means $\sum_{j=1}^{N}$.

3.18 (*a*) If N numbers $X_1, X_2, \ldots, X_N$ have deviations from any number A given by $d_1 = X_1 - A$, $d_2 = X_2 - A, \ldots, d_N = X_N - A$, respectively, prove that

$$\bar{X} = A + \frac{\sum_{j=1}^{N} d_j}{N} = A + \frac{\sum d}{N}$$

(*b*) In case $X_1, X_2, \ldots, X_K$ have respective frequencies $f_1, f_2, \ldots, f_K$ and $d_1 = X_1 - A, \ldots, d_K = X_K - A$, show that the result in part (*a*) is replaced with

$$\bar{X} = A + \frac{\sum_{j=1}^{K} f_j d_j}{\sum_{j=1}^{K} f_j} = A + \frac{\sum fd}{N} \qquad \text{where } \sum_{j=1}^{K} f_j = \sum f = N$$

SOLUTION

(*a*) **First method**

Since $d_j = X_j - A$ and $X_j = A + d_j$, we have

$$\bar{X} = \frac{\sum X_j}{N} = \frac{\sum (A + d_j)}{N} = \frac{\sum A + \sum d_j}{N} = \frac{NA + \sum d_j}{N} = A + \frac{\sum d_j}{N}$$

where we have used $\sum$ in place of $\sum_{j=1}^{N}$ for brevity.

Second method

We have $d = X - A$, or $X = A + d$, omitting the subscripts on d and X. Thus, by Problem 3.17,

$$\bar{X} = \bar{A} + \bar{d} = A + \frac{\sum d}{N}$$

since the mean of a number of constants all equal to A is A.

(*b*)
$$\bar{X} = \frac{\sum_{j=1}^{K} f_j X_j}{\sum_{j=1}^{K} f_j} = \frac{\sum f_j X_j}{N} = \frac{\sum f_j (A + d_j)}{N} = \frac{\sum A f_j + \sum f_j d_j}{N} = \frac{A \sum f_j + \sum f_j d_j}{N}$$

$$= \frac{AN + \sum f_j d_j}{N} = A + \frac{\sum f_j d_j}{N} = A + \frac{\sum fd}{N}$$

Note that *formally* the result is obtained from part (*a*) by replacing d_j with $f_j d_j$ and summing from $j = 1$ to K instead of from $j = 1$ to N. The result is equivalent to $\bar{X} = A + \bar{d}$, where $\bar{d} = (\sum fd)/N$.

THE ARITHMETIC MEAN COMPUTED FROM GROUPED DATA

3.19 Use the method of Problem 3.18(*a*) to find the arithmetic mean of the numbers 5, 8, 11, 9, 12, 6, 14, and 10, choosing as the "guessed mean" A the values (*a*) 9 and (*b*) 20.

SOLUTION

(*a*) The deviations of the given numbers from 9 are −4, −1, 2, 0, 3, −3, 5, and 1, and the sum of the deviations is $\sum d = -4-1+2+0+3-3+5+1 = 3$. Thus

$$\bar{X} = A + \frac{\sum d}{N} = 9 + \frac{3}{8} = 9.375$$

(*b*) The deviations of the given numbers from 20 are −15, −12, −9, −11, −8, −14, −6, and −10, and $\sum d = -85$. Thus

$$\bar{X} = A + \frac{\sum d}{N} = 20 + \frac{(-85)}{8} = 9.375$$

3.20 Use the method of Problem 3.18(*b*) to find the arithmetic mean of the heights of the 100 male students at XYZ University (see Problem 3.15).

SOLUTION

The work may be arranged as in Table 3.2. We take the guessed mean A to be the class mark 67 (which has the largest frequency), although any class mark can be used for A. Note that the computations are simpler than those in Problem 3.15. To shorten the labor even more, we can proceed as in Problem 3.22, where use is made of the fact that the deviations (column 2 of Table 3.2) are all integer multiples of the class-interval size.

Table 3.2

Class Mark (X)	Deviation $d = X - A$	Frequency (f)	fd
61	−6	5	−30
64	−3	18	−54
$A \longrightarrow$ 67	0	42	0
70	3	27	81
73	6	8	48
		$N = \sum f = 100$	$\sum fd = 45$

$$\bar{X} = A + \frac{\sum fd}{N} = 67 + \frac{45}{100} = 67.45 \text{ in}$$

3.21 Let $d_j = X_j - A$ denote the deviations of any class mark X_j in a frequency distribution from a given class mark A. Show that if all class intervals have equal size c, then (*a*) the deviations are all multiples of c (i.e., $d_j = cu_j$, where $u_j = 0, \pm 1, \pm 2, \ldots$) and (*b*) the arithmetic mean can be computed from the formula

$$\bar{X} = A + \left(\frac{\sum fu}{N}\right)c$$

SOLUTION

(*a*) The result is illustrated in Table 3.2 of Problem 3.20, where it is observed that the deviations in column 2 are all multiples of the class-interval size $c = 3$ in.

To see that the result is true in general, note that if $X_1, X_2, X_3, \ldots$ are successive class marks, their common difference will for this case be equal to c, so that $X_2 = X_1 + c$, $X_3 = X_1 + 2c$, and in general $X_j = X_1 + (j-1)c$. Then any two class marks X_p and X_q, for example, will differ by

$$X_p - X_q = [X_1 + (p-1)c] - [X_1 + (q-1)c] = (p-q)c$$

which is a multiple of c.

(*b*) By part (*a*), the deviations of all the class marks from any given one are multiples of c (i.e., $d_j = cu_j$). Then, using Problem 3.18(*b*), we have

$$\bar{X} = A + \frac{\sum f_j d_j}{N} = A + \frac{\sum f_j (cu_j)}{N} = A + c\frac{\sum f_j u_j}{N} = A + \left(\frac{\sum fu}{N}\right)c$$

Note that this is equivalent to the result $\bar{X} = A + c\bar{u}$, which can be obtained from $\bar{X} = A + \bar{d}$ by placing $d = cu$ and observing that $\bar{d} = c\bar{u}$ (see Problem 3.18).

3.22 Use the result of Problem 3.21(*b*) to find the mean height of the 100 male students at XYZ University (see Problem 3.20).

SOLUTION

The work may be arranged as in Table 3.3. The method is called the *coding method* and should be employed whenever possible.

Table 3.3

X	u	f	fu
61	−2	5	−10
64	−1	18	−18
$A \longrightarrow$ 67	0	42	0
70	1	27	27
73	2	8	16
		$N = 100$	$\sum fu = 15$

$$\bar{X} = A + \left(\frac{\sum fu}{N}\right)c = 67 + \left(\frac{15}{100}\right)(3) = 67.45 \text{ in}$$

3.23 Compute the mean weekly wage of the 65 employees at the P&R Company from the frequency distribution in Table 2.5, using (*a*) the long method and (*b*) the coding method.

SOLUTION

Tables 3.4 and 3.5 show the solutions to (*a*) and (*b*), respectively.

It might be supposed that error would be introduced into these tables since the class marks are actually \$254.995, \$264.995, etc., instead of \$255.00, \$265.00, etc. If in Table 3.4 these true class marks are used instead, then $\bar{X}$ turns out to be \$279.76 instead of \$279.77, and the difference is negligible.

$$\bar{X} = \frac{\sum fX}{N} = \frac{\$18{,}185.00}{65} = \$279.77 \qquad \bar{X} = A + \left(\frac{\sum fu}{N}\right)c = \$275.00 + \frac{31}{65}(\$10.00) = \$279.77$$

Table 3.4

X	f	fX
$255.00	8	$2040.00
265.00	10	2650.00
275.00	16	4400.00
285.00	14	3990.00
295.00	10	2950.00
305.00	5	1525.00
315.00	2	630.00
	$N = 65$	$\sum fX = \$18,185.00$

Table 3.5

	X	u	f	fu
	$255.00	−2	8	−16
	265.00	−1	10	−10
$A \longrightarrow$	275.00	0	16	0
	285.00	1	14	14
	295.00	2	10	20
	305.00	3	5	15
	315.00	4	2	8
			$N = 65$	$\sum fu = 31$

3.24 Using Table 2.9(d), find the mean wage of the 70 employees at the P&R Company.

SOLUTION

In this case the class intervals do not have equal size and we must use the long method, as shown in Table 3.6.

Table 3.6

X	f	fX
$255.00	8	$2040.00
265.00	10	2650.00
275.00	16	4400.00
285.00	15	4275.00
295.00	10	2950.00
310.00	8	2480.00
350.00	3	1050.00
	$N = 70$	$\sum fX = \$19,845.00$

$$\bar{X} = \frac{\sum fX}{N} = \frac{\$19,845.00}{70} = \$283.50$$

THE MEDIAN

3.25 The grades of a student on six examinations were 84, 91, 72, 68, 87, and 78. Find the median of the grades.

SOLUTION

Arranged in an array, the grades are 68, 72, 78, 84, 87, and 91. Since there is an even number of items, there are two middle values, 78 and 84, whose arithmetic mean $\frac{1}{2}(78+84) = 81$ is the required grade. Compare with Problem 3.6, where the arithmetic mean is 80.

3.26 The hourly wages of five employees in an office are \$4.52, \$5.96, \$5.28, \$11.20, and \$5.75. Find (a) the median hourly wage and (b) the mean hourly wage.

SOLUTION

(*a*) Arranged in an array, the wages are \$4.52, \$5.28, \$5.75, \$5.96, and \$11.20. Since there is an odd number of items, there is only one middle value, \$5.75, which is the required median.

(*b*) The arithmetic mean is

$$\frac{\$4.52+\$5.96+\$5.28+\$11.20+\$5.75}{5}=\$6.54$$

Note that the median is not affected by the extreme value \$11.20, while the mean is affected by it. In this case the median gives a better indication of the average hourly wage than does the mean.

3.27 If (*a*) 85 and (*b*) 150 numbers are arranged in an array, how would you find the median of the numbers?

SOLUTION

(*a*) Since there are 85 items, an odd number, there is only one middle value with 42 numbers below and 42 numbers above it. Thus the median is the 43d number in the array.

(*b*) Since there are 150 items, an even number, there are two middle values with 74 numbers below them and 74 numbers above them. The two middle values are the 75th and 76th numbers in the array, and their arithmetic mean is the required median.

Mathcad **3.28** From Problem 2.8, find the median weight of the 40 male college students at State University by using (*a*) the frequency distribution of Table 2.7 (reproduced here as Table 3.7) and (*b*) the original data.

SOLUTION

(*a*) **First method** (using interpolation)

The weights in the frequency distribution of Table 3.7 are assumed to be continuously distributed. In such case the median is that weight for which half the total frequency ($40/2=20$) lies above it and half lies below it.

Table 3.7

Weight (lb)	Frequency
118–126	3
127–135	5
136–144	9
145–153	12
154–162	5
163–171	4
172–180	2
	Total 40

Now the sum of the first three class frequencies is $3+5+9=17$. Thus to give the desired 20, we require three more of the 12 cases in the fourth class. Since the fourth class interval, 145–153, actually corresponds to weights 144.5 to 153.5, the median must lie 3/12 of the way between 144.5 and 153.5; that is, the median is

$$144.5+\frac{3}{12}(153.5-144.5)=144.5+\frac{3}{12}(9)=146.8\text{ lb}$$

Second method (using formula)

Since the sum of the first three and first four class frequencies are $3+5+9=17$ and $3+5+9+12=29$, respectively, it is clear that the median lies in the fourth class, which is therefore the median class. Then

$$\begin{aligned} L_1 &= \text{lower class boundary of median class} = 144.5 \\ N &= \text{number of items in the data} = 40 \\ (\textstyle\sum f)_1 &= \text{sum of all classes lower than the median class} = 3+5+9=17 \\ f_{\text{median}} &= \text{frequency of median class} = 12 \\ c &= \text{size of median class interval} = 9 \end{aligned}$$

and thus

$$\text{Median} = L_1 + \left(\frac{N/2-(\sum f)_1}{f_{\text{median}}}\right)c = 144.5 + \left(\frac{40/2-17}{12}\right)(9) = 146.8 \text{ lb}$$

(*b*) Arranged in an array, the original weights are

119, 125, 126, 128, 132, 135, 135, 135, 136, 138, 138, 140, 140, 142, 142, 144, 144, 145, 145, 146, 146, 147, 147, 148, 149, 150, 150, 152, 153, 154, 156, 157, 158, 161, 163, 164, 165, 168, 173, 176

The median is the arithmetic mean of the 20th and 21st weights in this array and is equal to 146 lb.

3.29 Show how the median weight in Problem 3.28 can be obtained from (*a*) a histogram and (*b*) a percentage ogive.

SOLUTION

(*a*) Figure 3-3(*a*) shows the histogram corresponding to the weights in Problem 3.28. The median is the abscissa corresponding to the line *LM*, which divides the histogram into two equal areas. Since area corresponds to frequency in a histogram, *LM* is such that the total area to the right and left of it is half the total frequency, or 20. Thus areas *AMLD* and *MBEL* correspond to frequencies of 3 and 9. Then $AM = \frac{3}{12}AB = \frac{3}{12}(9) = 2.25$, and the median has the value $144.5 + 2.25 = 146.75$, or 146.8 lb to the nearest tenth of a pound. The value can also be read approximately directly from the graph.

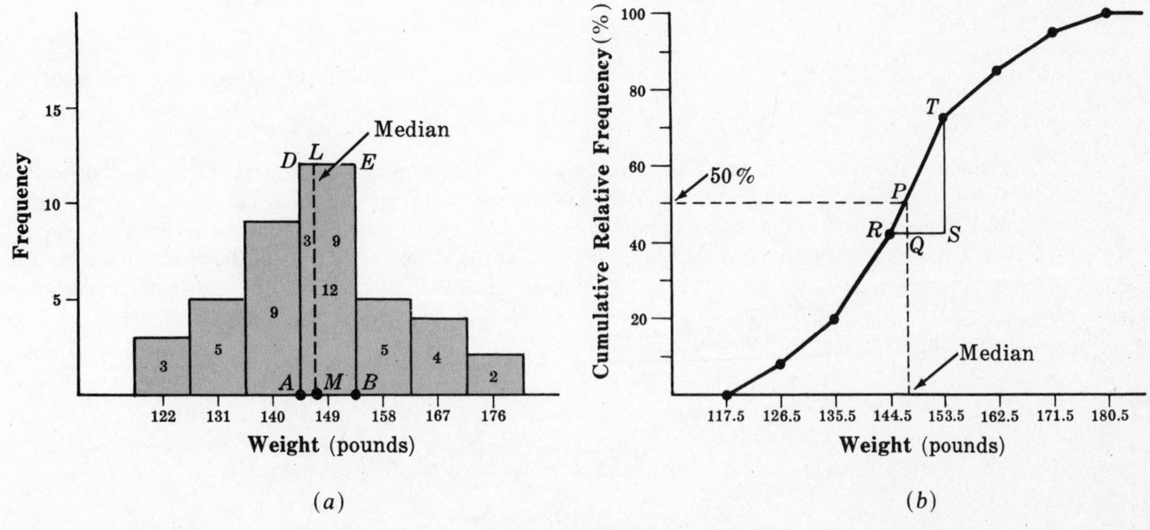

Fig. 3-3

(*b*) Figure 3-3(*b*) shows the relative cumulative-frequency polygon (or percentage ogive) corresponding to the weights in Problem 3.28. The median is the abscissa of point *P* on this ogive, whose ordinate is 50%. To compute its value, we see from the similar triangles *PQR* and *RST* that

$$\frac{RQ}{RS}=\frac{PQ}{ST} \quad \text{or} \quad \frac{RQ}{9}=\frac{50\%-42.5\%}{72.5\%-42.5\%}=\frac{1}{4} \quad \text{so that} \quad RQ=\frac{9}{4}=2.25$$

Thus $$\text{Median}=144.5+RQ=144.5+2.25=146.75\text{ lb}$$

or 146.8 lb to the nearest tenth of a pound. This value can also be read approximately directly from the graph.

3.30 Find the median wage of the 65 employees at the P&R Company (see Problem 2.3).

SOLUTION

Here $N=65$ and $N/2=32.5$. Since the sum of the first two and first three class frequencies are $8+10=18$ and $8+10+16=34$, respectively, the median class is the third class. Using the formula,

$$\text{Median}=L_1+\left(\frac{N/2-(\sum f)_1}{f_{\text{median}}}\right)c=\$269.995+\left(\frac{32.5-18}{16}\right)(\$10.00)=\$279.06$$

THE MODE

3.31 Find the mean, median, and mode for the sets (*a*) 3, 5, 2, 6, 5, 9, 5, 2, 8, 6 and (*b*) 51.6, 48.7, 50.3, 49.5, 48.9.

SOLUTION

(*a*) Arranged in an array, the numbers are 2, 2, 3, 5, 5, 5, 6, 6, 8, and 9.

$$\text{Mean}=\tfrac{1}{10}(2+2+3+5+5+5+6+6+8+9)=5.1$$
$$\text{Median}=\text{arithmetic mean of two middle numbers}=\tfrac{1}{2}(5+5)=5$$
$$\text{Mode}=\text{number occurring most frequently}=5$$

(*b*) Arranged in an array, the numbers are 48.7, 48.9, 49.5, 50.3, and 51.6.

$$\text{Mean}=\tfrac{1}{5}(48.7+48.9+49.5+50.3+51.6)=49.8$$
$$\text{Median}=\text{middle number}=49.5$$
$$\text{Mode}=\text{number occurring most frequently (nonexistent here)}$$

3.32 Develop a formula for determining the mode from data presented in a frequency distribution.

SOLUTION

Assume that Fig. 3-4 represents three rectangles of the histogram of the frequency distribution, the central rectangle corresponding to the modal class. Assume also that the class intervals have equal size.

We define the mode as the abscissa $\hat{X}$ of the point of intersection *P* of the constructed lines *QS* and *RT*.

Let $X=L_1$ and $X=U_1$ represent the lower and upper class boundaries of the modal class, and let Δ_1 and Δ_2 represent, respectively, the excess of the modal class frequency over the class frequencies to the left and right of the modal class.

From similar triangles *PQR* and *PST*, we have

$$\frac{EP}{RQ}=\frac{PF}{ST} \quad \text{or} \quad \frac{\hat{X}-L_1}{\Delta_1}=\frac{U_1-\hat{X}}{\Delta_2}$$

Then $\Delta_2(\hat{X}-L_1)=\Delta_1(U_1-\hat{X}) \qquad \Delta_2\hat{X}-\Delta_2L_1=\Delta_1U_1-\Delta_1\hat{X} \qquad (\Delta_1+\Delta_2)\hat{X}=\Delta_1U_1+\Delta_2L_1$

or $$\hat{X}=\frac{\Delta_1U_1+\Delta_2L_1}{\Delta_1+\Delta_2}$$

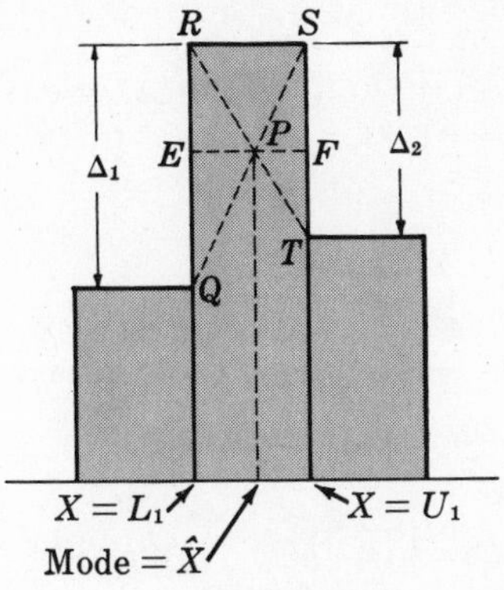

Fig. 3-4

Since $U_1 = L_1 + c$, where c is the class-interval size, this becomes

$$\hat{X} = \frac{\Delta_1(L_1 + c) + \Delta_2 L_1}{\Delta_1 + \Delta_2} = \frac{(\Delta_1 + \Delta_2)L_1 + \Delta_1 c}{\Delta_1 + \Delta_2} = L_1 + \left(\frac{\Delta_1}{\Delta_1 + \Delta_2}\right)c$$

The result has the following interesting interpretation. If a parabola is constructed so as to pass through the three midpoints of the tops of the rectangles in Fig. 3-4, the abscissa of the maximum of this parabola will be the same as the mode obtained above.

Mathcad **3.33** Find the modal wage of the 65 employees at the P&R Company (see Problem 3.23) by using the formula developed in Problem 3.32.

SOLUTION

Here $L_1 = \$269.995$, $\Delta_1 = 16 - 10 = 6$, $\Delta_2 = 16 - 14 = 2$, and $c = \$10.00$. Thus

$$\text{Mode} = L_1 + \left(\frac{\Delta_1}{\Delta_1 + \Delta_2}\right)c = \$269.995 + \left(\frac{6}{2+6}\right)(\$10.00) = \$277.50$$

THE EMPIRICAL RELATION BETWEEN THE MEAN, MEDIAN, AND MODE

3.34 (*a*) Use the empirical formula mean − mode = 3(mean − median) to find the modal wage of the 65 employees at the P&R Company.

(*b*) Compare your result with the mode obtained in Problem 3.33.

SOLUTION

(*a*) From Problems 3.23 and 3.30 we have mean = \$279.77 and median = \$279.06. Thus

$$\text{Mode} = \text{mean} - 3(\text{mean} - \text{median}) = \$279.77 - 3(\$279.77 - \$279.06) = \$277.64$$

(*b*) From Problem 3.33 the modal wage is \$277.50, so there is good agreement with the empirical result in this case.

THE GEOMETRIC MEAN

3.35 Find (*a*) the geometric mean and (*b*) the arithmetic mean of the numbers 3, 5, 6, 6, 7, 10, and 12. Assume that the numbers are exact.

SOLUTION

(*a*) Geometric mean $= G = \sqrt[7]{(3)(5)(6)(6)(7)(10)(12)} = \sqrt[7]{453{,}600}$. Using common logarithms, $\log G = \frac{1}{7}\log 453{,}600 = \frac{1}{7}(5.6567) = 0.8081$, and $G = 6.43$ (to the nearest hundredth). Alternatively, a calculator can be used.

Another method

$$\log G = \tfrac{1}{7}(\log 3 + \log 5 + \log 6 + \log 6 + \log 7 + \log 10 + \log 12)$$
$$= \tfrac{1}{7}(0.4771 + 0.6990 + 0.7782 + 0.7782 + 0.8451 + 1.0000 + 1.0792)$$
$$= 0.8081$$

and $$G = 6.43$$

(*b*) Arithmetic mean $= \hat{X} = \frac{1}{7}(3+5+6+6+7+10+12) = 7$. This illustrates the fact that the geometric mean of a set of unequal positive numbers is less than the arithmetic mean.

3.36 The numbers $X_1, X_2, \ldots, X_K$ occur with frequencies $f_1, f_2, \ldots, f_K$, where $f_1 + f_2 + \cdots + f_K = N$ is the total frequency.

(*a*) Find the geometric mean G of the numbers.

(*b*) Derive an expression for $\log G$.

(*c*) How can the results be used to find the geometric mean for data grouped into a frequency distribution?

SOLUTION

(*a*)
$$G = \sqrt[N]{\underbrace{X_1X_1\cdots X_1}_{f_1 \text{ times}}\ \underbrace{X_2X_2\cdots X_2}_{f_2 \text{ times}}\cdots\underbrace{X_KX_K\cdots X_K}_{f_K \text{ times}}} = \sqrt[N]{X_1^{f_1}X_2^{f_2}\cdots X_K^{f_K}}$$

where $N = \sum f$. This is sometimes called the *weighted geometric mean.*

(*b*)
$$\log G = \frac{1}{N}\log\left(X_1^{f_1}X_2^{f_2}\cdots X_K^{f_K}\right) = \frac{1}{N}(f_1\log X_1 + f_2\log X_2 + \cdots + f_K\log X_K)$$
$$= \frac{1}{N}\sum_{j=1}^{K} f_j \log X_j = \frac{\sum f \log X}{N}$$

where we assume that all the numbers are positive; otherwise, the logarithms are not defined.

Note that the logarithm of the geometric mean of a set of positive numbers is the arithmetic mean of the logarithms of the numbers.

(*c*) The result can be used to find the geometric mean for grouped data by taking $X_1, X_2, \ldots, X_K$ as class marks and $f_1, f_2, \ldots, f_K$ as the corresponding class frequencies.

3.37 During one year the ratio of milk prices per quart to bread prices per loaf was 3.00, whereas during the next year the ratio was 2.00.

(*a*) Find the arithmetic mean of these ratios for the 2-year period.

(*b*) Find the arithmetic mean of the ratios of bread prices to milk prices for the 2-year period.

(*c*) Discuss the advisability of using the arithmetic mean for averaging ratios.

(*d*) Discuss the suitability of the geometric mean for averaging ratios.

SOLUTION

(*a*)
$$\text{Mean ratio of milk to bread prices} = \tfrac{1}{2}(3.00 + 2.00) = 2.50$$

(*b*) Since the ratio of milk to bread prices for the first year is 3.00, the ratio of bread to milk prices is $1/3.00 = 0.333$. Similarly, the ratio of bread to milk prices for the second year is $1/2.00 = 0.500$. Thus

$$\text{Mean ratio of bread to milk prices} = \tfrac{1}{2}(0.333 + 0.500) = 0.417$$

(c) We would expect the mean ratio of milk to bread prices to be the reciprocal of the mean ratio of bread to milk prices if the mean is an appropriate average. However, $1/0.417 = 2.40 \neq 2.50$. This shows that the arithmetic mean is a poor average to use for ratios.

(d) Geometric mean of ratios of milk to bread prices $= \sqrt{(3.00)(2.00)} = \sqrt{6.00}$

Geometric mean of ratios of bread to milk prices $= \sqrt{(0.333)(0.500)} = \sqrt{0.0167} = 1/\sqrt{6.00}$

Since these averages are reciprocals, our conclusion is that the geometric mean is more suitable than the arithmetic mean for averaging ratios for this type of problem.

3.38 The bacterial count in a certain culture increased from 1000 to 4000 in 3 days. What was the average percentage increase per day?

SOLUTION

Since an increase from 1000 to 4000 is a 300% increase, one might be led to conclude that the average percentage increase per day would be $300\%/3 = 100\%$. This, however, would imply that during the first day the count went from 1000 to 2000, during the second day from 2000 to 4000, and during the third day from 4000 to 8000, which is contrary to the facts.

To determine this average percentage increase, let us denote it by r. Then

$$\begin{aligned}
\text{Total bacterial count after 1 day} &= 1000 + 1000r = 1000(1+r) \\
\text{Total bacterial count after 2 days} &= 1000(1+r) + 1000(1+r)r = 1000(1+r)^2 \\
\text{Total bacterial count after 3 days} &= 1000(1+r)^2 + 1000(1+r)^2 r = 1000(1+r)^3
\end{aligned}$$

This last expression must equal 4000. Thus $1000(1+r)^3 = 4000$, $(1+r)^3 = 4$, $1 + r = \sqrt[3]{4}$, and $r = \sqrt[3]{4} - 1 = 1.587 - 1 = 0.587$, so that $r = 58.7\%$.

In general, if we start with a quantity P and increase it at a constant rate r per unit of time, we will have after n units of time the amount

$$A = P(1+r)^n$$

This is called the *compound-interest formula* (see Problems 3.94 and 3.95).

THE HARMONIC MEAN

3.39 Find the harmonic mean H of the numbers 3, 5, 6, 6, 7, 10, and 12.

SOLUTION

$$\frac{1}{H} = \frac{1}{N}\sum \frac{1}{X} = \frac{1}{7}\left(\frac{1}{3} + \frac{1}{5} + \frac{1}{6} + \frac{1}{6} + \frac{1}{7} + \frac{1}{10} + \frac{1}{12}\right) = \frac{1}{7}\left(\frac{140 + 84 + 70 + 70 + 60 + 42 + 35}{420}\right)$$

$$= \frac{501}{2940}$$

and $$H = \frac{2940}{501} = 5.87$$

It is often convenient to express the fractions in decimal form first. Thus

$$\frac{1}{H} = \tfrac{1}{7}(0.3333 + 0.2000 + 0.1667 + 0.1667 + 0.1429 + 0.1000 + 0.0833)$$

$$= \frac{1.1929}{7}$$

and $$H = \frac{7}{1.1929} = 5.87$$

Comparison with Problem 3.35 illustrates the fact that the harmonic mean of several positive numbers not all equal is less than their geometric mean, which is in turn less than their arithmetic mean.

3.40 During four successive years, a home owner purchased oil for her furnace at respective costs of \$0.80, \$0.90, \$1.05, and \$1.25 per gallon (gal). What was the average cost of oil over the 4-year period?

SOLUTION

Case 1

Suppose that the home owner purchased the same quantity of oil each year, say 1000 gal. Then

$$\text{Average cost} = \frac{\text{total cost}}{\text{total quantity purchased}} = \frac{\$800 + \$900 + \$1050 + \$1250}{4000 \text{ gal}} = \$1.00/\text{gal}$$

This is the same as the arithmetic mean of the costs per gallon; that is, $\frac{1}{4}(\$0.80 + \$0.90 + \$1.05 + \$1.25) =$ 1.00/gal. This result would be the same even if x gallons were used each year.

Case 2

Suppose that the home owner spends the same amount of money each year, say \$1000. Then

$$\text{Average cost} = \frac{\text{total cost}}{\text{total quantity purchased}} = \frac{\$4000}{(1250 + 1111 + 952 + 800) \text{ gal}} = \$0.975/\text{gal}$$

This is the same as the harmonic mean of the costs per gallon:

$$\frac{4}{\dfrac{1}{0.80} + \dfrac{1}{0.90} + \dfrac{1}{1.05} + \dfrac{1}{1.25}} = 0.975$$

This result would be the same even if y dollars were spent each year.

Both averaging processes are correct, each average being computed under different prevailing conditions.

It should be noted that in case the number of gallons used changes from one year to another instead of remaining the same, the ordinary arithmetic mean of Case 1 is replaced by a weighted arithmetic mean. Similarly, if the total amount spent changes from one year to another, the ordinary harmonic mean of Case 2 is replaced by a weighted harmonic mean.

3.41 A person travels from A to B at an average speed of 30 miles per hour (mi/h) and returns from B to A along the same route at an average speed of 60 mi/h. Find the average speed for the entire trip.

SOLUTION

Assume that the distance from A to B is 60 miles (although any distance can be assumed). Then

$$\text{Time to move from } A \text{ to } B = \frac{60 \text{ mi}}{30 \text{ mi/h}} = 2 \text{ h} \qquad \text{Time from } B \text{ to } A = \frac{60 \text{ mi}}{60 \text{ mi/h}} = 1 \text{ h}$$

and

$$\text{Average speed for round-trip} = \frac{\text{total distance}}{\text{total time}} = \frac{120 \text{ mi}}{3 \text{ h}} = 40 \text{ mi/h}$$

The above average is the harmonic mean of 30 and 60; that is,

$$\frac{2}{1/30 + 1/60} = 40 \text{ mi/h}$$

If the distances traveled are not all equal, a weighted harmonic mean of the speeds would be used, where the weights are the respective distances (see Problem 3.102).

Note that one might very well be tempted to take the arithmetic mean of 30 and 60 mi/h to obtain 45 mi/h, but this is wrong.

THE ROOT MEAN SQUARE, OR QUADRATIC MEAN

3.42 Find the quadratic mean of the numbers 3, 5, 6, 6, 7, 10, and 12.

SOLUTION

$$\text{Quadratic mean} = \text{RMS} = \sqrt{\frac{3^2+5^2+6^2+6^2+7^2+10^2+12^2}{7}} = \sqrt{57} = 7.55$$

3.43 Prove that the quadratic mean of two positive unequal numbers, a and b, is greater than their geometric mean.

SOLUTION

We are required to show that $\sqrt{\frac{1}{2}(a^2+b^2)} > \sqrt{ab}$. If this is true, then by squaring both sides, $\frac{1}{2}(a^2+b^2) > ab$, so that $a^2+b^2 > 2ab$, $a^2-2ab+b^2 > 0$, or $(a-b)^2 > 0$. But this last inequality is true, since the square of any real number not equal to zero must be positive.

The proof consists in establishing the reversal of the above steps. Thus starting with $(a-b)^2 > 0$, which we know to be true, we can show that $a^2+b^2 > 2ab$, $\frac{1}{2}(a^2+b^2) > ab$, and finally $\sqrt{\frac{1}{2}(a^2+b^2)} > \sqrt{ab}$, as required.

Note that $\sqrt{\frac{1}{2}(a^2+b^2)} = \sqrt{ab}$ if and only if $a = b$.

QUARTILES, DECILES, AND PERCENTILES

3.44 Find (a) the quartiles Q_1, Q_2, and Q_3 and (b) the deciles $D_1, D_2, \ldots, D_9$ for the wages of the 65 employees at the P&R Company (see Problem 2.3).

SOLUTION

(a) The first quartile Q_1 is that wage obtained by counting $N/4 = 65/4 = 16.25$ of the cases, beginning with the first (lowest) class. Since the first class contains 8 cases, we must take 8.25 (16.25 − 8) of the 10 cases from the second class. Using the method of linear interpolation, we have

$$Q_1 = \$259.995 + \frac{8.25}{10}(\$10.00) = \$268.25$$

The second quartile Q_2 is obtained by counting the first $2N/4 = N/2 = 65/2 = 32.5$ of the cases. Since the first two classes comprise 18 cases, we must take $32.5 - 18 = 14.5$ of the 16 cases from the third class; thus

$$Q_2 = \$269.995 + \frac{14.5}{16}(\$10.00) = \$279.06$$

Note that Q_2 is actually the median.

The third quartile Q_3 is obtained by counting the first $3N/4 = \frac{3}{4}(65) = 48.75$ of the cases. Since the first four classes comprise 48 cases, we must take $48.75 - 48 = 0.75$ of the 10 cases from the fifth class; thus

$$Q_3 = \$289.995 + \frac{0.75}{10}(\$10.00) = \$290.75$$

Hence 25% of the employees earn \$268.25 or less, 50% earn \$279.06 or less, and 75% earn \$290.75 or less.

(*b*) The first, second, ..., ninth deciles are obtained by counting $N/10, 2N/10, \ldots, 9N/10$ of the cases, beginning with the first (lowest) class. Thus

$$D_1 = \$249.995 + \frac{6.5}{8}(\$10.00) = \$258.12 \qquad D_6 = \$279.995 + \frac{5}{14}(\$10.00) = \$283.57$$

$$D_2 = \$259.995 + \frac{5}{10}(\$10.00) = \$265.00 \qquad D_7 = \$279.995 + \frac{11.5}{14}(\$10.00) = \$288.21$$

$$D_3 = \$269.995 + \frac{1.5}{16}(\$10.00) = \$270.94 \qquad D_8 = \$289.995 + \frac{4}{10}(\$10.00) = \$294.00$$

$$D_4 = \$269.995 + \frac{8}{16}(\$10.00) = \$275.00 \qquad D_9 = \$299.995 + \frac{0.5}{5}(\$10.00) = \$301.00$$

$$D_5 = \$269.995 + \frac{14.5}{16}(\$10.00) = \$279.06$$

Hence 10% of the employees earn \$258.12 or less, 20% earn \$265.00 or less, ..., 90% earn \$301.00 or less.

Note that the fifth decile is the median. The second, fourth, sixth, and eighth deciles, which divide the distribution into five equal parts and which are called *quintiles*, are sometimes used in practice.

3.45 Determine (*a*) the 35th and (*b*) the 60th percentiles for the distribution in Problem 3.44.

SOLUTION

(*a*) The 35th percentile, denoted by P_{35}, is obtained by counting the first $35N/100 = 35(65)/100 = 22.75$ of the cases, beginning with the first (lowest) class. Then, as in Problem 3.44,

$$P_{35} = \$269.995 + \frac{4.75}{16}(\$10.00) = \$272.97$$

This means that 35% of the employees earn \$272.97 or less.

(*b*) The 60th percentile is $P_{60} = \$279.995 + \frac{5}{14}(\$10.00) = \$283.57$. Note that this is the same as the sixth decile or third quintile.

3.46 Show how the results of Problems 3.44 and 3.45 can be obtained from a percentage ogive.

SOLUTION

The percentage ogive corresponding to the data of Problems 3.44 and 3.45 is shown in Fig. 3-5.

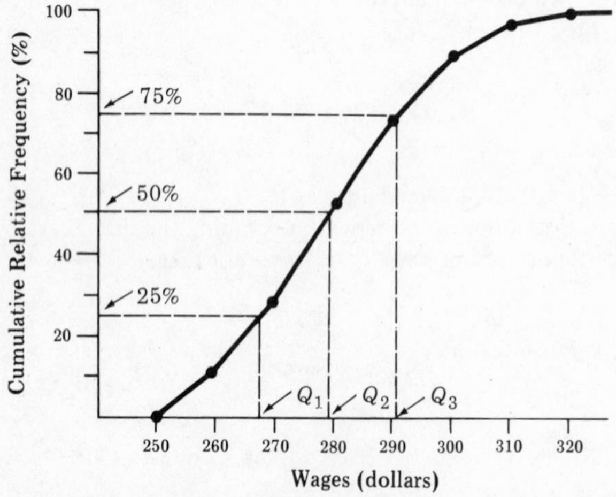

Fig. 3-5

The first quartile is the abscissa of that point on the ogive whose ordinate is 25%. Similarly, the second and third quartiles are the abscissas of those points on the ogive with ordinates 50% and 75%, respectively.

The deciles and percentiles can be similarly obtained. For example, the seventh decile and 35th percentile are the abscissas of those points on the ogive corresponding to ordinates of 70% and 35%, respectively.

Supplementary Problems

SUMMATION NOTATION

3.47 Write the terms in each of the following indicated sums:

(a) $\sum_{j=1}^{4} (X_j+2)$ (c) $\sum_{j=1}^{3} U_j(U_j+6)$ (e) $\sum_{j=1}^{4} 4X_jY_j$

(b) $\sum_{j=1}^{5} f_jX_j^2$ (d) $\sum_{k=1}^{N} (Y_k^2-4)$

3.48 Express each of the following by using the summation notation:

(a) $(X_1+3)^3+(X_2+3)^3+(X_3+3)^3$

(b) $f_1(Y_1-a)^2+f_2(Y_2-a)^2+\cdots+f_{15}(Y_{15}-a)^2$

(c) $(2X_1-3Y_1)+(2X_2-3Y_2)+\cdots+(2X_N-3Y_N)$

(d) $(X_1/Y_1-1)^2+(X_2/Y_2-1)^2+\cdots+(X_8/Y_8-1)^2$

(e) $\dfrac{f_1a_1^2+f_2a_2^2+\cdots+f_{12}a_{12}^2}{f_1+f_2+\cdots+f_{12}}$

3.49 Prove that $\sum_{j=1}^{N}(X_j-1)^2=\sum_{j=1}^{N}X_j^2-2\sum_{j=1}^{N}X_j+N$.

3.50 Prove that $\sum (X+a)(Y+b)=\sum XY+a\sum Y+b\sum X+Nab$, where a and b are constants. What subscript notation is implied?

3.51 Two variables, U and V, assume the values $U_1=3$, $U_2=-2$, $U_3=5$, and $V_1=-4$, $V_2=-1$, $V_3=6$, respectively. Calculate (a) $\sum UV$, (b) $\sum (U+3)(V-4)$, (c) $\sum V^2$, (d) $(\sum U)(\sum V)^2$, (e) $\sum UV^2$, (f) $\sum (U^2-2V^2+2)$, and (g) $\sum (U/V)$.

3.52 Given $\sum_{j=1}^{4} X_j=7$, $\sum_{j=1}^{4} Y_j=-3$, and $\sum_{j=1}^{4} X_jY_j=5$, find (a) $\sum_{j=1}^{4}(2X_j+5Y_j)$ and (b) $\sum_{j=1}^{4}(X_j-3)(2Y_j+1)$.

THE ARITHMETIC MEAN

3.53 A student received grades of 85, 76, 93, 82, and 96 in five subjects. Determine the arithmetic mean of the grades.

3.54 The reaction times of an individual to certain stimuli were measured by a psychologist to be 0.53, 0.46, 0.50, 0.49, 0.52, 0.53, 0.44, and 0.55 second, respectively. Determine the mean reaction time of the individual to the stimuli.

3.55 A set of numbers consists of six 6's, seven 7's, eight 8's, nine 9's and ten 10's. What is the arithmetic mean of the numbers?

3.56 A student's grades in the laboratory, lecture, and recitation parts of a physics course were 71, 78, and 89, respectively.

(*a*) If the weights accorded these grades are 2, 4, and 5, respectively, what is an appropriate average grade?

(*b*) What is the average grade if equal weights are used?

3.57 Three teachers of economics reported mean examination grades of 79, 74, and 82 in their classes, which consisted of 32, 25, and 17 students, respectively. Determine the mean grade for all the classes.

3.58 The mean annual salary paid to all employees in a company was \$15,000. The mean annual salaries paid to male and female employees of the company were \$15,600 and \$12,600, respectively. Determine the percentages of males and females employed by the company.

3.59 Table 3.8 shows the distribution of the maximum loads in short tons (1 short ton = 2000 lb) supported by certain cables produced by a company. Determine the mean maximum loading, using (*a*) the "long method" and (*b*) the coding method.

Table 3.8

Maximum Load (short tons)	Number of Cables
9.3–9.7	2
9.8–10.2	5
10.3–10.7	12
10.8–11.2	17
11.3–11.7	14
11.8–12.2	6
12.3–12.7	3
12.8–13.2	1
	Total 60

3.60 Find $\bar{X}$ for the data in Table 3.9, using (*a*) the "long method" and (*b*) the coding method.

Table 3.9

X	462	480	498	516	534	552	570	588	606	624
f	98	75	56	42	30	21	15	11	6	2

3.61 Table 3.10 shows the distribution of the diameters of the heads of rivets manufactured by a company. Compute the mean diameter.

3.62 Compute the mean for the data in Table 3.11.

3.63 Compute the mean lifetime of tubes manufactured by the L&M Tube Company of Problem 2.20.

3.64 (*a*) Use the frequency distribution obtained in Problem 2.27 to compute the mean diameter of the ball bearings.

(*b*) Compute the mean directly from the raw data and compare it with part (*a*), explaining any discrepancy.

Table 3.10

Diameter (cm)	Frequency
0.7247–0.7249	2
0.7250–0.7252	6
0.7253–0.7255	8
0.7256–0.7258	15
0.7259–0.7261	42
0.7262–0.7264	68
0.7265–0.7267	49
0.7268–0.7270	25
0.7271–0.7273	18
0.7274–0.7276	12
0.7277–0.7279	4
0.7280–0.7282	1
	Total 250

Table 3.11

Class	Frequency
10 to under 15	3
15 to under 20	7
20 to under 25	16
25 to under 30	12
30 to under 35	9
35 to under 40	5
40 to under 45	2
	Total 54

THE MEDIAN

3.65 Find the mean and median of these sets of numbers: (*a*) 5, 4, 8, 3, 7, 2, 9 and (*b*) 18.3, 20.6, 19.3, 22.4, 20.2, 18.8, 19.7, 20.0.

3.66 Find the median grade of Problem 3.53.

3.67 Find the median reaction time of Problem 3.54.

3.68 Find the median of the set of numbers in Problem 3.55.

3.69 Find the median of the maximum loads of the cables in Table 3.8 of Problem 3.59.

3.70 Find the median $\tilde{X}$ for the distribution in Table 3.9 of Problem 3.60.

3.71 Find the median diameter of the rivet heads in Table 3.10 of Problem 3.61.

3.72 Find the median of the distribution in Table 3.11 of Problem 3.62.

Table 3.12

Age (years)	Male (thousands)	Female (thousands)
18–19	121	481
20–24	2,441	4,184
25–29	5,930	6,952
30–34	6,587	7,193
35–44	11,788	11,893
45–54	9,049	9,022
55–64	8,749	8,171
65–74	5,786	4,654
75 and over	2,581	1,524

Source: U.S. Bureau of the Census.

3.73 Table 3.12 shows the total number of marriages (including possible repetitions) in the United States for males and females of different age groups during the year 1984.

(*a*) Find the median ages of males and females for these marriages.

(*b*) Why is the median a more suitable measure of central tendency than is the mean in this case?

3.74 Find the median sales on farms for the data of Problem 2.31.

3.75 Find the median lifetime of the tubes in Problem 2.20.

THE MODE

3.76 Find the mean, median, and mode for each set of numbers: (*a*) 7, 4, 10, 9, 15, 12, 7, 9, 7 and (*b*) 8, 11, 4, 3, 2, 5, 10, 6, 4, 1, 10, 8, 12, 6, 5, 7.

3.77 Find the modal grade in Problem 3.53.

3.78 Find the modal reaction time in Problem 3.54.

3.79 Find the mode of the set of numbers in Problem 3.55.

3.80 Find the mode of the maximum loads of the cables of Problem 3.59.

3.81 Find the mode $\hat{X}$ for the distribution in Table 3.9 of Problem 3.60.

3.82 Find the modal diameter of the rivet heads in Table 3.10 of Problem 3.61.

3.83 Find the mode of the distribution in Problem 3.62.

3.84 Find the modal lifetime of the tubes in Problem 2.20.

3.85 Is it possible to determine the mode for the distributions of Problems 3.73 and 2.31? Give reasons for your answer.

3.86 Use the empirical formula Mean − mode = 3(mean − median) to compute the mode for the distributions of Problems 3.59, 3.60, 3.61, 3.62, and 2.20. Compare the results with those obtained from formula (*9*) in this chapter, explaining any agreement or disagreement.

3.87 Prove the statement made at the end of Problem 3.32.

THE GEOMETRIC MEAN

3.88 Find the geometric mean of the numbers (*a*) 4.2 and 16.8 and (*b*) 3.00 and 6.00.

3.89 Find (*a*) the geometric mean G and (*b*) the arithmetic mean $\bar{X}$ of the set 2, 4, 8, 16, 32.

3.90 Find the geometric mean of the sets (*a*) 3, 5, 8, 3, 7, 2 and (*b*) 28.5, 73.6, 47.2, 31.5, 64.8.

3.91 Find the geometric mean for the distributions in (*a*) Problem 3.59 and (*b*) Problem 3.60. Verify that the geometric mean is less than or equal to the arithmetic mean for these cases.

3.92 If the price of a commodity doubles in a period of 4 years, what is the average percentage increase per year?

3.93 In 1970 and 1980 the population of the United States was 203.3 million and 226.5 million, respectively.

(*a*) What was the average percentage increase per year?

(*b*) Estimate the population in 1974.

(*c*) If the average percentage increase of population per year from 1980 to 1990 is the same as in part (*a*), what would the population be in 1990?

3.94 A principal of \$1000 is invested at an 8% annual rate of interest. What will the total amount be after 6 years if the original principal is not withdrawn?

3.95 If in Problem 3.94 the interest is compounded quarterly (i.e., there is a 2% increase in the money every 3 months), what will the total amount be after 6 years?

3.96 Find two numbers whose arithmetic mean is 9.0 and whose geometric mean is 7.2.

THE HARMONIC MEAN

3.97 Find the harmonic mean of the numbers (*a*) 2, 3, and 6 and (*b*) 3.2, 5.2, 4.8, 6.1, and 4.2.

3.98 Find the (*a*) arithmetic mean, (*b*) geometric mean, and (*c*) harmonic mean of the numbers 0, 2, 4, and 6.

3.99 If $X_1, X_2, X_3, \ldots$ represent the class marks in a frequency distribution with corresponding class frequencies $f_1, f_2, f_3, \ldots$, respectively, prove that the harmonic mean H of the distribution is given by

$$\frac{1}{H}=\frac{1}{N}\left(\frac{f_1}{X_1}+\frac{f_2}{X_2}+\frac{f_3}{X_3}+\cdots\right)=\frac{1}{N}\sum\frac{f}{X}$$

where $N=f_1+f_2+\cdots=\sum f$.

3.100 Use Problem 3.99 to find the harmonic mean of the distributions in (*a*) Problem 3.59 and (*b*) Problem 3.60. Compare with Problem 3.91.

3.101 Cities *A*, *B*, and *C* are equidistant from each other. A motorist travels from *A* to *B* at 30 mi/h, from *B* to *C* at 40 mi/h, and from *C* to *A* at 50 mi/h. Determine his average speed for the entire trip.

3.102 (*a*) An airplane travels distances of d_1, d_2, and d_3 miles at speeds v_1, v_2, and v_3 mi/h, respectively. Show that the average speed is given by V, where

$$\frac{d_1+d_2+d_3}{V}=\frac{d_1}{v_1}+\frac{d_2}{v_2}+\frac{d_3}{v_3}$$

This is a weighted harmonic mean.

(*b*) Find V if $d_1=2500$, $d_2=1200$, $d_3=500$, $v_1=500$, $v_2=400$, and $v_3=250$.

3.103 Prove that the geometric mean of two positive numbers *a* and *b* is (*a*) less than or equal to the arithmetic mean and (*b*) greater than or equal to the harmonic mean of the numbers. Can you extend the proof to more than two numbers?

THE ROOT MEAN SQUARE, OR QUADRATIC MEAN

3.104 Find the root mean square (or quadratic mean) of the numbers (*a*) 11, 23, and 35 and (*b*) 2.7, 3.8, 3.2, and 4.3.

3.105 Show that the root mean square of two positive numbers, *a* and *b*, is (*a*) greater than or equal to the arithmetic mean and (*b*) greater than or equal to the harmonic mean. Can you extend the proof to more than two numbers?

3.106 Derive a formula that can be used to find the root mean square for grouped data and apply it to one of the frequency distributions already considered.

QUARTILES, DECILES, AND PERCENTILES

3.107 Table 3.13 shows a frequency distribution of grades on a final examination in college algebra. (*a*) Find the quartiles of the distribution, and (*b*) interpret clearly the significance of each.

Table 3.13

Grade	Number of Students
90–100	9
80– 89	32
70– 79	43
60– 69	21
50– 59	11
40– 49	3
30– 39	1
	Total 120

3.108 Find the quartiles Q_1, Q_2, and Q_3 for the distributions in (*a*) Problem 3.59 and (*b*) Problem 3.60. Interpret clearly the significance of each.

3.109 Find (*a*) the second decile, (*b*) the fourth decile, (*c*) the 90th percentile, and (*d*) the 68th percentile for the data of Problem 3.73, interpreting clearly the significance of each.

3.110 Find (*a*) P_{10}, (*b*) P_{90}, (*c*) P_{25}, and (*d*) P_{75} for the data of Problem 3.59, interpreting clearly the significance of each.

3.111 (*a*) Can all quartiles and deciles be expressed as percentiles? Explain.

(*b*) Can all quantiles be expressed as percentiles? Explain.

3.112 For the data of Problem 3.107, determine (*a*) the lowest grade scored by the top 25% of the class and (*b*) the highest grade scored by the lowest 20% of the class. Interpret your answers in terms of percentiles.

3.113 Interpret the results of Problem 3.107 graphically by using (*a*) a percentage histogram, (*b*) a percentage frequency polygon, and (*c*) a percentage ogive.

3.114 Answer Problem 3.113 for the results of Problem 3.108.

3.115 (*a*) Develop a formula, similar to that of equation (*8*) in this chapter, for computing any percentile from a frequency distribution.

(*b*) Illustrate the use of the formula by applying it to obtain the results of Problem 3.110.

Chapter 4

The Standard Deviation and Other Measures of Dispersion

DISPERSION, OR VARIATION

The degree to which numerical data tend to spread about an average value is called the *dispersion*, or *variation*, of the data. Various measures of this dispersion (or variation) are available, the most common being the range, mean deviation, semi-interquartile range, 10–90 percentile range, and standard deviation.

THE RANGE

The *range* of a set of numbers is the difference between the largest and smallest numbers in the set.

EXAMPLE 1. The range of the set 2, 3, 3, 5, 5, 5, 8, 10, 12 is $12-2=10$. Sometimes the range is given by simply quoting the smallest and largest numbers; in the above set, for instance, the range could be indicated as 2 to 12, or 2–12.

THE MEAN DEVIATION

The *mean deviation*, or *average deviation*, of a set of N numbers $X_1, X_2, \ldots, X_N$ is abbreviated MD and is defined by

$$\text{Mean deviation (MD)} = \frac{\sum_{j=1}^{N} |X_j - \bar{X}|}{N} = \frac{\sum |X-\bar{X}|}{N} = \overline{|X-\bar{X}|} \tag{1}$$

where $\bar{X}$ is the arithmetic mean of the numbers and $|X_j - \bar{X}|$ is the absolute value of the deviation of X_j from $\bar{X}$. (The *absolute value* of a number is the number without the associated sign and is indicated by two vertical lines placed around the number; thus $|-4|=4$, $|+3|=3$, $|6|=6$, and $|-0.84|=0.84$.)

EXAMPLE 2. Find the mean deviation of the set 2, 3, 6, 8, 11.

$$\text{Arithmetic mean } (\bar{X}) = \frac{2+3+6+8+11}{5} = 6$$

$$\text{MD} = \frac{|2-6|+|3-6|+|6-6|+|8-6|+|11-6|}{5} = \frac{|-4|+|-3|+|0|+|2|+|5|}{5} = \frac{4+3+0+2+5}{5} = 2.8$$

If $X_1, X_2, \ldots, X_K$ occur with frequencies $f_1, f_2, \ldots, f_K$, respectively, the mean deviation can be written as

$$\text{MD} = \frac{\sum_{j=1}^{K} f_j |X_j - \bar{X}|}{N} = \frac{\sum f|X-\bar{X}|}{N} = \overline{|X-\bar{X}|} \tag{2}$$

where $N = \sum_{j=1}^{K} f_j = \sum f$. This form is useful for grouped data, where the X_j's represent class marks and the f_j's are the corresponding class frequencies.

Occasionally the mean deviation is defined in terms of absolute deviations from the median or other average instead of from the mean. An interesting property of the sum $\sum_{j=1}^{N} |X_j - a|$ is that it is a minimum when a is the median (i.e., the mean deviation about the median is a minimum).

Note that it would be more appropriate to use the terminology *mean absolute deviation* than *mean deviation.*

THE SEMI-INTERQUARTILE RANGE

The *semi-interquartile range*, or *quartile deviation*, of a set of data is denoted by Q and is defined by

$$Q = \frac{Q_3 - Q_1}{2} \tag{3}$$

where Q_1 and Q_3 are the first and third quartiles for the data (see Problems 4.6 and 4.7). The interquartile range $Q_3 - Q_1$ is sometimes used, but the semi-interquartile range is more common as a measure of dispersion.

THE 10–90 PERCENTILE RANGE

The *10–90 percentile range* of a set of data is defined by

$$\text{10–90 percentile range} = P_{90} - P_{10} \tag{4}$$

where P_{10} and P_{90} are the 10th and 90th percentiles for the data (see Problem 4.8). The semi-10–90 percentile range, $\frac{1}{2}(P_{90} - P_{10})$, can also be used but is not commonly employed.

THE STANDARD DEVIATION

The *standard deviation* of a set of N numbers $X_1, X_2, \ldots, X_N$ is denoted by s and is defined by

$$s = \sqrt{\frac{\sum_{j=1}^{N} (X_j - \bar{X})^2}{N}} = \sqrt{\frac{\sum (X - \bar{X})^2}{N}} = \sqrt{\frac{\sum x^2}{N}} = \sqrt{\overline{(X - \bar{X})^2}} \tag{5}$$

where x represents the deviations of each of the numbers X_j from the mean $\bar{X}$. Thus s is the root mean square of the deviations from the mean, or, as it is sometimes called, the *root-mean-square deviation* (see page 62).

If $X_1, X_2, \ldots, X_K$ occur with frequencies $f_1, f_2, \ldots, f_K$, respectively, the standard deviation can be written

$$s = \sqrt{\frac{\sum_{j=1}^{K} f_j(X_j - \bar{X})^2}{N}} = \sqrt{\frac{\sum f(X - \bar{X})^2}{N}} = \sqrt{\frac{\sum fx^2}{N}} = \sqrt{\overline{(X - \bar{X})^2}} \tag{6}$$

where $N = \sum_{j=1}^{K} f_j = \sum f$. In this form it is useful for grouped data.

Sometimes the standard deviation of a sample's data is defined with $(N-1)$ replacing N in the denominators of the expressions in equations (5) and (6) because the resulting value represents a better estimate of the standard deviation of a population from which the sample is taken. For large values of N (certainly $N > 30$), there is practically no difference between the two definitions. Also, when the better estimate is needed we can always obtain it by multiplying the standard deviation computed according to the first definition by $\sqrt{N/(N-1)}$. Hence we shall adhere to the form (5) and (6).

THE VARIANCE

The *variance* of a set of data is defined as the square of the standard deviation and is thus given by s^2 in equations (*5*) and (*6*).

When it is necessary to distinguish the standard deviation of a population from the standard deviation of a sample drawn from this population, we often use the symbol s for the latter and σ (lowercase Greek *sigma*) for the former. Thus s^2 and σ^2 would represent the *sample variance* and *population variance*, respectively.

SHORT METHODS FOR COMPUTING THE STANDARD DEVIATION

Equations (*5*) and (*6*) can be written, respectively, in the equivalent forms

$$s = \sqrt{\frac{\sum_{j=1}^{N} X_j^2}{N} - \left(\frac{\sum_{j=1}^{N} X_j}{N}\right)^2} = \sqrt{\frac{\sum X^2}{N} - \left(\frac{\sum X}{N}\right)^2} = \sqrt{\overline{X^2} - \bar{X}^2} \tag{7}$$

$$s = \sqrt{\frac{\sum_{j=1}^{K} f_j X_j^2}{N} - \left(\frac{\sum_{j=1}^{K} f_j X_j}{N}\right)^2} = \sqrt{\frac{\sum fX^2}{N} - \left(\frac{\sum fX}{N}\right)^2} = \sqrt{\overline{X^2} - \bar{X}^2} \tag{8}$$

where $\overline{X^2}$ denotes the mean of the squares of the various values of X, while $\bar{X}^2$ denotes the square of the mean of the various values of X (see Problems 4.12 to 4.14).

If $d_j = X_j - A$ are the deviations of X_j from some arbitrary constant A, results (*7*) and (*8*) become, respectively,

$$s = \sqrt{\frac{\sum_{j=1}^{N} d_j^2}{N} - \left(\frac{\sum_{j=1}^{N} d_j}{N}\right)^2} = \sqrt{\frac{\sum d^2}{N} - \left(\frac{\sum d}{N}\right)^2} = \sqrt{\overline{d^2} - \bar{d}^2} \tag{9}$$

$$s = \sqrt{\frac{\sum_{j=1}^{K} f_j d_j^2}{N} - \left(\frac{\sum_{j=1}^{K} f_j d_j}{N}\right)^2} = \sqrt{\frac{\sum fd^2}{N} - \left(\frac{\sum fd}{N}\right)^2} = \sqrt{\overline{d^2} - \bar{d}^2} \tag{10}$$

(See Problems 4.15 and 4.17.)

When data are grouped into a frequency distribution whose class intervals have equal size c, we have $d_j = cu_j$ or $X_j = A + cu_j$ and result (*10*) becomes

$$s = c\sqrt{\frac{\sum_{j=1}^{K} f_j u_j^2}{N} - \left(\frac{\sum_{j=1}^{K} f_j u_j}{N}\right)^2} = c\sqrt{\frac{\sum fu^2}{N} - \left(\frac{\sum fu}{N}\right)^2} = c\sqrt{\overline{u^2} - \bar{u}^2} \tag{11}$$

This last formula provides a very short method for computing the standard deviation and should always be used for grouped data when the class-interval sizes are equal. It is called the *coding method* and is exactly analogous to that used in Chapter 3 for computing the arithmetic mean of grouped data. (See Problems 4.16 to 4.19.)

PROPERTIES OF THE STANDARD DEVIATION

1. The standard deviation can be defined as

$$s = \sqrt{\frac{\sum_{j=1}^{N} (X_j - a)^2}{N}}$$

where a is an average besides the arithmetic mean. Of all such standard deviations, the minimum is that for which $a = \bar{X}$, because of Property 2 in Chapter 3 (page 59). This property provides an important reason for defining the standard deviation as above. For a proof of this property, see Problem 4.27.

2. For normal distributions (see Chapter 7), it turns out that (as shown in Fig. 4-1):

   (*a*) 68.27% of the cases are included between $\bar{X} - s$ and $\bar{X} + s$ (i.e., one standard deviation on either side of the mean).

   (*b*) 95.45% of the cases are included between $\bar{X} - 2s$ and $\bar{X} + 2s$ (i.e., two standard deviations on either side of the mean).

   (*c*) 99.73% of the cases are included between $\bar{X} - 3s$ and $\bar{X} + 3s$ (i.e., three standard deviations on either side of the mean).

   For moderately skewed distributions, the above percentages may hold approximately (see Problem 4.24).

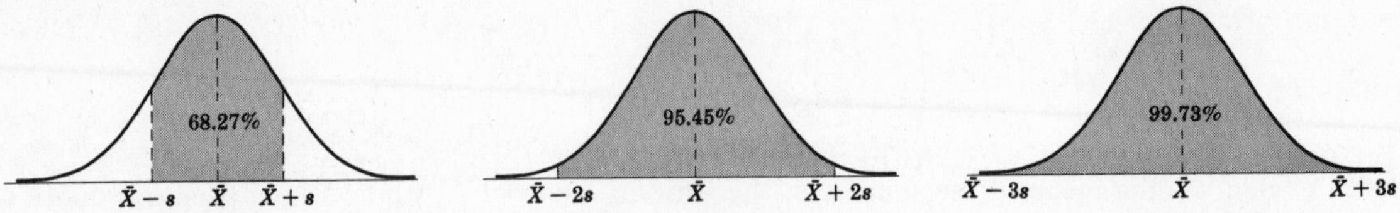

Fig. 4-1

3. Suppose that two sets consisting of N_1 and N_2 numbers (or two frequency distributions with total frequencies N_1 and N_2) have variances given by s_1^2 and s_2^2, respectively, and have the *same* mean $\bar{X}$. Then the *combined*, or *pooled*, *variance* of both sets (or both frequency distributions) is given by

$$s^2 = \frac{N_1 s_1^2 + N_2 s_2^2}{N_1 + N_2} \tag{12}$$

   Note that this is a weighted arithmetic mean of the variances. This result can be generalized to three or more sets.

CHARLIER'S CHECK

Charlier's check in computations of the mean and standard deviation by the coding method makes use of the identities

$$\sum f(u+1) = \sum fu + \sum f = \sum fu + N$$

$$\sum f(u+1)^2 = \sum f(u^2 + 2u + 1) = \sum fu^2 + 2\sum fu + \sum f = \sum fu^2 + 2\sum fu + N$$

(See Problem 4.20.)

SHEPPARD'S CORRECTION FOR VARIANCE

The computation of the standard deviation is somewhat in error as a result of grouping the data into classes (grouping error). To adjust for grouping error, we use the formula

$$\text{Corrected variance} = \text{variance from grouped data} - \frac{c^2}{12} \tag{13}$$

where c is the class-interval size. The correction $c^2/12$ (which is subtracted) is called *Sheppard's correction.* It is used for distributions of continuous variables where the "tails" go gradually to zero in both directions.

Statisticians differ as to *when* and *whether* Sheppard's correction should be applied. It should certainly not be applied before one examines the situation thoroughly, for it often tends to *overcorrect,* thus replacing an old error with a new one. In this book, unless otherwise indicated, we shall not be using Sheppard's correction.

EMPIRICAL RELATIONS BETWEEN MEASURES OF DISPERSION

For moderately skewed distributions, we have the empirical formulas

$$\text{Mean deviation} = \tfrac{4}{5}(\text{standard deviation})$$

$$\text{Semi-interquartile range} = \tfrac{2}{3}(\text{standard deviation})$$

These are consequences of the fact that for the normal distribution we find that the mean deviation and semi-interquartile range are equal, respectively, to 0.7979 and 0.6745 times the standard deviation.

ABSOLUTE AND RELATIVE DISPERSION; COEFFICIENT OF VARIATION

The actual variation, or dispersion, as determined from the standard deviation or other measure of dispersion is called the *absolute dispersion.* However, a variation (or dispersion) of 10 inches (in) in measuring a distance of 1000 feet (ft) is quite different in effect from the same variation of 10 in in a distance of 20 ft. A measure of this effect is supplied by the *relative dispersion,* which is defined by

$$\text{Relative dispersion} = \frac{\text{absolute dispersion}}{\text{average}} \tag{14}$$

If the absolute dispersion is the standard deviation s and if the average is the mean $\bar{X}$, then the relative dispersion is called the *coefficient of variation,* or *coefficient of dispersion*; it is denoted by V and is given by

$$\text{Coefficient of variation } (V) = \frac{s}{\bar{X}} \tag{15}$$

and is generally expressed as a percentage. Other possibilities also occur (see Problem 4.30).

Note that the coefficient of variation is independent of the units used. For this reason, it is useful in comparing distributions where the units may be different. A disadvantage of the coefficient of variation is that it fails to be useful when $\bar{X}$ is close to zero.

STANDARDIZED VARIABLE: STANDARD SCORES

The variable that measures the deviation from the mean in units of the standard deviation is called a *standardized variable,* is a dimensionless quantity (i.e., is independent of the units used), and is given by

$$z = \frac{X - \bar{X}}{s} \tag{16}$$

If the deviations from the mean are given in units of the standard deviation, they are said to be expressed in *standard units,* or *standard scores.* These are of great value in the comparison of distributions (see Problem 4.31).

Solved Problems

THE RANGE

4.1 Find the range of the sets (a) 12, 6, 7, 3, 15, 10, 18, 5 and (b) 9, 3, 8, 8, 9, 8, 9, 18.

SOLUTION

In both cases, range = largest number − smallest number = 18 − 3 = 15. However, as seen from the arrays of sets (a) and (b),

(a) 3, 5, 6, 7, 10, 12, 15, 18 (b) 3, 8, 8, 8, 9, 9, 9, 18

there is much more variation, or dispersion, in (a) than in (b). In fact, (b) consists mainly of 8's and 9's.

Since the range indicates no difference between the sets, it is not a very good measure of dispersion in this case. Where extreme values are present, the range is generally a poor measure of dispersion.

An improvement is achieved by throwing out the extreme cases, 3 and 18. Then for set (a) the range is $(15-5)=10$, while for set (b) the range is $(9-8)=1$, clearly showing that (a) has greater dispersion than (b). However, this is not the way the range is defined. The semi-interquartile range and the 10–90 percentile range were designed to improve on the range by eliminating extreme cases.

4.2 Find the range of heights of the students at XYZ University as given in Table 2.1.

SOLUTION

There are two ways of defining the range for grouped data.

First method

$$\text{Range} = \text{class mark of highest class} - \text{class mark of lowest class}$$
$$= 73 - 61 = 12 \text{ in}$$

Second method

$$\text{Range} = \text{upper class boundary of highest class} - \text{lower class boundary of lowest class}$$
$$= 74.5 - 59.5 = 15 \text{ in}$$

The first method tends to eliminate extreme cases to some extent.

THE MEAN DEVIATION

Mathcad **4.3** Find the mean deviation of the sets of numbers in Problem 4.1.

SOLUTION

(a) The arithmetic mean is

$$\bar{X} = \frac{12+6+7+3+15+10+18+5}{8} = \frac{76}{8} = 9.5$$

The mean deviation is

$$\text{MD} = \frac{\sum |X-\bar{X}|}{N}$$
$$= \frac{|12-9.5|+|6-9.5|+|7-9.5|+|3-9.5|+|15-9.5|+|10-9.5|+|18-9.5|+|5-9.5|}{8}$$
$$= \frac{2.5+3.5+2.5+6.5+5.5+0.5+8.5+4.5}{8} = \frac{34}{8} = 4.25$$

(*b*)

$$\bar{X} = \frac{9+3+8+8+9+8+9+18}{8} = \frac{72}{8} = 9$$

$$\text{MD} = \frac{\sum |X - \bar{X}|}{N}$$

$$= \frac{|9-9|+|3-9|+|8-9|+|8-9|+|9-9|+|8-9|+|9-9|+|18-9|}{8}$$

$$= \frac{0+6+1+1+0+1+0+9}{8} = 2.25$$

The mean deviation indicates that set (*b*) shows less dispersion than set (*a*), as it should.

4.4 Find the mean deviation of the heights of the 100 male students at XYZ University (see Table 3.2 of Problem 3.20).

SOLUTION

From Problem 3.20, $\bar{X} = 67.45$ in. The work can be arranged as in Table 4.1. It is also possible to devise a coding method for computing the mean deviation (see Problem 4.47).

Table 4.1

Height (in)	Class Mark (X)	$\lvert X-\bar{X}\rvert = \lvert X-67.45\rvert$	Frequency (f)	$f\lvert X-\bar{X}\rvert$
60–62	61	6.45	5	32.25
63–65	64	3.45	18	62.10
66–68	67	0.45	42	18.90
69–71	70	2.55	27	68.85
72–74	73	5.55	8	44.40
			$N = \sum f = 100$	$\sum f\lvert X-\bar{X}\rvert = 226.50$

$$\text{MD} = \frac{\sum f|X-\bar{X}|}{N} = \frac{226.50}{100} = 2.26 \text{ in}$$

4.5 Determine the percentage of the students' heights in Problem 4.4 that fall within the ranges (*a*) $\bar{X} \pm \text{MD}$, (*b*) $\bar{X} \pm 2\text{ MD}$, (*c*) $\bar{X} \pm 3\text{ MD}$.

SOLUTION

(*a*) The range from 65.19 to 69.71 in is $\bar{X} \pm MD = 67.45 \pm 2.26$. This range includes all individuals in the third class $+\frac{1}{3}(65.5-65.19)$ of the students in the second class$+\frac{1}{3}(69.71-68.5)$ of the students in the fourth class (since the class-interval size is 3 in, the upper class boundary of the second class is 65.5 in, and the lower class boundary of the fourth class is 68.5 in). The number of students in the range $\bar{X} \pm \text{MD}$ is

$$42 + \frac{0.31}{3}(18) + \frac{1.21}{3}(27) = 42 + 1.86 + 10.89 = 54.75 \quad \text{or} \quad 55$$

which is 55% of the total.

(*b*) The range from 62.93 to 71.97 in is $\bar{X} \pm 2\text{ MD} = 67.45 \pm 2(2.26) = 67.45 \pm 4.52$. The number of students in the range $\bar{X} \pm 2\text{ MD}$ is

$$18 - \left(\frac{62.93-62.5}{3}\right)(18) + 42 + 27 + \left(\frac{71.97-71.5}{3}\right)(8) = 85.67 \quad \text{or} \quad 86$$

which is 86% of the total.

(*c*) The range from 60.67 to 74.23 in is $\bar{X} \pm 3$ MD $= 67.45 \pm 3(2.26) = 67.45 \pm 6.78$. The number of students in the range $\bar{X} \pm 3$ MD is

$$5 - \left(\frac{60.67 - 59.5}{3}\right)(5) + 18 + 42 + 27 + \left(\frac{74.5 - 74.23}{3}\right)(8) = 97.33 \qquad \text{or} \qquad 97$$

which is 97% of the total.

THE SEMI-INTERQUARTILE RANGE

4.6 Find the semi-interquartile range for the height distribution of the students at XYZ University (see Table 4.1 of Problem 4.4).

SOLUTION

The lower and upper quartiles are $Q_1 = 65.5 + \frac{2}{42}(3) = 65.64$ in and $Q_3 = 68.5 + \frac{10}{27}(3) = 69.61$ in, respectively, and the semi-interquartile range (or quartile deviation) is $Q = \frac{1}{2}(Q_3 - Q_1) = \frac{1}{2}(69.61 - 65.64) = 1.98$ in. Note that 50% of the cases lie between Q_1 and Q_3 (i.e., 50 students have heights between 65.64 and 69.61 in).

We can consider $\frac{1}{2}(Q_1 + Q_3) = 67.63$ in to be a measure of central tendency (i.e., average height). It follows that 50% of the heights lie in the range 67.63 ± 1.98 in.

4.7 Find the semi-interquartile range for the wages of the 65 employees at the P&R Company (see Table 2.5 of Problem 2.3).

SOLUTION

From Problem 3.44, $Q_1 = \$268.25$ and $Q_3 = \$290.75$. Thus the semi-interquartile range $Q = \frac{1}{2}(Q_3 - Q_1) = \frac{1}{2}(\$290.75 - \$268.25) = \$11.25$. Since $\frac{1}{2}(Q_1 + Q_3) = \$279.50$, we can conclude that 50% of the employees earn wages lying in the range $\$279.50 \pm \$11.25$.

THE 10–90 PERCENTILE RANGE

4.8 Find the 10–90 percentile range of the heights of the students at XYZ University (see Table 2.1).

SOLUTION

Here $P_{10} = 62.5 + \frac{5}{18}(3) = 63.33$ in, and $P_{90} = 68.5 + \frac{25}{27}(3) = 71.27$ in. Thus the 10–90 percentile range is $P_{90} - P_{10} = 71.27 - 63.33 = 7.94$ in. Since $\frac{1}{2}(P_{10} + P_{90}) = 67.30$ in and $\frac{1}{2}(P_{90} - P_{10}) = 3.97$ in, we can conclude that 80% of the students have heights in the range 67.30 ± 3.97 in.

THE STANDARD DEVIATION

Mathcad **4.9** Find the standard deviation s of each set of numbers in Problem 4.1.

SOLUTION

(*a*)
$$\bar{X} = \frac{\sum X}{N} = \frac{12+6+7+3+15+10+18+5}{8} = \frac{76}{8} = 9.5$$

$$s = \sqrt{\frac{\sum (X - \bar{X})^2}{N}}$$

$$= \sqrt{\frac{(12-9.5)^2 + (6-9.5)^2 + (7-9.5)^2 + (3-9.5)^2 + (15-9.5)^2 + (10-9.5)^2 + (18-9.5)^2 + (5-9.5)^2}{8}}$$

$$= \sqrt{23.75} = 4.87$$

(b)

$$\bar{X} = \frac{9+3+8+8+9+8+9+18}{8} = \frac{72}{8} = 9$$

$$s = \sqrt{\frac{\sum (X-\bar{X})^2}{N}}$$

$$= \sqrt{\frac{(9-9)^2+(3-9)^2+(8-9)^2+(8-9)^2+(9-9)^2+(8-9)^2+(9-9)^2+(18-9)^2}{8}}$$

$$= \sqrt{15} = 3.87$$

The above results should be compared with those of Problem 4.3. It will be noted that the standard deviation does indicate that set (b) shows less dispersion than set (a). However, the effect is masked by the fact that extreme values affect the standard deviation much more than they affect the mean deviation. This is to be expected, of course, since the deviations are squared in computing the standard deviation.

4.10 Find the variance of the sets of numbers in Problem 4.1.

SOLUTION

Variance $= s^2$. Thus from Problem 4.9 we have (a) $s^2 = 23.75$ and (b) $s^2 = 15$.

4.11 Find the standard deviation of the heights of the 100 male students at XYZ University (see Table 2.1).

SOLUTION

From Problem 3.15, 3.20, or 3.22, $\bar{X} = 67.45$ in. The work can be arranged as in Table 4.2.

Table 4.2

Height (in)	Class Mark (X)	$X-\bar{X} = X-67.45$	$(X-\bar{X})^2$	Frequency (f)	$f(X-\bar{X})^2$
60–62	61	−6.45	41.6025	5	208.0125
63–65	64	−3.45	11.9025	18	214.2450
66–68	67	−0.45	0.2025	42	8.5050
69–71	70	2.55	6.5025	27	175.5675
72–74	73	5.55	30.8025	8	246.4200
				$N = \sum f = 100$	$\sum f(X-\bar{X})^2 = 852.7500$

$$s = \sqrt{\frac{\sum f(X-\bar{X})^2}{N}} = \sqrt{\frac{852.7500}{100}} = \sqrt{8.5275} = 2.92 \text{ in}$$

COMPUTING THE STANDARD DEVIATIONS FROM GROUPED DATA

4.12 (a) Prove that

$$s = \sqrt{\frac{\sum X^2}{N} - \left(\frac{\sum X}{N}\right)^2} = \sqrt{\overline{X^2} - \bar{X}^2}$$

(b) Use the formula in part (a) to find the standard deviation of the set 12, 6, 7, 3, 15, 10, 18, 5.

SOLUTION

(*a*) By definition,

$$s = \sqrt{\frac{\sum (X-\bar{X})^2}{N}}$$

Then
$$s^2 = \frac{\sum (X-\bar{X})^2}{N} = \frac{\sum (X^2 - 2\bar{X}X + \bar{X}^2)}{N} = \frac{\sum X^2 - 2\bar{X}\sum X + N\bar{X}^2}{N}$$

$$= \frac{\sum X^2}{N} - 2\bar{X}\frac{\sum X}{N} + \bar{X}^2 = \frac{\sum X^2}{N} - 2\bar{X}^2 + \bar{X}^2 = \frac{\sum X^2}{N} - \bar{X}^2$$

$$= \overline{X^2} = \bar{X}^2 = \frac{\sum X^2}{N} - \left(\frac{\sum X}{N}\right)^2$$

or
$$s = \sqrt{\frac{\sum X^2}{N} - \left(\frac{\sum X}{N}\right)^2} = \sqrt{\overline{X^2} - \bar{X}^2}$$

Note that in the above summations we have used the abbreviated form, with X replacing X_j and with $\sum$ replacing $\sum_{j=1}^{N}$.

Another method

$$s^2 = \overline{(X-\bar{X})^2} = \overline{X^2 - 2X\bar{X} + \bar{X}^2} = \overline{X^2} - \overline{2X\bar{X}} + \overline{\bar{X}^2} = \overline{X^2} - 2\bar{X}\bar{X} + \bar{X}^2 = \overline{X^2} - \bar{X}^2$$

(*b*)
$$\overline{X^2} = \frac{\sum X^2}{N} = \frac{(12)^2 + (6)^2 + (7)^2 + (3)^2 + (15)^2 + (10)^2 + (18)^2 + (5)^2}{8} = \frac{912}{8} = 114$$

$$\bar{X} = \frac{\sum X}{N} = \frac{12+6+7+3+15+10+18+5}{8} = \frac{76}{8} = 9.5$$

Thus
$$s = \sqrt{\overline{X^2} - \bar{X}^2} = \sqrt{114 - 90.25} = \sqrt{23.75} = 4.87$$

This method should be compared with that of Problem 4.9(*a*).

4.13 Modify the formula of Problem 4.12(*a*) to allow for frequencies corresponding to the various values of X.

SOLUTION

The appropriate modification is

$$s = \sqrt{\frac{\sum fX^2}{N} - \left(\frac{\sum fX}{N}\right)^2} = \sqrt{\overline{X^2} - \bar{X}^2}$$

As in Problem 4.12(*a*), this can be established by starting with

$$s = \sqrt{\frac{\sum f(X-\bar{X})^2}{N}}$$

Then
$$s^2 = \frac{\sum f(X-\bar{X})^2}{N} = \frac{\sum f(X^2 - 2\bar{X}X + \bar{X}^2)}{N} = \frac{\sum fX^2 - 2\bar{X}\sum fX + \bar{X}^2 \sum f}{N}$$

$$= \frac{\sum fX^2}{N} - 2\bar{X}\frac{\sum fX}{N} + \bar{X}^2 = \frac{\sum fX^2}{N} - 2\bar{X}^2 + \bar{X}^2 = \frac{\sum fX^2}{N} - \bar{X}^2$$

$$= \frac{\sum fX^2}{N} - \left(\frac{\sum fX}{N}\right)^2$$

or
$$s = \sqrt{\frac{\sum fX^2}{N} - \left(\frac{\sum fX}{N}\right)^2}$$

Note that in the above summations we have used the abbreviated form, with X and f replacing X_j and f_j, $\sum$ replacing $\sum_{j=1}^{K}$, and $\sum_{j=1}^{K} f_j = N$.

4.14 Using the formula of Problem 4.13, find the standard deviation for the data in Table 4.2 of Problem 4.11.

SOLUTION

The work can be arranged as in Table 4.3, where $\bar{X} = (\sum fX)/N = 67.45$ in, as obtained in Problem 3.15. Note that this method, like that of Problem 4.11, entails much tedious computation. Problem 4.17 shows how the coding method simplifies the calculations immensely.

Table 4.3

Height (in)	Class Mark (X)	X^2	Frequency (f)	fX^2
60–62	61	3721	5	18,605
63–65	64	4096	18	73,728
66–68	67	4489	42	188,538
69–71	70	4900	27	132,300
72–74	73	5329	8	42,632
			$N = \sum f = 100$	$\sum fX^2 = 455,803$

$$s = \sqrt{\frac{\sum fX^2}{N} - \left(\frac{\sum fX}{N}\right)^2} = \sqrt{\frac{455,803}{100} - (67.45)^2} = \sqrt{8.5275} = 2.92 \text{ in}$$

4.15 If $d = X - A$ are the deviations of X from an arbitrary constant A, prove that

$$s = \sqrt{\frac{\sum fd^2}{N} - \left(\frac{\sum fd}{N}\right)^2}$$

SOLUTION

Since $d = X - A$, $X = A + d$, and $\bar{X} = A + \bar{d}$ (see Problem 3.18), then

$$X - \bar{X} = (A + d) - (A + \bar{d}) = d - \bar{d}$$

so that
$$s = \sqrt{\frac{\sum f(X - \bar{X})^2}{N}} = \sqrt{\frac{\sum f(d - \bar{d})^2}{N}} = \sqrt{\frac{\sum fd^2}{N} - \left(\frac{\sum fd}{N}\right)^2}$$

using the result of Problem 4.13 and replacing X and $\bar{X}$ with d and $\bar{d}$, respectively.

Another method

$$s^2 = \overline{(X - \bar{X})^2} = \overline{(d - \bar{d})^2} = \overline{d^2 - 2\bar{d}d + \bar{d}^2}$$

$$= \overline{d^2} - 2\bar{d}^2 + \bar{d}^2 = \overline{d^2} - \bar{d}^2 = \frac{\sum fd^2}{N} - \left(\frac{\sum fd}{N}\right)^2$$

and the result follows on taking the positive square root.

4.16 Show that if each class mark X in a frequency distribution having class intervals of equal size c is coded into a corresponding value u according to the relation $X = A + cu$, where A is a given class mark, then the standard deviation can be written as

$$s = c\sqrt{\frac{\sum fu^2}{N} - \left(\frac{\sum fu}{N}\right)^2} = c\sqrt{\overline{u^2} - \bar{u}^2}$$

SOLUTION

This follows at once from Problem 4.15 since $d = X - A = cu$. Thus, since c is a constant,

$$s = \sqrt{\frac{\sum f(cu)^2}{N} - \left(\frac{\sum f(cu)}{N}\right)^2} = \sqrt{c^2\frac{\sum fu^2}{N} - c^2\left(\frac{\sum fu}{N}\right)^2} = c\sqrt{\frac{\sum fu^2}{N} - \left(\frac{\sum fu}{N}\right)^2}$$

Another method

We can also prove the result directly without using Problem 4.15. Since $X = A + cu$, $\bar{X} = A + c\bar{u}$, and $X - \bar{X} = c(u - \bar{u})$, then

$$s^2 = \overline{(X - \bar{X})^2} = \overline{c^2(u - \bar{u})^2} = c^2\overline{(u^2 - 2\bar{u}u + \bar{u}^2)} = c^2(\overline{u^2} - 2\bar{u}^2 + \bar{u}^2) = c^2(\overline{u^2} - \bar{u}^2)$$

and

$$s = c\sqrt{\overline{u^2} - \bar{u}^2} = c\sqrt{\frac{\sum fu^2}{N} - \left(\frac{\sum fu}{N}\right)^2}$$

4.17 Find the standard deviation of the heights of the students at XYZ University (see Table 2.1) by using (*a*) the formula derived in Problem 4.15 and (*b*) the coding method of Problem 4.16.

SOLUTION

In Tables 4.4 and 4.5, A is arbitrarily chosen as being equal to the class mark 67. Note that in Table 4.4 the deviations $d = X - A$ are all multiples of the class-interval size $c = 3$. This factor is removed in Table 4.5. As a result, the computations in Table 4.5 are greatly simplified (compare them with those of Problems 4.11 and 4.14). For this reason, the coding method should be used wherever possible.

(*a*) See Table 4.4.

Table 4.4

Class Mark (X)	$d = X - A$	Frequency (f)	fd	fd^2
61	−6	5	−30	180
64	−3	18	−54	162
$A \rightarrow 67$	0	42	0	0
70	3	27	81	243
73	6	8	48	288
		$N = \sum f = 100$	$\sum fd = 45$	$\sum fd^2 = 873$

$$s = \sqrt{\frac{\sum fd^2}{N} - \left(\frac{\sum fd}{N}\right)^2} = \sqrt{\frac{873}{100} - \left(\frac{45}{100}\right)^2} = \sqrt{8.5275} = 2.92 \text{ in}$$

(*b*) See Table 4.5.

Table 4.5

Class Mark (X)	$u = \frac{X - A}{c}$	Frequency (f)	fu	fu^2
61	−2	5	−10	20
64	−1	18	−18	18
$A \rightarrow 67$	0	42	0	0
70	1	27	27	27
73	2	8	16	32
		$N = \sum f = 100$	$\sum fu = 15$	$\sum fu^2 = 97$

$$s = c\sqrt{\frac{\sum fu^2}{N} - \left(\frac{\sum fu}{N}\right)^2} = 3\sqrt{\frac{97}{100} - \left(\frac{15}{100}\right)^2} = 3\sqrt{0.9475} = 2.92 \text{ in}$$

Mathcad **4.18** Using coding methods, find (a) the mean and (b) the standard deviation for the wage distribution of the 65 employees at the P&R Company (see Table 2.4 of Problem 2.3).

SOLUTION

The work can be arranged simply, as shown in Table 4.6.

Table 4.6

X	u	f	fu	fu^2
\$255.00	−2	8	−16	32
265.00	−1	10	−10	10
$A \rightarrow$ 275.00	0	16	0	0
285.00	1	14	14	14
295.00	2	10	20	40
305.00	3	5	15	45
315.00	4	2	8	32
		$N = \sum f = 65$	$\sum fu = 31$	$\sum fu^2 = 173$

(a)
$$\bar{X} = A + c\bar{u} = A + c\frac{\sum fu}{N} = \$275.00 + (\$10.00)\left(\frac{31}{65}\right) = \$279.77$$

(b)
$$s = c\sqrt{\overline{u^2} - \bar{u}^2} = c\sqrt{\frac{\sum fu^2}{N} - \left(\frac{\sum fu}{N}\right)^2} = (\$10.00)\sqrt{\frac{173}{65} - \left(\frac{31}{65}\right)^2} = (\$10.00)\sqrt{2.4341} = \$15.60$$

4.19 Table 4.7 shows the IQ's of 480 school children at a certain elementary school. Using the coding method, find (a) the mean and (b) the standard deviation.

Table 4.7

Class mark (X)	70	74	78	82	86	90	94	98	102	106	110	114	118	122	126
Frequency (f)	4	9	16	28	45	66	85	72	54	38	27	18	11	5	2

SOLUTION

The intelligence quotient is

$$\text{IQ} = \frac{\text{mental age}}{\text{chronological age}}$$

expressed as a percentage. For example, an 8-year-old child who (according to certain educational procedures) has a mentality equivalent to that of a 10-year-old child would have an IQ of $10/8 = 1.25 = 125\%$, or simply 125, the % sign being understood.

To find the mean and standard deviation of the IQ's in Table 4.7, we can arrange the work as in Table 4.8.

(a)
$$\bar{X} = A + c\bar{u} = A + c\frac{\sum fu}{N} = 94 + 4\left(\frac{236}{480}\right) = 95.97$$

(b)
$$s = c\sqrt{\overline{u^2} - \bar{u}^2} = c\sqrt{\frac{\sum fu^2}{N} - \left(\frac{\sum fu}{N}\right)^2} = 4\sqrt{\frac{3404}{480} - \left(\frac{236}{480}\right)^2} = 4\sqrt{6.8499} = 10.47$$

Table 4.8

	X	u	f	fu	fu^2
	70	−6	4	−24	144
	74	−5	9	−45	225
	78	−4	16	−64	256
	82	−3	28	−84	252
	86	−2	45	−90	180
	90	−1	66	−66	66
$A \rightarrow$	94	0	85	0	0
	98	1	72	72	72
	102	2	54	108	216
	106	3	38	114	342
	110	4	27	108	432
	114	5	18	90	450
	118	6	11	66	396
	122	7	5	35	245
	126	8	2	16	128
			$N = \sum f = 480$	$\sum fu = 236$	$\sum fu^2 = 3404$

CHARLIER'S CHECK

4.20 Use Charlier's check to help verify the computations of (a) the mean and (b) the standard deviation performed in Problem 4.19.

SOLUTION

To supply the required check, the columns of Table 4.9 are added to those of Table 4.8 (with the exception of column 2, which is repeated in Table 4.9 for convenience).

(a) From Table 4.9, $\sum f(u+1) = 716$; from Table 4.8, $\sum fu + N = 236 + 480 = 716$. This provides the required check on the mean.

(b) From Table 4.9, $\sum f(u+1)^2 = 4356$; from Table 4.8, $\sum fu^2 + 2\sum fu + N = 3404 + 2(236) + 480 = 4356$. This provides the required check on the standard deviation.

SHEPPARD'S CORRECTION FOR VARIANCE

4.21 Apply Sheppard's correction to determine the standard deviation of the data in (a) Problem 4.17, (b) Problem 4.18, and (c) Problem 4.19.

SOLUTION

(a) $s^2 = 8.5275$, and $c = 3$. Corrected variance $= s^2 - c^2/12 = 8.5275 - 3^2/12 = 7.7775$. Corrected standard deviation $= \sqrt{\text{correct variance}} = \sqrt{7.7775} = 2.79$ in.

(b) $s^2 = 243.41$, and $c = 10$. Corrected variance $= s^2 - c^2/12 = 243.41 - 10^2/12 = 235.08$. Corrected standard deviation $= \sqrt{235.08} = \$15.33$.

(c) $s^2 = 109.60$, and $c = 4$. Corrected variance $= s^2 - c^2/12 = 109.60 - 4^2/12 = 108.27$. Corrected standard deviation $= \sqrt{108.27} = 10.41$.

Table 4.9

$u+1$	f	$f(u+1)$	$f(u+1)^2$
−5	4	−20	100
−4	9	−36	144
−3	16	−48	144
−2	28	−56	112
−1	45	−45	45
0	66	0	0
1	85	85	85
2	72	144	288
3	54	162	486
4	38	152	608
5	27	135	675
6	18	108	648
7	11	77	539
8	5	40	320
9	2	18	162
	$N=\sum f=480$	$\sum f(u+1)=716$	$\sum f(u+1)^2=4356$

4.22 For the second frequency distribution of Problem 2.8, find (*a*) the mean, (*b*) the standard deviation, (*c*) the standard deviation using Sheppard's correction, and (*d*) the actual standard deviation from the ungrouped data.

SOLUTION

The work is arranged in Table 4.10.

Table 4.10

	X	u	f	fu	fu^2
	122	−3	3	−9	27
	131	−2	5	−10	20
	140	−1	9	−9	9
$A \rightarrow$	149	0	12	0	0
	158	1	5	5	5
	167	2	4	8	16
	176	3	2	6	18
			$N=\sum f=40$	$\sum fu=-9$	$\sum fu^2=95$

(*a*) $$\bar{X}=A+c\bar{u}=A+c\frac{\sum fu}{N}=149+9\left(\frac{-9}{40}\right)=147.0 \text{ lb}$$

(*b*) $$s=c\sqrt{\overline{u^2}-\bar{u}^2}=c\sqrt{\frac{\sum fu^2}{N}-\left(\frac{\sum fu}{N}\right)^2}=9\sqrt{\frac{95}{40}-\left(\frac{-9}{40}\right)^2}=9\sqrt{2.324375}=13.7 \text{ lb}$$

(*c*) Corrected variance $= s^2-c^2/12=188.27-9^2/12=181.52$. Corrected standard deviation $= 13.5$ lb.

(*d*) To compute the standard deviation from the actual weights of the students given in the problem, it is convenient first to subtract a suitable number, say $A = 150$ lb, from each weight and then use the method of Problem 4.15. The deviations $d = X - A = X - 150$ are then given in the following table:

−12	14	0	−18	−6	−25	−1	7
−4	8	−10	−3	−14	−2	2	−6
18	−24	−12	26	13	−31	4	15
−4	23	−8	−3	−15	3	−10	−15
11	−5	−15	−8	0	6	−5	−22

from which we find that $\sum d = -128$ and $\sum d^2 = 7052$. Then

$$s = \sqrt{\overline{d^2} - \bar{d}^2} = \sqrt{\frac{\sum d^2}{N} - \left(\frac{\sum d}{N}\right)^2} = \sqrt{\frac{7052}{40} - \left(\frac{-128}{40}\right)^2} = \sqrt{166.06} = 12.9 \text{ lb}$$

Hence Sheppard's correction supplied some improvement in this case.

EMPIRICAL RELATIONS BETWEEN MEASURES OF DISPERSION

4.23 For the distribution of the heights of the students at XYZ University, discuss the validity of the empirical formulas (*a*) mean deviation $= \frac{4}{5}$(standard deviation) and (*b*) semi-interquartile range $= \frac{2}{3}$(standard deviation).

SOLUTION

(*a*) From Problems 4.4 and 4.11, mean deviation ÷ standard deviation $= 2.26/2.92 = 0.77$, which is close to $\frac{4}{5}$.

(*b*) From Problems 4.6 and 4.11, semi-interquartile range ÷ standard deviation $= 1.98/2.92 = 0.68$, which is close to $\frac{2}{3}$.

Thus the empirical formulas are valid in this case.

Note that in the above we have not used the standard deviation with Sheppard's correction for grouping, since no corresponding correction has been made for the mean deviation or semi-interquartile range.

PROPERTIES OF THE STANDARD DEVIATION

4.24 Determine the percentage of the students' IQ's in Problem 4.19 that fall within the ranges (*a*) $\bar{X} \pm s$, (*b*) $\bar{X} \pm 2s$, and (*c*) $\bar{X} \pm 3s$.

SOLUTION

(*a*) The range of IQ's from 85.5 to 106.4 is $\bar{X} \pm s = 95.97 \pm 10.47$. The number of IQ's in the range $\bar{X} \pm s$ is

$$\left(\frac{88 - 85.5}{4}\right)(45) + 66 + 85 + 72 + 54 + \left(\frac{106.4 - 104}{4}\right)(38) = 339$$

The percentage of IQ's in the range $\bar{X} \pm s$ is $339/480 = 70.6\%$.

(*b*) The range of IQ's from 75.0 to 116.9 is $\bar{X} \pm 2s = 95.97 \pm 2(10.47)$. The number of IQ's in the range $\bar{X} \pm 2s$ is

$$\left(\frac{76 - 75.0}{4}\right)(9) + 16 + 28 + 45 + 66 + 85 + 72 + 54 + 38 + 27 + 18 + \left(\frac{116.9 - 116}{4}\right)(11) = 451$$

The percentage of IQ's in the range $\bar{X} \pm 2s$ is $451/480 = 94.0\%$.

(c) The range of IQ's from 64.6 to 127.4 is $\bar{X} \pm 3s = 95.97 \pm 3(10.47)$. The number of IQ's in the range $\bar{X} \pm 3s$ is

$$480 - \left(\frac{128 - 127.4}{4}\right)(2) = 479.7 \qquad \text{or} \qquad 480$$

The percentage of IQ's in the range $\bar{X} \pm 3s$ is $479.7/480 = 99.9\%$, or practically 100%.

The percentages in parts (a), (b), and (c) agree favorably with those to be expected for a normal distribution: 68.27%, 95.45%, and 99.73%, respectively.

Note that we have not used Sheppard's correction for the standard deviation. If this is used, the results in this case agree closely with the above. Note also that the above results can also be obtained by using Table 4.11 of Problem 4.32.

4.25 Given the sets 2, 5, 8, 11, 14, and 2, 8, 14, find (a) the mean of each set, (b) the variance of each set, (c) the mean of the combined (or pooled) sets, and (d) the variance of the combined sets.

SOLUTION

(a) Mean of first set $= \frac{1}{5}(2+5+8+11+14) = 8$. Mean of second set $= \frac{1}{3}(2+8+14) = 8$.

(b) Variance of first set $= s_1^2 = \frac{1}{5}[(2-8)^2+(5-8)^2+(8-8)^2+(11-8)^2+(14-8)^2] = 18$. Variance of second set $= s_2^2 = \frac{1}{3}[(2-8)^2+(8-8)^2+(14-8)^2] = 24$.

(c) The mean of the combined sets is

$$\frac{2+5+8+11+14+2+8+14}{5+3} = 8$$

(d) The variance of the combined sets is

$$s^2 = \frac{(2-8)^2+(5-8)^2+(8-8)^2+(11-8)^2+(14-8)^2+(2-8)^2+(8-8)^2+(14-8)^2}{5+3} = 20.25$$

Another method (by formula)

$$s^2 = \frac{N_1 s_1^2 + N_2 s_2^2}{N_1 + N_2} = \frac{(5)(18)+(3)(24)}{5+3} = 20.25$$

4.26 Work Problem 4.25 for the sets 2, 5, 8, 11, 14 and 10, 16, 22.

SOLUTION

Here the means of the two sets are 8 and 16, respectively, while the variances are the *same* as the sets of the preceding problem, namely, $s_1^2 = 18$ and $s_2^2 = 24$.

$$\text{Mean of combined sets} = \frac{2+5+8+11+14+10+16+22}{5+3} = 11$$

$$s^2 = \frac{(2-11)^2+(5-11)^2+(8-11)^2+(11-11)^2+(14-11)^2+(10-11)^2+(16-11)^2+(22-11)^2}{5+3} = 35.25$$

Note that the formula

$$s^2 = \frac{N_1 s_1^2 + N_2 s_2^2}{N_1 + N_2}$$

which gives the value 20.25, is *not* applicable in this case since the means of the two sets are *not* the same.

4.27 (*a*) Prove that w^2+pw+q, where p and q are given constants, is a minimum if and only $w=-\frac{1}{2}p$.

(*b*) Using part (*a*), prove that

$$\frac{\sum_{j=1}^{N}(X_j-a)^2}{N} \quad \text{or briefly} \quad \frac{\sum(X-a)^2}{N}$$

is a minimum if and only if $a=\bar{X}$.

SOLUTION

(*a*) We have $w^2+pw+q=(w+\frac{1}{2}p)^2+q-\frac{1}{4}p^2$. Since $(q-\frac{1}{4}p^2)$ is a constant, the expression has the least value (i.e., is a minimum) if and only if $w+\frac{1}{2}p=0$ (i.e., $w=-\frac{1}{2}p$).

(*b*)
$$\frac{\sum(X-a)^2}{N}=\frac{\sum(X^2-2aX+a^2)}{N}=\frac{\sum X^2-2a\sum X+Na^2}{N}=a^2-2a\frac{\sum X}{N}+\frac{\sum X^2}{N}$$

Comparing this last expression with (w^2+pw+q), we have

$$w=a \qquad p=-2\frac{\sum X}{N} \qquad q=\frac{\sum X^2}{N}$$

Thus the expression is a minimum when $a=-\frac{1}{2}p=(\sum X)/N=\bar{X}$, using the result of part (*a*).

ABSOLUTE AND RELATIVE DISPERSION: COEFFICIENT OF VARIATION

Mathcad **4.28** A manufacturer of television tubes has two types of tubes, A and B. Respectively, the tubes have mean lifetimes of $\bar{X}_A=1495$ hours and $\bar{X}_B=1875$ hours, and standard deviations of $s_A=280$ hours and $s_B=310$ hours. Which tube has the greater (*a*) absolute dispersion and (*b*) relative dispersion?

SOLUTION

(*a*) The absolute dispersion of A is $s_A=280$ hours, and of B is $s_B=310$ hours. Thus tube B has the greater absolute dispersion.

(*b*) The coefficients of variation are

$$A=\frac{s_A}{\bar{X}_A}=\frac{280}{1495}=18.7\% \qquad B=\frac{s_B}{\bar{X}_B}=\frac{310}{1875}=16.5\%$$

Thus tube A has the greater relative variation, or dispersion.

4.29 Find the coefficients of variation, V, for the data of (*a*) Problem 4.14 and (*b*) Problem 4.18, using both uncorrected and corrected standard deviations.

SOLUTION

(*a*)
$$V(\text{uncorrected})=\frac{s(\text{uncorrected})}{\bar{X}}=\frac{2.92}{67.45}=0.0433=4.3\%$$

$$V(\text{corrected})=\frac{s(\text{corrected})}{\bar{X}}=\frac{2.79}{67.45}=0.0413=4.1\% \qquad \text{by Problem 4.21}(a)$$

(*b*)
$$V(\text{uncorrected})=\frac{s(\text{uncorrected})}{\bar{X}}=\frac{15.60}{79.77}=0.196=19.6\%$$

$$V(\text{corrected})=\frac{s(\text{corrected})}{\bar{X}}=\frac{15.33}{79.77}=0.192=19.2\% \qquad \text{by Problem 4.21}(b)$$

4.30 (*a*) Define a measure of relative dispersion that could be used for a set of data for which the quartiles are known.

(*b*) Illustrate the calculation of the measure defined in part (*a*) by using the data of Problem 4.6.

SOLUTION

(*a*) If Q_1 and Q_3 are given for a set of data, then $\frac{1}{2}(Q_1 + Q_3)$ is a measure of the data's central tendency, or average, while $Q = \frac{1}{2}(Q_3 - Q_1)$, the semi-interquartile range, is a measure of the data's dispersion. We can thus define a measure of relative dispersion as

$$V_Q = \frac{\frac{1}{2}(Q_3 - Q_1)}{\frac{1}{2}(Q_1 + Q_3)} = \frac{Q_3 - Q_1}{Q_3 + Q_1}$$

which we call the *quartile coefficient of variation*, or *quartile coefficient of relative dispersion.*

(*b*)
$$V_Q = \frac{Q_3 - Q_1}{Q_3 + Q_1} = \frac{69.61 - 65.64}{69.61 + 65.64} = \frac{3.97}{135.25} = 0.0293 = 2.9\%$$

STANDARDIZED VARIABLE; STANDARD SCORES

4.31 A student received a grade of 84 on a final examination in mathematics for which the mean grade was 76 and the standard deviation was 10. On the final examination in physics, for which the mean grade was 82 and the standard deviation was 16, she received a grade of 90. In which subject was her relative standing higher?

SOLUTION

The standardized variable $z = (X - \bar{X})/s$ measures the deviation of X from the mean $\bar{X}$ in terms of standard deviation s. For mathematics, $z = (84 - 76)/10 = 0.8$; for physics, $z = (90 - 82)/16 = 0.5$. Thus the student had a grade 0.8 of a standard deviation above the mean in mathematics, but only 0.5 of a standard deviation above the mean in physics. Thus her relative standing was higher in mathematics.

The variable $z = (X - \bar{X})/s$ is often used in educational testing, where it is known as a *standard score.*

4.32 (a) Convert the IQ's of Problem 4.19 into standard scores, and (*b*) construct a graph of relative frequency versus standard score.

SOLUTION

(*a*) The work of converting the data into standard scores can be arranged as in Table 4.11.

Added to the table for use in part (*b*) are the IQ class marks 66 and 130, which have frequency zero. Also, Sheppard's correction for the standard deviation has not been used; the corrected scores for this problem would be practically the same (to the indicated accuracy) as those shown in Table 4.11.

(*b*) The graph of relative frequency versus z score (relative-frequency polygon) is shown in Fig. 4-2. The horizontal axis is measured in terms of the standard deviation s as a unit. Note that the distribution is moderately asymmetrical and slightly skewed to the right.

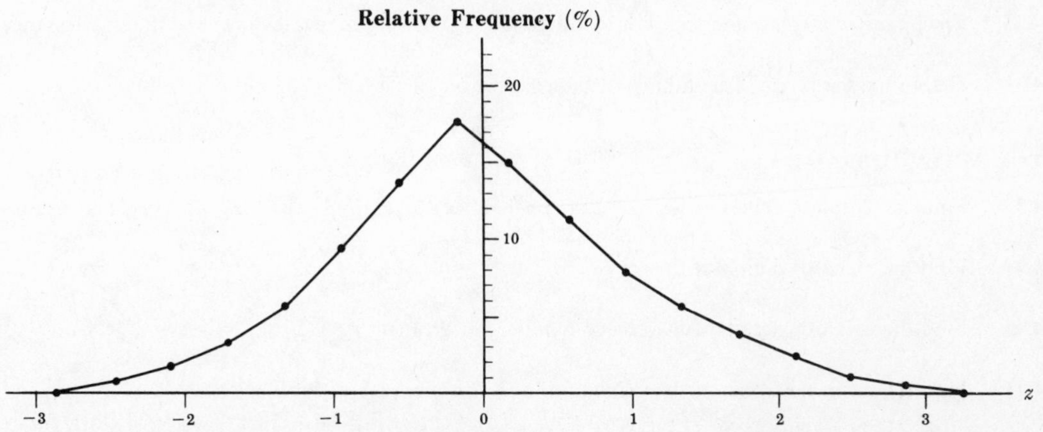

Fig. 4-2

Table 4.11. $\bar{X} = 96.0$, $s = 10.5$

IQ (X)	$X - \bar{X}$	$z = \dfrac{X - \bar{X}}{s}$	Frequency (f)	Relative Frequency (f)/N (%)
66	−30.0	−2.86	0	0.0
70	−26.0	−2.48	4	0.8
74	−22.0	−2.10	9	1.9
78	−18.0	−1.71	16	3.3
82	−14.0	−1.33	28	5.8
86	−10.0	−0.95	45	9.4
90	−6.0	−0.57	66	13.8
94	−2.0	−0.19	85	17.7
98	2.0	0.19	72	15.0
102	6.0	0.57	54	11.2
106	10.0	0.95	38	7.9
110	14.0	1.33	27	5.6
114	18.0	1.71	18	3.8
118	22.0	2.10	11	2.3
122	26.0	2.48	5	1.0
126	30.0	2.86	2	0.4
130	34.0	3.24	0	0.0
			480	100

$\bar{X} = 96.0$, $s = 10.5$

Supplementary Problems

THE RANGE

4.33 Find the range of the sets (*a*) 5, 3, 8, 4, 7, 6, 12, 4, 3 and (*b*) 8.772, 6.453, 10.624, 8.628, 9.434, 6.351.

4.34 Find the range of the maximum loads given in Table 3.8 of Problem 3.59.

4.35 Find the range of the rivet diameters in Table 3.10 of Problem 3.61.

4.36 The largest of 50 measurements is 8.34 kilograms (kg). If the range is 0.46 kg, find the smallest measurement.

4.37 Determine the range of data in (*a*) Problem 3.62, (*b*) Problem 3.73, and (*c*) Problem 2.20.

THE MEAN DEVIATION

4.38 Find the absolute values of (*a*) −18.2, (*b*) +3.58, (*c*) 6.21, (*d*) 0, (*e*) $-\sqrt{2}$, and (*f*) $4.00 - 2.36 - 3.52$.

4.39 Find the mean deviation of the set (*a*) 3, 7, 9, 5 and (*b*) 2.4, 1.6, 3.8, 4.1, 3.4.

4.40 Find the mean deviation of the sets of numbers in Problem 4.33.

4.41 Find the mean deviation of the maximum loads in Table 3.8 of Problem 3.59.

4.42 (*a*) Find the mean deviation (MD) of the rivet diameters in Table 3.10 of Problem 3.61.

(*b*) What percentage of the rivet diameters lie between ($\bar{X} \pm$ MD), ($\bar{X} \pm 2$MD), and ($\bar{X} \pm 3$ MD)?

4.43 For the set 8, 10, 9, 12, 4, 8, 2, find the mean deviation (*a*) from the mean and (*b*) from the median. Verify that the mean deviation from the median is not greater than the mean deviation from the mean.

4.44 For the distribution in Table 3.9 of Problem 3.60, find the mean deviation (*a*) about the mean and (*b*) about the median. Use the results of Problems 3.60 and 3.70.

4.45 For the distribution in Table 3.11 of Problem 3.62, find the mean deviation (*a*) about the mean and (*b*) about the median. Use the results of Problems 3.6.2 and 3.72.

4.46 Explain why the mean deviation is or is not an appropriate measure of dispersion for the distribution in Table 3.12 of Problem 3.73.

4.47 Derive coding formulas for computing the mean deviation (*a*) about the mean and (*b*) about the median from a frequency distribution. Apply these formulas to verify the results of Problems 4.44 and 4.45.

THE SEMI-INTERQUARTILE RANGE

4.48 Find the semi-interquartile range for the distributions of (*a*) Problem 3.59, (*b*) Problem 3.60, and (*c*) Problem 3.107. Interpret the results clearly in each case.

4.49 Find the semi-interquartile range for the distributions of (*a*) Problem 2.31 and (*b*) Problem 3.73, interpreting the results clearly in each case. As compared to other measures of dispersion, explain the advantages of the semi-interquartile range for this type of distribution.

4.50 Prove that for any frequency distribution the total percentage of cases falling in the interval $\frac{1}{2}(Q_1+Q_3) \pm \frac{1}{2}(Q_3-Q_1)$ is 50%. Is the same true for the interval $Q_2 \pm \frac{1}{2}(Q_3-Q_1)$? Explain your answer.

4.51 (*a*) How would you graph the semi-interquartile range corresponding to a given frequency distribution?

(*b*) What is the relationship of the semi-interquartile range to the ogive of the distribution?

THE 10–90 PERCENTILE RANGE

4.52 Find the 10–90 percentile range for the distributions of (*a*) Problem 3.59 and (*b*) Problem 3.107. Interpret the results clearly in each case.

4.53 Find the 10–90 percentile range for the distributions of (*a*) Problem 2.31 and (*b*) Problem 3.73. Interpret the results clearly in each case. What advantage does the 10–90 percentile range have over other measures of dispersion? What disadvantages does it have?

4.54 What advantages or disadvantages would a 20–80 percentile range have in comparison to a 10–90 percentile range?

4.55 Answer Problem 4.51 with reference to the (*a*) 10–90 percentile range, (*b*) 20–80 percentile range, and (*c*) 25–75 percentile range. What is the relationship between (*c*) and the semi-interquartile range?

THE STANDARD DEVIATION

4.56 Find the standard deviation of the sets (*a*) 3, 6, 2, 1, 7, 5; (*b*) 3.2, 4.6, 2.8, 5,2, 4.4; and (*c*) 0, 0, 0, 0, 0, 1, 1, 1.

4.57 (*a*) By adding 5 to each of the numbers in the set 3, 6, 2, 1, 7, 5, we obtain the set 8, 11, 7, 6, 12, 10. Show that the two sets have the same standard deviation but different means. How are the means related?

(*b*) By multiplying each of the numbers 3, 6, 2, 1, 7, and 5 by 2 and then adding 5, we obtain the set 11, 17, 9, 7, 19, 15. What is the relationship between the standard deviations and the means for the two sets?

(*c*) What properties of the mean and standard deviation are illustrated by the particular sets of numbers in parts (*a*) and (*b*)?

4.58 Find the standard deviation of the set of numbers in the arithmetic progression 4, 10, 16, 22, . . . , 154.

4.59 Find the standard deviation for the distributions of (*a*) Problem 3.59, (*b*) Problem 3.60, and (*c*) Problem 3.107.

4.60 Demonstrate the use of Charlier's check in each part of Problem 4.59.

4.61 Find (*a*) the mean and (*b*) the standard deviation for the distribution of Problem 2.17, and explain the significance of the results obtained.

4.62 (*a*) Explain why the standard deviation is not an appropriate measure of dispersion for the distribution of Problem 2.31.

(*b*) What measure of dispersion could be used in its place? Illustrate your answer.

4.63 (*a*) Find the standard deviation s of the rivet diameters in Table 3.10 of Problem 3.61.

(*b*) What percentage of the rivet diameters lies between $\bar{X} \pm s$, $\bar{X} \pm 2s$, and $\bar{X} \pm 3s$?

(*c*) Compare the percentages in part (*b*) with those which would theoretically be expected if the distribution were normal, and account for any observed differences.

4.64 Apply Sheppard's correction to each standard deviation in Problem 4.59. In each case, discuss whether such application is or is not justified.

4.65 What modifications occur in Problem 4.63 when Sheppard's correction is applied?

4.66 (*a*) Find the mean and standard deviation for the data of Problem 2.8.

(*b*) Construct a frequency distribution for the data and find the standard deviation.

(*c*) Compare the result of part (*b*) with that of part (*a*). Determine whether an application of Sheppard's correction produces better results.

4.67 Work Problem 4.66 for the data of Problem 2.27.

4.68 (*a*) Of a total of N numbers, the fraction p are 1's, while the fraction $q = 1 - p$ are 0's. Prove that the standard deviation of the set of numbers is $\sqrt{pq}$.

(*b*) Apply the result of part (*a*) to Problem 4.56(*c*).

4.69 (*a*) Prove that the variance of the set of n numbers a, $a + d$, $a + 2d, \ldots, a + (n-1)d$ (i.e., an arithmetic progression with the first term a and common difference d) is given by $\frac{1}{12}(n^2 - 1)d^2$.

(*b*) Use part (*a*) in Problem 4.58. [*Hint:* Use $1 + 2 + 3 \cdots + (n-1) = \frac{1}{2}n(n-1)$, $1^2 + 2^2 + 3^2 + \cdots + (n-1)^2 = \frac{1}{6}n(n-1)(2n-1)$.]

4.70 Generalize and prove Property 3 of this chapter (page 90).

EMPIRICAL RELATIONS BETWEEN MEASURES OF DISPERSION

4.71 By comparing the standard deviations obtained in Problem 4.59 with the corresponding mean deviations of Problems 4.41, 4.42 and 4.44, determine whether the following empirical relation holds: Mean deviation = $\frac{4}{5}$(standard deviation). Account for any differences that may occur.

4.72 By comparing the standard deviations obtained in Problem 4.59 with the corresponding semi-interquartile ranges of Problem 4.48, determine whether the following empirical relation holds: Semi-interquartile range = $\frac{2}{3}$(standard deviation). Account for any differences that may occur.

4.73 What empirical relation would you expect to exist between the semi-interquartile range and the mean deviation for bell-shaped distributions that are moderately skewed?

4.74 A frequency distribution that is approximately normal has a semi-interquartile range equal to 10. What values would you expect for (*a*) the standard deviation and (*b*) the mean deviation?

ABSOLUTE AND RELATIVE DISPERSION; COEFFICIENT OF VARIATION

4.75 On a final examination in statistics, the mean grade of a group of 150 students was 78 and the standard deviation was 8.0. In algebra, however, the mean final grade of the group was 73 and the standard deviation was 7.6. In which subject was there the greater (*a*) absolute dispersion and (*b*) relative dispersion?

4.76 Find the coefficient of variation for the data of (*a*) Problem 3.59 and (*b*) Problem 3.107.

4.77 (*a*) Why is it not possible to calculate the coefficient of variation for the distribution of Problem 2.31?

(*b*) Calculate the quartile coefficient of relative dispersion for this distribution. [See Problems 3.108(*c*) and 4.30.]

4.78 (*a*) Describe a measure of relative dispersion that utilizes the semi-interquartile range.

(*b*) Illustrate the calculation of this measure by using the data of Problem 3.73.

STANDARDIZED VARIABLES; STANDARD SCORES

4.79 On the examinations referred to in Problem 4.75, a student scored 75 in statistics and 71 in algebra. In which examination was his relative standing higher?

4.80 Convert the set 6, 2, 8, 7, 5 into standard scores.

4.81 Prove that the mean and standard deviation of a set of standard scores are equal to 0 and 1, respectively. Use Problem 4.80 to illustrate this.

4.82 (*a*) Convert the grades of problem 3.107 into standard scores, and (*b*) construct a graph of relative frequency versus standard score.

Chapter 5

Moments, Skewness, and Kurtosis

MOMENTS

If $X_1, X_2, \ldots, X_N$ are the N values assumed by the variable X, we define the quantity

$$\overline{X^r} = \frac{X_1^r + X_2^r + \cdots + X_N^r}{N} = \frac{\sum_{j=1}^{N} X_j^r}{N} = \frac{\sum X^r}{N} \tag{1}$$

called the rth *moment*. The first moment with $r = 1$ is the arithmetic mean $\bar{X}$.

The rth *moment about the mean* $\bar{X}$ is defined as

$$m_r = \frac{\sum_{j=1}^{N} (X_j - \bar{X})^r}{N} = \frac{\sum (X - \bar{X})^r}{N} = \overline{(X - \bar{X})^r} \tag{2}$$

If $r = 1$, then $m_1 = 0$ (see Problem 3.16). If $r = 2$, then $m_2 = s^2$, the variance.

The rth *moment about any origin* A is defined as

$$m'_r = \frac{\sum_{j=1}^{N} (X_j - A)^r}{N} = \frac{\sum (X - A)^r}{N} = \frac{\sum d^r}{N} = \overline{(X - A)^r} \tag{3}$$

where $d = X - A$ are the deviations of X from A. If $A = 0$, equation (*3*) reduces to equation (*1*). For this reason, equation (*1*) is often called the rth *moment about zero.*

MOMENTS FOR GROUPED DATA

If $X_1, X_2, \ldots, X_K$ occur with frequencies $f_1, f_2, \ldots, f_K$, respectively, the above moments are given by

$$\overline{X^r} = \frac{f_1X_1^r + f_2X_2^r + \cdots + f_KX_K^r}{N} = \frac{\sum_{j=1}^{K} f_jX_j^r}{N} = \frac{\sum fX^r}{N} \tag{4}$$

$$m_r = \frac{\sum_{j=1}^{K} f_j(X_j - \bar{X})^r}{N} = \frac{\sum f(X - \bar{X})^r}{N} = \overline{(X - \bar{X})^r} \tag{5}$$

$$m'_r = \frac{\sum_{j=1}^{K} f_j(X_j - A)^r}{N} = \frac{\sum f(X - A)^r}{N} = \overline{(X - A)^r} \tag{6}$$

where $N = \sum_{j=1}^{K} f_j = \sum f$. The formulas are suitable for calculating moments from grouped data.

RELATIONS BETWEEN MOMENTS

The following relations exist between moments about the mean m_r and moments about an arbitrary origin m'_r:

$$\begin{aligned} m_2 &= m'_2 - m'^2_1 \\ m_3 &= m'_3 - 3m'_1 m'_2 + 2m'^3_1 \\ m_4 &= m'_4 - 4m'_1 m'_3 + 6m'^2_1 m'_2 - 3m'^4_1 \end{aligned} \tag{7}$$

etc. (see Problem 5.5). Note that $m'_1 = \bar{X} - A$.

COMPUTATION OF MOMENTS FOR GROUPED DATA

The coding method given in previous chapters for computing the mean and standard deviation can also be used to provide a short method for computing moments. This method uses the fact that $X_j = A + cu_j$ (or briefly, $X = A + cu$), so that from equation (6) we have

$$m'_r = c^r \frac{\sum fu^r}{N} = c^r \overline{u^r} \tag{8}$$

which can be used to find m_r by applying equations (7).

CHARLIER'S CHECK AND SHEPPARD'S CORRECTIONS

Charlier's check in computing moments by the coding method uses the identities

$$\begin{aligned} \sum f(u+1) &= \sum fu + N \\ \sum f(u+1)^2 &= \sum fu^2 + 2\sum fu + N \\ \sum f(u+1)^3 &= \sum fu^3 + 3\sum fu^2 + 3\sum fu + N \\ \sum f(u+1)^4 &= \sum fu^4 + 4\sum fu^3 + 6\sum fu^2 + 4\sum fu + N \end{aligned} \tag{9}$$

Sheppard's corrections for moments (extending the ideas on page 90) are as follows:

$$\text{Corrected } m_2 = m_2 - \tfrac{1}{12}c^2 \qquad \text{Corrected } m_4 = m_4 - \tfrac{1}{2}c^2 m_2 + \tfrac{7}{240}c^4$$

The moments m_1 and m_3 need no correction.

MOMENTS IN DIMENSIONLESS FORM

To avoid particular units, we can define the *dimensionless moments* about the mean as

$$a_r = \frac{m_r}{s^r} = \frac{m_r}{(\sqrt{m_2})^r} = \frac{m_r}{\sqrt{m_2^r}} \tag{10}$$

where $s = \sqrt{m_2}$ is the standard deviation. Since $m_1 = 0$ and $m_2 = s^2$, we have $a_1 = 0$ and $a_2 = 1$.

SKEWNESS

Skewness is the degree of asymmetry, or departure from symmetry, of a distribution. If the frequency curve (smoothed frequency polygon) of a distribution has a longer tail to the right of the central maximum than to the left, the distribution is said to be *skewed to the right*, or to have *positive skewness.* If the reverse is true, it is said to be *skewed to the left*, or to have *negative skewness.*

For skewed distributions, the mean tends to lie on the same side of the mode as the longer tail (see Figs. 3-1 and 3-2). Thus a measure of the asymmetry is supplied by the difference: mean − mode.

This can be made dimensionless if we divide it by a measure of dispersion, such as the standard deviation, leading to the definition

$$\text{Skewness} = \frac{\text{mean} - \text{mode}}{\text{standard deviation}} = \frac{\bar{X} - \text{mode}}{s} \tag{11}$$

To avoid using the mode, we can employ the empirical formula (*10*) of Chapter 3 and define

$$\text{Skewness} = \frac{3(\text{mean} - \text{median})}{\text{standard deviation}} = \frac{3(\bar{X} - \text{median})}{s} \tag{12}$$

Equations (*11*) and (*12*) are called, respectively, *Pearson's first and second coefficients of skewness.*

Other measures of skewness, defined in terms of quartiles and percentiles, are as follows:

$$\text{Quartile coefficient of skewness} = \frac{(Q_3 - Q_2) - (Q_2 - Q_1)}{Q_3 - Q_1} = \frac{Q_3 - 2Q_2 + Q_1}{Q_3 - Q_1} \tag{13}$$

$$\text{10–90 percentile coefficient of skewness} = \frac{(P_{90} - P_{50}) - (P_{50} - P_{10})}{P_{90} - P_{10}} = \frac{P_{90} - 2P_{50} + P_{10}}{P_{90} - P_{10}} \tag{14}$$

An important measure of skewness uses the third moment about the mean expressed in dimensionless form and is given by

$$\text{Moment coefficient of skewness} = a_3 = \frac{m_3}{s^3} = \frac{m_3}{(\sqrt{m_2})^3} = \frac{m_3}{\sqrt{m_2^3}} \tag{15}$$

Another measure of skewness is sometimes given by $b_1 = a_3^2$. For perfectly symmetrical curves, such as the normal curve, a_3 and b_1 are zero.

KURTOSIS

Kurtosis is the degree of peakedness of a distribution, usually taken relative to a normal distribution. A distribution having a relatively high peak, such as the curve of Fig. 5-1(a), is called *leptokurtic*, while the curve of Fig. 5-1(b), which is flat-topped, is called *platykurtic.* The normal distribution shown in Fig. 5-1(c), which is not very peaked or very flat-topped, is called *mesokurtic.*

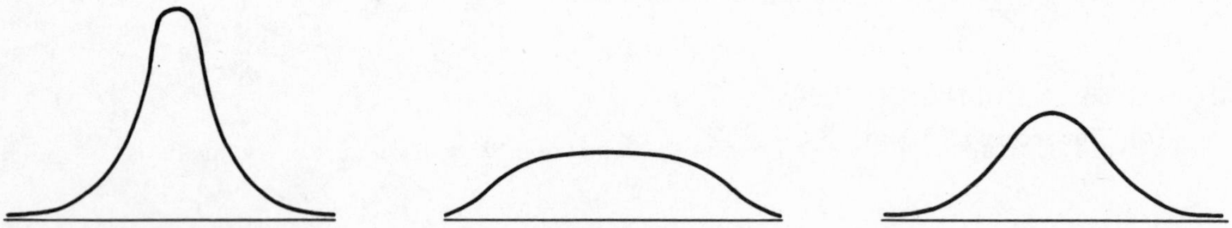

(*a*) **Leptokurtic** (*b*) **Platykurtic** (*c*) **Mesokurtic**

Fig. 5-1

One measure of kurtosis uses the fourth moment about the mean expressed in dimensionless form and is given by

$$\text{Moment coefficient of kurtosis} = a_4 = \frac{m_4}{s^4} = \frac{m_4}{m_2^2} \tag{16}$$

which is often denoted by b_2. For the normal distribution, $b_2 = a_4 = 3$. For this reason, the kurtosis is sometimes defined by $(b_2 - 3)$, which is positive for a leptokurtic distribution, negative for a platykurtic distribution, and zero for the normal distribution.

Another measure of kurtosis is based on both quartiles and percentiles and is given by

$$\kappa = \frac{Q}{P_{90} - P_{10}} \tag{17}$$

where $Q = \frac{1}{2}(Q_3 - Q_1)$ is the semi-interquartile range. We refer to κ (the lowercase Greek letter *kappa*) as the *percentile coefficient of kurtosis*; for the normal distribution, κ has the value 0.263 (see Problem 5.14).

POPULATION MOMENTS, SKEWNESS, AND KURTOSIS

When it is necessary to distinguish a sample's moments, measures of skewness, and measures of kurtosis from those corresponding to a population of which the sample is a part, it is often the custom to use Latin symbols for the former and Greek symbols for the latter. Thus if the sample's moments are denoted by m_r and m'_r, the corresponding Greek symbols would be μ_r and μ'_r (μ is the Greek letter *mu*). Subscripts are always denoted by Latin symbols.

Similarly, if the sample's measures of skewness and kurtosis are denoted by a_3 and a_4, respectively, the population's skewness and kurtosis would be α_3 and α_4 (α is the Greek letter *alpha*).

We already know from Chapter 4 that the standard deviation of a sample and of a population are denoted by s and σ, respectively.

Solved Problems

MOMENTS

5.1 Find the (*a*) first, (*b*) second, (*c*) third, and (*d*) fourth moments of the set 2, 3, 7, 8, 10.

SOLUTION

(*a*) The first moment, or arithmetic mean, is

$$\bar{X} = \frac{\sum X}{N} = \frac{2+3+7+8+10}{5} = \frac{30}{5} = 6$$

(*b*) The second moment is

$$\overline{X^2} = \frac{\sum X^2}{N} = \frac{2^2+3^2+7^2+8^2+10^2}{5} = \frac{226}{5} = 45.2$$

(*c*) The third moment is

$$\overline{X^3} = \frac{\sum X^3}{N} = \frac{2^3+3^3+7^3+8^3+10^3}{5} = \frac{1890}{5} = 378$$

(*d*) The fourth moment is

$$\overline{X^4} = \frac{\sum X^4}{N} = \frac{2^4+3^4+7^4+8^4+10^4}{5} = \frac{16,594}{5} = 3318.8$$

5.2 Find the (*a*) first, (*b*) second (*c*) third, and (*d*) fourth moments about the mean for the set of numbers in Problem 5.1.

SOLUTION

(a) $m_1 = \overline{(X - \bar{X})} = \dfrac{\sum (X - \bar{X})}{N} = \dfrac{(2-6)+(3-6)+(7-6)+(8-6)+(10-6)}{5} = \dfrac{0}{5} = 0$.

m_1 is always equal to zero since $\overline{X - \bar{X}} = \bar{X} - \bar{X} = 0$ (see Problem 3.16).

(b) $m_2 = \overline{(X - \bar{X})^2} = \dfrac{\sum (X - \bar{X})^2}{N} = \dfrac{(2-6)^2+(3-6)^2+(7-6)^2+(8-6)^2+(10-6)^2}{6} = \dfrac{46}{5} = 9.2$

Note that m_2 is the variance s^2.

(c) $m_3 = \overline{(X - \bar{X})^3} = \dfrac{\sum (X - \bar{X})^3}{N} = \dfrac{(2-6)^3+(3-6)^3+(7-6)^3+(8-6)^3+(10-6)^3}{5} = \dfrac{-18}{5} = -3.6$

(d) $m_4 = \overline{(X - \bar{X})^4} = \dfrac{\sum (X - \bar{X})^4}{N} = \dfrac{(2-6)^4+(3-6)^4+(7-6)^4+(8-6)^4+(10-6)^4}{5} = \dfrac{610}{5} = 122$

5.3 Find the (a) first, (b) second, (c) third, and (d) fourth moments about the origin 4 for the set of numbers in Problem 5.1.

SOLUTION

(a) $m_1' = \overline{(X - 4)} = \dfrac{\sum (X - 4)}{N} = \dfrac{(2-4)+(3-4)+(7-4)+(8-4)+(10-4)}{5} = 2$

(b) $m_2' = \overline{(X - 4)^2} = \dfrac{\sum (X - 4)^2}{N} = \dfrac{(2-4)^2+(3-4)^2+(7-4)^2+(8-4)^2+(10-4)^2}{5} = \dfrac{66}{5} = 13.2$

(c) $m_3' = \overline{(X - 4)^3} = \dfrac{\sum (X - 4)^3}{N} = \dfrac{(2-4)^3+(3-4)^3+(7-4)^3+(8-4)^3+(10-4)^3}{5} = \dfrac{298}{5} = 59.6$

(d) $m_4' = \overline{(X - 4)^4} = \dfrac{\sum (X - 4)^4}{N} = \dfrac{(2-4)^4+(3-4)^4+(7-4)^4+(8-4)^4+(10-4)^4}{5} = \dfrac{1650}{5} = 330$

5.4 Using the results of Problems 5.2 and 5.3, verify the relations between the moments (a) $m_2 = m_2' - m_1'^2$, (b) $m_3 = m_3' - 3m_1'm_2' + 2m_1'^3$, and (c) $m_4 = m_4' - 4m_1'm_3' + 6m_1'^2m_2' - 3m_1'^4$.

SOLUTION

From Problem 5.3 we have $m_1' = 2$, $m_2' = 13.2$, $m_3' = 59.6$, and $m_4' = 330$. Thus:

(a) $m_2 = m_2' - m_1'^2 = 13.2 - (2)^2 = 13.2 - 4 = 9.2$

(b) $m_3 = m_3' - 3m_1'm_2' + 2m_1'^3 = 59.6 - (3)(2)(13.2) + 2(2)^3 = 59.6 - 79.2 + 16 = -3.6$

(c) $m_4 = m_4' - 4m_1'm_3' + 6m_1'^2m_2' - 3m_1'^4 = 330 - 4(2)(59.6) + 6(2)^2(13.2) - 3(2)^4 = 122$

in agreement with Problem 5.2.

5.5 Prove that (a) $m_2 = m_2' - m_1'^2$, (b) $m_3 = m_3' - 3m_1'm_2' + 2m_1'^3$, and (c) $m_4 = m_4' - 4m_1'm_3' + 6m_1'^2m_2' - 3m_1'^4$.

SOLUTION

If $d = X - A$, then $X = A + d$, $\bar{X} = A + \bar{d}$, and $X - \bar{X} = d - \bar{d}$. Thus:

(a)
$$\begin{aligned} m_2 &= \overline{(X - \bar{X})^2} = \overline{(d - \bar{d})^2} = \overline{d^2 - 2\bar{d}d + \bar{d}^2} \\ &= \overline{d^2} - 2\bar{d}^2 + \bar{d}^2 = \overline{d^2} - \bar{d}^2 = m_2' - m_1'^2 \end{aligned}$$

(b)
$$\begin{aligned} m_3 &= \overline{(X-\bar{X})^3} = \overline{(d-\bar{d})^3} = \overline{(d^3 - 3d^2\bar{d} + 3d\bar{d}^2 - \bar{d}^3)} \\ &= \overline{d^3} - 3\bar{d}\,\overline{d^2} + 3\bar{d}^3 - \bar{d}^3 = \overline{d^3} - 3\bar{d}\,\overline{d^2} + 2\bar{d}^3 = m_3' - 3m_1'm_2' + 2m_1'^3 \end{aligned}$$

(c)
$$\begin{aligned} m_4 &= \overline{(X-\bar{X})^4} = \overline{(d-\bar{d})^4} = \overline{(d^4 - 4d^3\bar{d} + 6d^2\bar{d}^2 - 4d\bar{d}^3 + \bar{d}^4)} \\ &= \overline{d^4} - 4\bar{d}\,\overline{d^3} + 6\bar{d}^2\overline{d^2} - 4\bar{d}^4 + \bar{d}^4 = \overline{d^4} - 4\bar{d}\,\overline{d^3} + 6\bar{d}^2\overline{d^2} - 3\bar{d}^4 \\ &= m_4' - 4m_1'm_3' + 6m_1'^2 m_2' - 3m_1'^4 \end{aligned}$$

By extension of this method, we can derive similar results for m_5, m_6, etc.

COMPUTATION OF MOMENTS FROM GROUPED DATA

5.6 Find the first four moments about the mean for the height distribution of Problem 3.22.

SOLUTION

Table 5.1

X	u	f	fu	fu^2	fu^3	fu^4
61	−2	5	−10	20	−40	80
64	−1	18	−18	18	−18	18
67	0	42	0	0	0	0
70	1	27	27	27	27	27
73	2	8	16	32	64	128
		$N = \sum f = 100$	$\sum fu = 15$	$\sum fu^2 = 97$	$\sum fu^3 = 33$	$\sum fu^4 = 253$

The work can be arranged as in Table 5.1, from which we have

$$m_1' = c\frac{\sum fu}{N} = (3)\left(\frac{15}{100}\right) = 0.45 \qquad m_3' = c^3\frac{\sum fu^3}{N} = (3)^3\left(\frac{33}{100}\right) = 8.91$$

$$m_2' = c^2\frac{\sum fu^2}{N} = (3)^2\left(\frac{97}{100}\right) = 8.73 \qquad m_4' = c^4\frac{\sum fu^4}{N} = (3)^4\left(\frac{253}{100}\right) = 204.93$$

Thus
$$\begin{aligned} m_1 &= 0 \\ m_2 &= m_2' - m_1'^2 = 8.73 - (0.45)^2 = 8.5275 \\ m_3 &= m_3' - 3m_1'm_2' + m_1'^3 = 8.91 - 3(0.45)(8.73) + 2(0.45)^3 = -2.6932 \\ m_4 &= m_4' - 4m_1'm_3' + 6m_1'^2 m_2' - 3m_1'^4 \\ &= 204.93 - 4(0.45)(8.91) + 6(0.45)^2(8.73) - 3(0.45)^4 = 199.3759 \end{aligned}$$

5.7 Find (a) m_1', (b) m_2', (c) m_3', (d) m_4', (e) m_1, (f) m_2, (g) m_3, (h) m_4, (i) $\bar{X}$, (j) s, (k) $\overline{X^2}$, and (l) $\overline{X^3}$ for the distribution in Table 4.7 of Problem 4.19.

SOLUTION

The work can be arranged as in Table 5.2.

(a) $m_1' = c\dfrac{\sum fu}{N} = (4)\left(\dfrac{236}{480}\right) = 1.9667$

(b) $m_2' = c^2\dfrac{\sum fu^2}{N} = (4)^2\left(\dfrac{3404}{480}\right) = 113.4667$

Table 5.2

	X	u	f	fu	fu^2	fu^3	fu^4
	70	−6	4	−24	144	−864	5184
	74	−5	9	−45	225	−1125	5625
	78	−4	16	−64	256	−1024	4096
	82	−3	28	−84	252	−756	2268
	86	−2	45	−90	180	−360	720
	90	−1	66	−66	66	−66	66
$A \rightarrow$	94	0	85	0	0	0	0
	98	1	72	72	72	72	72
	102	2	54	108	216	432	864
	106	3	38	114	342	1026	3078
	110	4	27	108	432	1728	6912
	114	5	18	90	450	2250	11250
	118	6	11	66	396	2376	14256
	122	7	5	35	245	1715	12005
	126	8	2	16	128	1024	8192
			$N=\sum f=480$	$\sum fu=236$	$\sum fu^2=3404$	$\sum fu^3=6428$	$\sum fu^4=74{,}588$

(c) $m'_3 = c^3 \dfrac{\sum fu^3}{N} = (4)^3\left(\dfrac{6428}{480}\right) = 857.0667$

(d) $m'_4 = c^4 \dfrac{\sum fu^4}{N} = (4)^4\left(\dfrac{74{,}588}{480}\right) = 39{,}780.2667$

(e) $m_1 = 0$

(f) $m_2 = m'_2 - m'^2_1 = 113.4667 - (1.9667)^2 = 109.5988$

(g) $m_3 = m'_3 - 3m'_1m'_2 + 2m'^3_1 = 857.0667 - 3(1.9667)(113.4667) + 2(1.9667)^3 = 202.8158$

(h) $m_4 = m'_4 - 4m'_1m'_3 + 6m'^2_1m'_2 - 3m'^4_1 = 35{,}627.2853$

(i) $\bar{X} = \overline{(A+d)} = A + m'_1 = A + c\dfrac{\sum fu}{N} = 94 + 1.9667 = 95.97$

(j) $s = \sqrt{m_2} = \sqrt{109.5988} = 10.47$

(k) $\overline{X^2} = \overline{(A+d)^2} = \overline{(A^2+2Ad+d^2)} = A^2 + 2A\bar{d} + \overline{d^2} = A^2 + 2Am'_1 + m'_2$
$= (94)^2 + 2(94)(1.9667) + 113.4667 = 9319.2063$, or 9319 to four significant figures

(l) $\overline{X^3} = \overline{(A+d)^3} = \overline{(A^3+3A^2d+3Ad^2+d^3)} = A^3 + 3A^2\bar{d} + 3A\overline{d^2} + \overline{d^3}$
$= A^3 + 3A^2m'_1 + 3Am'_2 + m'_3 = 915{,}571.9597$, or 915,600 to four significant figures

CHARLIER'S CHECK

5.8 Illustrate the use of Charlier's check for the computations in Problem 5.7.

SOLUTION

To supply the required check, we add to Table 5.2 the columns shown in Table 5.3 (with the exception of column 2, which is repeated in Table 5.3 for convenience).

In each of the following groupings, the first is taken from Table 5.3 and the second is taken from Table 5.2. Equality of results in each grouping provides the required check.

$$\sum f(u+1) = 716$$
$$\sum fu + N = 236 + 480 = 716$$

$$\sum f(u+1)^2 = 4356$$
$$\sum fu^2 + 2\sum fu + N = 3404 + 2(236) + 480 = 4356$$

$$\sum f(u+1)^3 = 17{,}828$$
$$\sum fu^3 + 3\sum fu^2 + 3\sum fu + N = 6428 + 3(3404) + 3(236) + 480 = 17{,}828$$

$$\sum f(u+1)^4 = 122{,}148$$
$$\sum fu^4 + 4\sum fu^3 + 6\sum fu^2 + 4\sum fu + N = 74{,}588 + 4(6428) + 6(3404) + 4(236) + 480 = 122{,}148$$

Table 5.3

$u+1$	f	$f(u+1)$	$f(u+1)^2$	$f(u+1)^3$	$f(u+1)^4$
−5	4	−20	100	−500	2500
−4	9	−36	144	−576	2304
−3	16	−48	144	−432	1296
−2	28	−56	112	−224	448
−1	45	−45	45	−45	45
0	66	0	0	0	0
1	85	85	85	85	85
2	72	144	288	576	1152
3	54	162	486	1458	4374
4	38	152	608	2432	9728
5	27	135	675	3375	16875
6	18	108	648	3888	23328
7	11	77	539	3773	26411
8	5	40	320	2560	20480
9	2	18	162	1458	13122
	$N = \sum f$ $= 480$	$\sum f(u+1)$ $= 716$	$\sum f(u+1)^2$ $= 4356$	$\sum f(u+1)^3$ $= 17828$	$\sum f(u+1)^4$ $= 122148$

SHEPPARD'S CORRECTIONS FOR MOMENTS

5.9 Apply Sheppard's corrections to determine the moments about the mean for the data in (*a*) Problem 5.6 and (*b*) Problem 5.7.

SOLUTION

(*a*) Corrected $m_2 = m_2 - c^2/12 = 8.5275 - 3^2/12 = 7.7775$

Corrected $m_4 = m_4 - \frac{1}{2}c^2 m_2 + \frac{7}{240}c^4$

$= 199.3759 - \frac{1}{2}(3)^2(8.5275) + \frac{7}{240}(3)^4$

$= 163.3646$

m_1 and m_3 need no correction.

(*b*) Corrected $m_2 = m_2 - c^2/12 = 109.5988 - 4^2/12 = 108.2655$

Corrected $m_4 = m_4 - \frac{1}{2}c^2 m_2 + \frac{7}{240}c^4$

$= 35{,}627.2853 - \frac{1}{2}(4)^2(109.5988) + \frac{7}{240}(4)^4$

$= 34{,}757.9616$

SKEWNESS

5.10 Find Pearson's (*a*) first and (*b*) second coefficients of skewness for the wage distribution of the 65 employees at the P&R Company (see Problems 3.44 and 4.18).

SOLUTION

Mean = \$279.76, median = \$279.06, mode = \$277.50, and standard deviation s = \$15.60. Thus:

(*a*) $$\text{First coefficient of skewness} = \frac{\text{mean} - \text{mode}}{s} = \frac{\$279.76 - \$277.50}{\$15.60} = 0.1448, \text{ or } 0.14$$

(*b*) $$\text{Second coefficient of skewness} = \frac{3(\text{mean} - \text{median})}{s} = \frac{3(\$279.76 - \$279.06)}{\$15.60} = 0.1346, \text{ or } 0.13$$

If the corrected standard deviation is used [see Problem 4.21(*b*)], these coefficients become, respectively:

(*a*) $$\frac{\text{Mean} - \text{mode}}{\text{Corrected } s} = \frac{\$279.76 - \$277.50}{\$15.33} = 0.1474, \text{ or } 0.15$$

(*b*) $$\frac{3(\text{mean} - \text{median})}{\text{Corrected } s} = \frac{3(\$279.76 - \$279.06)}{\$15.33} = 0.1370, \text{ or } 0.14$$

Since the coefficients are positive, the distribution is skewed positively (i.e., to the right).

5.11 Find the (*a*) quartile and (*b*) percentile coefficients of skewness for the distribution of Problem 5.10 (see Problem 3.44).

SOLUTION

$Q_1 = \$268.25$, $Q_2 = P_{50} = \$279.06$, $Q_3 = \$290.75$, $P_{10} = D_1 = \$258.12$, and $P_{90} = D_9 = \$301.00$. Thus:

(*a*) $$\text{Quartile coefficient of skewness} = \frac{Q_3 - 2Q_2 + Q_1}{Q_3 - Q_1} = \frac{\$290.75 - 2(\$279.06) + \$268.25}{\$290.75 - \$268.25} = 0.0391$$

(*b*) $$\text{Percentile coefficient of skewness} = \frac{P_{90} - 2P_{50} + P_{10}}{P_{90} - P_{10}} = \frac{\$301.00 - 2(\$279.06) + \$258.12}{\$301.00 - \$258.12} = 0.0233$$

Mathcad **5.12** Find the moment coefficient of skewness, a_3, for (*a*) the height distribution of students at XYZ University (see Problem 5.6) and (*b*) the IQ's of elementary school children (see Problem 5.7).

SOLUTION

(*a*) $m_2 = s^2 = 8.5275$, and $m_3 = -2.6932$. Thus

$$a_3 = \frac{m_3}{s^3} = \frac{m_3}{(\sqrt{m_2})^3} = \frac{-2.6932}{(\sqrt{8.5275})^3} = -0.1081 \quad \text{or} \quad -0.11$$

If Sheppard's corrections for grouping are used [see Problem 5.9(*a*)], then

$$\text{Corrected } a_3 = \frac{m_3}{(\sqrt{\text{corrected } m_2})^3} = \frac{-2.6932}{(\sqrt{7.7775})^3} = -0.1242 \quad \text{or} \quad -0.12$$

(*b*) $$a_3 = \frac{m_3}{s^3} = \frac{m_3}{(\sqrt{m_2})^3} = \frac{202.8158}{(\sqrt{109.5988})^3} = 0.1768 \quad \text{or} \quad 0.18$$

If Sheppard's corrections for grouping are used [see Problem 5.9(*b*)], then

$$\text{Corrected } a_3 = \frac{m_3}{(\sqrt{\text{corrected } m_2})^3} = \frac{202.8158}{(\sqrt{108.2655})^3} = 0.1800 \quad \text{or} \quad 0.18$$

Note that both distributions are moderately skewed, distribution (*a*) to the left (negatively) and distribution (*b*) to the right (positively). Distribution (*b*) is more skewed than (*a*); that is, (*a*) is more symmetrical than (*b*), as is evidenced by the fact that the numerical value (or absolute value) of the skewness coefficient for (*b*) is greater than that for (*a*).

KURTOSIS

Mathcad **5.13** Find the moment coefficient of kurtosis, a_4, for the data of (a) Problem 5.6 and (b) Problem 5.7.

SOLUTION

(a)
$$a_4 = \frac{m_4}{s^4} = \frac{m_4}{m_2^2} = \frac{199.3759}{(8.5275)^2} = 2.7418 \quad \text{or} \quad 2.74$$

If Sheppard's corrections are used [see Problem 5.9(a)], then

$$\text{Corrected } a_4 = \frac{\text{corrected } m_4}{(\text{corrected } m_2)^2} = \frac{163.3646}{(7.7775)^2} = 2.7007 \quad \text{or} \quad 2.70$$

(b)
$$a_4 = \frac{m_4}{s^4} = \frac{m_4}{m_2^2} = \frac{35{,}627.2853}{(109.5988)^2} = 2.9660 \quad \text{or} \quad 2.97$$

If Sheppard's corrections are used [see Problem 5.9(b)], then

$$\text{Corrected } a_4 = \frac{\text{corrected } m_4}{(\text{corrected } m_2)^2} = \frac{34{,}757.9616}{(108.2655)^2} = 2.9653 \quad \text{or} \quad 2.97$$

Since for a normal distribution $a_4 = 3$, it follows that both distributions (a) and (b) are *platykurtic* with respect to the normal distribution (i.e., less peaked than the normal distribution).

Insofar as peakedness is concerned, distribution (b) approximates the normal distribution much better than does distribution (a). However, from Problem 5.12 distribution (a) is more symmetrical than (b), so that as far as symmetry is concerned, (a) approximates the normal distribution better than (b) does.

5.14 (a) Calculate the percentile coefficient of kurtosis, $\kappa = Q/(P_{90} - P_{10})$, for the distribution of Problem 5.11.

(b) How well would it be approximated by a normal distribution?

SOLUTION

(a) $Q = \frac{1}{2}(Q_3 - Q_1) = \frac{1}{2}(\$290.75 - \$268.25) = \$11.25$, $P_{90} - P_{10} = \$301.00 - \$258.12 = \$42.88$. Thus $\kappa = Q/(P_{90} - P_{10}) = 0.262$.

(b) Since κ for the normal distribution is 0.263, it follows that the given distribution is *mesokurtic* (i.e., about as peaked as the normal). Thus the kurtosis of the distribution is about the same as it should be for a normal distribution and leads us to believe that it would be approximated well by a normal distribution insofar as kurtosis is concerned.

Supplementary Problems

MOMENTS

5.15 Find the (a) first, (b) second, (c) third, and (d) fourth moments for the set 4, 7, 5, 9, 8, 3, 6.

5.16 Find the (a) first, (b) second, (c) third, and (d) fourth moments about the mean for the set of numbers in Problem 5.15.

5.17 Find the (a) first, (b) second (c) third, and (d) fourth moments about the number 7 for the set of numbers in Problem 5.15.

5.18 Using the results of Problems 5.16 and 5.17, verify the relations between the moments (a) $m_2 = m_2' - m_1'^2$, (b) $m_3 = m_3' - 3m_1'm_2' + 2m_1'^3$, and ($c$) $m_4 = m_4' - 4m_1'm_3' + 6m_1'^2m_2' - 3m_1'^4$.

5.19 Find the first four moments about the mean of the set of numbers in the arithmetic progression 2, 5, 8, 11, 14, 17.

5.20 Prove that (*a*) $m_2' = m_2 + h^2$, (*b*) $m_3' = m_3 + 3hm_2 + h^3$, and (*c*) $m_4' = m_4 + 4hm_3 + 6h^2m_2 + h^4$, where $h = m_1'$.

5.21 If the first moment about the number 2 is equal to 5, what is the mean?

5.22 If the first four moments of a set of numbers about the number 3 are equal to −2, 10, −25, and 50, determine the corresponding moments (*a*) about the mean, (*b*) about the number 5, and (*c*) about zero.

5.23 Find the first four moments about the mean of the numbers 0, 0, 0, 1, 1, 1, 1, and 1.

5.24 (*a*) Prove that $m_5 = m_5' - 5m_1'm_4' + 10m_1'^2m_3' - 10m_1'^3m_2' + 4m_1'^5$.

(*b*) Derive a similar formula for m_6.

5.25 Of a total of N numbers, the fraction p are 1's, while the fraction $q = 1 - p$ are 0's. Find (*a*) m_1, (*b*) m_2, (*c*) m_3, and (*d*) m_4 for the set of numbers. Compare with Problem 5.23.

5.26 Prove that the first four moments about the mean of the arithmetic progression $a, a+d, a+2d, \ldots, a+(n-1)d$ are $m_1 = 0$, $m_2 = \frac{1}{12}(n^2-1)d^2$, $m_3 = 0$, and $m_4 = \frac{1}{240}(n^2-1)(3n^2-7)d^4$. Compare with Problem 5.19 (see also Problem 4.69). [*Hint:* $1^4 + 2^4 + 3^4 + \cdots + (n-1)^4 = \frac{1}{30}n(n-1)(2n-1)(3n^2-3n-1)$.]

Table 5.4

X	f
12	1
14	4
16	6
18	10
20	7
22	2
	Total 30

MOMENTS FOR GROUPED DATA

5.27 Calculate the first four moments about the mean for the distribution of Table 5.4.

5.28 Illustrate the use of Charlier's check for the computations in Problem 5.27.

5.29 Apply Sheppard's corrections to the moments obtained in Problem 5.27.

5.30 Calculate the first four moments about the mean for the distribution of Problem 3.59 (*a*) without Sheppard's corrections and (*b*) with Sheppard's corrections.

5.31 Find (*a*) m_1, (*b*) m_2, (*c*) m_3, (*d*) m_4, (*e*) $\bar{X}$, (*f*) s, (*g*) $\overline{X^2}$, (*h*) $\overline{X^3}$, (*i*) $\overline{X^4}$, and (*j*) $\overline{(X+1)^3}$ for the distribution of Problem 3.62.

SKEWNESS

5.32 Find the moment coefficient of skewness, a_3, for the distribution of Problem 5.27 (*a*) without and (*b*) with Sheppard's corrections.

5.33 Find the moment coefficient of skewness, a_3, for the distribution of Problem 3.59 (see Problem 5.30).

5.34 The second moments about the mean of two distributions are 9 and 16, while the third moments about the mean are -8.1 and -12.8, respectively. Which distribution is more skewed to the left?

5.35 Find Pearson's (*a*) first and (*b*) second coefficients of skewness for the distribution of Problem 3.59, and account for the difference.

5.36 Find the (*a*) quartile and (*b*) percentile coefficients of skewness for the distribution of Problem 3.59. Compare your results with those of Problem 5.35 and explain.

5.37 (*a*) Explain why Pearson's coefficients of skewness are not appropriate for the distribution of Problem 2.31.

(*b*) Find the quartile coefficient of skewness for this distribution, and interpret the result.

KURTOSIS

5.38 Find the moment coefficient of kurtosis, a_4, for the distribution of Problem 5.27 (*a*) without and (*b*) with Sheppard's corrections.

5.39 Find the moment coefficient of kurtosis for the distribution of Problem 3.59 (*a*) without and (*b*) with Sheppard's corrections (see Problem 5.30).

5.40 The fourth moments about the mean of the two distributions of Problem 5.34 are 230 and 780, respectively. Which distribution more nearly approximates the normal distribution from the viewpoint of (*a*) peakedness and (*b*) skewness?

5.41 Which of the distributions in Problem 5.40 is (*a*) leptokurtic, (*b*) mesokurtic, and (*c*) platykurtic?

5.42 The standard deviation of a symmetrical distribution is 5. What must be the value of the fourth moment about the mean in order that the distribution be (*a*) leptokurtic, (*b*) mesokurtic, and (*c*) platykurtic?

5.43 (*a*) Calculate the percentile coefficient of kurtosis, κ, for the distribution of Problem 3.59.

(*b*) Compare your result with the theoretical value 0.263 for the normal distribution, and interpret.

(*c*) How do you reconcile this result with that of Problem 5.39?

Chapter 6

Elementary Probability Theory

DEFINITIONS OF PROBABILITY

Classic Definition

Suppose that an event E can happen in h ways out of a total of n possible equally likely ways. Then the probability of occurrence of the event (called its *success*) is denoted by

$$p = \Pr\{E\} = \frac{h}{n}$$

The probability of nonoccurrence of the event (called its *failure*) is denoted by

$$q = \Pr\{\text{not } E\} = \frac{n-h}{n} = 1 - \frac{h}{n} = 1 - p = 1 - \Pr\{E\}$$

Thus $p + q = 1$, or $\Pr\{E\} + \Pr\{\text{not } E\} = 1$. The event "not E" is sometimes denoted by $\bar{E}$, $\tilde{E}$, or $\sim E$.

EXAMPLE 1. Let E be the event that the number 3 or 4 turns up in a single toss of a die. There are six ways in which the die can fall, resulting in the numbers 1, 2, 3, 4, 5, or 6; and if the die is *fair* (i.e., not *loaded*), we can *assume* these six ways to be equally likely. Since E can occur in two of these ways, we have $p = \Pr\{E\} = \frac{2}{6} = \frac{1}{3}$.

The probability of not getting a 3 or 4 (i.e., getting a 1, 2, 5, or 6) is $q = \Pr\{\bar{E}\} = 1 - \frac{1}{3} = \frac{2}{3}$.

Note that the probability of an event is a number between 0 and 1. If the event cannot occur, its probability is 0. If it must occur (i.e., its occurrence is *certain*), its probability is 1.

If p is the probability that an event will occur, the *odds* in favor of its happening are $p:q$ (read "p to q"); the odds against its happening are $q:p$. Thus the odds against a 3 or 4 in a single toss of a fair die are $q:p = \frac{2}{3}:\frac{1}{3} = 2:1$ (i.e., 2 to 1).

Relative-Frequency Definition

The classic definition of probability has a disadvantage in that the words "equally likely" are vague. In fact, since these words seem to be synonymous with "equally probable," the definition is *circular* because we are essentially defining probability in terms of itself. For this reason, a statistical definition of probability has been advocated by some people. According to this the estimated probability, or *empirical probability*, of an event is taken to be the *relative frequency* of occurrence of the event when the number of observations is very large. The probability itself is the *limit* of the relative frequency as the number of observations increases indefinitely.

EXAMPLE 2. If 1000 tosses of a coin result in 529 heads, the relative frequency of heads is $529/1000 = 0.529$. If another 1000 tosses results in 493 heads, the relative frequency in the total of 2000 tosses is $(529 + 493)/2000 = 0.511$. According to the statistical definition, by continuing in this manner we should ultimately get closer and closer to a number that represents the probability of a head in a single toss of the coin. From the results so far presented, this should be 0.5 to one significant figure. To obtain more significant figures, further observations must be made.

The statistical definition, although useful in practice, has difficulties from a mathematical point of view, since an actual limiting number may not really exist. For this reason, modern probability theory has been developed *axiomatically*; that is, the theory leaves the concept of probability undefined, much the same as *point* and *line* are undefined in geometry.

CONDITIONAL PROBABILITY; INDEPENDENT AND DEPENDENT EVENTS

If E_1 and E_2 are two events, the probability that E_2 occurs given that E_1 has occurred is denoted by $\Pr\{E_2 | E_1\}$, or $\Pr\{E_2 \text{ given } E_1\}$, and is called the *conditional probability* of E_2 given that E_1 has occurred.

If the occurrence or nonoccurrence of E_1 does not affect the probability of occurrence of E_2, then $\Pr\{E_2 | E_1\} = \Pr\{E_2\}$ and we say that E_1 and E_2 are *independent events*; otherwise, they are *dependent events.*

If we denote by E_1E_2 the event that "both E_1 and E_2 occur," sometimes called a *compound event*, then

$$\Pr\{E_1E_2\} = \Pr\{E_1\} \Pr\{E_2 | E_1\} \tag{1}$$

In particular,

$$\Pr\{E_1E_2\} = \Pr\{E_1\} \Pr\{E_2\} \qquad \text{for independent events} \tag{2}$$

For three events E_1, E_2, and E_3, we have

$$\Pr\{E_1E_2E_3\} = \Pr\{E_1\} \Pr\{E_2 | E_1\} \Pr\{E_3 | E_1E_2\} \tag{3}$$

That is, the probability of occurrence of E_1, E_2, and E_3 is equal to (the probability of E_1) $\times$ (the probability of E_2 given that E_1 has occurred) $\times$ (the probability of E_3 given that both E_1 and E_2 have occurred). In particular,

$$\Pr\{E_1E_2E_3\} = \Pr\{E_1\} \Pr\{E_2\} \Pr\{E_3\} \qquad \text{for independent events} \tag{4}$$

In general, if $E_1, E_2, E_3, \ldots, E_n$ are n independent events having respective probabilities $p_1, p_2, p_3, \ldots, p_n$, then the probability of occurrence of E_1 and E_2 and E_3 and $\cdots E_n$ is $p_1p_2p_3 \cdots p_n$.

EXAMPLE 3. Let E_1 and E_2 be the events "heads on fifth toss" and "heads on sixth toss" of a coin, respectively. Then E_1 and E_2 are independent events, and thus the probability of heads on both the fifth and sixth tosses is (assuming the coin to be fair)

$$\Pr\{E_1E_2\} = \Pr\{E_1\} \Pr\{E_2\} = \left(\frac{1}{2}\right)\left(\frac{1}{2}\right) = \frac{1}{4}$$

EXAMPLE 4. If the probability that A will be alive in 20 years is 0.7 and the probability that B will be alive in 20 years is 0.5, then the probability that they will both be alive in 20 years is $(0.7)(0.5) = 0.35$.

EXAMPLE 5. Suppose that a box contains 3 white balls and 2 black balls. Let E_1 be the event "first ball drawn is black" and E_2 the event "second ball drawn is black," where the balls are not replaced after being drawn. Here E_1 and E_2 are dependent events.

The probability that the first ball drawn is black is $\Pr\{E_1\} = 2/(3+2) = \frac{2}{5}$. The probability that the second ball drawn is black, given that the first ball drawn was black, is $\Pr\{E_2 | E_1\} = 1/(3+1) = \frac{1}{4}$. Thus the probability that both balls drawn are black is

$$\Pr\{E_1E_2\} = \Pr\{E_1\} \Pr\{E_2 | E_1\} = \frac{2}{5} \cdot \frac{1}{4} = \frac{1}{10}$$

MUTUALLY EXCLUSIVE EVENTS

Two or more events are called *mutually exclusive* if the occurrence of any one of them excludes the occurrence of the others. Thus if E_1 and E_2 are mutually exclusive events, then $\Pr\{E_1E_2\} = 0$.

If $E_1 + E_2$ denotes the event that "either E_1 or E_2 or both occur," then

$$\Pr\{E_1 + E_2\} = \Pr\{E_1\} + \Pr\{E_2\} - \Pr\{E_1E_2\} \tag{5}$$

In particular,

$$\Pr\{E_1 + E_2\} = \Pr\{E_1\} + \Pr\{E_2\} \qquad \text{for mutually exclusive events} \qquad (6)$$

As an extension of this, if $E_1, E_2, \ldots, E_n$ are n mutually exclusive events having respective probabilities of occurrence $p_1, p_2, \ldots, p_n$, then the probability of occurrence of either E_1 or E_2 or $\cdots E_n$ is $p_1 + p_2 + \cdots + p_n$.

Result (5) can also be generalized to three or more mutually exclusive events (see Problem 6.38).

EXAMPLE 6. If E_1 is the event "drawing an ace from a deck of cards" and E_2 is the event "drawing a king," then $\Pr\{E_1\} = \frac{4}{52} = \frac{1}{13}$ and $\Pr\{E_2\} = \frac{4}{52} = \frac{1}{13}$. The probability of drawing either an ace or a king in a single draw is

$$\Pr\{E_1 + E_2\} = \Pr\{E_1\} + \Pr\{E_2\} = \frac{1}{13} + \frac{1}{13} = \frac{2}{13}$$

since both an ace and a king cannot be drawn in a single draw and are thus mutually exclusive events.

EXAMPLE 7. If E_1 is the event "drawing an ace" from a deck of cards and E_2 is the event "drawing a spade," then E_1 and E_2 are not mutually exclusive since the ace of spades can be drawn. Thus the probability of drawing either an ace or a spade or both is

$$\Pr\{E_1 + E_2\} = \Pr\{E_1\} + \Pr\{E_2\} - \Pr\{E_1 E_2\} = \frac{4}{52} + \frac{13}{52} - \frac{1}{52} = \frac{16}{52} = \frac{4}{13}$$

PROBABILITY DISTRIBUTIONS

Discrete

If a variable X can assume a discrete set of values $X_1, X_2, \ldots, X_K$ with respective probabilities $p_1, p_2, \ldots, p_K$, where $p_1 + p_2 + \cdots + p_K = 1$, we say that a *discrete probability distribution* for X has been defined. The function $p(X)$, which has the respective values $p_1, p_2, \ldots, p_K$ for $X = X_1, X_2, \ldots, X_K$, is called the *probability function*, or *frequency function*, of X. Because X can assume certain values with given probabilities, it is often called a *discrete random variable*. A random variable is also known as a *chance variable* or *stochastic variable*.

EXAMPLE 8. Let a pair of fair dice be tossed and let X denote the sum of the points obtained. Then the probability distribution is as shown in Table 6.1. For example, the probability of getting sum 5 is $\frac{4}{36} = \frac{1}{9}$; thus in 900 tosses of the dice we would expect 100 tosses to give the sum 5.

Table 6.1

X	2	3	4	5	6	7	8	9	10	11	12
$p(X)$	1/36	2/36	3/36	4/36	5/36	6/36	5/36	4/36	3/36	2/36	1/36

Note that this is analogous to a relative-frequency distribution with probabilities replacing the relative frequencies. Thus we can think of probability distributions as theoretical or ideal limiting forms of relative-frequency distributions when the number of observations made is very large. For this reason, we can think of probability distributions as being distributions of *populations*, whereas relative-frequency distributions are distributions of *samples* drawn from this population.

The probability distribution can be represented graphically by plotting $p(X)$ against X, just as for relative-frequency distributions (see Problem 6.11).

By cumulating probabilities, we obtain *cumulative probability distributions*, which are analogous to cumulative relative-frequency distributions. The function associated with this distribution is sometimes called a *distribution function*.

Continuous

The above ideas can be extended to the case where the variable X may assume a continuous set of values. The relative-frequency polygon of a sample becomes, in the theoretical or limiting case of a population, a continuous curve (such as shown in Fig. 6-1) whose equation is $Y = p(X)$. The total area under this curve bounded by the X axis is equal to 1, and the area under the curve between lines $X = a$ and $X = b$ (shaded in Fig. 6-1) gives the probability that X lies between a and b, which can be denoted by $\Pr\{a < X < b\}$.

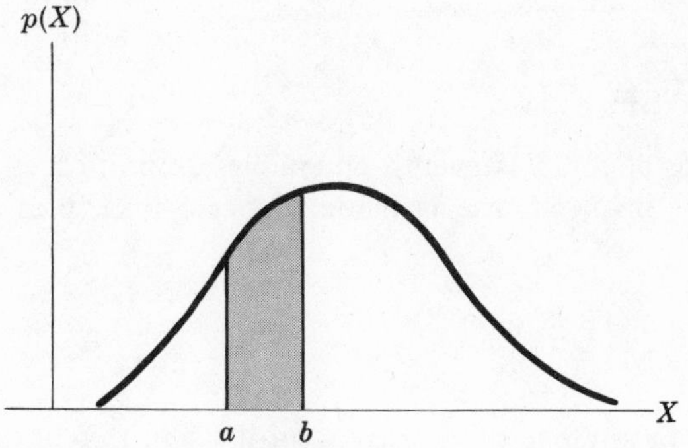

Fig. 6-1

We call $p(X)$ a *probability density function*, or briefly a *density function*, and when such a function is given we say that a *continuous probability distribution* for X has been defined. The variable X is then often called a *continuous random variable*.

As in the discrete case, we can define cumulative probability distributions and the associated distribution functions.

MATHEMATICAL EXPECTATION

If p is the probability that a person will receive a sum of money S, the *mathematical expectation* (or simply the *expectation*) is defined as pS.

EXAMPLE 9. If the probability that a man wins a \$10 prize is $\frac{1}{5}$, his expectation is $\frac{1}{5}(\$10) = \$2$.

The concept of expectation is easily extended. If X denotes a discrete random variable that can assume the values $X_1, X_2, \ldots, X_K$ with respective probabilities $p_1, p_2, \ldots, p_K$, where $p_1 + p_2 + \cdots + p_K = 1$, the *mathematical expectation* of X (or simply the *expectation* of X), denoted by $E(X)$, is defined as

$$E(X) = p_1X_1 + p_2X_2 + \cdots + p_KX_K = \sum_{j=1}^{K} p_jX_j = \sum pX \tag{7}$$

If the probabilities p_j in this expectation are replaced with the relative frequencies f_j/N, where $N = \sum f_j$, the expectation reduces to $(\sum fX)/N$, which is the arithmetic mean $\bar{X}$ of a sample of size N in which $X_1, X_2, \ldots, X_K$ appear with these relative frequencies. As N gets larger and larger, the relative frequencies f_j/N approach the probabilities p_j. Thus we are led to the interpretation that $E(X)$ represents the mean of the population from which the sample is drawn. If we call m the sample mean, we can denote the population mean by the corresponding Greek letter μ (mu).

Expectation can also be defined for continuous random variables, but the definition requires the use of calculus.

RELATION BETWEEN POPULATION, SAMPLE MEAN, AND VARIANCE

If we select a sample of size N at random from a population (i.e., we assume that all such samples are equally probable), then it is possible to show that the *expected value of the sample mean m is the population mean μ.*

It does not follow, however, that the expected value of any quantity computed from a sample is the corresponding population quantity. For example, the expected value of the sample variance as we have defined it is not the population variance, but $(N-1)/N$ times this variance. This is why some statisticians choose to define the sample variance as our variance multiplied by $N(N-1)$.

COMBINATORIAL ANALYSIS

In obtaining probabilities of complex events, an enumeration of cases is often difficult, tedious, or both. To facilitate the labor involved, use is made of basic principles studied in a subject called *combinatorial analysis.*

Fundamental Principle

If an event can happen in any one of n_1 ways, and if when this has occurred another event can happen in any one of n_2 ways, then the number of ways in which both events can happen in the specified order is $n_1 n_2$.

EXAMPLE 10. If there are 3 candidates for governor and 5 for mayor, the two offices can be filled in $3 \cdot 5 = 15$ ways.

Factorial *n*

Factorial n, denoted by $n!$, is defined as

$$n! = n(n-1)(n-2)\cdots 1 \tag{8}$$

Thus $5! = 5 \cdot 4 \cdot 3 \cdot 2 \cdot 1 = 120$, and $4!3! = (4 \cdot 3 \cdot 2 \cdot 1)(3 \cdot 2 \cdot 1) = 144$. It is convenient to define $0! = 1$.

Permutations

A permutation of n different objects taken r at a time is an *arrangement* of r out of the n objects, with attention given to the order of arrangement. The number of permutations of n objects taken r at a time is denoted by ${}_nP_r$, $P(n, r)$, or $P_{n,r}$ and is given by

$${}_nP_r = n(n-1)(n-2)\cdots(n-r+1) = \frac{n!}{(n-r)!} \tag{9}$$

In particular, the number of permutations of n objects taken n at a time is

$${}_n^nP = n(n-1)(n-2)\cdots 1 = n!$$

EXAMPLE 11. The number of permutations of the letters a, b, and c taken two at a time is ${}_3P_2 = 3 \cdot 2 = 6$. These are *ab*, *ba*, *ac*, *ca*, *bc*, and *cb*.

The number of permutations of n objects consisting of groups of which n_1 are alike, n_2 are alike, $\cdots$ is

$$\frac{n!}{n_1!\,n_2!\cdots} \qquad \text{where } n = n_1 + n_2 + \cdots \tag{10}$$

EXAMPLE 12. The number of permutations of letters in the word *statistics* is

$$\frac{10!}{3!\,3!\,1!\,2!\,1!} = 50{,}400$$

since there are $3s$'s, $3t$'s, $1a$, $2i$'s, and $1c$.

COMBINATIONS

A combination of n different objects taken r at a time is a selection of r out of the n objects, with no attention given to the order of arrangement. The number of combinations of n objects taken r at a time is denoted by the symbol $\binom{n}{r}$ and is given by

$$\binom{n}{r} = \frac{n(n-1)\cdots(n-r+1)}{r!} = \frac{n!}{r!(n-r)!} \tag{11}$$

EXAMPLE 13. The number of combinations of the letters a, b, and c taken two at a time is

$$\binom{3}{2} = \frac{3 \cdot 2}{2!} = 3$$

These are *ab*, *ac*, and *bc*. Note that *ab* is the same combination as *ba*, but not the same permutation.

STIRLING'S APPROXIMATION TO *n*!

When n is large, a direct evaluation of $n!$ is impractical. In such case, use is made of an approximate formula developed by James Stirling:

$$n! \approx \sqrt{2\pi n}\, n^n e^{-n} \tag{12}$$

where $e = 2.71828\cdots$ is the natural base of logarithms (see Problem 6.31).

RELATION OF PROBABILITY TO POINT SET THEORY

In modern probability theory, we think of all possible outcomes (or results) of an experiment, game, etc., as points in a space (which can be of one, two, three, etc., dimensions), called a *sample space S*. If S contains only a finite number of points, then with each point we can associate a nonnegative number, called a *probability*, such that the sum of all numbers corresponding to all points in S add to 1. An event is a *set* (or *collection*) of points in S, such as indicated by E_1 or E_2 in Fig. 6-2; this figure is called an *Euler diagram* or *Venn diagram*.

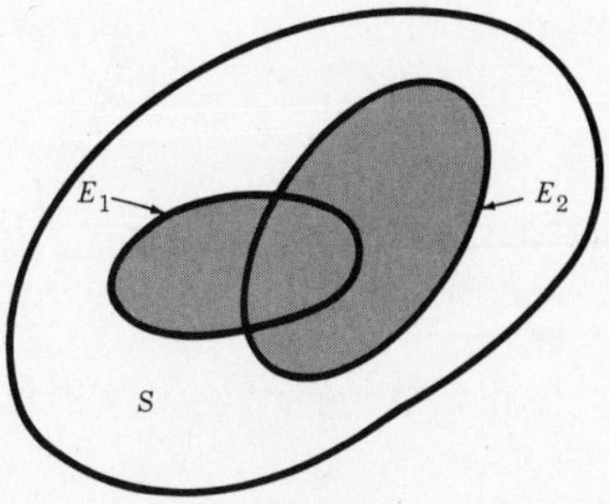

Fig. 6-2

The event $E_1 + E_2$ is the set of points that are *either in* E_1 *or* E_2 *or both*, while the event E_1E_2 is the set of points *common to both* E_1 *and* E_2. Thus the probability of an event such as E_1 is the sum of the probabilities associated with all points contained in the set E_1. Similarly, the probability of $E_1 + E_2$, denoted by $\Pr\{E_1 + E_2\}$, is the sum of the probabilities associated with all points contained in the set $E_1 + E_2$. If E_1 and E_2 have no points in common (i.e., the events are mutually exclusive), then $\Pr\{E_1 + E_2\} = \Pr\{E_1\} + \Pr\{E_2\}$. If they have points in common, then $\Pr\{E_1 + E_2\} = \Pr\{E_1\} + \Pr\{E_2\} - \Pr\{E_1E_2\}$.

The set $E_1 + E_2$ is sometimes denoted by $E_1 \cup E_2$ and is called the *union* of the two sets. The set E_1E_2 is sometimes denoted by $E_1 \cap E_2$ and is called the *intersection* of the two sets. Extensions to more than two sets can be made; thus instead of $E_1 + E_2 + E_3$ and $E_1E_2E_3$, we could use the notations $E_1 \cup E_2 \cup E_3$ and $E_1 \cap E_2 \cap E_3$, respectively.

The symbol ϕ (the Greek letter *phi*) is sometimes used to denote a set with no points in it, called the *null set*. The probability associated with an event corresponding to this set is zero (i.e., $\Pr\{\phi\} = 0$). If E_1 and E_2 have no points in common, we can write $E_1E_2 = \phi$, which means that the corresponding events are mutually exclusive, whereby $\Pr\{E_1E_2\} = 0$.

With this modern approach, a random variable is a function defined at each point of the sample space. For example, in Problem 6.37 the random variable is the sum of the coordinates of each point.

In the case where S has an infinite number of points, the above ideas can be extended by using concepts of calculus.

Solved Problems

FUNDAMENTAL RULES OF PROBABILITY

6.1 Determine the probability p, or an estimate of it, for each of the following events:

(*a*) An odd number appears in a single toss of a fair die.

(*b*) At least one head appears in two tosses of a fair coin.

(*c*) An ace, 10 of diamonds, or 2 of spades appears in drawing a single card from a well-shuffled ordinary deck of 52 cards.

(*d*) The sum 7 appears in a single toss of a pair of fair dice.

(*e*) A tail appears in the next toss of a coin if out of 100 tosses 56 were heads.

SOLUTION

(*a*) Out of six possible equally likely cases, three cases (where the die comes up 1, 3, or 5) are favorable to the event. Thus $p = \frac{3}{6} = \frac{1}{2}$.

(*b*) If H denotes "head" and T denotes "tail," the two tosses can lead to four cases: HH, HT, TH, and TT, all equally likely. Only the first three cases are favorable to the event. Thus $p = \frac{3}{4}$.

(*c*) The event can occur in six ways (ace of spades, ace of hearts, ace of clubs, ace of diamonds, 10 of diamonds, and 2 of spades) out of 52 equally likely cases. Thus $p = \frac{6}{52} = \frac{3}{26}$.

(*d*) Each of the six faces of one die can be associated with each of the six faces of the other die, so that the total number of cases that can arise, all equally likely, is $6 \cdot 6 = 36$. These can be denoted by $(1,1), (2,1), (3,1), \ldots, (6,6)$.

There are six ways of obtaining the sum 7, denoted by $(1,6)$, $(2,5)$, $(3,4)$, $(4,3)$, $(5,2)$, and $(6,1)$ [see Problem 6.37(*a*)]. Thus $p = \frac{6}{36} = \frac{1}{6}$.

(*e*) Since $100 - 56 = 44$ tails were obtained in 100 tosses, the *estimated* (or *empirical*) *probability* of a tail is the relative frequency $44/100 = 0.44$.

6.2 An experiment consists of tossing a coin and a die. If E_1 is the event that "head" comes up in tossing the coin and E_2 is the event that "3 or 6" comes up in tossing the die, state in words the meaning of each of the following:

(*a*) $\bar{E}_1$ (*c*) E_1E_2 (*e*) $\Pr\{E_1 | E_2\}$

(*b*) $\bar{E}_2$ (*d*) $\Pr\{E_1\bar{E}_2\}$ (*f*) $\Pr\{\bar{E}_1 + \bar{E}_2\}$

SOLUTION

(*a*) Tails on the coin and anything on the die

(*b*) 1, 2, 4, or 5 on the die and anything on the coin

(*c*) Heads on the coin and 3 or 6 on the die

(*d*) Probability of heads on the coin and 1, 2, 4, or 5 on the die

(*e*) Probability of heads on the coin, given that a 3 or 6 has come up on the die

(*f*) Probability of tails on the coin or 1, 2, 4, or 5 on the die, or both

6.3 A ball is drawn at random from a box containing 6 red balls, 4 white balls, and 5 blue balls. Determine the probability that the ball drawn is (*a*) red, (*b*) white, (*c*) blue, (*d*) not red, and (*e*) red or white.

SOLUTION

Let R, W, and B denote the events of drawing a red ball, white ball, and blue ball, respectively. Then:

(*a*)
$$\Pr\{R\} = \frac{\text{ways of choosing a red ball}}{\text{total ways of choosing a ball}} = \frac{6}{6+4+5} = \frac{6}{15} = \frac{2}{5}$$

(*b*)
$$\Pr\{W\} = \frac{4}{6+4+5} = \frac{4}{15}$$

(*c*)
$$\Pr\{B\} = \frac{5}{6+4+5} = \frac{5}{15} = \frac{1}{3}$$

(*d*)
$$\Pr\{\bar{R}\} = 1 - \Pr\{R\} = 1 - \frac{2}{5} = \frac{3}{5} \qquad \text{by part } (a)$$

(*e*)
$$\Pr\{R + W\} = \frac{\text{ways of choosing a red or white ball}}{\text{total ways of choosing a ball}} = \frac{6+4}{6+4+5} = \frac{10}{15} = \frac{2}{3}$$

Another method

$$\Pr\{R + W\} = \Pr\{\bar{B}\} = 1 - \Pr\{B\} = 1 - \frac{1}{3} = \frac{2}{3} \qquad \text{by part } (c)$$

Note that $\Pr\{R + W\} = \Pr\{R\} + \Pr\{W\}$ (i.e., $\frac{2}{3} = \frac{2}{5} + \frac{4}{15}$). This is an illustration of the general rule $\Pr\{E_1 + E_2\} = \Pr\{E_1\} + \Pr\{E_2\}$ that is true for *mutually exclusive* events E_1 and E_2.

6.4 A fair die is tossed twice. Find the probability of getting a 4, 5, or 6 on the first toss and a 1, 2, 3, or 4 on the second toss.

SOLUTION

Let E_1 = event "4, 5, or 6" on the first toss, and let E_2 = event "1, 2, 3, or 4" on the second toss. Each of the six ways in which the die can fall on the first toss can be associated with each of the six ways in which it can fall on the second toss, a total of $6 \cdot 6 = 36$ ways, all equally likely. Each of the three ways in which E_1 can occur can be associated with each of the four ways in which E_2 can occur, to give $3 \cdot 4 = 12$ ways in which both E_1 and E_2, or E_1E_2 occur. Thus $\Pr\{E_1E_2\} = 12/36 = 1/3$.

Note that $\Pr\{E_1E_2\} = \Pr\{E_1\}\Pr\{E_2\}$ (i.e., $\frac{1}{3} = \frac{3}{6} \cdot \frac{4}{6}$) is valid for the *independent events* E_1 and E_2.

6.5 Two cards are drawn from a well-shuffled ordinary deck of 52 cards. Find the probability that they are both aces if the first card is (*a*) replaced and (*b*) not replaced.

SOLUTION

Let E_1 = event "ace" on the first draw, and let E_2 = event "ace" on the second draw.

(*a*) If the first card is replaced, E_1 and E_2 are independent events. Thus Pr{both cards drawn are aces} = $\Pr\{E_1 E_2\} = \Pr\{E_1\}\Pr\{E_2\} = (\frac{4}{52})(\frac{4}{52}) = \frac{1}{169}$.

(*b*) The first card can be drawn in any one of 52 ways, and the second card can be drawn in any one of 51 ways since the first card is not replaced. Thus both cards can be drawn in $52 \cdot 51$ ways, all equally likely.

There are four ways in which E_1 can occur and three ways in which E_2 can occur, so that both E_1 and E_2, or E_1E_2, can occur in $4 \cdot 3$ ways. Thus $\Pr\{E_1E_2\} = (4 \cdot 3)/(52 \cdot 51) = \frac{1}{221}$.

Note that $\Pr\{E_2|E_1\}$ = Pr{second card is an ace given that first card is an ace} $= \frac{3}{51}$. Thus our result is an illustration of the general rule that $\Pr\{E_1E_2\} = \Pr\{E_1\}\Pr\{E_2|E_1\}$ when E_1 and E_2 are dependent events.

6.6 Three balls are drawn successively from the box of Problem 6.3. Find the probability that they are drawn in the order red, white, and blue if each ball is (*a*) replaced and (*b*) not replaced.

SOLUTION

Let R = event "red" on the first draw, W = event "white" on the second draw, and B = event "blue" on the third draw. We require $\Pr\{RWB\}$.

(*a*) If each ball is replaced, then R, W, and B are independent events and

$$\Pr\{RWB\} = \Pr\{R\}\Pr\{W\}\Pr\{B\} = \left(\frac{6}{6+4+5}\right)\left(\frac{4}{6+4+5}\right)\left(\frac{5}{6+4+5}\right) = \left(\frac{6}{15}\right)\left(\frac{4}{15}\right)\left(\frac{5}{15}\right) = \frac{8}{225}$$

(*b*) If each ball is not replaced, then R, W, and B are dependent events and

$$\Pr\{RWB\} = \Pr\{R\}\Pr\{W|R\}\Pr\{B|WR\} = \left(\frac{6}{6+4+5}\right)\left(\frac{4}{5+4+5}\right)\left(\frac{5}{5+3+5}\right)$$

$$= \left(\frac{6}{15}\right)\left(\frac{4}{14}\right)\left(\frac{5}{13}\right) = \frac{4}{91}$$

where $\Pr\{B|WR\}$ is the conditional probability of getting a blue ball if a white and red ball have already been chosen.

6.7 Find the probability of a 4 turning up at least once in two tosses of a fair die.

SOLUTION

Let E_1 = event "4" on the first toss, E_2 = event "4" on the second toss, and $E_1 + E_2$ = event "4" on the first toss or "4" on the second toss or both = event that at least one 4 turns up. We require $\Pr\{E_1 + E_2\}$.

First method

The total number or equally likely ways in which both dice can fall is $6 \cdot 6 = 36$. Also,

Number of ways in which E_1 occurs but not E_2 = 5
Number of ways in which E_2 occurs but not E_1 = 5
Number of ways in which both E_1 and E_2 occur = 1

Thus the number of ways in which at least one of the events E_1 or E_2 occurs is $5+5+1 = 11$, and thus $\Pr\{E_1 + E_2\} = \frac{11}{36}$.

Second method

Since E_1 and E_2 are not mutually exclusive, $\Pr\{E_1+E_2\}=\Pr\{E_1\}+\Pr\{E_2\}-\Pr\{E_1E_2\}$. Also, since E_1 and E_2 are independent, $\Pr\{E_1E_2\}=\Pr\{E_1\}\Pr\{E_2\}$. Thus $\Pr\{E_1+E_2\}=\Pr\{E_1\}+\Pr\{E_2\}-\Pr\{E_1\}\Pr\{E_2\}=\frac{1}{6}+\frac{1}{6}-(\frac{1}{6})(\frac{1}{6})=\frac{11}{36}$.

Third method

$$\Pr\{\text{at least one 4 comes up}\}+\Pr\{\text{no 4 comes up}\}=1$$

Thus

$$\begin{aligned}\Pr\{\text{at least one 4 comes up}\} &= 1-\Pr\{\text{no 4 comes up}\}\\ &= 1-\Pr\{\text{no 4 on first toss and no 4 on second toss}\}\\ &= 1-\Pr\{\bar{E}_1\bar{E}_2\}=1-\Pr\{\bar{E}_1\}\Pr\{\bar{E}_2\}\\ &= 1-\left(\frac{5}{6}\right)\left(\frac{5}{6}\right)=\frac{11}{36}\end{aligned}$$

6.8 One bag contains 4 white balls and 2 black balls; another contains 3 white balls and 5 black balls. If one ball is drawn from each bag, find the probability that (*a*) both are white, (*b*) both are black, and (*c*) one is white and one is black.

SOLUTION

Let W_1 = event "white" ball from the first bag, and let W_2 = event "white" ball from the second bag.

(*a*)
$$\Pr\{W_1W_2\}=\Pr\{W_1\}\Pr\{W_2\}=\left(\frac{4}{4+2}\right)\left(\frac{3}{3+5}\right)=\frac{1}{4}$$

(*b*)
$$\Pr\{\bar{W}_1\bar{W}_2\}=\Pr\{\bar{W}_1\}\Pr\{\bar{W}_2\}=\left(\frac{2}{4+2}\right)\left(\frac{5}{3+5}\right)=\frac{5}{24}$$

(*c*) The event "one is white and one is black" is the same as the event "either the first is white and the second is black *or* the first is black and the second is white"; that is, $W_1\bar{W}_2+\bar{W}_1W_2$. Since events $W_1\bar{W}_2$ and $\bar{W}_1W_2$ are mutually exclusive, we have

$$\begin{aligned}\Pr\{W_1\bar{W}_2+\bar{W}_1W_2\} &= \Pr\{W_1\bar{W}_2\}+\Pr\{\bar{W}_1W_2\}\\ &= \Pr\{W_1\}\Pr\{\bar{W}_2\}+\Pr\{\bar{W}_1\}\Pr\{W_2\}\\ &= \left(\frac{4}{4+2}\right)\left(\frac{5}{3+5}\right)+\left(\frac{2}{4+2}\right)\left(\frac{3}{3+5}\right)=\frac{13}{24}\end{aligned}$$

Another method

The required probability is $1-\Pr\{W_1W_2\}-\Pr\{\bar{W}_1\bar{W}_2\}=1-\frac{1}{4}-\frac{5}{24}=\frac{13}{24}$.

6.9 *A* and *B* play 12 games of chess, of which 6 are won by *A*, 4 are won by *B*, and 2 end in a tie. They agree to play a tournament consisting of 3 games. Find the probability that (*a*) *A* wins all 3 games, (*b*) 2 games end in a tie, (*c*) *A* and *B* win alternately, and (*d*) *B* wins at least 1 game.

SOLUTION

Let A_1, A_2, and A_3 denote the events "*A* wins" in the first, second, and third games, respectively; let B_1, B_2, and B_3 denote the events "*B* wins" in the first, second, and third games, respectively; and let T_1, T_2, and T_3 denote the events "there is a tie" in the first, second, and third games, respectively.

On the basis of their past experience (empirical probability), we shall assume that $\Pr\{A \text{ wins any one game}\}=\frac{6}{12}=\frac{1}{2}$, that $\Pr\{B \text{ wins any one game}\}=\frac{4}{12}=\frac{1}{3}$, and that $\Pr\{\text{any one game ends in a tie}\}=\frac{2}{12}=\frac{1}{6}$.

(*a*) $\Pr\{A \text{ wins all 3 games}\} = \Pr\{A_1 A_2 A_3\} = \Pr\{A_1\}\Pr\{A_2\}\Pr\{A_3\} = \left(\frac{1}{2}\right)\left(\frac{1}{2}\right)\left(\frac{1}{2}\right) = \frac{1}{8}$

assuming that the results of each game are independent of the results of any others, which appears to be justifiable (unless, of course, the players happen to be *psychologically influenced* by the other one's winning or losing).

(*b*) $\Pr\{2 \text{ games end in a tie}\} = \Pr\{1\text{st and 2d } or \text{ 1st and 3d } or \text{ 2d and 3d games end in a tie}\}$

$$= \Pr\{T_1 T_2 \bar{T}_3\} + \Pr\{T_1 \bar{T}_2 T_3\} + \Pr\{\bar{T}_1 T_2 T_3\}$$
$$= \Pr\{T_1\}\Pr\{T_2\}\Pr\{\bar{T}_3\} + \Pr\{T_1\}\Pr\{\bar{T}_2\}\Pr\{T_3\} + \Pr\{\bar{T}_1\}\Pr\{T_2\}\Pr\{T_3\}$$
$$= \left(\frac{1}{6}\right)\left(\frac{1}{6}\right)\left(\frac{5}{6}\right) + \left(\frac{1}{6}\right)\left(\frac{5}{6}\right)\left(\frac{1}{6}\right) + \left(\frac{5}{6}\right)\left(\frac{1}{6}\right)\left(\frac{1}{6}\right) = \frac{15}{216} = \frac{5}{72}$$

(*c*) $\Pr\{A \text{ and } B \text{ win alternately}\} = \Pr\{A \text{ wins then } B \text{ wins then } A \text{ wins } or\ B \text{ wins then } A \text{ wins then } B \text{ wins}\}$

$$= \Pr\{A_1 B_2 A_3 + B_1 A_2 B_3\} = \Pr\{A_1 B_2 A_3\} + \Pr\{B_1 A_2 B_3\}$$
$$= \Pr\{A_1\}\Pr\{B_2\}\Pr\{A_3\} + \Pr\{B_1\}\Pr\{A_2\}\Pr\{B_3\}$$
$$= \left(\frac{1}{2}\right)\left(\frac{1}{3}\right)\left(\frac{1}{2}\right) + \left(\frac{1}{3}\right)\left(\frac{1}{2}\right)\left(\frac{1}{3}\right) = \frac{5}{36}$$

(*d*) $\Pr\{B \text{ wins at least 1 game}\} = 1 - \Pr\{B \text{ wins no game}\}$

$$= 1 - \Pr\{\bar{B}_1 \bar{B}_2 \bar{B}_3\} = 1 - \Pr\{\bar{B}_1\}\Pr\{\bar{B}_2\}\Pr\{\bar{B}_3\}$$
$$= 1 - \left(\frac{2}{3}\right)\left(\frac{2}{3}\right)\left(\frac{2}{3}\right) = \frac{19}{27}$$

PROBABILITY DISTRIBUTIONS

6.10 Find the probability of boys and girls in families with three children, assuming equal probabilities for boys and girls.

SOLUTION

Let B = event "boy in the family," and let G = event "girl in the family." Thus, according to the assumption of equal probabilities, $\Pr\{B\} = \Pr\{G\} = \frac{1}{2}$. In families of three children the following mutually exclusive events can occur with the corresponding indicated probabilities:

(*a*) Three boys (BBB):

$$\Pr\{BBB\} = \Pr\{B\}\Pr\{B\}\Pr\{B\} = \frac{1}{8}$$

Here we assume that the birth of a boy is not influenced in any manner by the fact that a previous child was also a boy, that is, we assume that the events are independent.

(*b*) Three girls (GGG): As in part (*a*) or by symmetry,

$$\Pr\{GGG\} = \frac{1}{8}$$

(*c*) Two boys and one girl ($BBG + BGB + GBB$):

$$\Pr\{BBG + BGB + GBB\} = \Pr\{BBG\} + \Pr\{BGB\} + \Pr\{GBB\}$$
$$= \Pr\{B\}\Pr\{B\}\Pr\{G\} + \Pr\{B\}\Pr\{G\}\Pr\{B\} + \Pr\{G\}\Pr\{B\}\Pr\{B\}$$
$$= \frac{1}{8} + \frac{1}{8} + \frac{1}{8} = \frac{3}{8}$$

(*d*) Two girls and one boy ($GGB + GBG + BGG$): As in part (*c*) or by symmetry, the probability is $\frac{3}{8}$.

If we call X the *random variable* showing the number of boys in families with three children, the probability distribution is as shown in Table 6.2.

Table 6.2

Number of boys X	0	1	2	3
Probability $p(X)$	1/8	3/8	3/8	1/8

6.11 Graph the distribution of Problem 6.10.

SOLUTION

The graph can be represented either as in Fig. 6-3 or Fig. 6-4. Note that the sum of the areas of the rectangles in Fig. 6-4 is 1; in this figure, called a *probability histogram*, we are considering X as a continuous variable even though it is actually discrete, a procedure that is often found useful. Figure 6-3, on the other hand, is used when one does not wish to consider the variable as continuous.

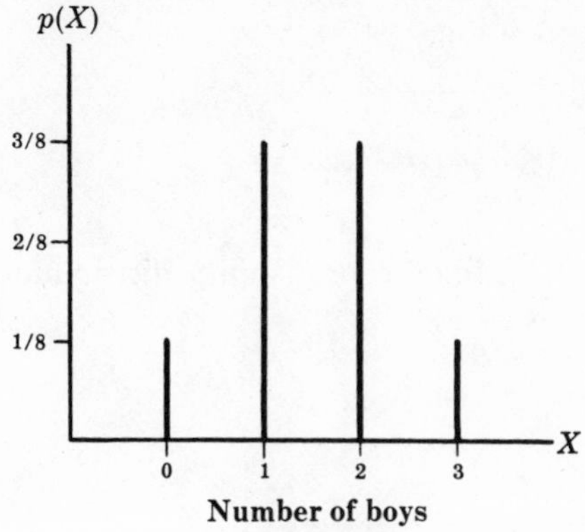

Fig. 6-3

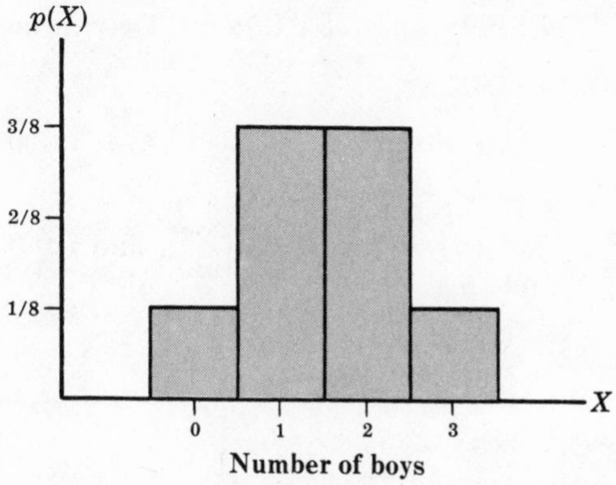

Fig. 6-4

Mathcad **6.12** A continuous random variable X having values only between 0 and 4 has a density function given by $p(X) = \frac{1}{2} - aX$, where a is a constant.

(*a*) Calculate a.

(*b*) Find $\Pr\{1 < X < 2\}$.

SOLUTION

(*a*) The graph of $p(X) = \frac{1}{2} - aX$ is a straight line, as shown in Fig. 6-5. To find a, first we must realize that the total area under the line between $X = 0$ and $X = 4$ and above the X axis must be 1: at $X = 0$, $p(X) = \frac{1}{2}$, and at $X = 4$, $p(X) = \frac{1}{2} - 4a$. Then we must choose a so that the trapezoidal area $= 1$. Trapezoidal area $= \frac{1}{2}(\text{height})(\text{sum of bases}) = \frac{1}{2}(4)(\frac{1}{2} + \frac{1}{2} - 4a) = 2(1 - 4a) = 1$, from which $(1 - 4a) = \frac{1}{2}$, $4a = \frac{1}{2}$, and $a = \frac{1}{8}$. Thus $(\frac{1}{2} - 4a)$ is actually equal to zero, and so the correct graph is as shown in Fig. 6-6.

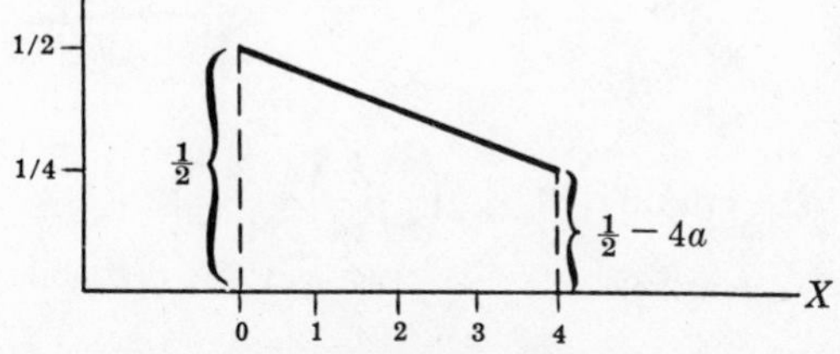

Fig. 6-5

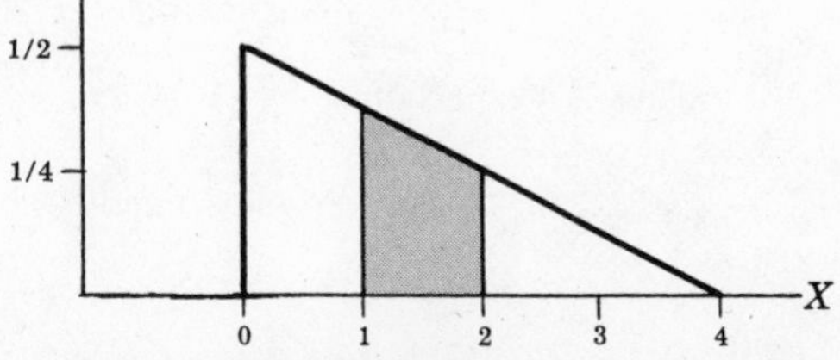

Fig. 6-6

(*b*) The required probability is the area between $X = 1$ and $X = 2$, shown shaded in Fig. 6-6. From part (*a*), $p(X) = \frac{1}{2} - \frac{1}{8}X$; thus $p(1) = \frac{3}{8}$ and $p(2) = \frac{1}{4}$ are the ordinates at $X = 1$ and $X = 2$, respectively. The required trapezoidal area is $\frac{1}{2}(1)(\frac{3}{8} + \frac{1}{4}) = \frac{5}{16}$, which is the required probability.

MATHEMATICAL EXPECTATION

6.13 If a man purchases a raffle ticket, he can win a first prize of \$5000 or a second prize of \$2000 with probabilities 0.001 and 0.003. What should be a fair price to pay for the ticket?

SOLUTION

His expectation is (\$5000)(0.001) + (\$2000)(0.003) = \$5 + \$6 = \$11, which is a fair price to pay.

6.14 In a given business venture a lady can make a profit of \$300 with probability 0.6 or take a loss of \$100 with probability 0.4. Determine her expectation.

SOLUTION

Her expectation is (\$300)(0.6) + (−\$100)(0.4) = \$180 − \$40 = \$140.

6.15 Find (*a*) $E(X)$, (*b*) $E(X^2)$, and (*c*) $E[(X - \bar{X})^2]$ for the probability distribution shown in Table 6.3.

Table 6.3

X	8	12	16	20	24
$p(X)$	1/8	1/6	3/8	1/4	1/12

SOLUTION

(*a*) $E(X) = \sum Xp(X) = (8)(\frac{1}{8}) + (12)(\frac{1}{6}) + (16)(\frac{3}{8}) + (20)(\frac{1}{4}) + (24)(\frac{1}{12}) = 16$; this represents the *mean* of the distribution.

(*b*) $E(X^2) = \sum X^2p(X) = (8)^2(\frac{1}{8}) + (12)^2(\frac{1}{6}) + (16)^2(\frac{3}{8}) + (20)^2(\frac{1}{4}) + (24)^2(\frac{1}{12}) = 276$; this represents the *second moment* about the origin zero.

(*c*) $E[(X - \bar{X})^2] = \sum(X - \bar{X})^2p(X) = (8 - 16)^2(\frac{1}{8}) + (12 - 16)^2(\frac{1}{6}) + (16 - 16)^2(\frac{3}{8}) + (20 - 16)^2(\frac{1}{4}) + (24 - 16)^2(\frac{1}{12}) = 20$; this represents the *variance* of the distribution.

6.16 A bag contains 2 white balls and 3 black balls. Each of four persons, *A*, *B*, *C*, and *D*, in the order named, draws one ball and does not replace it. The first to draw a white ball receives \$10. Determine the expectations of *A*, *B*, *C*, and *D*.

SOLUTION

Since only 3 black balls are present, one person must win on his or her first attempt. Denote by *A*, *B*, *C*, and *D* the events "*A* wins," "*B* wins," "*C* wins," and "*D* wins," respectively.

$$\Pr\{A \text{ wins}\} = \Pr\{A\} = \frac{2}{3+2} = \frac{2}{5}$$

Thus *A*'s expectation $= \frac{2}{5}(\$10) = \$4$.

$$\Pr\{A \text{ loses and } B \text{ wins}\} = \Pr\{\bar{A}B\} = \Pr\{\bar{A}\}\Pr\{B \mid \bar{A}\} = \left(\frac{3}{5}\right)\left(\frac{2}{4}\right) = \frac{3}{10}$$

Thus B's expectation = \$3.

$$\Pr\{A \text{ and } B \text{ lose and } C \text{ wins}\} = \Pr\{\bar{A}\bar{B}C\} = \Pr\{\bar{A}\}\Pr\{\bar{B}\,|\,\bar{A}\}\Pr\{C\bar{A}\bar{B}\} = \left(\frac{3}{5}\right)\left(\frac{2}{4}\right)\left(\frac{2}{3}\right) = \frac{1}{5}$$

Thus C's expectation = \$2.

$$\begin{aligned}\Pr\{A, B, \text{ and } C \text{ lose and } D \text{ wins}\} &= \Pr\{\bar{A}\bar{B}\bar{C}D\}\\ &= \Pr\{\bar{A}\}\Pr\{\bar{B}\,|\,\bar{A}\}\Pr\{\bar{C}\,|\,\bar{A}\bar{B}\}\Pr\{D\,|\,\bar{A}\bar{B}\bar{C}\}\\ &= \left(\frac{3}{5}\right)\left(\frac{2}{4}\right)\left(\frac{1}{3}\right)\left(\frac{1}{1}\right) = \frac{1}{10}\end{aligned}$$

Thus D's expectation = \$1.

Check: \$4 + \$3 + \$2 + \$1 = \$10, and $\frac{2}{5} + \frac{3}{10} + \frac{1}{5} + \frac{1}{10} = 1$.

PERMUTATIONS

6.17 In how many ways can 5 differently colored marbles be arranged in a row?

SOLUTION

We must arrange the 5 marbles in 5 positions: — — — — —. The first position can be occupied by any one of 5 marbles (i.e., there are 5 ways of filling the first position). When this has been done, there are 4 ways of filling the second position. Then there are 3 ways of filling the third position, 2 ways of filling the fourth position, and finally only 1 way of filling the last position. Therefore:

$$\text{Number of arrangements of 5 marbles in a row} = 5 \cdot 4 \cdot 3 \cdot 2 \cdot 1 = 5! = 120$$

In general,

$$\text{Number of arrangements of } n \text{ different objects in a row} = n(n-1)(n-2)\cdots 1 = n!$$

This is also called the number of *permutations* of n different objects taken n at a time and is denoted by ${}_nP_n$.

6.18 In how many ways can 10 people be seated on a bench if only 4 seats are available?

SOLUTION

The first seat can be filled in any one of 10 ways, and when this has been done there are 9 ways of filling the second seat, 8 ways of filling the third seat, and 7 ways of filling the fourth seat. Therefore:

$$\text{Number of arrangements of 10 people taken 4 at a time} = 10 \cdot 9 \cdot 8 \cdot 7 = 5040$$

In general,

$$\text{Number of arrangements of } n \text{ different objects taken } r \text{ at a time} = n(n-1)\cdots(n-r+1)$$

This is also called the number of *permutations* of n different objects taken r at a time and is denoted by ${}_nP_r$, $P(n, r)$ or $P_{n,r}$. Note that when $r = n$, ${}_nP_n = n!$, as in Problem 6.17.

6.19 Evaluate $(a)\ {}_8P_3$, $(b)\ {}_6P_4$, $(c)\ {}_{15}P_1$, and ${}_3P_3$.

SOLUTION

$(a)\ {}_8P_3 = 8 \cdot 7 \cdot 6 = 336$, $(b)\ {}_6P_4 = 6 \cdot 5 \cdot 4 \cdot 3 = 360$, $(c)\ {}_{15}P_1 = 15$, and $(d)\ {}_3P_3 = 3 \cdot 2 \cdot 1 = 6$.

6.20 It is required to seat 5 men and 4 women in a row so that the women occupy the even places. How many such arrangements are possible?

SOLUTION

The men may be seated in ${}_5P_5$ ways and the women in ${}_4P_4$ ways; each arrangement of the men may be associated with each arrangement of the women. Hence the required number of arrangements is ${}_5P_5 \cdot {}_4P_4 = 5!4! = (120)(24) = 2880$.

6.21 How many four-digit numbers can be formed with the 10 digits 0, 1, 2, 3, . . . , 9, if (*a*) repetitions are allowed, (*b*) repetitions are not allowed, and (*c*) the last digit must be zero and repetitions are not allowed?

SOLUTION

(*a*) The first digit can be any one of 9 (since 0 is not allowed). The second, third and fourth digits can be any one of 10. Then $9 \cdot 10 \cdot 10 \cdot 10 = 9000$ numbers can be formed.

(*b*) The first digit can be any one of 9 (any one but 0).
The second digit can be any one of 9 (any but that used for the first digit).
The third digit can be any one of 8 (any but those used for the first two digits).
The fourth digit can be any one of 7 (any but those used for the first three digits).
Thus $9 \cdot 9 \cdot 8 \cdot 7 = 4536$ numbers can be formed.

Another method

The first digit can be any one of 9 and the remaining three can be chosen in ${}_9P_3$ ways. Thus $9 \cdot {}_9P_3 = 9 \cdot 9 \cdot 8 \cdot 7 = 4536$ numbers can be formed.

(*c*) The first digit can be chosen in 9 ways, the second in 8 ways, and the third in 7 ways. Thus $9 \cdot 8 \cdot 7 = 504$ numbers can be formed.

Another method

The first digit can be chosen in 9 ways and the next two digits in ${}_8P_2$ ways. Thus $9 \cdot {}_8P_2 = 9 \cdot 8 \cdot 7 = 504$ numbers can be found.

6.22 Four different mathematics books, 6 different physics books, and 2 different chemistry books are to be arranged on a shelf. How many different arrangements are possible if (*a*) the books in each particular subject must all stand together and (*b*) only the mathematics books must stand together?

SOLUTION

(*a*) The mathematics books can be arranged among themselves in ${}_4P_4 = 4!$ ways, the physics books in ${}_6P_6 = 6!$ ways, the chemistry books in ${}_2P_2 = 2!$ ways, and the three groups in ${}_3P_3 = 3!$ ways. Thus the required number of arrangements $= 4!6!2!3! = 207{,}360$.

(*b*) Consider the 4 mathematics books as one big book. Then we have 9 books that can be arranged in ${}_9P_9 = 9!$ ways. In all of these ways the mathematics books are together. But the mathematics books can be arranged among themselves in ${}_4P_4 = 4!$ ways. Thus the required number of arrangements $= 9!4! = 8{,}709{,}120$.

6.23 Five red marbles, 2 white marbles, and 3 blue marbles are arranged in a row. If all the marbles of the same color are not distinguishable from each other, how many different arrangements are possible?

SOLUTION

Assume that there are P different arrangements. Multiplying P by the numbers of ways of arranging (*a*) the 5 red marbles among themselves, (*b*) the 2 white marbles among themselves, and (*c*) the 3 blue marbles among themselves (i.e., multiplying P by $5!2!3!$), we obtain the number of ways of arranging the

10 marbles if they are distinguishable (i.e., 10!). Thus

$$(5!2!3!)P = 10! \qquad \text{and} \qquad P = \frac{10!}{5!2!3!}$$

In general, the number of different arrangements of n objects of which n_1 are alike, n_2 are alike, ..., n_k are alike is

$$\frac{n!}{n_1!\,n_2!\cdots n_k!}$$

where $n_1 + n_2 + \cdots + n_k = n$.

6.24 In how many ways can 7 people be seated at a round table if (*a*) they can sit anywhere and (*b*) 2 particular people must not sit next to each other?

SOLUTION

(*a*) Let 1 of them be seated anywhere. Then the remaining 6 people can be seated in $6! = 720$ ways, which is the total number of ways of arranging the 7 people in a circle.

(*b*) Consider the 2 particular people as 1 person. Then there are 6 people altogether and they can be arranged in 5! ways. But the 2 people considered as 1 can be arranged among themselves in 2! ways. Thus the number of ways of arranging 6 people at a round table with 2 particular people sitting together $= 5!2! = 240$.

Then using part (*a*), the total number of ways in which 6 people can be seated at a round table so that the 2 particular people do not sit together $= 720 - 240 = 480$ ways.

COMBINATIONS

6.25 In how many ways can 10 objects be split into two groups containing 4 and 6 objects, respectively.

SOLUTION

This is the same as the number of arrangements of 10 objects of which 4 objects are alike and 6 other objects are alike. By Problem 6.23, this is

$$\frac{10!}{4!6!} = \frac{10 \cdot 9 \cdot 8 \cdot 7}{4!} = 210$$

The problem is equivalent to finding the number of selections of 4 out of 10 objects (or 6 out of 10 objects), the order of selection being immaterial.

In general the number of selections of r out of n objects, called the number of *combinations* of n things taken r at a time, is denoted by $\binom{n}{r}$ and is given by

$$\binom{n}{r} = \frac{n!}{r!(n-r)!} = \frac{n(n-1)\cdots(n-r+1)}{r!} = \frac{{}_nP_r}{r!}$$

6.26 Evaluate (*a*) $\binom{7}{4}$, (*b*) $\binom{6}{5}$, and (*c*) $\binom{4}{4}$.

SOLUTION

(*a*) $$\binom{7}{4} = \frac{7!}{4!3!} = \frac{7 \cdot 6 \cdot 5 \cdot 4}{4!} = \frac{7 \cdot 6 \cdot 5}{3 \cdot 2 \cdot 1} = 35$$

(*b*) $$\binom{6}{5} = \frac{6!}{5!1!} = \frac{6 \cdot 5 \cdot 4 \cdot 3 \cdot 2}{5!} = 6 \qquad \text{or} \qquad \binom{6}{5} = \binom{6}{1} = 6$$

(*c*) $\binom{4}{4}$ is the number of selections of 4 objects taken all at a time, and there is only one such selection; thus $\binom{4}{4} = 1$. Note that formally

$$\binom{4}{4} = \frac{4!}{4!0!} = 1$$

if we *define* $0! = 1$.

6.27 In how many ways can a committee of 5 people be chosen out of 9 people?

SOLUTION

$$\binom{9}{5} = \frac{9!}{5!4!} = \frac{9 \cdot 8 \cdot 7 \cdot 6 \cdot 5}{5!} = 126$$

6.28 Out of 5 mathematicians and 7 physicists, a committee consisting of 2 mathematicians and 3 physicists is to be formed. In how many ways can this be done if (*a*) any mathematician and any physicist can be included, (*b*) one particular physicist must be on the committee, and (*c*) two particular mathematicians cannot be on the committee?

SOLUTION

(*a*) Two mathematicians out of 5 can be selected in $\binom{5}{2}$ ways, and 3 physicists out of 7 can be selected in $\binom{7}{3}$ ways. The total number of possible selections is

$$\binom{5}{2} \cdot \binom{7}{3} = 10 \cdot 35 = 350$$

(*b*) Two mathematicians out of 5 can be selected in $\binom{5}{2}$ ways, and 2 additional physicists out of 6 can be selected in $\binom{6}{2}$ ways. The total number of possible selections is

$$\binom{5}{2} \cdot \binom{6}{2} = 10 \cdot 15 = 150$$

(*c*) Two mathematicians out of 3 can be selected in $\binom{3}{2}$ ways, and 3 physicists out of 7 can be selected in $\binom{7}{3}$ ways. The total number possible selections is

$$\binom{3}{2} \cdot \binom{7}{3} = 3 \cdot 35 = 105$$

6.29 A girl has 5 flowers, each of a different variety. How many different bouquets can she form?

SOLUTION

Each flower can be dealt with in 2 ways: It can be chosen or not chosen. Since each of the 2 ways of dealing with a flower is associated with 2 ways of dealing with each of the other flowers, the number of ways of dealing with the 5 flowers $= 2^5$. But these 2^5 ways include the case in which no flower is chosen. Hence the required number of bouquets $= 2^5 - 1 = 31$.

Another method

She can select either 1 out of 5 flowers, 2 out of 5 flowers, ..., 5 out of 5 flowers. Thus the required number of bouquets is

$$\binom{5}{1} + \binom{5}{2} + \binom{5}{3} + \binom{5}{4} + \binom{5}{5} = 5 + 10 + 10 + 5 + 1 = 31$$

In general, for any positive integer *n*,

$$\binom{n}{1} + \binom{n}{2} + \binom{n}{3} + \cdots + \binom{n}{n} = 2^n - 1$$

6.30 From 7 consonants and 5 vowels, how many words can be formed consisting of 4 different consonants and 3 different vowels? The words need not have meaning.

SOLUTION

The 4 different consonants can be selected in $\binom{7}{4}$ ways, the 3 different vowels can be selected in $\binom{5}{3}$ ways, and the resulting 7 different letters (4 consonants and 3 vowels) can then be arranged among themselves in ${}_7P_7 = 7!$ ways. Thus the number of words is

$$\binom{7}{4} \cdot \binom{5}{3} \cdot 7! = 35 \cdot 10 \cdot 5040 = 1{,}764{,}000$$

STIRLING'S APPROXIMATION TO *n*!

6.31 Evaluate 50!.

SOLUTION

For large n, we have $n! \approx \sqrt{2\pi n}\, n^n e^{-n}$; thus

$$50! \approx \sqrt{2\pi(50)}\, 50^{50} e^{-50} = S$$

To evaluate S, use logarithms to the base 10. Thus

$$\begin{aligned}\log S = \log(\sqrt{100\pi}\,50^{50} e^{-50}) &= \tfrac{1}{2}\log 100 + \tfrac{1}{2}\log \pi + 50\log 50 - 50 \log e\\ &= \tfrac{1}{2}\log 100 + \tfrac{1}{2}\log 3.142 + 50\log 50 - 50\log 2.718\\ &= \tfrac{1}{2}(2) + \tfrac{1}{2}(0.4972) + 50(1.6990) - 50(0.4343) = 64.4846\end{aligned}$$

from which $S = 3.05 \times 10^{64}$, a number that has 65 digits.

PROBABILITY AND COMBINATORIAL ANALYSIS

6.32 A box contains 8 red, 3 white, and 9 blue balls. If 3 balls are drawn at random, determine the probability that (*a*) all 3 are red, (*b*) all 3 are white, (*c*) 2 are red and 1 is white, (*d*) at least 1 is white, (*e*) 1 of each color is drawn, and (*f*) the balls are drawn in the order red, white, blue.

SOLUTION

(*a*) **First method**

Let R_1, R_2, and R_3 denote the events "red ball on first draw," "red ball on second draw," and "red ball on third draw," respectively. Then $R_1R_2R_3$ denotes the event that all 3 balls drawn are red.

$$\Pr\{R_1R_2R_3\} = \Pr\{R_1\}\Pr\{R_2|R_1\}\Pr\{R_3|R_1R_2\} = \left(\frac{8}{20}\right)\left(\frac{7}{19}\right)\left(\frac{6}{18}\right) = \frac{14}{285}$$

Second method

$$\text{Required probability} = \frac{\text{number of selections of 3 out of 8 red balls}}{\text{number of selections of 3 out of 20 balls}} = \frac{\binom{8}{3}}{\binom{20}{3}} = \frac{14}{285}$$

(*b*) Using the second method of part (*a*),

$$\Pr\{\text{all 3 are white}\} = \frac{\binom{3}{3}}{\binom{20}{3}} = \frac{1}{1140}$$

The first method of part (*a*) can also be used.

(*c*)
$$\Pr\{2 \text{ are red and } 1 \text{ is white}\} = \frac{\binom{\text{selections of 2 out}}{\text{of 8 red balls}}\binom{\text{selections of 1 out}}{\text{of 3 white balls}}}{\text{number of selections of 3 out of 20 balls}} = \frac{\binom{8}{2}\binom{3}{1}}{\binom{20}{3}} = \frac{7}{95}$$

(*d*)
$$\Pr\{\text{none is white}\} = \frac{\binom{17}{3}}{\binom{20}{3}} = \frac{34}{57} \quad \text{so} \quad \Pr\{\text{at least 1 is white}\} = 1 - \frac{34}{57} = \frac{23}{57}$$

(*e*)
$$\Pr\{1 \text{ of each color is drawn}\} = \frac{\binom{8}{1}\binom{3}{1}\binom{9}{1}}{\binom{20}{3}} = \frac{18}{95}$$

(*f*) Using part (*e*),

$$\Pr\{\text{balls drawn in order red, white, blue}\} = \frac{1}{3!}\Pr\{1 \text{ of each color is drawn}\} = \frac{1}{6}\left(\frac{18}{95}\right) = \frac{3}{95}$$

Another method

$$\Pr\{R_1 W_2 B_2\} = \Pr\{R_1\}\Pr\{W_2 | R_1\}\Pr\{B_3 | R_1 W_2\} = \left(\frac{8}{20}\right)\left(\frac{3}{19}\right)\left(\frac{9}{18}\right) = \frac{3}{95}$$

6.33 Five cards are drawn from a pack of 52 well-shuffled cards. Find the probability that (*a*) 4 are aces; (*b*) 4 are aces and 1 is a king; (*c*) 3 are 10's and 2 are jacks; (*d*) a 9, 10, jack, queen, and king are obtained in any order; (*e*) 3 are of any one suit and 2 are of another; and (*f*) at least 1 ace is obtained.

SOLUTION

(*a*)
$$\Pr\{4 \text{ aces}\} = \binom{4}{4} \cdot \frac{\binom{48}{1}}{\binom{52}{5}} = \frac{1}{54{,}145}$$

(*b*)
$$\Pr\{4 \text{ aces and } 1 \text{ king}\} = \binom{4}{4} \cdot \frac{\binom{4}{1}}{\binom{52}{5}} = \frac{1}{649{,}740}$$

(*c*)
$$\Pr\{3 \text{ are 10's and 2 are jacks}\} = \binom{4}{3} \cdot \frac{\binom{4}{2}}{\binom{52}{5}} = \frac{1}{108{,}290}$$

(*d*)
$$\Pr\{9, 10, \text{jack, queen, king in any order}\} = \frac{\binom{4}{1}\cdot\binom{4}{1}\cdot\binom{4}{1}\cdot\binom{4}{1}\cdot\binom{4}{1}}{\binom{52}{5}} = \frac{64}{162{,}435}$$

(*e*) Since there are 4 ways of choosing the first suit and 3 ways of choosing the second suit,

$$\Pr\{3 \text{ of any one suit, 2 of another}\} = \frac{4\binom{13}{3}\cdot 3\binom{13}{2}}{\binom{52}{5}} = \frac{429}{4165}$$

(*f*) $$\Pr\{\text{no ace}\} = \frac{\binom{48}{5}}{\binom{52}{5}} = \frac{35{,}673}{54{,}145} \quad \text{and} \quad \Pr\{\text{at least 1 ace}\} = 1 - \frac{35{,}673}{54{,}145} = \frac{18{,}482}{54{,}145}$$

6.34 Determine the probability of 3 sixes in 5 tosses of a fair die.

SOLUTION

Let the tosses of the die be represented by the 5 spaces - - - - -. In each space we will have either the events 6 or non-6 ($\bar{6}$); for example, three 6's and two non-6's can occur as $6\,6\,\bar{6}\,6\,\bar{6}$ or as $6\,\bar{6}\,6\,\bar{6}\,6$, etc.

Now the probability of an event such as $6\,6\,\bar{6}\,6\,\bar{6}$ is

$$\Pr\{6\,6\,\bar{6}\,6\,\bar{6}\} = \Pr\{6\}\Pr\{6\}\Pr\{\bar{6}\}\Pr\{6\}\Pr\{\bar{6}\} = \frac{1}{6}\cdot\frac{1}{6}\cdot\frac{5}{6}\cdot\frac{1}{6}\cdot\frac{5}{6} = \left(\frac{1}{6}\right)^3\left(\frac{5}{6}\right)^2$$

Similarly, $\Pr\{6\,\bar{6}\,6\,\bar{6}\,6\} = (\frac{1}{6})^3(\frac{5}{6})^2$, etc., for all events in which three 6's and two non-6's occur. But there are $\binom{5}{3} = 10$ such events, and these events are mutually exclusive; hence the required probability is

$$\Pr\{6\,6\,\bar{6}\,6\,\bar{6} \text{ or } 6\,\bar{6}\,6\,\bar{6}\,6 \text{ or etc.}\} = \binom{5}{3}\left(\frac{1}{6}\right)^3\left(\frac{5}{6}\right)^2 = \frac{125}{3888}$$

In general, if $p = \Pr\{E\}$ and $q = \Pr\{\bar{E}\}$, then by using the same reasoning as given above, the probability of getting exactly X E's in N trials is $\binom{N}{X}p^Xq^{N-X}$.

6.35 A factory finds that, on average, 20% of the bolts produced by a given machine will be defective for certain specified requirements. If 10 bolts are selected at random from the day's production of this machine, find the probability (*a*) that exactly 2 will be defective, (*b*) that 2 or more will be defective, and (*c*) that more than 5 will be defective.

SOLUTION

(*a*) Using reasoning similar to that of Problem 6.34,

$$\Pr\{2 \text{ defective bolts}\} = \binom{10}{2}(0.2)^2(0.8)^8 = 45(0.04)(0.1678) = 0.3020$$

(*b*)
$$\begin{aligned}\Pr\{2 \text{ or more defective bolts}\} &= 1 - \Pr\{0 \text{ defective bolts}\} - \Pr\{1 \text{ defective bolt}\}\\ &= 1 - \binom{10}{0}(0.2)^0(0.8)^{10} - \binom{10}{1}(0.2)^1(0.8)^9\\ &= 1 - (0.8)^{10} - 10(0.2)(0.8)^9\\ &= 1 - 0.1074 - 0.2684 = 0.6242\end{aligned}$$

(*c*)
$$\begin{aligned}\Pr\{\text{more than 5 defective bolts}\} &= \Pr\{6 \text{ defective bolts}\} + \Pr\{7 \text{ defective bolts}\}\\ &\quad + \Pr\{8 \text{ defective bolts}\} + \Pr\{9 \text{ defective bolts}\}\\ &\quad + \Pr\{10 \text{ defective bolts}\}\\ &= \binom{10}{6}(0.2)^6(0.8)^4 + \binom{10}{7}(0.2)^7(0.8)^3 + \binom{10}{8}(0.2)^8(0.8)^2\\ &\quad + \binom{10}{9}(0.2)^9(0.8) + \binom{10}{10}(0.2)^{10}\\ &= 0.00637\end{aligned}$$

6.36 If 1000 samples of 10 bolts each were taken in Problem 6.35, in how many of these samples would we expect to find (*a*) exactly 2 defective bolts, (*b*) 2 or more defective bolts, (*c*) more than 5 defective bolts?

SOLUTION

(a) Expected number = (1000)(0.3020) = 302, by Problem 6.35(a).

(b) Expected number = (1000)(0.6242) = 624, by Problem 6.35(b).

(c) Expected number = (1000)(0.00637) = 6, by Problem 6.35(c).

SAMPLE SPACES AND EULER DIAGRAMS

6.37 (a) Set up a sample space for the single toss of a pair of fair dice.

(b) From the sample space determine the probability that the sum in tossing a pair of dice is either 7 or 11.

SOLUTION

(a) The sample space consists of the set of points shown in Fig. 6-7. The first coordinate of each point is the number on one die, and the second coordinate is the number on the other die. There are 36 points in all, and to each point we assign a probability of $\frac{1}{36}$. The sum of the probabilities for all points in the space is 1.

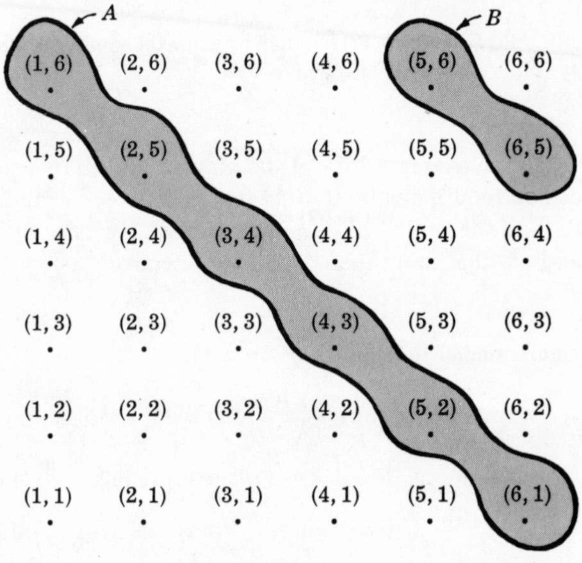

Fig. 6-7

(b) The sets of points corresponding to the events "sum 7" and "sum 11" are indicated by A and B, respectively.

$\Pr\{A\}$ = sum of probabilities associated with each point in $A = \frac{6}{36}$

$\Pr\{B\}$ = sum of probabilities associated with each point in $B = \frac{2}{36}$

$\Pr\{A+B\}$ = sum of probabilities of points in A or B or both $= (6+2)/36 = \frac{8}{36} = \frac{2}{9}$

Note that in this case $\Pr\{A+B\} = \Pr\{A\} + \Pr\{B\}$. This is because A and B have no points in common (i.e., they are mutually exclusive events).

6.38 Using a sample space, show that:

(a) $\Pr\{A+B\} = \Pr\{A\} + \Pr\{B\} - \Pr\{AB\}$

(b) $\Pr\{A+B+C\} = \Pr\{A\} + \Pr\{B\} + \Pr\{C\} - \Pr\{AB\} - \Pr\{BC\} - \Pr\{AC\} + \Pr\{ABC\}$

SOLUTION

(*a*) Let A and B be two sets of points having points in common represented by AB, as in Fig. 6-8; A is composed of $A\bar{B}$ and AB, while B is composed of $B\bar{A}$ and AB. The totality of points in $A+B$ (either A or B or both) = totality of points in A + totality of points in B − totality of points in AB. Since the probability of an event or set is the sum of the probabilities associated with the points of the set, we have

$$\Pr\{A+B\} = \Pr\{A\} + \Pr\{B\} - \Pr\{AB\}$$

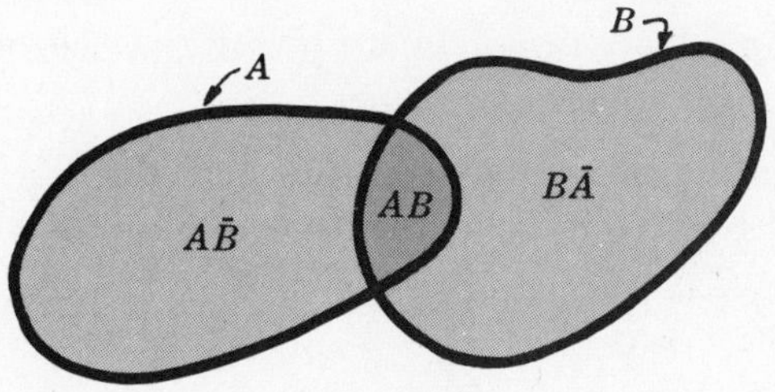

Fig. 6-8

Another method

Let $A - AB$ denote the set of points in A but not in B (this is the same as $A\bar{B}$); then $A - AB$ and B are mutually exclusive (i.e., have no points in common). Also, $\Pr\{A - AB\} = \Pr\{A\} - \Pr\{AB\}$. Thus

$$\Pr\{A+B\} = \Pr\{A-AB\} + \Pr\{B\} = \Pr\{A\} - \Pr\{AB\} + \Pr\{B\} = \Pr\{A\} + \Pr\{B\} - \Pr\{AB\}$$

(*b*) Let A, B, and C be three sets of points, as shown in Fig. 6-9. The symbol $AB\bar{C}$ means the set of points in A and B but not in C, and the other symbols have similar meanings.

We can consider points that are either in A or B or C as points included in the seven mutually exclusive sets of Fig. 6-9, four of which have been shown shaded and three unshaded. The required probability is given by

$$\Pr\{A+B+C\} = \Pr\{A\bar{B}\bar{C}\} + \Pr\{B\bar{C}\bar{A}\} + \Pr\{C\bar{A}\bar{B}\} + \Pr\{AB\bar{C}\} + \Pr\{BC\bar{A}\} + \Pr\{CA\bar{B}\} + \Pr\{ABC\}$$

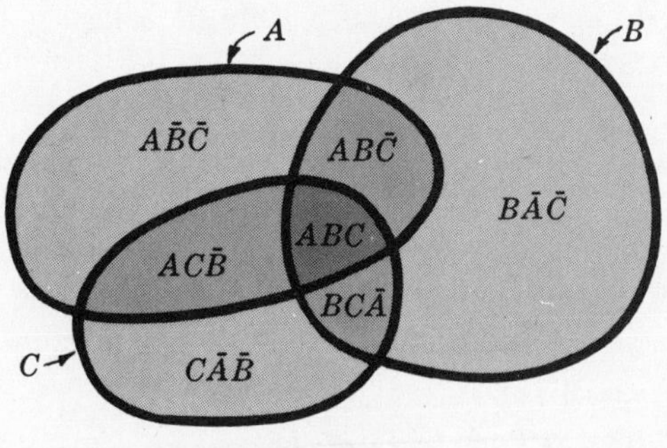

Fig. 6-9

Now to obtain $A\bar{B}\bar{C}$, for example, we remove points common to A and B and to A and C, but in so doing we have removed points common to A, B, and C twice. Hence $A\bar{B}\bar{C} = A - AB - AC + ABC$ and

$$\Pr\{A\bar{B}\bar{C}\} = \Pr\{A\} - \Pr\{AB\} - \Pr\{AC\} + \Pr\{ABC\}$$

Similarly, we find

$$\Pr\{B\bar{C}\bar{A}\} = \Pr\{B\} - \Pr\{BC\} - \Pr\{BA\} + \Pr\{BCA\}$$
$$\Pr\{C\bar{A}\bar{B}\} = \Pr\{C\} - \Pr\{CA\} - \Pr\{CB\} + \Pr\{CAB\}$$
$$\Pr\{BC\bar{A}\} = \Pr\{BC\} - \Pr\{ABC\}$$
$$\Pr\{CA\bar{B}\} = \Pr\{CA\} - \Pr\{BCA\}$$
$$\Pr\{AB\bar{C}\} = \Pr\{AB\} - \Pr\{CAB\}$$
$$\Pr\{ABC\} = \Pr\{ABC\}$$

Adding these seven equations and considering that $\Pr\{AB\} = \Pr\{BA\}$, etc., we obtain

$$\Pr\{A+B+C\} = \Pr\{A\} + \Pr\{B\} + \Pr\{C\} - \Pr\{AB\} - \Pr\{BC\} - \Pr\{AC\} + \Pr\{ABC\}$$

6.39 A survey of 500 students taking one or more courses in algebra, physics, and statistics during one semester revealed the following numbers of students in the indicated subjects:

Algebra	329	Algebra and physics	83
Physics	186	Algebra and statistics	217
Statistics	295	Physics and statistics	63

How many students were taking (a) all three subjects, (b) algebra but not statistics, (c) physics but not algebra, (d) statistics but not physics, (e) algebra or statistics but not physics, and (f) algebra but not physics or statistics?

SOLUTION

Let A denote the set of all students taking algebra, and denote by (A) the number of students belonging to this set. Similarly, let (B) denote the number taking physics and (C) the number taking statistics. Then $(A+B+C)$ denotes the number taking *either* algebra, physics, or statistics or combinations, (AB) the number taking both algebra and physics, etc. As in Problem 6.38, it follows that

$$(A+B+C) = (A) + (B) + (C) - (AB) - (BC) - (AC) + (ABC)$$

(a) Substituting the given numbers in this expression, we find

$$500 = 329 + 186 + 295 - 83 - 63 - 217 + (ABC)$$

or $(ABC) = 53$, which is the number of students taking algebra, physics, *and* statistics. Note that the (empirical) probability of a student taking all three subjects is $\frac{53}{500}$.

(b) To obtain the required information, it is convenient to construct an Euler diagram showing the number of students belonging to each set. Starting with the fact that 53 students are taking all three subjects, we deduce that the number taking both algebra and statistics but not physics is $217 - 53 = 164$, which is shown in Fig. 6-10. From the given information the other numbers shown are obtained.

From the given data, the number taking algebra but not statistics $= 329 - 217$; or from Fig. 6-10, $82 + 30 = 112$.

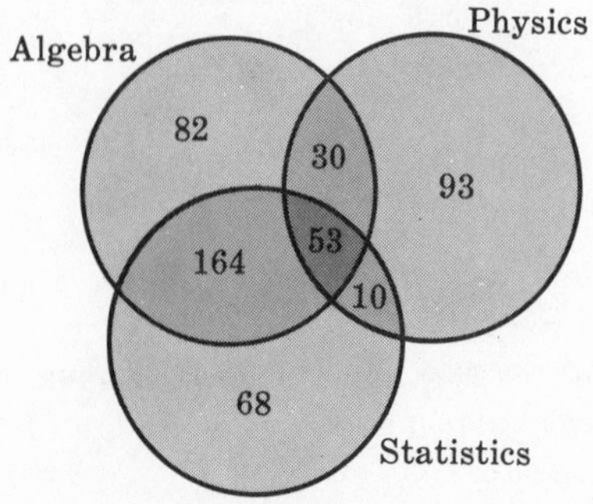

Fig. 6-10

(*c*) Number taking physics but not algebra $= 93 + 10 = 103$

(*d*) Number taking statistics but not physics $= 68 + 164 = 232$

(*e*) Number taking algebra or statistics but not physics $= 82 + 164 + 68 = 314$

(*f*) Number taking algebra but not physics or statistics $= 82$

Supplementary Problems

FUNDAMENTAL RULES OF PROBABILITY

6.40 Determine the probability p, or an estimate of it, for each of the following events:

(*a*) A king, ace, jack of clubs, or queen of diamonds appears in drawing a single card from a well-shuffled ordinary deck of cards.

(*b*) The sum 8 appears in a single toss of a pair of fair dice.

(*c*) A nondefective bolt will be found if out of 600 bolts already examined, 12 were defective.

(*d*) A 7 or 11 comes up in a single toss of a pair of fair dice.

(*e*) At least one head appears in three tosses of a fair coin.

6.41 An experiment consists of drawing three cards in succession from a well-shuffled ordinary deck of cards. Let E_1 be the event "king" on the first draw, E_2 the event "king" on the second draw, and E_3 the event "king" on the third draw. State in words the meaning of each of the following:

(*a*) $\Pr\{E_1\bar{E}_2\}$ (*c*) $\bar{E}_1 + \bar{E}_2$ (*e*) $\bar{E}_1\bar{E}_2\bar{E}_3$

(*b*) $\Pr\{E_1 + E_2\}$ (*d*) $\Pr\{E_3 | E_1\bar{E}_2\}$ (*f*) $\Pr\{E_1E_2 + \bar{E}_2E_3\}$

6.42 A ball is drawn at random from a box containing 10 red, 30 white, 20 blue, and 15 orange marbles. Find the probability that the ball drawn is (*a*) orange or red, (*b*) not red or blue, (*c*) not blue, (*d*) white, and (*e*) red, white, or blue.

6.43 Two marbles are drawn in succession from the box of Problem 6.42, replacement being made after each drawing. Find the probability that (*a*) both are white, (*b*) the first is red and the second is white, (*c*) neither is orange, (*d*) they are either red or white or both (red and white), (*e*) the second is not blue, (*f*) the first is orange, (*g*) at least one is blue, (*h*) at most one is red, (*i*) the first is white but the second is not, and (*j*) only one is red.

6.44 Work Problem 6.43 if there is no replacement after each drawing.

6.45 Find the probability of scoring a total of 7 points (*a*) once, (*b*) at least once, and (*c*) twice in two tosses of a pair of fair dice.

6.46 Two cards are drawn successively from an ordinary deck of 52 well-shuffled cards. Find the probability that (*a*) the first card is not a 10 of clubs or an ace, (*b*) the first card is an ace but the second is not, (*c*) at least one card is a diamond, (*d*) the cards are not of the same suit, (*e*) not more than one card is a picture card (jack, queen, king), (*f*) the second card is not a picture card, (*g*) the second card is not a picture card given that the first was a picture card, and (*h*) the cards are picture cards or spades or both.

6.47 A box contains 9 tickets numbered from 1 to 9 inclusive. If 3 tickets are drawn from the box one at a time, find the probability that they are alternately either (1) odd, even, odd or (2) even, odd, even.

6.48 The odds in favor of A winning a game of chess against B are 3:2. If three games are to be played, what are the odds (a) in favor of A's winning at least two games out of the three and (b) against A losing the first two games to B?

6.49 A purse contains 2 silver coins and 4 copper coins, and a second purse contains 4 silver coins and 3 copper coins. If a coin is selected at random from one of the two purses, what is the probability that it is a silver coin?

6.50 The probability that a man will be alive in 25 years is $\frac{3}{5}$, and the probability that his wife will be alive in 25 years is $\frac{2}{3}$. Find the probability that (a) both will be alive, (b) only the man will be alive, (c) only the wife will be alive, and (d) at least one will be alive.

6.51 Out of 800 families with 4 children each, what percentage would be expected to have (a) 2 boys and 2 girls, (b) at least 1 boy, (c) no girls, and (d) at most 2 girls? Assume equal probabilities for boys and girls.

PROBABILITY DISTRIBUTIONS

6.52 If X is the random variable showing the number of boys in families with 4 children (see Problem 6.51), (a) construct a table showing the probability distribution of X and (b) represent the distribution in part (a) graphically.

6.53 A continuous random variable X that can assume values only between $X=2$ and 8 inclusive has a density function given by $a(X+3)$, where a is a constant. (a) Calculate a. Find (b) $\Pr\{3<X<5\}$, (c) $\Pr\{X \geq 4\}$, and (d) $\Pr\{|X-5|<0.5\}$.

6.54 Three marbles are drawn without replacement from an urn containing 4 red and 6 white marbles. If X is a random variable that denotes the total number of red marbles drawn, (a) construct a table showing the probability distribution of X and (b) graph the distribution.

6.55 For Problem 6.54, find (a) $\Pr\{X=2\}$ and (b) $(\Pr\{1 \leq X \leq 3\}$, and interpret the results.

MATHEMATICAL EXPECTATION

6.56 What is a fair price to pay to enter a game in which one can win \$25 with probability 0.2 and \$10 with probability 0.4?

6.57 If it rains, an umbrella salesman can earn \$30 per day. If it is fair, he can lose \$6 per day. What is his expectation if the probability of rain is 0.3?

6.58 A and B play a game in which they toss a fair coin three times. The one obtaining heads first wins the game. If A tosses the coin first and if the total value of the stakes is \$20, how much should be contributed by each in order that the game be considered fair?

6.59 Find (a) $E(X)$, (b) $E(X^2)$, (c) $E[(X-\bar{X})^2]$, and (d) $E(X^3)$ for the probability distribution of Table 6.4.

Table 6.4

X	-10	-20	30
$p(X)$	1/5	3/10	1/2

6.60 Referring to Problem 6.54, find the (a) mean, (b) variance, and (c) standard deviation of the distribution of X, and interpret your results.

6.61 A random variable assumes the value 1 with probability p, and 0 with probability $q=1-p$. Prove that (a) $E(X)=p$ and (b) $E[(X-\bar{X})^2]=pq$.

6.62 Prove that (*a*) $E(2X+3)=2E(X)+3$ and (*b*) $E[(X-\bar{X})^2]=E(X^2)-[E(X)]^2$.

6.63 Let X and Y be two random variables having the same distribution. Show that $E(X+Y)=E(X)+E(Y)$.

PERMUTATIONS

6.64 Evaluate (*a*) ${}_4P_2$, (*b*) ${}_7P_5$, and (*c*) ${}_{10}P_3$.

6.65 For what value of n is ${}_{n+1}P_3={}_nP_4$?

6.66 In how many ways can 5 people be seated on a sofa if there are only 3 seats available?

6.67 In how many ways can 7 books be arranged on a shelf if (*a*) any arrangement is possible, (*b*) 3 particular books must always stand together, and (*c*) 2 particular books must occupy the ends?

6.68 How many numbers consisting of five different digits each can be made from the digits 1, 2, 3, . . . , 9 if (*a*) the numbers must be odd and (*b*) the first two digits of each number are even?

6.69 Solve Problem 6.68 if repetitions of the digits are allowed.

6.70 How many different three-digit numbers can be made with three 4's, four 2's, and two 3's?

6.71 In how many ways can 3 men and 3 women be seated at a round table if (*a*) no restriction is imposed, (*b*) 2 particular women must not sit together, and (*c*) each woman is to be between 2 men?

COMBINATIONS

6.72 Evaluate (*a*) $\binom{7}{3}$, (*b*) $\binom{8}{4}$, and (*c*) $\binom{10}{8}$.

6.73 For what value of n does $3\binom{n+1}{3}=7\binom{n}{2}$?

6.74 In how many ways can 6 questions be selected out of 10?

6.75 How many different committees of 3 men and 4 women can be formed from 8 men and 6 women?

6.76 In how many ways can 2 men, 4 women, 3 boys, and 3 girls be selected from 6 men, 8 women, 4 boys, and 5 girls if (*a*) no restrictions are imposed and (*b*) a particular man and woman must be selected?

6.77 In how many ways can a group of 10 people be divided into (*a*) two groups consisting of 7 and 3 people and (*b*) three groups consisting of 4, 3, and 2 people?

6.78 From 5 statisticians and 6 economists a committee consisting of 3 statisticians and 2 economists is to be formed. How many different committees can be formed if (*a*) no restrictions are imposed, (*b*) 2 particular statisticians must be on the committee, and (*c*) 1 particular economist cannot be on the committee?

6.79 Find the number of (*a*) combinations and (*b*) permutations of four letters each that can be made from the letters of the word *Tennessee*?

6.80 Prove that $1-\binom{n}{1}+\binom{n}{2}-\binom{n}{3}+\cdots+(-1)^n\binom{n}{n}=0$.

STIRLING'S APPROXIMATION TO $n!$

6.81 In how many ways can 30 individuals be selected out of 100?

6.82 Show that $\binom{2n}{n} = 2^{2n}/\sqrt{\pi n}$ approximately, for large values of n.

MISCELLANEOUS PROBLEMS

6.83 Three cards are drawn from a deck of 52 cards. Find the probability that (*a*) two are jacks and one is a king, (*b*) all cards are of one suit, (*c*) all cards are of different suits, and (*d*) at least two aces are drawn.

6.84 Find the probability of at least two 7's in four tosses of a pair of dice.

6.85 If 10% of the rivets produced by a machine are defective, what is the probability that out of 5 rivets chosen at random (*a*) none will be defective, (*b*) 1 will be defective, and (*c*) at least 2 will be defective?

6.86 (*a*) Set up a sample space for the outcomes of 2 tosses of a fair coin, using 1 to represent "heads" and 0 to represent "tails."

(*b*) From this sample space determine the probability of at least one head.

(*c*) Can you set up a sample space for the outcomes of 3 tosses of a coin? If so, determine with the aid of it the probability of at most two heads?

6.87 A sample poll of 200 voters revealed the following information concerning three candidates (A, B, and C) of a certain party who were running for three different offices:

28 in favor of both A and B	122 in favor of B or C but not A
98 in favor of A or B but not C	64 in favor of C but not A or B
42 in favor of B but not A or C	14 in favor of A and C but not B

How many of the voters were in favor of (*a*) all three candidates, (*b*) A irrespective of B or C, (*c*) B irrespective of A or C, (*d*) C irrespective of A or B, (*e*) A and B but not C, and (*f*) only one of the candidates?

6.88 (*a*) Prove that for any events E_1 and E_2, $\Pr\{E_1+E_2\} \le \Pr\{E_1\}+\Pr\{E_2\}$.

(*b*) Generalize the result in part (*a*).

6.89 Let E_1, E_2, and E_3 be three different events, at least one of which is known to have occurred. Suppose that any of these events can result in another event A, which is also known to have occurred. If all the probabilities $\Pr\{E_1\}$, $\Pr\{E_2\}$, $\Pr\{E_3\}$ and $\Pr\{A|E_1\}$, $\Pr\{A|E_2\}$, $\Pr\{A|E_3\}$ are assumed known, prove that

$$\Pr\{E_1|A\} = \frac{\Pr\{E_1\}\Pr\{A|E_1\}}{\Pr\{E_1\}\Pr\{A|E_1\}+\Pr\{E_2\}\Pr\{A|E_2\}+\Pr\{E_3\}\Pr\{A|E_3\}}$$

with similar results for $\Pr\{E_2|A\}$ and $\Pr\{E_3|A\}$. This is known as *Bayes' rule* or *theorem.* It is useful in computing probabilities of various *hypotheses* E_1, E_2, or E_3 that have resulted in the event A. The result can be generalized.

6.90 Each of three identical jewelry boxes has two drawers. In each drawer of the first box there is a gold watch. In each drawer of the second box there is a silver watch. In one drawer of the third box there is a gold watch, while in the other drawer there is a silver watch. If we select a box at random, open one of the drawers, and find it to contain a silver watch, what is the probability that the other drawer has the gold watch? [*Hint:* Apply Problem 6.89.]

6.91 Find the probability of winning a state lottery in which one is required to choose six of the numbers 1, 2, 3, . . . , 40 in any order.

6.92 Work Problem 6.91 if one is required to choose (*a*) five, (*b*) four, and (*c*) three of the numbers.

6.93 In the game of poker, five cards from a standard deck of 52 cards are dealt to each player. Determine the odds against the player receiving:

(*a*) A royal flush (the ace, king, queen, jack, and 10 of the same suit)

(*b*) A straight flush (any five cards in sequence and of the same suit, such as the 3, 4, 5, 6, and 7 of spades)

(*c*) Four of a kind (such as four 7's)

(*d*) A full house (3 of one kind and 2 of another, such as three kings and two 10's)

6.94 *A* and *B* decide to meet between 3 and 4 P.M. but agree that each should wait no longer than 10 minutes for the other. Determine the probability that they meet.

6.95 Two points are chosen at random on a line segment whose length is $a > 0$. Find the probability that the three line segments thus formed can be the sides of a triangle.

Chapter 7

The Binomial, Normal, and Poisson Distributions

THE BINOMIAL DISTRIBUTION

If p is the probability that an event will happen in any single trial (called the probability of a *success*) and $q = 1 - p$ is the probability that it will fail to happen in any single trial (called the probability of a *failure*), then the probability that the event will happen exactly X times in N trials (i.e., X successes and $N - X$ failures will occur) is given by

$$p(X) = \binom{N}{X} p^X q^{N-X} = \frac{N!}{X!(N-X)!} p^X q^{N-X} \tag{1}$$

where $X = 0, 1, 2, \ldots, N$; $N! = N(N-1)(N-2) \cdots 1$; and $0! = 1$ by definition (see Problem 6.34).

EXAMPLE 1. The probability of getting exactly 2 heads in 6 tosses of a fair coin is

$$\binom{6}{2}\left(\frac{1}{2}\right)^2\left(\frac{1}{2}\right)^{6-2} = \frac{6}{2!4!}\left(\frac{1}{2}\right)^6 = \frac{15}{64}$$

using formula (*1*) with $N = 6$, $X = 2$, and $p = q = \frac{1}{2}$.

EXAMPLE 2. The probability of getting at least 4 heads in 6 tosses of a fair coin is

$$\binom{6}{4}\left(\frac{1}{2}\right)^4\left(\frac{1}{2}\right)^{6-4} + \binom{6}{5}\left(\frac{1}{2}\right)^5\left(\frac{1}{2}\right)^{6-5} + \binom{6}{6}\left(\frac{1}{2}\right)^6\left(\frac{1}{2}\right)^{6-6} = \frac{15}{64} + \frac{6}{64} + \frac{1}{64} = \frac{11}{32}$$

The discrete probability distribution (1) is often called the *binomial distribution* since for $X = 0, 1, 2, \ldots, N$ it corresponds to successive terms of the *binomial formula*, or *binomial expansion*,

$$(q+p)^N = q^N + \binom{N}{1} q^{N-1}p + \binom{N}{2} q^{N-2}p^2 + \cdots + p^N \tag{2}$$

where $1, \binom{N}{1}, \binom{N}{2}, \ldots$ are called the *binomial coefficients*.

EXAMPLE 3.

$$\begin{aligned}(q+p)^4 &= q^4 + \binom{4}{1} q^3p + \binom{4}{2} q^2p^2 + \binom{4}{3} qp^3 + p^4 \\ &= q^4 + 4q^3p + 6q^2p^2 + 4qp^3 + p^4\end{aligned}$$

Distribution (*1*) is also called the *Bernoulli distribution* after James Bernoulli, who discovered it at the end of the seventeenth century. Some properties of the binomial distribution are listed in Table 7.1.

EXAMPLE 4. In 100 tosses of a fair coin the mean number of heads is $\mu = Np = (100)(\frac{1}{2}) = 50$; this is the *expected* number of heads in 100 tosses of the coin. The standard deviation is $\sigma = \sqrt{Npq} = \sqrt{(100)(\frac{1}{2})(\frac{1}{2})} = 5$.

THE NORMAL DISTRIBUTION

One of the most important examples of a continuous probability distribution is the *normal distribution*, *normal curve*, or *gaussian distribution*. It is defined by the equation

$$Y = \frac{1}{\sigma\sqrt{2\pi}} e^{-\frac{1}{2}(X-\mu)^2/\sigma^2} \tag{3}$$

Table 7.1 Binomial Distribution

Mean	$\mu = Np$
Variance	$\sigma^2 = Npq$
Standard deviation	$\sigma = \sqrt{Npq}$
Moment coefficient of skewness	$\alpha_3 = \dfrac{q-p}{\sqrt{Npq}}$
Moment coefficient of kurtosis	$\alpha_4 = 3 + \dfrac{1-6pq}{Npq}$

where μ = mean, σ = standard deviation, $\pi = 3.14159\cdots$, and $e = 2.71828\cdots$. The total area bounded by curve (*3*) and the X axis is 1; hence the area under the curve between two ordinates $X = a$ and $X = b$, where $a < b$, represents the probability that X lies between a and b. This probability is denoted by $\Pr\{a < X < b\}$.

When the variable X is expressed in terms of standard units $[z = (X - \mu)/\sigma]$, equation (*3*) is replaced by the so-called *standard form*

$$Y = \frac{1}{\sqrt{2\pi}} e^{-\frac{1}{2}z^2} \tag{4}$$

In such case we say that z is *normally distributed with mean 0 and variance 1.* Figure 7-1 is a graph of this standardized normal curve. It shows that the areas included between $z = -1$ and $+1$, $z = -2$ and $+2$, and $z = -3$ and $+3$ are equal, respectively, to 68.27%, 95.45%, and 99.73% of the total area, which is 1. The table in Appendix II shows the areas under this curve bounded by the ordinates at $z = 0$ and any positive value of z. From this table the area between any two ordinates can be found by using the symmetry of the curve about $z = 0$.

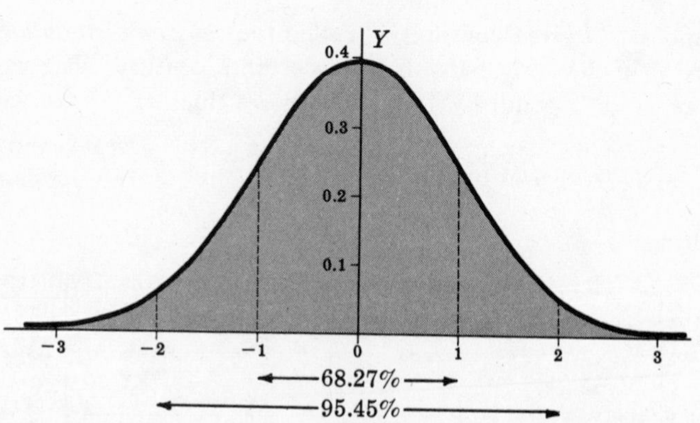

Fig. 7-1

Some properties of the normal distribution given by equation (*3*) are listed in Table 7.2.

Table 7.2 Normal Distribution

Mean	μ
Variance	σ^2
Standard deviation	σ
Moment coefficient of skewness	$\alpha_3 = 0$
Moment coefficient of kurtosis	$\alpha_4 = 3$
Mean deviation	$\sigma\sqrt{2/\pi} = 0.7979\sigma$

RELATION BETWEEN THE BINOMIAL AND NORMAL DISTRIBUTIONS

If N is large and if neither p nor q is too close to zero, the binomial distribution can be closely approximated by a normal distribution with standardized variable given by

$$z = \frac{X - Np}{\sqrt{Npq}}$$

The approximation becomes better with increasing N, and in the limiting case it is exact; this is shown in Tables 7.1 and 7.2, where it is clear that as N increases, the skewness and kurtosis for the binomial distribution approach that of the normal distribution. In practice the approximation is very good if both Np and Nq are greater than 5.

THE POISSON DISTRIBUTION

The discrete probability distribution

$$p(X) = \frac{\lambda^X e^{-\lambda}}{X!} \qquad X = 0, 1, 2, \ldots \tag{5}$$

where $e = 2.71828 \cdots$ and λ is a given constant, is called the *Poisson distribution* after Siméon-Denis Poisson, who discovered it in the early part of the nineteenth century. The values of $p(X)$ can be computed by using the table in Appendix VIII (which gives values of $e^{-\lambda}$ for various values of λ) or by using logarithms.

Some properties of the Poisson distribution are listed in Table 7.3.

Table 7.3 Poisson's Distribution

Mean	$\mu = \lambda$
Variance	$\sigma^2 = \lambda$
Standard deviation	$\sigma = \sqrt{\lambda}$
Moment coefficient of skewness	$\alpha_3 = 1/\sqrt{\lambda}$
Moment coefficient of kurtosis	$\alpha_4 = 3 + 1/\lambda$

RELATION BETWEEN THE BINOMIAL AND POISSON DISTRIBUTIONS

In the binomial distribution (*1*), if N is large while the probability p of the occurrence of an event is close to 0, so that $q = 1 - p$ is close to 1, the event is called a *rare event.* In practice we shall consider an event to be rare if the number of trials is at least 50 ($N \geq 50$) while Np is less than 5. In such case the binomial distribution (*1*) is very closely approximated by the Poisson distribution (*5*) with $\lambda = Np$. This is indicated by comparing Tables 7.1 and 7.3—for by placing $\lambda = Np$, $q \approx 1$, and $p \approx 0$ in Table 7.1, we get the results in Table 7.3.

Since there is a relation between the binomial and normal distributions, it follows that there also is a relation between the Poisson and normal distributions. It can in fact be shown that the Poisson distribution approaches a normal distribution with standardized variable $(X - \lambda)/\sqrt{\lambda}$ as λ increases indefinitely.

THE MULTINOMIAL DISTRIBUTION

If events $E_1, E_2, \ldots, E_K$ can occur with probabilities $p_1, p_2, \ldots, p_K$, respectively, then the probability that $E_1, E_2, \ldots, E_K$ will occur $X_1, X_2, \ldots, X_K$ times, respectively, is

$$\frac{N!}{X_1!X_2!\cdots X_K!} p_1^{X_1} p_2^{X_2} \cdots p_K^{X_K} \tag{6}$$

where $X_1 + X_2 + \cdots + X_K = N$. This distribution, which is a generalization of the binomial distribution, is called the *multinomial distribution* since equation (*6*) is the general term in the *multinomial expansion* $(p_1 + p_2 + \cdots + p_K)^N$.

EXAMPLE 5. If a fair die is tossed 12 times, the probability of getting 1, 2, 3, 4, 5, and 6 points exactly twice each is

$$\frac{12!}{2!2!2!2!2!2!}\left(\frac{1}{6}\right)^2\left(\frac{1}{6}\right)^2\left(\frac{1}{6}\right)^2\left(\frac{1}{6}\right)^2\left(\frac{1}{6}\right)^2\left(\frac{1}{6}\right)^2 = \frac{1925}{559,872} = 0.00344$$

The *expected* numbers of times that $E_1, E_2, \ldots, E_K$ will occur in N trials are $Np_1, Np_2, \ldots, Np_K$, respectively.

FITTING THEORETICAL DISTRIBUTIONS TO SAMPLE FREQUENCY DISTRIBUTIONS

When one has some indication of the distribution of a population by probabilistic reasoning or otherwise, it is often possible to fit such theoretical distributions (also called *model* or *expected* distributions) to frequency distributions obtained from a sample of the population. The method used consists in general of employing the mean and standard deviation of the sample to estimate the mean and sample of the population (see Problems 7.31, 7.33, and 7.34).

In order to test the *goodness of fit* of the theoretical distributions, we use the *chi-square test* (which is given in Chapter 12). In attempting to determine whether a normal distribution represents a good fit for given data, it is convenient to use *normal-curve graph paper*, or *probability graph paper* as it is sometimes called (see Problem 7.32).

Solved Problems

THE BINOMIAL DISTRIBUTION

7.1 Evaluate the following:

(*a*) $5!$ (*c*) $\binom{8}{3}$ (*e*) $\binom{4}{4}$

(*b*) $\dfrac{6!}{2!4!}$ (*d*) $\binom{7}{5}$ (*f*) $\binom{4}{0}$

SOLUTION

(*a*) $5! = 5 \cdot 4 \cdot 3 \cdot 2 \cdot 1 = 120$

(*b*) $\dfrac{6!}{2!4!} = \dfrac{6 \cdot 5 \cdot 4 \cdot 3 \cdot 2 \cdot 1}{(2 \cdot 1)(4 \cdot 3 \cdot 2 \cdot 1)} = \dfrac{6 \cdot 5}{2 \cdot 1} = 15$

(*c*) $\binom{8}{3} = \dfrac{8!}{3!(8-3)!} = \dfrac{8!}{3!5!} = \dfrac{8 \cdot 7 \cdot 6 \cdot 5 \cdot 4 \cdot 3 \cdot 2 \cdot 1}{(3 \cdot 2 \cdot 1)(5 \cdot 4 \cdot 3 \cdot 2 \cdot 1)} = \dfrac{8 \cdot 7 \cdot 6}{3 \cdot 2 \cdot 1} = 56$

(*d*) $\binom{7}{5} = \dfrac{7!}{5!2!} = \dfrac{7 \cdot 6 \cdot 5 \cdot 4 \cdot 3 \cdot 2 \cdot 1}{(5 \cdot 4 \cdot 3 \cdot 2 \cdot 1)(2 \cdot 1)} = \dfrac{7 \cdot 6}{2 \cdot 1} = 21$

(*e*) $\binom{4}{4} = \dfrac{4!}{4!0!} = 1$ since $0! = 1$ by definition

(*f*) $\binom{4}{0} = \dfrac{4!}{0!4!} = 1$

7.2 Find the probability that in tossing a fair coin three times there will appear (*a*) 3 heads, (*b*) 2 heads and 1 tail, (*c*) 2 tails and 1 head, and (*d*) 3 tails.

SOLUTION

First method

Let H denote "heads" and T denote "tails," and suppose that we designate HTH to mean head on first toss, tail on second toss, and then head on third toss. Since two possibilities (head or tail) can occur on each toss, we have a total of $(2)(2)(2) = 8$ possible outcomes. These are

HHH HHT HTH HTT TTH THH THT TTT

Because each of these possibilities is equally likely, the probability of each is $\frac{1}{8}$.

(*a*) Three heads (HHH) occur only once; thus the probability of 3 heads is $\frac{1}{8}$.

(*b*) Two heads and 1 tail occur three times (HHT, HTH, and THH); thus Pr{2 heads and 1 tail} $= \frac{3}{8}$.

(*c*) Two tails and 1 head occur three times (HTT, TTH, and THT); thus Pr{2 tails and 1 head} $= \frac{3}{8}$.

(*d*) Three tails (TTT) occur only once; thus Pr{TTT} = Pr{3 tails} $= \frac{1}{8}$.

Second method [using formula (*1*)]

(*a*) $\Pr\{3 \text{ heads}\} = \binom{3}{3}\left(\dfrac{1}{2}\right)^3\left(\dfrac{1}{2}\right)^0 = (1)\left(\dfrac{1}{8}\right)(1) = \dfrac{1}{8}$

(*b*) $\Pr\{2 \text{ heads and 1 tail}\} = \binom{3}{2}\left(\dfrac{1}{2}\right)^2\left(\dfrac{1}{2}\right) = (3)\left(\dfrac{1}{4}\right)\left(\dfrac{1}{2}\right) = \dfrac{3}{8}$

(c) $\Pr\{1 \text{ head and } 2 \text{ tails}\} = \binom{3}{1}\left(\frac{1}{2}\right)^1\left(\frac{1}{2}\right)^2 = (3)\left(\frac{1}{2}\right)\left(\frac{1}{4}\right) = \frac{3}{8}$

(d) $\Pr\{3 \text{ tails}\} = \binom{3}{0}\left(\frac{1}{2}\right)^0\left(\frac{1}{2}\right)^3 = (1)(1)\left(\frac{1}{8}\right) = \frac{1}{8}$

We can also proceed as in Problem 6.10.

7.3 Find the probability that in five tosses of a fair die a 3 appears (*a*) at no time, (*b*) once, (*c*) twice, (*d*) three times, and (*e*) four times.

SOLUTION

The probability of 3 in a single toss $= p = \frac{1}{6}$, and the probability of no 3 in a single toss $= q = 1 - p = \frac{5}{6}$; thus:

(a) $\Pr\{3 \text{ occurs zero times}\} = \binom{5}{0}\left(\frac{1}{6}\right)^0\left(\frac{5}{6}\right)^5 = (1)(1)\left(\frac{5}{6}\right)^5 = \frac{3125}{7776}$

(b) $\Pr\{3 \text{ occurs one time}\} = \binom{5}{1}\left(\frac{1}{6}\right)^1\left(\frac{5}{6}\right)^4 = (5)\left(\frac{1}{6}\right)\left(\frac{5}{6}\right)^4 = \frac{3125}{7776}$

(c) $\Pr\{3 \text{ occurs two times}\} = \binom{5}{2}\left(\frac{1}{6}\right)^2\left(\frac{5}{6}\right)^3 = (10)\left(\frac{1}{36}\right)\left(\frac{125}{216}\right) = \frac{625}{3888}$

(d) $\Pr\{3 \text{ occurs three times}\} = \binom{5}{3}\left(\frac{1}{6}\right)^3\left(\frac{5}{6}\right)^2 = (10)\left(\frac{1}{216}\right)\left(\frac{25}{36}\right) = \frac{125}{3888}$

(e) $\Pr\{3 \text{ occurs four times}\} = \binom{5}{4}\left(\frac{1}{6}\right)^4\left(\frac{5}{6}\right)^1 = (5)\left(\frac{1}{1296}\right)\left(\frac{5}{6}\right) = \frac{25}{7776}$

(f) $\Pr\{3 \text{ occurs five times}\} = \binom{5}{5}\left(\frac{1}{6}\right)^5\left(\frac{5}{6}\right)^0 = (1)\left(\frac{1}{7776}\right)(1) = \frac{1}{7776}$

Note that these probabilities represent the terms in the binomial expansion

$$\left(\frac{5}{6}+\frac{1}{6}\right)^5 = \left(\frac{5}{6}\right)^5 + \binom{5}{1}\left(\frac{5}{6}\right)^4\left(\frac{1}{6}\right) + \binom{5}{2}\left(\frac{5}{6}\right)^3\left(\frac{1}{6}\right)^2 + \binom{5}{3}\left(\frac{5}{6}\right)^2\left(\frac{1}{6}\right)^3 + \binom{5}{4}\left(\frac{5}{6}\right)\left(\frac{1}{6}\right)^4 + \left(\frac{1}{6}\right)^5 = 1$$

7.4 Write the binomial expansion for $(a)(q+p)^4$ and $(b)(q+p)^6$.

SOLUTION

(a)
$$\begin{aligned}(q+p)^4 &= q^4 + \binom{4}{1}q^3p + \binom{4}{2}q^2p^2 + \binom{4}{3}qp^3 + p^4 \\ &= q^4 + 4q^3p + 6q^2p^2 + 4qp^3 + p^4\end{aligned}$$

(b)
$$\begin{aligned}(q+p)^6 &= q^6 + \binom{6}{1}q^5p + \binom{6}{2}q^4p^2 + \binom{6}{3}q^3p^3 + \binom{6}{4}q^2p^4 + \binom{6}{5}qp^5 + p^6 \\ &= q^6 + 6q^5p + 15q^4p^2 + 20q^3p^3 + 15q^2p^4 + 6qp^5 + p^6\end{aligned}$$

The coefficients 1, 4, 6, 4, 1 and 1, 6, 15, 20, 15, 6, 1 are called the *binomial coefficients* corresponding to $N = 4$ and $N = 6$, respectively. By writing these coefficients for $N = 0, 1, 2, 3, \ldots$, as shown in the following array, we obtain an arrangement called *Pascal's triangle.* Note that the first and last numbers in each row are 1 and that any other number can be obtained by adding the two numbers to the right and left of it in the preceding row.

$$
\begin{array}{ccccccccccccc}
 & & & & & & 1 & & & & & & \\
 & & & & & 1 & & 1 & & & & & \\
 & & & & 1 & & 2 & & 1 & & & & \\
 & & & 1 & & 3 & & 3 & & 1 & & & \\
 & & 1 & & 4 & & 6 & & 4 & & 1 & & \\
 & 1 & & 5 & & 10 & & 10 & & 5 & & 1 & \\
1 & & 6 & & 15 & & 20 & & 15 & & 6 & & 1
\end{array}
$$

7.5 Find the probability that in a family of 4 children there will be (*a*) at least 1 boy and (*b*) at least 1 boy and 1 girl. Assume that the probability of a male birth is $\frac{1}{2}$.

SOLUTION

(*a*)
$$\Pr\{1 \text{ boy}\} = \binom{4}{1}\left(\frac{1}{2}\right)^1\left(\frac{1}{2}\right)^3 = \frac{1}{4} \qquad \Pr\{3 \text{ boys}\} = \binom{4}{3}\left(\frac{1}{2}\right)^3\left(\frac{1}{2}\right) = \frac{1}{4}$$

$$\Pr\{2 \text{ boys}\} = \binom{4}{2}\left(\frac{1}{2}\right)^2\left(\frac{1}{2}\right)^2 = \frac{3}{8} \qquad \Pr\{4 \text{ boys}\} = \binom{4}{4}\left(\frac{1}{2}\right)^4\left(\frac{1}{2}\right)^0 = \frac{1}{16}$$

Thus
$$\Pr\{\text{at least 1 boy}\} = \Pr\{1 \text{ boy}\} + \Pr\{2 \text{ boys}\} + \Pr\{3 \text{ boys}\} + \Pr\{4 \text{ boys}\}$$
$$= \frac{1}{4} + \frac{3}{8} + \frac{1}{4} + \frac{1}{16} = \frac{15}{16}$$

Another method

$$\Pr\{\text{at least 1 boy}\} = 1 - \Pr\{\text{no boy}\} = 1 - \left(\frac{1}{2}\right)^4 = 1 - \frac{1}{16} = \frac{15}{16}$$

(*b*)
$$\Pr\{\text{at least 1 boy and 1 girl}\} = 1 - \Pr\{\text{no boy}\} - \Pr\{\text{no girl}\} = 1 - \frac{1}{16} - \frac{1}{16} = \frac{7}{8}$$

7.6 Out of 2000 families with 4 children each, how many would you expect to have (*a*) at least 1 boy, (*b*) 2 boys, (*c*) 1 or 2 girls, and (*d*) no girls? Refer to Problem 7.5(*a*).

SOLUTION

(*a*) Expected number of families with at least 1 boy $= 2000(\frac{15}{16}) = 1875$

(*b*) Expected number of families with 2 boys $= 2000 \cdot \Pr\{2 \text{ boys}\} = 2000(\frac{3}{8}) = 750$

(*c*) $\Pr\{1 \text{ or } 2 \text{ girls}\} = \Pr\{1 \text{ girl}\} + \Pr\{2 \text{ girls}\} = \Pr\{1 \text{ boy}\} + \Pr\{2 \text{ boys}\} = \frac{1}{4} + \frac{3}{8} = \frac{5}{8}$
Expected number of families with 1 or 2 girls $= 2000(\frac{5}{8}) = 1250$

(*d*) Expected number of families with no girls $= 2000(\frac{1}{16}) = 125$

Mathcad **7.7** If 20% of the bolts produced by a machine are defective, determine the probability that, out of 4 bolts chosen at random, (*a*) 1, (*b*), 0, and (*c*) at most 2 bolts will be defective.

SOLUTION

The probability of a defective bolt is $p = 0.2$, and the probability of a nondefective bolt is $q = 1 - p = 0.8$.

(*a*)
$$\Pr\{1 \text{ defective bolt out of } 4\} = \binom{4}{1}(0.2)^1(0.8)^3 = 0.4096$$

(*b*) $$\Pr\{0 \text{ defective bolts}\} = \binom{4}{0}(0.2)^0(0.8)^4 = 0.4096$$

(*c*) $$\Pr\{2 \text{ defective bolts}\} = \binom{4}{2}(0.2)^2(0.8)^2 = 0.1536$$

Thus

$$\begin{aligned}\Pr\{\text{at most 2 defective bolts}\} &= \Pr\{0 \text{ defective bolts}\} + \Pr\{1 \text{ defective bolt}\} + \Pr\{2 \text{ defective bolts}\}\\ &= 0.4096 + 0.4096 + 0.1536 = 0.9728\end{aligned}$$

7.8 The probability that an entering college student will graduate is 0.4. Determine the probability that out of 5 students (*a*) none, (*b*), 1, (*c*) at least 1, and (*d*) all will graduate.

SOLUTION

(*a*) $\Pr\{\text{none will graduate}\} = \binom{5}{0}(0.4)^0(0.6)^5 = 0.07776$ or about 0.08

(*b*) $\Pr\{1 \text{ will graduate}\} = \binom{5}{1}(0.4)^1(0.6)^4 = 0.2592$ or about 0.26

(*c*) $\Pr\{\text{at least 1 will graduate}\} = 1 - \Pr\{\text{none will graduate}\} = 0.92224$ or about 0.92

(*d*) $\Pr\{\text{all will graduate}\} = \binom{5}{5}(0.4)^5(0.6)^0 = 0.01024$ or about 0.01

7.9 What is the probability of getting a total of 9 (*a*) twice and (*b*) at least twice in 6 tosses of a pair of dice?

SOLUTION

Each of the 6 ways in which the first die can fall can be associated with each of the 6 ways in which the second die can fall; thus there are $6 \cdot 6 = 36$ ways in which both dice can fall. These are: 1 on the first die and 1 on the second die, 1 on the first die and 2 on the second die, etc., denoted by (1, 1), (1, 2), etc.

Of these 36 ways (all equally likely if the dice are fair), a total of 9 occurs in 4 cases: (3, 6), (4, 5), (5, 4), and (6, 3). Thus the probability of a total of 9 in a single toss of a pair of dice is $p = \frac{4}{36} = \frac{1}{9}$, and the probability of not getting a total of 9 in a single toss of a pair of dice is $q = 1 - p = \frac{8}{9}$.

(*a*) $$\Pr\{2 \text{ nines in 6 tosses}\} = \binom{6}{2}\left(\frac{1}{9}\right)^2\left(\frac{8}{9}\right)^{6-2} = \frac{61{,}440}{531{,}441}$$

(*b*) $$\begin{aligned}\Pr\{\text{at least 2 nines}\} &= \Pr\{2 \text{ nines}\} + \Pr\{3 \text{ nines}\} + \Pr\{4 \text{ nines}\} + \Pr\{5 \text{ nines}\} + \Pr\{6 \text{ nines}\}\\ &= \binom{6}{2}\left(\frac{1}{9}\right)^2\left(\frac{8}{9}\right)^4 + \binom{6}{3}\left(\frac{1}{9}\right)^3\left(\frac{8}{9}\right)^3 + \binom{6}{4}\left(\frac{1}{9}\right)^4\left(\frac{8}{9}\right)^2 + \binom{6}{5}\left(\frac{1}{9}\right)^5\left(\frac{8}{9}\right)^1 + \binom{6}{6}\left(\frac{1}{9}\right)^6\left(\frac{8}{9}\right)^0\\ &= \frac{61{,}440}{531{,}441} + \frac{10{,}240}{531{,}441} + \frac{960}{531{,}441} + \frac{48}{531{,}441} + \frac{1}{531{,}441} = \frac{72{,}689}{531{,}441}\end{aligned}$$

Another method

$$\begin{aligned}\Pr\{\text{at least 2 nines}\} &= 1 - \Pr\{0 \text{ nines}\} - \Pr\{1 \text{ nine}\}\\ &= 1 - \binom{6}{0}\left(\frac{1}{9}\right)^0\left(\frac{8}{9}\right)^6 - \binom{6}{1}\left(\frac{1}{9}\right)^1\left(\frac{8}{9}\right)^5 = \frac{72{,}689}{531{,}441}\end{aligned}$$

7.10 Evaluate (*a*) $\sum_{X=0}^{N} Xp(X)$ and (*b*) $\sum_{X=0}^{N} X^2p(X)$, where $p(X) = \binom{N}{X} p^x q^{N-X}$.

SOLUTION

(*a*) Since $q + p = 1$,

$$\sum_{X=0}^{N} Xp(X) = \sum_{X=1}^{N} X \frac{N!}{X!(N-X)!} p^X q^{N-X} = Np \sum_{X=1}^{N} \frac{(N-1)!}{(X-1)!(N-X)!} p^{X-1} q^{N-X}$$
$$= Np(q+p)^{N-1} = Np$$

(*b*)
$$\sum_{X=0}^{N} X^2p(X) = \sum_{X=1}^{N} \frac{N!}{X!(N-X)!} p^X q^{N-X} = \sum_{X=1}^{N} [X(X-1)+X] \frac{N!}{X!(N-X)!} p^X q^{N-X}$$
$$= \sum_{X=2}^{N} X(X-1) \frac{N!}{X!(N-X)!} p^X q^{N-X} + \sum_{X=1}^{N} X \frac{N!}{X!(N-X)!} p^X q^{N-X}$$
$$= N(N-1)p^2 \sum_{X=2}^{N} \frac{(N-2)!}{(X-2)!(N-X)!} p^{X-2} q^{N-X} + Np = N(N-1)p^2(q+p)^{N-2} + Np$$
$$= N(N-1)p^2 + Np$$

Note: The results in parts (*a*) and (*b*) are the *expectations* of X and X^2, denoted by $E(X)$ and $E(X^2)$, respectively (see Chapter 6).

7.11 If a variable is binomially distributed, determine its (*a*) mean μ and (*b*) variance σ^2.

SOLUTION

(*a*) By Problem 7.10(*a*),

$$\mu = \text{expectation of variable} = \sum_{X=0}^{N} Xp(X) = Np$$

(*b*) Using $\mu = Np$ and the results of Problem 7.10,

$$\sigma^2 = \sum_{X=0}^{N} (X-\mu)^2 p(X) = \sum_{X=0}^{N} (X^2 - 2\mu X + \mu^2) p(X) = \sum_{X=0}^{N} X^2 p(X) - 2\mu \sum_{X=0}^{N} Xp(X) + \mu^2 \sum_{X=0}^{N} p(X)$$
$$= N(N-1)p^2 + Np - 2(Np)(Np) + (Np)^2(1) = Np - Np^2 = Np(1-p) = Npq$$

It follows that the standard deviation of a binomially distributed variable is $\sigma = \sqrt{Npq}$.

Another method

By Problem 6.62(*b*),

$$E[(X-\bar{X})]^2 = E(X^2) - [E(X)]^2 = N(N-1)p^2 + Np - N^2p^2 = Np - Np^2 = Npq$$

7.12 If the probability of a defective bolt is 0.1, find (*a*) the mean and (*b*) the standard deviation for the distribution of defective bolts in a total of 400.

SOLUTION

(*a*) The mean is $Np = 400(0.1) = 40$; that is, we can *expect* 40 bolts to be defective.

(*b*) The variance is $Npq = 400(0.1)(0.9) = 36$. Hence the standard deviation is $\sqrt{36} = 6$.

7.13 Find the moment coefficients of (*a*) skewness and (*b*) kurtosis of the distribution in Problem 7.12.

SOLUTION

(*a*)
$$\text{Moment coefficient of skewness} = \frac{q-p}{\sqrt{Npq}} = \frac{0.9-0.1}{6} = 0.133$$

Since this is positive, the distribution is skewed to the right.

(*b*) $$\text{Moment coefficient of kurtosis} = 3 + \frac{1-6pq}{Npq} = 3 + \frac{1-6(0.1)(0.9)}{36} = 3.01$$

The distribution is slightly *leptokurtic* with respect to the normal distribution (i.e., slightly more peaked; see Chapter 5).

THE NORMAL DISTRIBUTION

7.14 On a final examination in mathematics, the mean was 72 and the standard deviation was 15. Determine the standard scores (i.e., grades in standard-deviation units) of students receiving the grades (*a*) 60, (*b*) 93, and (*c*) 72.

SOLUTION

(*a*) $z = \frac{X - \bar{X}}{s} = \frac{60-72}{15} = -0.8$ (*c*) $z = \frac{X - \bar{X}}{s} = \frac{72-72}{15} = 0$

(*b*) $z = \frac{X - \bar{X}}{s} = \frac{93-72}{15} = 1.4$

7.15 Referring to Problem 7.14, find the grades corresponding to the standard scores (*a*) -1 and (*b*) 1.6.

SOLUTION

(*a*) $X = \bar{X} + zs = 72 + (-1)(15) = 57$ (*b*) $X = \bar{X} + zs = 72 + (1.6)(15) = 96$

7.16 Two students were informed that they received standard scores of 0.8 and -0.4, respectively, on a multiple-choice examination in English. If their grades were 88 and 64, respectively, find the mean and the standard deviation of the examination grades.

SOLUTION

Using the equation $X = \bar{X} + zs$, we have $88 = \bar{X} + 0.8s$ for the first student and $64 = \bar{X} - 0.4s$ for the second student. Solving both equations simultaneously, the mean $\bar{X} = 72$ and the standard deviation $s = 20$.

7.17 Find the area under the normal curve in each of the following cases, (*a*) to (*g*), which corresponds to Figs. 7-2(*a*) to 7-2(*g*), respectively. Use Appendix II.

(*a*) Between $z = 0$ and $z = 1.2$
(*b*) Between $z = -0.68$ and $z = 0$
(*c*) Between $z = -0.46$ and $z = 2.21$
(*d*) Between $z = 0.81$ and $z = 1.94$
(*e*) To the left of $z = -0.6$
(*f*) To the right of $z = -1.28$
(*g*) To the right of $z = 2.05$, and to the left of $z = -1.44$

SOLUTION

(*a*) In Appendix II, proceed downward under the column marked z until reaching entry 1.2; then proceed right to the column marked 0. The result, 0.3849, is the required area and represents the probability that z is between 0 and 1.2, denoted by $\Pr\{0 \le z \le 1.2\}$.

(*b*) The required area is that between $z = 0$ and $z = 0.68$ (by symmetry). To find this area, proceed downward under the column marked z in Appendix II until reaching 0.6; then proceed right to the column marked 8. The result, 0.2517, is the required area and represents the probability that z is between -0.68 and 0, denoted by $\Pr\{-0.68 \le z \le 0\}$.

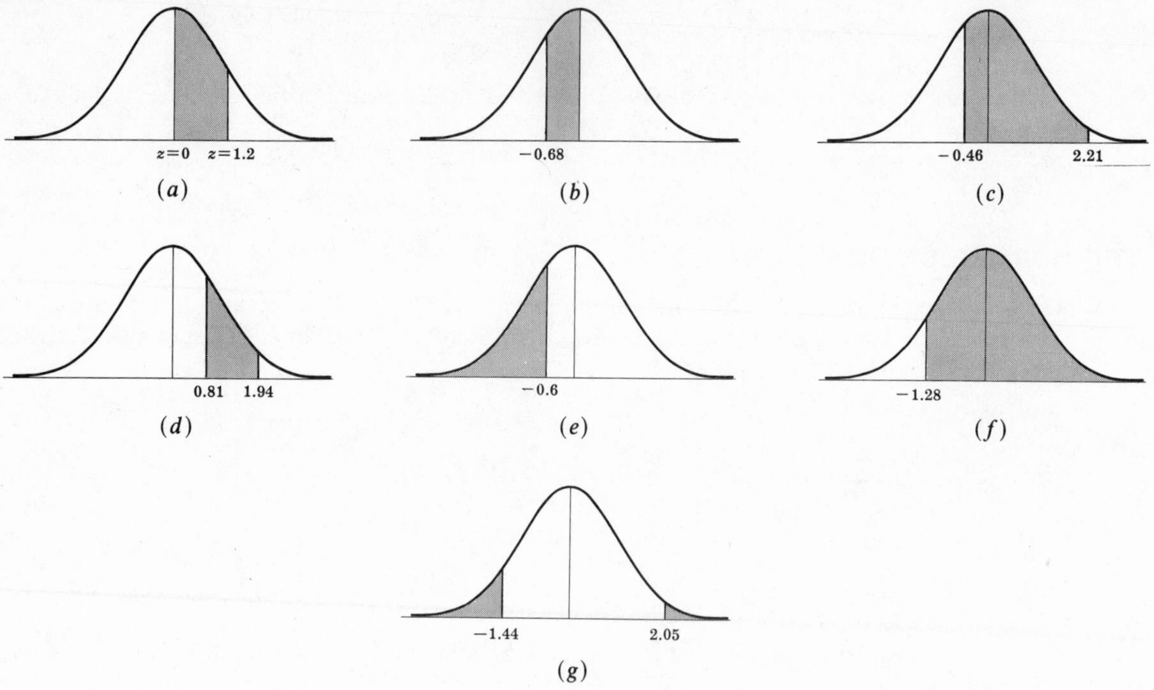

Fig. 7-2

(*c*) Required area = (area between $z = -0.46$ and $z = 0$) + (area between $z = 0$ and $z = 2.21$)
= (area between $z = 0$ and $z = 0.46$) + (area between $z = 0$ and $z = 2.21$)
$= 0.1772 + 0.4864 = 0.6636$

(*d*) Required area = (area between $z = 0$ and $z = 1.94$) − (area between $z = 0$ and $z = 0.81$)
$= 0.4738 - 0.2910 = 0.1828$

(*e*) Required area = (area to left of $z = 0$) − (area between $z = -0.6$ and $z = 0$)
= (area to left of $z = 0$) − (area between $z = 0$ and $z = 0.6$)
$= 0.5 - 0.2258 = 0.2742$

(*f*) Required area = (area between $z = -1.28$ and $z = 0$) + (area to right of $z = 0$)
$= 0.3997 + 0.5 = 0.8997$

(*g*) Required area = total area − (area between $z = -1.44$ and $z = 0$) − (area between $z = 0$ and $z = 2.05$)
$= 1 - 0.4251 - 0.4798 = 1 - 0.9049 = 0.0951$

Mathcad **7.18** Determine the value or values of z in each of the following cases, (*a*) to (*c*), which correspond to Figs. 7-3(*a*) to 7-3(*c*), respectively. The word "area" refers to that area under the normal curve.

(*a*) The area between 0 and z is 0.3770.

(*b*) The area to the left of z is 0.8621.

(*c*) The area between −1.5 and z is 0.0217.

SOLUTION

(*a*) In Appendix II the entry 0.3770 is located to the right of the row marked 1.1 and under the column marked 6; thus the required $z = 1.16$. By symmetry, $z = -1.16$ is another value of z; thus $z = \pm 1.16$.

(*b*) Since the area is greater than 0.5, z must be positive. The area between 0 and $z = 0.8621 - 0.5 = 0.3621$, from which $z = 1.09$.

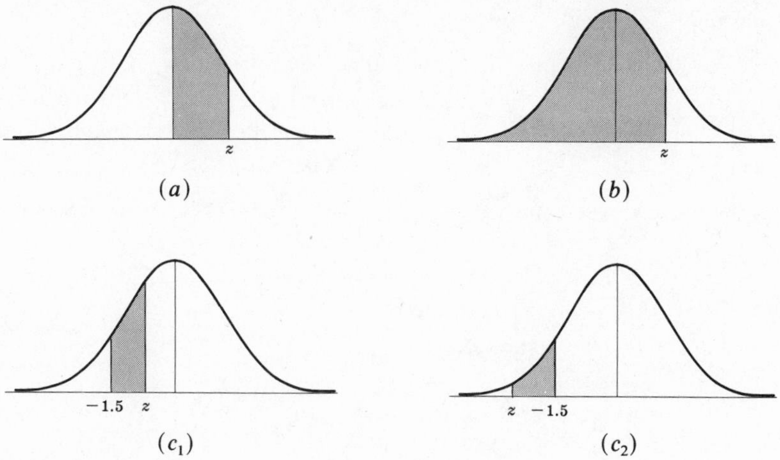

Fig. 7-3

(c) If z were positive, the area would be greater than the area between -1.5 and 0, which is 0.4332; hence z must be negative.

Case 1 [z is negative but to the right of -1.5; see Fig. 7-3(c_1)]

The area between -1.5 and z = (area between -1.5 and 0) − (area between 0 and z), and $0.0217 = 0.4332$ − (area between 0 and z). Thus the area between 0 and $z = 0.4332 - 0.0217 = 0.4115$, from which $z = -1.35$.

Case 2 [z is negative but to the left of -1.5; see Fig. 7-3(c_2)]

The area between z and -1.5 = (area between z and 0) − (area between -1.5 and 0), and 0.0217 = (area between 0 and z) − 0.4332. Thus the area between 0 and $z = 0.0217 + 0.4332 = 0.4549$, and $z = -1.694$ by using linear interpolation; or, with slightly less precision, $z = -1.69$.

7.19 Find the ordinates of the normal curve at (a) $z = 0.84$, (b) $z = -1.27$, and (c) $z = -0.05$.

SOLUTION

(a) In Appendix I, proceed downward under the column headed z until reaching the entry 0.8; then proceed right to the column headed 4. The entry 0.2803 is the required ordinate.

(b) By symmetry: (ordinate at $z = -1.27$) = (ordinate at $z = 1.27$) = 0.1781.

(c) (Ordinate at $z = -0.05$) = (ordinate at $z = 0.05$) = 0.3984.

7.20 The mean weight of 500 male students at a certain college is 151 pounds (lb), and the standard deviation is 15 lb. Assuming that the weights are normally distributed, find how many students weigh (a) between 120 and 155 lb and (b) more than 185 lb.

SOLUTION

(a) Weights recorded as being between 120 and 155 lb can actually have any value from 119.5 to 155.5 lb, assuming that they are recorded to the nearest pound.

$$119.5 \text{ lb in standard units} = \frac{119.5 - 151}{15} = -2.10$$

$$155.5 \text{ lb in standard units} = \frac{155.5 - 151}{15} = 0.30$$

As shown in Fig. 7-4(a),

$$\begin{aligned}\text{Required proportion of students} &= (\text{area between } z=-2.10 \text{ and } z=0.30)\\ &= (\text{area between } z=-210 \text{ and } z=0)\\ &\quad +(\text{area between } z=0 \text{ and } z=0.30)\\ &= 0.4821+0.1179=0.6000\end{aligned}$$

Thus the number of students weighing between 120 and 155 lb is 500(0.6000) = 300.

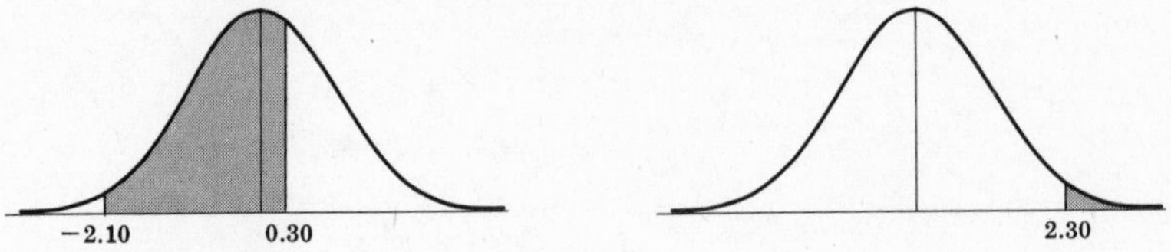

(a) (b)

Fig. 7-4

(b) Students weighing more than 185 lb must weigh at least 185.5 lb.

$$185.5 \text{ lb in standard units} = \frac{185.5-151}{15} = 2.30$$

As shown in Fig. 7-4(b),

$$\begin{aligned}\text{Required proportion of students} &= (\text{area to right of } z=2.30)\\ &= (\text{area to right of } z=0)-(\text{area between } z=0 \text{ and } z=2.30)\\ &= 0.5-0.4893=0.0107\end{aligned}$$

Thus the number of students weighing more than 185 lb is 500(0.0107) = 5.

If W denotes the weight of a student at random, we can summarize the above results in terms of probability by writing

$$\Pr\{119.5 \le W \le 155.5\} = 0.6000 \qquad \text{and} \qquad \Pr\{W \ge 185.5\} = 0.0107$$

7.21 Determine how many of the 500 students in Problem 7.20 weigh (a) less than 128 lb, (b) 128 lb, and (c) less than or equal to 128 lb.

SOLUTION

(a) Students weighing less than 128 lb must weigh less than 127.5 lb.

$$127.5 \text{ lb in standard units} = \frac{127.5-151}{15} = -1.57$$

As shown in Fig. 7-5(a),

$$\begin{aligned}\text{Required proportion of students} &= (\text{area to left of } z=-1.57)\\ &= (\text{area to left of } z=0)-\text{area between } z=-1.57 \text{ and } z=0)\\ &= 0.5-0.4418=0.0582\end{aligned}$$

Thus the number of students weighing less than 128 lb is 500(0.0582) = 29.

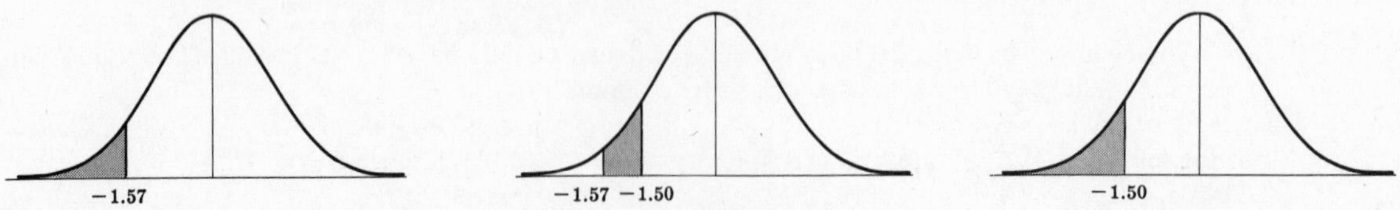

(a) (b) (c)

Fig. 7-5

(*b*) Students weighing 128 lb weigh between 127.5 and 128.5 lb.

$$127.5 \text{ lb in standard units} = \frac{127.5 - 151}{15} = -1.57$$

$$128.5 \text{ lb in standard units} = \frac{128.5 - 151}{15} = -1.50$$

As shown in Fig. 7-5(b),

$$\begin{aligned}\text{Required proportion of students} &= (\text{area between } z = -1.57 \text{ and } z = -1.50)\\ &= (\text{area between } z = -1.57 \text{ and } z = 0)\\ &\quad -(\text{area between } z = -1.50 \text{ and } z = 0)\\ &= 0.4418 - 0.4332 = 0.0086\end{aligned}$$

Thus the number of students weighing 128 lb is 500(0.0086) = 4.

(*c*) Students weighing less than or equal to 128 lb must weigh less than 128.5 lb.

$$128.5 \text{ lb in standard units} = \frac{128.5 - 151}{15} = -1.50$$

As shown in Fig. 7-5(*c*),

$$\begin{aligned}\text{Required proportion of students} &= (\text{area to left of } z = -1.50)\\ &= (\text{area to left of } z = 0) - (\text{area between } z = -1.50 \text{ and } z = 0)\\ &= 0.5 - 0.4332 = 0.0668\end{aligned}$$

Thus the number of students weighing 128 lb or less is 500(0.0668) = 33.

Another method [using parts (*a*) and (*b*)]

The number of students weighing less than or equal to 128 lb is (number weighing less than 128 lb) + (number weighing 128 lb) = 29 + 4 = 33.

7.22 The grades on a short quiz in biology were 0, 1, 2, . . . , 10 points, depending on the number answered correctly out of 10 questions. The mean grade was 6.7 and the standard deviation was 1.2. Assuming the grades to be normally distributed, determine (*a*) the percentage of students scoring 6 points, (*b*) the maximum grade of the lowest 10% of the class, and (*c*) the minimum grade of the highest 10% of the class.

SOLUTION

(*a*) To apply the normal distribution to discrete data, it is necessary to treat the data as if they were continuous. Thus a score of 6 points is considered to be 5.5 to 6.5 points.

$$5.5 \text{ in standard units} = \frac{5.5 - 6.7}{1.2} = -1.0$$

$$6.5 \text{ in standard units} = \frac{6.5 - 6.7}{1.2} = -0.17$$

As shown in Fig. 7-6(*a*),

$$\begin{aligned}\text{Required proportion} &= (\text{area between } z = -1 \text{ and } z = -0.17)\\ &= (\text{area between } z = -1 \text{ and } z = 0) - (\text{area between } z = -0.17 \text{ and } z = 0)\\ &= 0.3413 - 0.0675 = 0.2738 = 27\%\end{aligned}$$

(*b*) Let X_1 be the required maximum grade and z_1 the grade in standard units. From Fig. 7-6(*b*) the area to the left of z_1 is 10% = 0.10; hence: (area between z_1 and 0) = 0.40, and $z_1 = -1.28$ (very closely). Thus $z_1 = (X_1 - 6.7)/1.2 = -1.28$; and $X_1 = 5.2$, or 5 to the nearest integer.

(*c*) Let X_2 be the required minimum grade and z_2 the grade in standard units. From part (*b*), by symmetry, $z_2 = 1.28$. Thus $(X_2 = 6.7)/1.2 = 1.28$; and $X_2 = 8.2$, or 8 to the nearest integer.

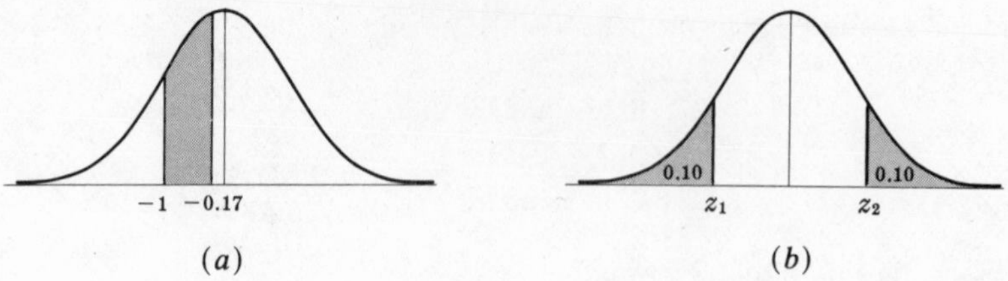

Fig. 7-6

7.23 The mean inside diameter of a sample of 200 washers produced by a machine is 0.502 inches (in), and the standard deviation is 0.005 in. The purpose for which these washers are intended allows a maximum tolerance in the diameter of 0.496 to 0.508 in; otherwise, the washers are considered defective. Determine the percentage of defective washers produced by the machine, assuming that the diameters are normally distributed.

SOLUTION

$$0.496 \text{ in standard units} = \frac{0.496-0.502}{0.005} = -1.2$$

$$0.508 \text{ in standard units} = \frac{0.508-0.502}{0.005} = 1.2$$

As shown in Fig. 7-7,

$$\begin{aligned}\text{Proportion of nondefective washers} &= (\text{area under normal curve between } z=-1.2 \text{ and } z=1.2)\\ &= (\text{twice the area between } z=0 \text{ and } z=1.2)\\ &= 2(0.3849) = 0.7698 \quad \text{or} \quad 77\%\end{aligned}$$

Thus the percentage of defective washers is $100\% - 77\% = 23\%$.

Note that if we think of the interval 0.496 to 0.508 in as actually representing diameters of from 0.4955 to 0.5085 in, the above result is modified slightly. To two significant figures, however, the results are the same.

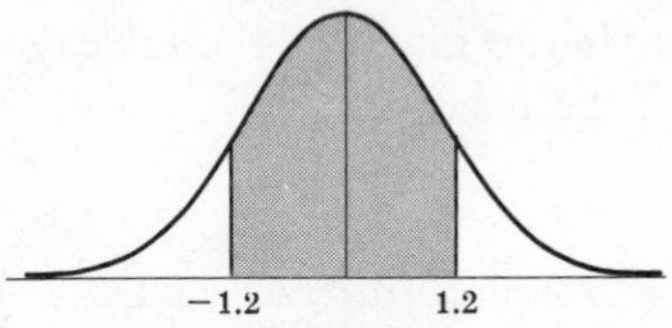

Fig. 7-7

NORMAL APPROXIMATION TO THE BINOMIAL DISTRIBUTION

7.24 Find the probability of getting between 3 and 6 heads inclusive in 10 tosses of a fair coin by using (*a*) the binomial distribution and (*b*) the normal approximation to the binomial distribution.

SOLUTION

(*a*)

$$\Pr\{3 \text{ heads}\} = \binom{10}{3}\left(\frac{1}{2}\right)^3\left(\frac{1}{2}\right)^7 = \frac{15}{128} \qquad \Pr\{5 \text{ heads}\} = \binom{10}{5}\left(\frac{1}{2}\right)^5\left(\frac{1}{2}\right)^5 = \frac{63}{256}$$

$$\Pr\{4 \text{ heads}\} = \binom{10}{4}\left(\frac{1}{2}\right)^4\left(\frac{1}{2}\right)^6 = \frac{105}{512} \qquad \Pr\{6 \text{ heads}\} = \binom{10}{6}\left(\frac{1}{2}\right)^6\left(\frac{1}{2}\right)^4 = \frac{105}{512}$$

Thus

$$\Pr\{\text{between 3 and 6 heads inclusive}\} = \frac{15}{128} + \frac{105}{512} + \frac{63}{256} + \frac{105}{512} = \frac{99}{128} = 0.7734$$

(*b*) The probability distribution for the number of heads in 10 tosses of the coin is graphed in Figs. 7-8(*a*) and 7-8(*b*), where Fig. 7-8(*b*) treats the data as if they were continuous. The required probability is the sum of the areas of the shaded rectangles in Fig. 7-8(*b*) and can be approximated by the area under the corresponding normal curve, shown dashed.

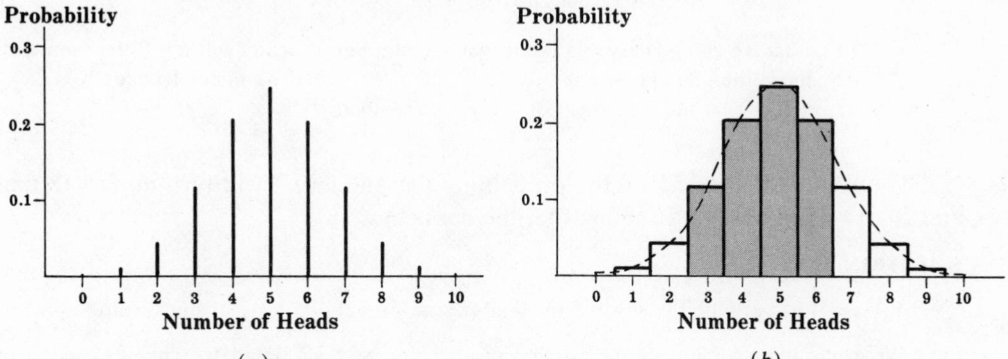

Fig. 7-8

Considering the data to be continuous, it follows that 3 to 6 heads can be considered as 2.5 to 6.5 heads. Also, the mean and variance for the binomial distribution are given by $\mu = Np = 10(\frac{1}{2}) = 5$ and $\sigma = \sqrt{Npq} = \sqrt{(10)(\frac{1}{2})(\frac{1}{2})} = 1.58$.

$$2.5 \text{ in standard units} = \frac{2.5-5}{1.58} = -1.58$$

$$6.5 \text{ in standard units} = \frac{6.5-5}{1.58} = 0.95$$

As shown in Fig. 7-9,

$$\begin{aligned}\text{Required probability} &= (\text{area between } z=-1.58 \text{ and } z=0.95)\\ &= (\text{area between } z=-1.58 \text{ and } z=0)+(\text{area between } z=0 \text{ and } z=0.95)\\ &= 0.4429+0.3289=0.7718\end{aligned}$$

which compares very well with the true value of 0.7734 obtained in part (*a*). The accuracy is even better for larger values of *N*.

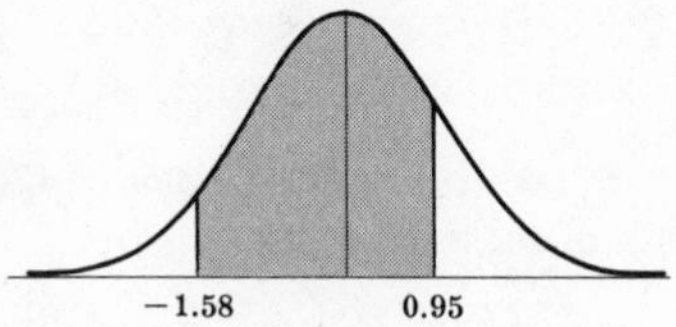

Fig. 7-9

7.25 A fair coin is tossed 500 times. Find the probability that the number of heads will not differ from 250 by (*a*) more than 10 and (*b*) more than 30.

SOLUTION

$$\mu = Np = (500)(\tfrac{1}{2}) = 250 \qquad \sigma = \sqrt{Npq} = \sqrt{(500)(\tfrac{1}{2})(\tfrac{1}{2})} = 11.18$$

(*a*) We require the probability that the number of heads will lie between 240 and 260 or, considering the data to be continuous, between 239.5 and 260.5. Since 239.5 in standard units is $(239.5-250)/11.18 = -0.94$, and 260.5 in standard units is 0.94, we have

$$\begin{aligned}\text{Required probability} &= (\text{area under normal curve between } z=-0.94 \text{ and } z=0.94)\\ &= (\text{twice area between } z=0 \text{ and } z=0.94) = 2(0.3264) = 0.6528\end{aligned}$$

(*b*) We require the probability that the number of heads will lie between 220 and 280 or, considering the data to be continuous, between 219.5 and 280.5. Since 219.5 in standard units is $(219.5-250)/11.18 = -2.73$, and 280.5 in standard units is 2.73, we have

$$\begin{aligned}\text{Required probability} &= (\text{twice area under normal curve between } z=0 \text{ and } z=-2.73)\\ &= 2(0.4968) = 0.9936\end{aligned}$$

It follows that we can be very confident that the number of heads will not differ from that expected (250) by more than 30. Thus if it turned out that the *actual* number of heads was 280, we would strongly believe that the coin was not fair (i.e., was loaded).

7.26 A die is tossed 120 times. Find the probability that the face 4 will turn up (*a*) 18 times or less and (*b*) 14 times or less, assuming that the die is fair.

SOLUTION

The face 4 has probability $p=\frac{1}{6}$ of turning up and probability $q=\frac{5}{6}$ of not turning up.

(*a*) We want the probability of the number of 4's being between 0 and 18. This is exactly equal to

$$\binom{120}{18}\left(\frac{1}{6}\right)^{18}\left(\frac{5}{6}\right)^{102}+\binom{120}{17}\left(\frac{1}{6}\right)^{17}\left(\frac{5}{6}\right)^{103}+\cdots+\binom{120}{0}\left(\frac{1}{6}\right)^{0}\left(\frac{5}{6}\right)^{120}$$

but since the labor involved in the computation is overwhelming, we use the normal approximation.

Considering the data to be continuous, it follows that 0 to 18 fours can be considered as -0.5 to 18.5 fours. Also,

$$\mu = Np = 120(\tfrac{1}{6}) = 20 \qquad \text{and} \qquad \sigma=\sqrt{Npq}=\sqrt{(120)(\tfrac{1}{6})(\tfrac{5}{6})}=4.08$$

Since -0.5 in standard units is $(-0.5-20)/4.08 = -5.02$, and 18.5 in standard units is -0.37, we have

$$\begin{aligned}\text{Required probability} &= (\text{area under normal curve between } z=-5.02 \text{ and } z=-0.37)\\ &= (\text{area between } z=0 \text{ and } z=-5.02)\\ &\quad -(\text{area between } z=0 \text{ and } z=-0.37)\\ &= 0.5-0.1443=0.3557\end{aligned}$$

(*b*) We proceed as in part (*a*), replacing 18 with 14. Since -0.5 in standard units is -5.02, and 14.5 in standard units is $(14.5-20)/4.08=-1.35$, we have

$$\begin{aligned}\text{Required probability} &= (\text{area under normal curve between } z=-5.02 \text{ and } z=-1.35)\\ &= (\text{area between } z=0 \text{ and } z=-5.02)\\ &\quad -(\text{area between } z=0 \text{ and } z=-1.35)\\ &= 0.5-0.4115=0.0885\end{aligned}$$

It follows that if we were to take repeated samples of 120 tosses of a die, a 4 should turn up 14 times or less in about one-tenth of these samples.

THE POISSON DISTRIBUTION

7.27 Ten percent of the tools produced in a certain manufacturing process turn out to be defective. Find the probability that in a sample of 10 tools chosen at random exactly two will be defective by using (*a*) the binomial distribution and (*b*) the Poisson approximation to the binomial distribution.

SOLUTION

The probability of a defective tool is $p=0.1$.

(*a*) $$\Pr\{2 \text{ defective tools in } 10\} = \binom{10}{2}(0.1)^2(0.9)^8 = 0.1937 \qquad \text{or} \qquad 0.19$$

(*b*) With $\lambda = Np = 10(0.1) = 1$ and using $e = 2.718$,

$$\Pr\{2 \text{ defective tools in } 10\} = \frac{\lambda^X e^{-\lambda}}{X!} = \frac{(1)^2 e^{-1}}{2!} = \frac{e^{-1}}{2} = \frac{1}{2e} = 0.1839 \quad \text{or} \quad 0.18$$

In general, the approximation is good if $p \le 0.1$ and $\lambda = Np \le 5$.

7.28 If the probability that an individual suffers a bad reaction from injection of a given serum is 0.001, determine the probability that out of 2000 individuals (*a*) exactly 3 and (*b*) more than 2 individuals will suffer a bad reaction.

SOLUTION

$$\Pr\{X \text{ individuals suffer bad reaction}\} = \frac{\lambda^X e^{-\lambda}}{X!} = \frac{2^X e^{-2}}{X!}$$

where $\lambda = Np = (2000)(0.001) = 2$.

(*a*) $$\Pr\{3 \text{ individuals suffer bad reaction}\} = \frac{2^3 e^{-2}}{3!} = \frac{4}{3e^2} = 0.180$$

(*b*) $$\Pr\{0 \text{ suffers}\} = \frac{2^0 e^{-2}}{0!} = \frac{1}{e^2} \qquad \Pr\{1 \text{ suffers}\} = \frac{2^1 e^{-2}}{1!} = \frac{2}{e^2} \qquad \Pr\{2 \text{ suffer}\} = \frac{2^2 e^{-2}}{2!} = \frac{2}{e^2}$$

$$\begin{aligned}\Pr\{\text{more than 2 suffer}\} &= 1 - \Pr\{0 \text{ or } 1 \text{ or } 2 \text{ suffer}\}\\ &= 1 - \left(\frac{1}{e^2} + \frac{2}{e^2} + \frac{2}{e^2}\right) = 1 - \frac{5}{e^2} = 0.323\end{aligned}$$

Note that according to the binomial distribution, the required probabilities for parts (*a*) and (*b*) are, respectively,

(*a*) $$\binom{2000}{3}(0.001)^3(0.999)^{1997}$$

(*b*) $$1 - \left\{\binom{2000}{0}(0.001)^0(0.999)^{2000} + \binom{2000}{1}(0.001)^1(0.999)^{1999} + \binom{2000}{2}(0.001)^2(0.999)^{1998}\right\}$$

which would be more difficult to evaluate directly.

7.29 A Poisson distribution is given by

$$p(X) = \frac{(0.72)^X e^{-0.72}}{X!}$$

Find (*a*) $p(0)$, (*b*) $p(1)$, (*c*) $p(2)$, and (*d*) $p(3)$.

SOLUTION

(*a*) $$p(0) = \frac{(0.72)^0 e^{-0.72}}{0!} = \frac{(1)\, e^{-0.72}}{1} = e^{-0.72} = 0.4868 \qquad \text{using Appendix VIII}$$

(*b*) $$p(1) = \frac{(0.72)^1 e^{-0.72}}{1!} = 0.72\, e^{-0.72} = (0.72)(0.4868) = 0.3505$$

(*c*) $$p(2) = \frac{(0.72)^2 e^{-0.72}}{2!} = \frac{(0.5184)\, e^{-0.72}}{2} = (0.2592)(0.4868) = 0.1262$$

Another method

$$p(2) = \frac{0.72}{2} p(1) = (0.36)(0.3505) = 0.1262$$

(*d*) $$p(3) = \frac{(0.72)^3 e^{-0.72}}{3!} = \frac{0.72}{3} p(2) = (0.24)(0.1262) = 0.0303$$

THE MULTINOMIAL DISTRIBUTION

7.30 A box contains 5 red balls, 4 white balls, and 3 blue balls. A ball is selected at random from the box, its color is noted, and then the ball is replaced. Find the probability that out of 6 balls selected in this manner, 3 are red, 2 are white, and 1 is blue.

SOLUTION

Pr{red at any drawing} = $\frac{5}{12}$, Pr{white at any drawing} = $\frac{4}{12}$, and Pr{blue at any drawing} = $\frac{3}{12}$; thus

$$\Pr\{3 \text{ are red, 2 are white, 1 is blue}\} = \frac{6!}{3!2!1!}\left(\frac{5}{12}\right)^3\left(\frac{4}{12}\right)^2\left(\frac{3}{12}\right)^1 = \frac{625}{5184}$$

FITTING OF DATA BY THEORETICAL DISTRIBUTIONS

7.31 Fit a binomial distribution to the data of Problem 2.17.

SOLUTION

We have Pr{X heads in a toss of 5 pennies} = $p(X) = \binom{5}{X} p^X q^{5-X}$, where p and q are the respective probabilities of a head and a tail on a single toss of a penny. By Problem 7.11(*a*), the mean number of heads is $\mu = Np = 5p$. For the actual (or observed) frequency distribution, the mean number of heads is

$$\frac{\sum fX}{\sum f} = \frac{(38)(0) + (144)(1) + (342)(2) + (287)(3) + (164)(4) + (25)(5)}{1000} = \frac{2470}{1000} = 2.47$$

Equating the theoretical and actual means, $5p = 2.47$, or $p = 0.494$. Thus the fitted binomial distribution is given by $p(X) = \binom{5}{X}(0.494)^X(0.506)^{5-X}$.

Table 7.4 lists these probabilities as well as the expected (theoretical) and actual frequencies. The fit is seen to be fair. The goodness of fit is investigated in Problem 12.12.

Table 7.4

Number of Heads (X)	Pr{X heads}	Expected Frequency	Observed Frequency
0	0.0332	33.2, or 33	38
1	0.1619	161.9, or 162	144
2	0.3162	316.2, or 316	342
3	0.3087	308.7, or 309	287
4	0.1507	150.7, or 151	164
5	0.0294	29.4, or 29	25

7.32 Use probability graph paper to determine whether the frequency distribution of Table 2.1 can be closely approximated by a normal distribution.

SOLUTION

First the given frequency distribution is converted into a relative cumulative-frequency distribution, as shown in Table 7.5. Then the relative cumulative frequencies, expressed as percentages, are plotted against upper class boundaries on special probability graph paper, as shown in Fig. 7-10. The degree to which all plotted points lie on a line determines the closeness of fit of the given distribution to a normal distribution. From the above it is seen that there is a normal distribution that fits the data closely (see Problem 7.33).

Table 7.5

Height (in)	Relative Cumulative Frequency (%)
Less than 62.5	5.0
Less than 65.5	23.0 (c_1)
Less than 68.5	65.0
Less than 71.5	92.0
Less than 74.5	100.0

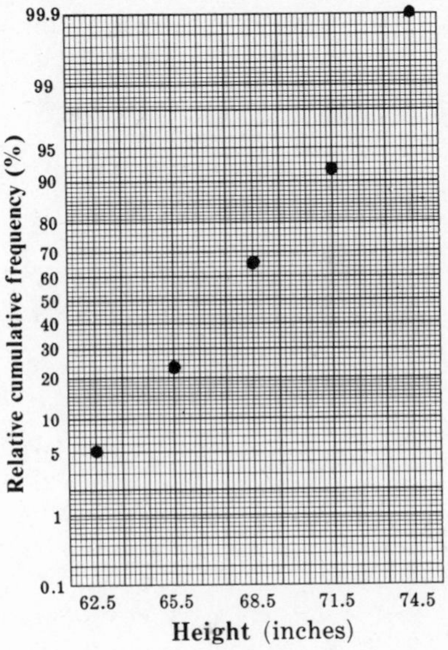

Fig. 7-10

Mathcad **7.33** Fit a normal curve to the data of Table 2.1.

SOLUTION

The work may be organized as in Table 7.6. In calculating z for the class boundaries, we use $z = (X - \bar{X})/s$, where the mean $\bar{X}$ and the standard deviation s have been obtained, respectively, in Problems 3.22 and 4.17.

Table 7.6

Heights (in)	Class Boundaries (X)	z for Class Boundaries	Area Under Normal Curve from 0 to z	Area for Each Class	Expected Frequency	Observed Frequency
	59.5	−2.72	0.4967			
60–62				0.0413	4.13, or 4	5
	62.5	−1.70	0.4554			
63–65				0.2068	20.68, or 21	18
	65.5	−0.67	0.2486			
66–68			} Add →	0.3892	38.92, or 39	42
	68.5	0.36	0.1406			
69–71				0.2771	27.71, or 28	27
	71.5	1.39	0.4177			
72–74				0.0743	7.43, or 7	8
	74.5	2.41	0.4920			

$\bar{X} = 67.45$ in $\qquad s = 2.92$ in

In column 4 of Table 7.6, the areas under the normal curve from 0 to z have been obtained from Appendix II. From this we find the areas under the normal curve between successive values of z, as shown in column 5. These are obtained by subtracting the successive areas in column 4 when the corresponding z's have the same sign, and adding them when the z's have opposite signs (which occurs only once in the table). The reason for this is at once clear from a diagram.

Multiplying the entries in column 5 (which represent relative frequencies) by the total frequency N (in this case $N = 100$) yields the expected frequencies, as shown in column 6. It is seen that they agree well with the actual (or observed) frequencies of column 7.

If desired, the standard deviation modified by using Sheppard's correction may be used [see Problem 4.21(a)].

The goodness of fit of the distribution is considered in Problem 12.13.

7.34 Table 7.7 shows the number of days, f, in a 50-day period during which X automobile accidents occurred in a city. Fit a Poisson distribution to the data.

SOLUTION

The mean number of accidents is

$$\lambda = \frac{\sum fX}{\sum f} = \frac{(21)(0)+(18)(1)+(7)(2)+(3)(3)+(1)(4)}{50} = \frac{45}{50} = 0.90$$

Thus, according to the Poisson distribution,

$$\Pr\{X \text{ accidents}\} = \frac{(0.90)^X e^{-0.90}}{X!}$$

Table 7.7

Number of Accidents (X)	Number of Days (f)
0	21
1	18
2	7
3	3
4	1
	Total 50

Table 7.8 lists the probabilities for 0, 1, 2, 3, and 4 accidents as obtained from this Poisson distribution, as well as the expected or theoretical number of days during which X accidents take place (obtained by multiplying the respective probabilities by 50). For convenience of comparison, column 4 repeats the actual number of days from Table 7.7.

Table 7.8

Number of Accidents (X)	Pr{X accidents}	Expected Number of Days	Actual Number of Days
0	0.4066	20.33, or 20	21
1	0.3659	18.30, or 18	18
2	0.1647	8.24, or 8	7
3	0.0494	2.47, or 2	3
4	0.0111	0.56, or 1	1

Note that the fit of the Poisson distribution to the given data is good.

For a true Poisson distribution, the variance $\sigma^2 = \lambda$. Computing the variance of the given distribution gives 0.97. This compares favorably with the value 0.90 for λ, and this can be taken as further evidence for the suitability of the Poisson distribution in approximating the sample data.

Supplementary Problems

THE BINOMIAL DISTRIBUTION

7.35 Evaluate (*a*) 7!, (*b*) 10!/(6!4!), (*c*) $\binom{9}{5}$, (*d*) $\binom{11}{8}$, and (*e*) $\binom{6}{1}$.

7.36 Expand (*a*) $(q+p)^7$ and (*b*) $(q+p)^{10}$.

7.37 Find the probability that in tossing a fair coin six times there will appear (*a*) 0, (*b*) 1, (*c*) 2, (*d*), 3, (*e*) 4, (*f*) 5, and (*g*) 6 heads.

7.38 Find the probability of (*a*) 2 or more heads and (*b*) fewer than 4 heads in a single toss of 6 fair coins.

7.39 If X denotes the number of heads in a single toss of 4 fair coins, find (*a*) $\Pr\{X=3\}$, (*b*) $\Pr\{X<2\}$, (*c*) $\Pr\{X \le 2\}$, and (*d*) $\Pr\{1 < X \le 3\}$.

7.40 Out of 800 families with 5 children each, how many would you expect to have (*a*) 3 boys, (*b*) 5 girls, and (*c*) either 2 or 3 boys? Assume equal probabilities for boys and girls.

7.41 Find the probability of getting a total of 11 (*a*) once and (*b*) twice in two tosses of a pair of fair dice.

7.42 What is the probability of getting a 9 exactly once in 3 throws with a pair of dice?

7.43 Find the probability of guessing correctly at least 6 of the 10 answers on a true-false examination.

7.44 An insurance salesperson sells policies to 5 men, all of identical age and in good health. According to the actuarial tables, the probability that a man of this particular age will be alive 30 years hence is $\frac{2}{3}$. Find the probability that in 30 years (*a*) all 5 men, (*b*) at least 3 men, (*c*) only 2 men, and (*d*) at least 1 man will be alive.

7.45 Compute the (*a*) mean, (*b*) standard deviation, (*c*) moment coefficient of skewness, and (*d*) moment coefficient of kurtosis for a binomial distribution in which $p=0.7$ and $N=60$. Interpret the results.

7.46 Show that if a binomial distribution with $N=100$ is symmetrical, its moment coefficient of kurtosis is 2.98.

7.47 Evaluate (*a*) $\sum (X-\mu)^3 p(X)$ and (*b*) $\sum (X-\mu)^4 p(X)$ for the binomial distribution.

7.48 Prove formulas (*1*) and (*2*) at the beginning of this chapter for the moment coefficients of skewness and kurtosis.

THE NORMAL DISTRIBUTION

7.49 On a statistics examination the mean was 78 and the standard deviation was 10.

(*a*) Determine the standard scores of two students whose grades were 93 and 62, respectively.

(*b*) Determine the grades of two students whose standard scores were −0.6 and 1.2, respectively.

7.50 Find (*a*) the mean and (*b*) the standard deviation on an examination in which grades of 70 and 88 correspond to standard scores of −0.6 and 1.4, respectively.

7.51 Find the area under the normal curve between (*a*) $z = -1.20$ and $z = 2.40$, (*b*) $z = 1.23$ and $z = 1.87$, and (*c*) $z = -2.35$ and $z = -0.50$.

7.52 Find the area under the normal curve (*a*) to the left of $z = -1.78$, (*b*) to the left of $z = 0.56$, (*c*) to the right of $z = -1.45$, (*d*) corresponding to $z \geq 2.16$, (*e*) corresponding to $-0.80 \leq z \leq 1.53$, and (*f*) to the left of $z = -2.52$ and to the right of $z = 1.83$.

7.53 If z is normally distributed with mean 0 and variance 1, find (*a*) $\Pr\{z \geq -1.64\}$, (*b*) $\Pr(-1.96 \leq z \leq 1.96\}$, and (*c*) $\Pr\{|z| \geq 1\}$.

7.54 Find the value of z such that (*a*) the area to the right of z is 0.2266, (*b*) the area to the left of z is 0.0314, (*c*) the area between −0.23 and z is 0.5722, (*d*) the area between 1.15 and z is 0.0730, and (*e*) the area between $-z$ and z is 0.9000.

7.55 Find z_1 if $\Pr\{z \geq z_1\} = 0.84$, where z is normally distributed with mean 0 and variance 1.

7.56 Find the ordinates of the normal curve at (*a*) $z = 2.25$, (*b*) $z = -0.32$, and (*c*) $z = -1.18$.

7.57 If the heights of 300 students are normally distributed with mean 68.0 in and standard deviation 3.0 in, how many students have heights (*a*) greater than 72 in, (*b*) less than or equal to 64 in, (*c*) between 65 and 71 in inclusive, and (*d*) equal to 68 in? Assume the measurements to be recorded to the nearest inch.

7.58 If the diameters of ball bearings are normally distributed with mean 0.6140 in and standard deviation 0.0025 in, determine the percentage of ball bearings with diameters (*a*) between 0.610 and 0.618 in inclusive, (*b*) greater than 0.617 in, (*c*) less than 0.608 in, and (*d*) equal to 0.615 in.

7.59 The mean grade on a final examination was 72 and the standard deviation was 9. The top 10% of the students are to receive A's. What is the minimum grade that a student must get in order to receive an A?

7.60 If a set of measurements is normally distributed, what percentage of the measurements differ from the mean by (*a*) more than half the standard deviation and (*b*) less than three-quarters of the standard deviation?

7.61 If $\bar{X}$ is the mean and s is the standard deviation of a set of normally distributed measurements, what percentage of the measurements are (*a*) within the range $\bar{X} \pm 2s$, (*b*) outside the range $\bar{X} \pm 1.2s$, and (*c*) greater than $\bar{X} - 1.5s$?

7.62 In Problem 7.61, find the constant a such that the percentage of the cases (*a*) within the range $\bar{X} \pm as$ is 75% and (*b*) less than $\bar{X} - as$ is 22%.

NORMAL APPROXIMATION TO THE BINOMIAL DISTRIBUTION

7.63 Find the probability that 200 tosses of a coin will result in (*a*) between 80 and 120 heads inclusive, (*b*) less than 90 heads, (*c*) less than 85 or more than 115 heads, and (*d*) exactly 100 heads.

7.64 Find the probability that on a true-false examination a student can guess correctly the answers to (*a*) 12 or more out of 20 questions and (*b*) 24 or more out of 40 questions.

7.65 Ten percent of the bolts that a machine produces are defective. Find the probability that in a random sample of 400 bolts produced by this machine, (*a*) at most 30, (*b*) between 30 and 50, (*c*) between 35 and 45, and (*d*) 55 or more of the bolts will be defective.

7.66 Find the probability of getting more than 25 sevens in 100 tosses of a pair of fair dice.

THE POISSON DISTRIBUTION

7.67 If 3% of the electric bulbs manufactured by a company are defective, find the probability that in a sample of 100 bulbs (*a*) 0, (*b*) 1, (*c*) 2, (*d*) 3, (*e*) 4, and (*f*) 5 bulbs will be defective.

7.68 In Problem 7.67, find the probability that (*a*) more than 5, (*b*) between 1 and 3, and (*c*) less than or equal to 2 bulbs will be defective.

7.69 A bag contains 1 red and 7 white marbles. A marble is drawn from the bag and its color is observed. Then the marble is put back into the bag and the contents are thoroughly mixed. Using (*a*) the binomial distribution and (*b*) the Poisson approximation to the binomial distribution, find the probability that in 8 such drawings a red ball is selected exactly 3 times.

7.70 According to the National Office of Vital Statistics of the U.S. Department of Health, Education, and Welfare, the average number of accidental drownings per year in the United States is 3.0 per 100,000 population. Find the probability that in a city of population 200,000 there will be (*a*) 0, (*b*) 2, (*c*) 6, (*d*) 8, (*e*) between 4 and 8, and (*f*) fewer than 3 accidental drownings per year.

7.71 Between the hours of 2 and 4 P.M. the average number of phone calls per minute coming into the switchboard of a company is 2.5. Find the probability that during one particular minute there will be (*a*) 0, (*b*) 1, (*c*) 2, (*d*) 3, (*e*) 4 or fewer, and (*f*) more than 6 phone calls.

THE MULTINOMIAL DISTRIBUTION

7.72 A fair die is tossed 6 times. Find the probability (*a*) that one 1, two 2's, and three 3's turn up and (*b*) that each side turns up only once.

7.73 A box contains a very large number of red, white, blue, and yellow marbles in the ratio 4:3:2:1, respectively. Find the probability that in 10 drawings (*a*) 4 red, 3 white, 2 blue, and 1 yellow marble will be drawn and (*b*) 8 red and 2 yellow marbles will be drawn.

7.74 Find the probability of not getting a 1, 2, or 3 in four tosses of a fair die.

FITTING OF DATA BY THEORETICAL DISTRIBUTIONS

7.75 Fit a binomial distribution to the data in Table 7.9.

Table 7.9

X	0	1	2	3	4
f	30	62	46	10	2

7.76 Use probability graph paper to determine whether the data of Problem 3.59 can be closely approximated by a normal distribution.

7.77 Fit a normal distribution to the data of Problem 3.59.

7.78 Fit a normal distribution to the data of Problem 3.61.

7.79 Fit a Poisson distribution to the data of Problem 7.75, and compare this fit with the fit obtained by using the binomial distribution.

7.80 For 10 Prussian army corps units over a period of 20 years (1875 to 1894), Table 7.10 shows the number of deaths per army corps per year resulting from the kick of a horse. Fit a Poisson distribution to the data.

Table 7.10

X	0	1	2	3	4
f	109	65	22	3	1

Chapter 8

Elementary Sampling Theory

SAMPLING THEORY

Sampling theory is a study of relationships existing between a population and samples drawn from the population. It is of great value in many connections. For example, it is useful in *estimating* unknown population quantities (such as population mean and variance), often called *population parameters* or briefly *parameters*, from a knowledge of corresponding sample quantities (such as sample mean and variance), often called *sample statistics* or briefly *statistics*. Estimation problems are considered in Chapter 9.

Sampling theory is also useful in determining whether the observed differences between two samples are due to chance variation or whether they are really significant. Such questions arise, for example, in testing a new serum for use in treatment of a disease or in deciding whether one production process is better than another. Their answers involve the use of so-called *tests of significance and hypotheses* that are important in the *theory of decisions*. These are considered in Chapter 10.

In general, a study of the inferences made concerning a population by using samples drawn from it, together with indications of the accuracy of such inferences by using probability theory, is called *statistical inference*.

RANDOM SAMPLES AND RANDOM NUMBERS

In order that the conclusions of sampling theory and statistical inference be valid, samples must be chosen so as to be *representative* of a population. A study of sampling methods and of the related problems that arise is called the *design of the experiment*.

One way in which a representative sample may be obtained is by a process called *random sampling*, according to which each member of a population has an equal chance of being included in the sample. One technique for obtaining a random sample is to assign numbers to each member of the population, write these numbers on small pieces of paper, place them in an urn, and then draw numbers from the urn, being careful to mix thoroughly before each drawing. An alternative method is to use a table of *random numbers* (see Appendix IX) specially constructed for such purposes. See Problem 8.6.

SAMPLING WITH AND WITHOUT REPLACEMENT

If we draw a number from an urn, we have the choice of replacing or not replacing the number into the urn before a second drawing. In the first case the number can come up again and again, whereas in the second it can only come up once. Sampling where each member of the population may be chosen more than once is called *sampling with replacement*, while if each member cannot be chosen more than once it is called *sampling without replacement*.

Populations are either finite or infinite. If, for example, we draw 10 balls successively without replacement from an urn containing 100 balls, we are sampling from a finite population; while if we toss a coin 50 times and count the number of heads, we are sampling from an infinite population.

A finite population in which sampling is with replacement can theoretically be considered infinite, since any number of samples can be drawn without exhausting the population. For many practical purposes, sampling from a finite population that is very large can be considered to be sampling from an infinite population.

SAMPLING DISTRIBUTIONS

Consider all possible samples of size N that can be drawn from a given population (either with or without replacement). For each sample, we can compute a statistic (such as the mean and the standard deviation) that will vary from sample to sample. In this manner we obtain a distribution of the statistic that is called its *sampling distribution.*

If, for example, the particular statistic used is the sample mean, then the distribution is called the *sampling distribution of means,* or the *sampling distribution of the mean.* Similarly, we could have sampling distributions of standard deviations, variances, medians, proportions, etc.

For each sampling distribution, we can compute the mean, standard deviation, etc. Thus we can speak of the mean and standard deviation of the sampling distribution of means, etc.

SAMPLING DISTRIBUTION OF MEANS

Suppose that all possible samples of size N are drawn without replacement from a finite population of size $N_p > N$. If we denote the mean and standard deviation of the sampling distribution of means by $\mu_{\bar{X}}$ and $\sigma_{\bar{X}}$ and the population mean and standard deviation by μ and σ, respectively, then

$$\mu_{\bar{X}} = \mu \qquad \text{and} \qquad \sigma_{\bar{X}} = \frac{\sigma}{\sqrt{N}}\sqrt{\frac{N_p - N}{N_p - 1}} \tag{1}$$

If the population is infinite or if sampling is with replacement, the above results reduce to

$$\mu_{\bar{X}} = \mu \qquad \text{and} \qquad \sigma_{\bar{X}} = \frac{\sigma}{\sqrt{N}} \tag{2}$$

For large values of N ($N \geq 30$), the sampling distribution of means is approximately a normal distribution with mean $\mu_{\bar{X}}$ and standard deviation $\sigma_{\bar{X}}$, irrespective of the population (so long as the population mean and variance are finite and the population size is at least twice the sample size). This result for an infinite population is a special case of the *central limit theorem* of advanced probability theory, which shows that the accuracy of the approximation improves as N gets larger. This is sometimes indicated by saying that the sampling distribution is *asymptotically normal.*

In case the population is normally distributed, the sampling distribution of means is also normally distributed even for small values of N (i.e., $N < 30$).

SAMPLING DISTRIBUTION OF PROPORTIONS

Suppose that a population is infinite and that the probability of occurrence of an event (called its success) is p, while the probability of nonoccurrence of the event is $q = 1 - p$. For example, the population may be all possible tosses of a fair coin in which the probability of the event "heads" is $p = \frac{1}{2}$. Consider all possible samples of size N drawn from this population, and for each sample determine the proportion P of successes. In the case of the coin, P would be the proportion of heads turning up in N tosses. We thus obtain a *sampling distribution of proportions* whose mean μ_P and standard deviation σ_P are given by

$$\mu_P = p \qquad \text{and} \qquad \sigma_P = \sqrt{\frac{pq}{N}} = \sqrt{\frac{p(1-p)}{N}} \tag{3}$$

which can be obtained from equations (*2*) by placing $\mu = p$ and $\sigma = \sqrt{pq}$. For large values of N ($N \geq 30$), the sampling distribution is very closely normally distributed. Note that the population is *binomially distributed.*

Equations (*3*) are also valid for a finite population in which sampling is with replacement. For finite populations in which sampling is without replacement, equations (*3*) are replaced by equations (*1*) with $\mu = p$ and $\sigma = \sqrt{pq}$.

Note that equations (*3*) are obtained most easily by dividing the mean and standard deviation (Np and $\sqrt{Npq}$) of the binomial distribution by N (see Chapter 7).

SAMPLING DISTRIBUTIONS OF DIFFERENCES AND SUMS

Suppose that we are given two populations. For each sample of size N_1 drawn from the first population, let us compute a statistic S_1; this yields a sampling distribution for the statistic S_1, whose mean and standard deviation we denote by μ_{S1} and σ_{S1}, respectively. Similarly, for each sample of size N_2 drawn from the second population, let us compute a statistic S_2; this yields a sampling distribution for the statistic S_2, whose mean and standard deviation are denoted by μ_{S2} and σ_{S2}. From all possible combinations of these samples from the two populations we can obtain a distribution of the differences, $S_1 - S_2$, which is called the *sampling distribution of differences of the statistics.* The mean and standard deviation of this sampling distribution, denoted respectively by μ_{S1-S2} and σ_{S1-S2}, are given by

$$\mu_{S1-S2} = \mu_{S1} - \mu_{S2} \qquad \text{and} \qquad \sigma_{S1-S2} = \sqrt{\sigma_{S1}^2 + \sigma_{S2}^2} \tag{4}$$

provided that the samples chosen do not in any way depend on each other (i.e., the samples are *independent*).

If S_1 and S_2 are the sample means from the two populations—which means we denote by $\bar{X}_1$ and $\bar{X}_2$, respectively—then the sampling distribution of the differences of means is given for infinite populations with means and standard deviations (μ_1, σ_1) and (μ_2, σ_2), respectively, by

$$\mu_{\bar{X}1-\bar{X}2} = \mu_{\bar{X}1} - \mu_{\bar{X}2} = \mu_1 - \mu_2 \qquad \text{and} \qquad \sigma_{\bar{X}1-\bar{X}2} = \sqrt{\sigma_{\bar{X}1}^2 + \sigma_{\bar{X}2}^2} = \sqrt{\frac{\sigma_1^2}{N_1} + \frac{\sigma_2^2}{N_2}} \tag{5}$$

using equations (*2*). The result also holds for finite populations if sampling is with replacement. Similar results can be obtained for finite populations in which sampling is without replacement by using equations (*1*).

Corresponding results can be obtained for the sampling distributions of differences of proportions from two binomially distributed populations with parameters (p_1, q_1) and (p_2, q_2), respectively. In this case S_1 and S_2 correspond to the proportion of successes, P_1 and P_2, and equations (*4*) yield the results

$$\mu_{P1-P2} = \mu_{P1} - \mu_{P2} = p_1 - p_2 \qquad \text{and} \qquad \sigma_{P1-P2} = \sqrt{\sigma_{P1}^2 + \sigma_{P2}^2} = \sqrt{\frac{p_1 q_1}{N_1} + \frac{p_2 q_2}{N_2}} \tag{6}$$

If N_1 and N_2 are large ($N_1, N_2 \geq 30$), the sampling distributions of differences of means or proportions are very closely normally distributed.

It is sometimes useful to speak of the *sampling distribution of the sum of statistics.* The mean and standard deviation of this distribution are given by

$$\mu_{S1+S2} = \mu_{S1} + \mu_{S2} \qquad \text{and} \qquad \sigma_{S1+S2} = \sqrt{\sigma_{S1}^2 + \sigma_{S2}^2} \tag{7}$$

assuming that the samples are *independent.*

STANDARD ERRORS

The standard deviation of a sampling distribution of a statistic is often called its *standard error.* Table 8.1 lists standard errors of sampling distributions for various statistics under the conditions of random sampling from an infinite (or very large) population or of sampling with replacement from a finite population. Also listed are special remarks giving conditions under which results are valid and other pertinent statements.

The quantities μ, σ, p, μ_r and $\bar{X}$, s, P, m_r denote, respectively, the population and sample means, standard deviations, proportions, and rth moments about the mean.

Table 8.1 Standard Errors for Some Sampling Distributions

Sampling Distribution	Standard Error	Special Remarks
Means	$\sigma_{\bar{X}} = \dfrac{\sigma}{\sqrt{N}}$	This is true for large or small samples. The sampling distribution of means is very nearly normal for $N \geq 30$ even when the population is nonnormal. $\mu_{\bar{X}} = \mu$, the population mean, in all cases.
Proportions	$\sigma_P = \sqrt{\dfrac{p(1-p)}{N}} = \sqrt{\dfrac{pq}{N}}$	The remarks made for means apply here as well. $\mu_P = p$ in all cases.
Standard deviations	(*1*) $\sigma_s = \dfrac{\sigma}{\sqrt{2N}}$ (*2*) $\sigma_s = \sqrt{\dfrac{\mu_4 - \mu_2^2}{4N\mu_2}}$	For $N \geq 100$, the sampling distribution of s is very nearly normal. σ_s is given by (*1*) only if the population is normal (or approximately normal). If the population is nonnormal, (*2*) can be used. Note that (*2*) reduces to (*1*) when $\mu_2 = \sigma^2$ and $\mu_4 = 3\sigma^4$, which is true for normal populations. For $N \geq 100$, $\mu_s = \sigma$ very nearly.
Medians	$\sigma_{\text{med}} = \sigma\sqrt{\dfrac{\pi}{2N}} = \dfrac{1.2533\sigma}{\sqrt{N}}$	For $N \geq 30$, the sampling distribution of the median is very nearly normal. The given result holds only if the population is normal (or approximately normal). $\mu_{\text{med}} = \mu$
First and third quartiles	$\sigma_{Q1} = \sigma_{Q3} = \dfrac{1.3626\sigma}{\sqrt{N}}$	The remarks made for medians apply here as well. μ_{Q1} and μ_{Q3} are very nearly equal to the first and third quartiles of the population. Note that $\sigma_{Q2} = \sigma_{\text{med}}$
Deciles	$\sigma_{D1} = \sigma_{D9} = \dfrac{1.7094\sigma}{\sqrt{N}}$ $\sigma_{D2} = \sigma_{D8} = \dfrac{1.4288\sigma}{\sqrt{N}}$ $\sigma_{D3} = \sigma_{D7} = \dfrac{1.3180\sigma}{\sqrt{N}}$ $\sigma_{D4} = \sigma_{D6} = \dfrac{1.2680\sigma}{\sqrt{N}}$	The remarks made for medians apply here as well. $\mu_{D1}, \mu_{D2}, \ldots$ are very nearly equal to the first, second, ... deciles of the population. Note that $\sigma_{D5} = \sigma_{\text{med}}$.
Semi-interquartile ranges	$\sigma_Q = \dfrac{0.7867\sigma}{\sqrt{N}}$	The remarks made for medians apply here as well. μ_Q is very nearly equal to the population semi-interquartile range.
Variances	(*1*) $\sigma_{S^2} = \sigma^2\sqrt{\dfrac{2}{N}}$ (*2*) $\sigma_{S^2} = \sqrt{\dfrac{\mu_4 - \dfrac{N-3}{N-1}\mu_2^2}{N}}$	The remarks made for standard deviation apply here as well. Note that (*2*) yields (*1*) in case the population is normal. $\mu_{S^2} = \sigma^2(N-1)/N$, which is very nearly σ^2 for large N.
Coefficients of variation	$\sigma_V = \dfrac{v}{\sqrt{2N}}\sqrt{1+2v^2}$	Here $v = \sigma/\mu$ is the population coefficient of variation. The given result holds for normal (or nearly normal) populations and $N \geq 100$.

It is noted that if the sample size N is large enough, the sampling distributions are normal or nearly normal. For this reason, the methods are known as *large sampling methods.* When $N < 30$, samples are called *small.* The theory of *small samples,* or *exact sampling theory* as it is sometimes called, is treated in Chapter 11.

When population parameters such as σ, p, or μ_r are unknown, they may be estimated closely by their corresponding sample statistics namely, s (or $\hat{s} = \sqrt{N/(N-1)}s$), P, and m_r—if the samples are large enough.

Solved Problems

SAMPLING DISTRIBUTION OF MEANS

8.1 A population consists of the five numbers 2, 3, 6, 8, and 11. Consider all possible samples of size 2 that can be drawn with replacement from this population. Find (*a*) the mean of the population, (*b*) the standard deviation of the population, (*c*) the mean of the sampling distribution of means, and (*d*) the standard deviation of the sampling distribution of means (i.e., the standard error of means).

SOLUTION

(*a*)
$$\mu = \frac{2+3+6+8+11}{5} = \frac{30}{5} = 6.0$$

(*b*)
$$\sigma^2 = \frac{(2-6)^2+(3-6)^2+(6-6)^2+(8-6)^2+(11-6)^2}{5} = \frac{16+9+0+4+25}{5} = 10.8$$

and $\sigma = 3.29$.

(*c*) There are $5(5) = 25$ samples of size 2 that can be drawn with replacement (since any one of the five numbers on the first draw can be associated with any one of the five numbers on the second draw). These are

(2, 2)	(2, 3)	(2, 6)	(2, 8)	(2, 11)
(3, 2)	(3, 3)	(3, 6)	(3, 8)	(3, 11)
(6, 2)	(6, 3)	(6, 6)	(6, 8)	(6, 11)
(8, 2)	(8, 3)	(8, 6)	(8, 8)	(8, 11)
(11, 2)	(11, 3)	(11, 6)	(11, 8)	(11, 11)

The corresponding sample means are

2.0	2.5	4.0	5.0	6.5	
2.5	3.0	4.5	5.5	7.0	
4.0	4.5	6.0	7.0	8.5	(*8*)
5.0	5.5	7.0	8.0	9.5	
6.5	7.0	8.5	9.5	11.0	

and the mean of sampling distribution of means is

$$\mu_{\bar{X}} = \frac{\text{sum of all sample means in } (8)}{25} = \frac{150}{25} = 6.0$$

illustrating the fact that $\mu_{\bar{X}} = \mu$.

(*d*) The variance $\sigma_{\bar{X}}^2$ of the sampling distribution of means is obtained by subtracting the mean 6 from each number in (*8*), squaring the result, adding all 25 numbers thus obtained, and dividing by 25. The final result is $\sigma_{\bar{X}}^2 = 135/25 = 5.40$, and thus $\sigma_{\bar{X}} = \sqrt{5.40} = 2.32$. This illustrates the fact that for finite populations involving sampling with replacement (or infinite populations), $\sigma_{\bar{X}}^2 = \sigma^2/N$ since the right-hand side is $10.8/2 = 5.40$, agreeing with the above value.

8.2 Solve Problem 8.1 for the case that the sampling is without replacement.

SOLUTION

As in parts (*a*) and (*b*) of Problem 8.1, $\mu = 6$ and $\sigma = 3.29$.

(*c*) There are $\binom{5}{2} = 10$ samples of size 2 that can be drawn without replacement (this means that we draw one number and then another number different from the first) from the population: (2, 3), (2, 6), (2, 8), (2, 11), (3, 6), (3, 8), (3, 11), (6, 8), (6, 11), and (8, 11). The selection (2, 3), for example, is considered the same as (3, 2).

The corresponding sample means are 2.5, 4.0, 5.0, 6.5, 4.5, 5.5, 7.0, 7.0, 8.5, and 9.5, and the mean of sampling distribution of means is

$$\mu_{\bar{X}} = \frac{2.5+4.0+5.0+6.5+4.5+5.5+7.0+7.0+8.5+9.5}{10} = 6.0$$

illustrating the fact that $\mu_{\bar{X}} = \mu$.

(*d*) The variance of sampling distribution of means is

$$\sigma_{\bar{X}}^2 = \frac{(2.5-6.0)^2+(4.0-6.0)^2+(5.0-6.0)^2+\cdots+(9.5-6.0)^2}{10} = 4.05$$

and $\sigma_{\bar{X}} = 2.01$. This illustrates

$$\sigma_{\bar{X}}^2 = \frac{\sigma^2}{N}\left(\frac{N_p - N}{N_p - 1}\right)$$

since the right side equals

$$\frac{10.8}{2}\left(\frac{5-2}{5-1}\right) = 4.05$$

as obtained above.

8.3 Assume that the heights of 3000 male students at a university are normally distributed with mean 68.0 inches (in) and standard deviation 3.0 in. If 80 samples consisting of 25 students each are obtained, what would be the expected mean and standard deviation of the resulting sampling distribution of means if the sampling were done (*a*) with replacement and (*b*) without replacement?

SOLUTION

The numbers of samples of size 25 that could be obtained theoretically from a group of 3000 students with and without replacement are $(3000)^{25}$ and $\binom{3000}{25}$, which are much larger than 80. Hence we do not get a true sampling distribution of means, but only an *experimental* sampling distribution. Nevertheless, since the number of samples is large, there should be close agreement between the two sampling distributions. Hence the expected mean and standard deviation would be close to those of the theoretical distribution. Thus we have:

(*a*) $\mu_{\bar{X}} = \mu = 68.0$ in and $\sigma_{\bar{X}} = \dfrac{\sigma}{\sqrt{N}} = \dfrac{3}{\sqrt{25}} = 0.6$ in

(*b*) $\mu_{\bar{X}} = 68.0$ in and $\delta_{\bar{X}} = \dfrac{\sigma}{\sqrt{N}}\sqrt{\dfrac{N_p - N}{N_p - 1}} = \dfrac{3}{\sqrt{25}}\sqrt{\dfrac{3000-25}{3000-1}}$

which is only very slightly less than 0.6 in and can therefore for all practical purposes be considered the same as in sampling with replacement.

Thus we would expect the experimental sampling distribution of means to be approximately normally distributed with mean 68.0 in and standard deviation 0.6 in.

Mathcad **8.4** In how many samples of Problem 8.3 would you expect to find the mean (a) between 66.8 and 68.3 in and (b) less than 66.4 in?

SOLUTION

The mean $\bar{X}$ of a sample in standard units is here given by

$$z = \frac{\bar{X} - \mu_{\bar{X}}}{\sigma_{\bar{X}}} = \frac{\bar{X} - 68.0}{0.6}$$

(a)

$$66.8 \text{ in standard units} = \frac{66.8 - 68.0}{0.6} = -2.0$$

$$68.3 \text{ in standard units} = \frac{68.3 - 68.0}{0.6} = 0.5$$

As shown in Fig. 8-1(a),

Proportion of samples with means between 66.8 and 68.3 in

$= (\text{area under normal curve between } z = -2.0 \text{ and } z = 0.5)$

$= (\text{area between } z = -2 \text{ and } z = 0) + (\text{area between } z = 0 \text{ and } z = 0.5)$

$= 0.4772 + 0.1915 = 0.6687$

Thus the expected number of samples is $(80)(0.6687) = 53.496$, or 53.

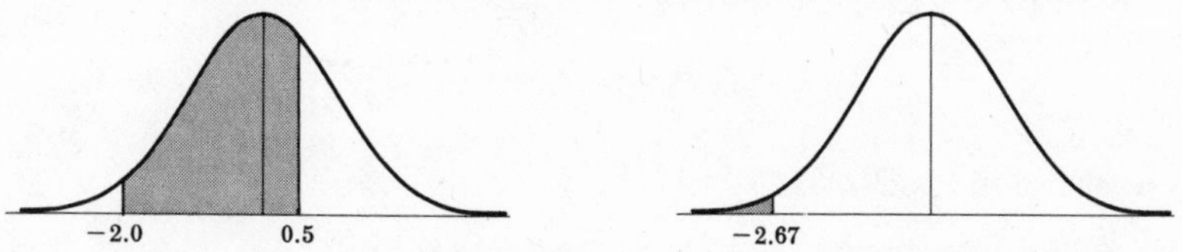

(a) (b)

Fig. 8-1

(b)

$$66.4 \text{ in standard units} = \frac{66.4 - 68.0}{0.6} = -2.67$$

As shown in Fig. 8.1(b),

Proportion of samples with means less than 66.4 in $= (\text{area under normal curve to left of } z = -2.67)$

$= (\text{area to left of } z = 0)$

$- (\text{area between } z = -2.67 \text{ and } z = 0)$

$= 0.5 - 0.4962 = 0.0038$

Thus the expected number of samples is $(80)(0.0038) = 0.304$, or zero.

8.5 Five hundred ball bearings have a mean weight of 5.02 grams (g) and a standard deviation of 0.30 g. Find the probability that a random sample of 100 ball bearings chosen from this group will have a combined weight of (a) between 496 and 500 g and (b) more than 510 g.

SOLUTION

For the sample distribution of means, $\mu_{\bar{X}} = \mu = 5.02$ g, and

$$\sigma_{\bar{X}} = \frac{\sigma}{\sqrt{N}}\sqrt{\frac{N_p - N}{N_p - 1}} = \frac{0.30}{\sqrt{100}}\sqrt{\frac{500 - 100}{500 - 1}} = 0.027 \text{ g}$$

(*a*) The combined weight will lie between 496 and 500 g if the mean weight of the 100 ball bearings lies between 4.96 and 5.00 g.

$$4.96 \text{ in standard units} = \frac{4.96 - 5.02}{0.027} = -2.22$$

$$5.00 \text{ in standard units} = \frac{5.00 - 5.02}{0.027} = -0.74$$

As shown in Fig. 8-2(*a*),

$$\begin{aligned}\text{Required probability} &= (\text{area between } z = -2.22 \text{ and } z = -0.74)\\ &= (\text{area between } z = -2.22 \text{ and } z = 0) - (\text{area between } z = -0.74 \text{ and } z = 0)\\ &= 0.4868 - 0.2704 = 0.2164\end{aligned}$$

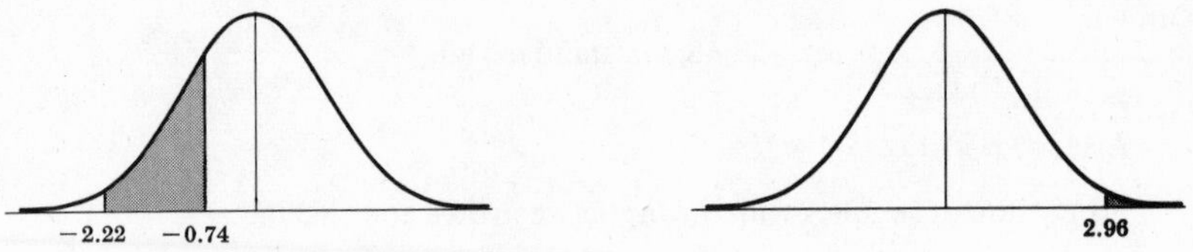

(*a*) (*b*)

Fig. 8-2

(*b*) The combined weight will exceed 510 g if the mean weight of the 100 bearings exceeds 5.10 g.

$$5.10 \text{ in standard units} = \frac{5.10 - 5.02}{0.027} = 2.96$$

As shown in Fig. 8-2(*b*),

$$\begin{aligned}\text{Required probability} &= (\text{area to right of } z = 2.96)\\ &= (\text{area to right of } z = 0) - (\text{area between } z = 0 \text{ and } z = 2.96)\\ &= 0.5 - 0.4985 = 0.0015\end{aligned}$$

Thus there are only 3 chances in 2000 of picking a sample of 100 ball bearings with a combined weight exceeding 510 g.

8.6 (*a*) Show how to select 30 random samples of 4 students each (with replacement) from Table 2.1 by using random numbers.

(*b*) Find the mean and standard deviation of the sampling distribution of means in part (*a*).

(*c*) Compare the results of part (*b*) with theoretical values, explaining any discrepancies.

SOLUTION

(*a*) Use two digits to number each of the 100 students: 00, 01, 02, ..., 99 (see Table 8.2). Thus the 5 students with heights 60–62 in are numbered 00–04, the 18 students with heights 63–65 in are numbered 05–22, etc. Each student number is called a *sampling number.*

We now draw sampling numbers from the random-number table (Appendix IX). From the first line we find the sequence 51, 77, 27, 46, 40, etc., which we take as random sampling numbers, each of which yields the height of a particular student. Thus 51 corresponds to a student having height 66–68 in, which we take as 67 in (the class mark). Similarly, 77, 27, and 46 yield heights of 70, 67, and 67 in, respectively.

By this process we obtain Table 8.3, which shows the sample numbers drawn, the corresponding heights, and the mean height for each of 30 samples. It should be mentioned that although we have entered the random-number table on the first line, we could have started *anywhere* and chosen any specified pattern.

Table 8.2

Height (in)	Frequency	Sampling Number
60–62	5	00–04
63–65	18	05–22
66–68	42	23–64
69–71	27	65–91
72–74	8	92–99

Table 8.3

Sample Number Drawn	Corresponding Height	Mean Height	Sample Number Drawn	Corresponding Height	Mean Height
1. 51, 77, 27, 46	67, 70, 67, 67	67.75	**16.** 11, 64, 55, 58	64, 67, 67, 67	66.25
2. 40, 42, 33, 12	67, 67, 67, 64	66.25	**17.** 70, 56, 97, 43	70, 67, 73, 67	69.25
3. 90, 44, 46, 62	70, 67, 67, 67	67.75	**18.** 74, 28, 93, 50	70, 67, 73, 67	69.25
4. 16, 28, 98, 93	64, 67, 73, 73	69.25	**19.** 79, 42, 71, 30	70, 67, 70, 67	68.50
5. 58, 20, 41, 86	67, 64, 67, 70	67.00	**20.** 58, 60, 21, 33	67, 67, 64, 67	66.25
6. 19, 64, 08, 70	64, 67, 64, 70	66.25	**21.** 75, 79, 74, 54	70, 70, 70, 67	69.25
7. 56, 24, 03, 32	67, 67, 61, 67	65.50	**22.** 06, 31, 04, 18	64, 67, 61, 64	64.00
8. 34, 91, 83, 58	67, 70, 70, 67	68.50	**23.** 67, 07, 12, 97	70, 64, 64, 73	67.75
9. 70, 65, 68, 21	70, 70, 70, 64	68.50	**24.** 31, 71, 69, 88	67, 70, 70, 70	69.25
10. 96, 02, 13, 87	73, 61, 64, 70	67.00	**25.** 11, 64, 21, 87	64, 67, 64, 70	66.25
11. 76, 10, 51, 08	70, 64, 67, 64	66.25	**26.** 03, 58, 57, 93	61, 67, 67, 73	67.00
12. 63, 97, 45, 39	67, 73, 67, 67	68.50	**27.** 53, 81, 93, 88	67, 70, 73, 70	70.00
13. 05, 81, 45, 93	64, 70, 67, 73	68.50	**28.** 23, 22, 96, 79	67, 64, 73, 70	68.50
14. 96, 01, 73, 52	73, 61, 70, 67	67.75	**29.** 98, 56, 59, 36	73, 67, 67, 67	68.50
15. 07, 82, 54, 24	64, 70, 67, 67	67.00	**30.** 08, 15, 08, 84	64, 64, 64, 70	65.50

(*b*) Table 8.4 gives the frequency distribution of the sample mean heights obtained in part (*a*). This is a *sampling distribution of means.* The mean and the standard deviation are obtained as usual by the coding methods of Chapters 3 and 4:

$$\text{Mean} = A + c\bar{u} = A + \frac{c\sum fu}{N} = 67.00 + \frac{(0.75)(23)}{30} = 67.58 \text{ in}$$

$$\text{Standard deviation} = c\sqrt{\overline{u^2} - \bar{u}^2} = c\sqrt{\frac{\sum fu^2}{N} - \left(\frac{\sum fu}{N}\right)^2} = 0.75\sqrt{\frac{123}{30} - \left(\frac{23}{30}\right)^2} = 1.41 \text{ in}$$

Table 8.4

Sample Mean	Tally	f	u	fu	fu^2
64.00	/	1	−4	−4	16
64.75		0	−3	0	0
65.50	//	2	−2	−4	8
66.25	~~////~~ /	6	−1	−6	6
$A \rightarrow$ 67.00	////	4	0	0	0
67.75	////	4	1	4	4
68.50	~~////~~ //	7	2	14	28
69.25	~~////~~	5	3	15	45
70.00	/	1	4	4	16
		$\sum f = N = 30$		$\sum fu = 23$	$\sum fu^2 = 123$

(c) The theoretical mean of the sampling distribution of means, given by $\mu_{\bar{X}}$, should equal the population mean μ, which is 67.45 in (see Problem 3.22), in agreement with the value 67.58 in of part (b).

The theoretical standard deviation (standard error) of the sampling distribution of means, given by $\sigma_{\bar{X}}$, should equal $\sigma/\sqrt{N}$, where the population standard deviation $\sigma = 2.92$ in (see Problem 4.17) and the sample size $N = 4$. Since $\sigma/\sqrt{N} = 2.92/\sqrt{4} = 1.46$ in, we have agreement with the value 1.41 in of part (b). The discrepancies result from the fact that only 30 samples were selected and the sample size was small.

SAMPLING DISTRIBUTION OF PROPORTIONS

8.7 Find the probability that in 120 tosses of a fair coin (a) between 40% and 60% will be heads and (b) $\frac{5}{8}$ or more will be heads.

SOLUTION

First method

We consider the 120 tosses of the coin to be a sample from the infinite population of all possible tosses of the coin. In this population the probability of heads is $p = \frac{1}{2}$ and the probability of tails is $q = 1 - p = \frac{1}{2}$.

(a) We require the probability that the number of heads in 120 tosses will be between (40% of 120) = 48 and (60% of 120) = 72. We proceed as in Chapter 7, using the normal approximation to the binomial. Since the number of heads is a discrete variable, we ask for the probability that the number of heads lies between 47.5 and 72.5.

$$\mu = \text{expected number of heads} = Np = 120(\tfrac{1}{2}) = 60 \qquad \text{and} \qquad \sigma = \sqrt{Npq} = \sqrt{(120)(\tfrac{1}{2})(\tfrac{1}{2})} = 5.48$$

$$47.5 \text{ in standard units} = \frac{47.5 - 60}{5.48} = -2.28$$

$$72.5 \text{ in standard units} = \frac{72.5 - 60}{5.48} = 2.28$$

As shown in Fig. 8-3,

$$\begin{aligned} \text{Required probability} &= (\text{area under normal curve between } z = -2.28 \text{ and } z = 2.28) \\ &= 2(\text{area between } z = 0 \text{ and } z = 2.28) \\ &= 2(0.4887) = 0.9774 \end{aligned}$$

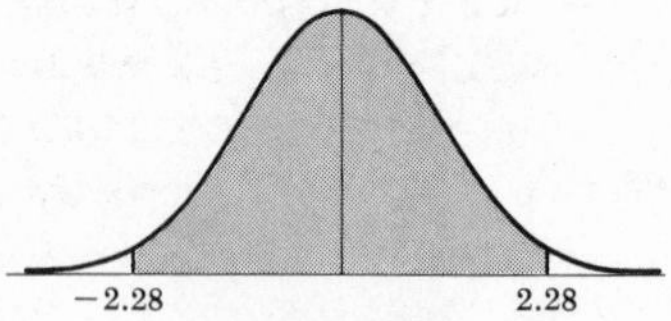

Fig. 8-3

Second method

$$\mu_P = p = \tfrac{1}{2} = 0.50 \qquad \sigma_P = \sqrt{\frac{pq}{N}} = \sqrt{\frac{(\frac{1}{2})(\frac{1}{2})}{120}} = 0.0456$$

$$40\% \text{ in standard units} = \frac{0.40 - 0.50}{0.0456} = -2.19$$

$$60\% \text{ in standard units} = \frac{0.60 - 0.50}{0.0456} = 2.19$$

$$\begin{aligned} \text{Required probability} &= (\text{area under normal curve between } z = -2.19 \text{ and } z = 2.19) \\ &= 2(0.4857) = 0.9714 \end{aligned}$$

Although this result is accurate to two significant figures, it does not agree exactly since we have not used the fact that the proportion is actually a discrete variable. To account for this, we subtract $1/2N = 1/2(120)$ from 0.40 and add $1/2N = 1/2(120)$ to 0.60; thus, since $1/240 = 0.00417$, the required proportions in standard units are

$$\frac{0.40-0.00417-0.50}{0.0456} = -2.28 \quad \text{and} \quad \frac{0.60+0.00417-0.50}{0.0456} = 2.28$$

so that agreement with the first method is obtained.

Note that (0.40 − 0.00417) and (0.60 + 0.00417) correspond to the proportions 47.5/120 and 72.5/120 in the first method.

(*b*) Using the second method of part (*a*), we find that since $\frac{5}{8} = 0.6250$,

$$(0.6250 - 0.00417) \text{ in standard units} = \frac{0.6250-0.00417-0.50}{0.0456} = 2.65$$

$$\begin{aligned}\text{Required probability} &= (\text{area under normal curve to right of } z = 2.65)\\ &= (\text{area to right of } z = 0) - (\text{area between } z = 0 \text{ and } z = 2.65)\\ &= 0.5 - 0.4960 = 0.0040\end{aligned}$$

8.8 Each person of a group of 500 people tosses a fair coin 120 times. How many people should be expected to report that (*a*) between 40% and 60% of their tosses resulted in heads and (*b*) $\frac{5}{8}$ or more of their tosses resulted in heads?

SOLUTION

This problem is closely related to Problem 8.7. Here we consider 500 samples, of size 120 each, from the infinite population of all possible tosses of a coin.

(*a*) Part (*a*) of Problem 8.7 states that of all possible samples, each consisting of 120 tosses of a coin, we can expect to find 97.74% with a percentage of heads between 40% and 60%. In 500 samples we can thus expect to find about (97.74% of 500) = 489 samples with this property. It follows that about 489 people would be expected to report that their experiment resulted in between 40% and 60% heads.

It is interesting to note that 500 − 489 = 11 people who would be expected to report that the percentage of heads was not between 40% and 60%. Such people might reasonably conclude that their coins were loaded even though they were fair. This type of error is an everpresent *risk* whenever we deal with probability.

(*b*) By reasoning as in part (*a*), we conclude that about (500)(0.0040) = 2 persons who would report that $\frac{5}{8}$ or more of their tosses resulted in heads.

Mathcad **8.9** It has been found that 2% of the tools produced by a certain machine are defective. What is the probability that in a shipment of 400 such tools (*a*) 3% or more and (*b*) 2% or less will prove defective?

SOLUTION

$$\mu_P = p = 0.02 \quad \text{and} \quad \sigma_P = \sqrt{\frac{pq}{N}} = \sqrt{\frac{(0.02)(0.98)}{400}} = \frac{0.14}{20} = 0.007$$

(*a*) **First method**

Using the correction for discrete variables, $1/2N = 1/800 = 0.00125$, we have

$$(0.03 - 0.00125) \text{ in standard units} = \frac{0.03-0.00125-0.02}{0.007} = 1.25$$

$$\text{Required probability} = (\text{area under normal curve to right of } z = 1.25) = 0.1056$$

If we had not used the correction, we would have obtained 0.0764.

Another method

(3% of 400) = 12 defective tools. On a continuous basis 12 or more tools means 11.5 or more.

$$\bar{X} = (2\% \text{ of } 400) = 8 \qquad \text{and} \qquad \sigma = \sqrt{Npq} = \sqrt{(400)(0.02)(0.98)} = 2.8$$

Then, 11.5 in standard units = (11.5 − 8)/2.8 = 1.25, and as before the required probability is 0.1056.

(*b*)
$$(0.02 + 0.00125) \text{ in standard units} = \frac{0.02 + 0.00125 - 0.02}{0.007} = 0.18$$

$$\text{Required probability} = (\text{area under normal curve to left of } z = 0.18)$$
$$= 0.5000 + 0.0714 = 0.5714$$

If we had not used the correction, we would have obtained 0.5000. The second method of part (*a*) can also be used.

8.10 The election returns showed that a certain candidate received 46% of the votes. Determine the probability that a poll of (*a*) 200 and (*b*) 1000 people selected at random from the voting population would have shown a majority of votes in favor of the candidate.

SOLUTION

(*a*)
$$\mu_P = p = 0.46 \qquad \text{and} \qquad \sigma_P = \sqrt{\frac{pq}{N}} = \sqrt{\frac{(0.46)(0.54)}{200}} = 0.0352$$

Since $1/2N = 1/400 = 0.0025$, a majority is indicated in the sample if the proportion in favor of the candidate is 0.50 + 0.0025 = 0.5025 or more. (This proportion can also be obtained by realizing that 101 or more indicates a majority, but as a continuous variable this is 100.5, and so the proportion is 100.5/200 = 0.5025.)

$$0.5025 \text{ in standard units} = \frac{0.5025 - 0.46}{0.0352} = 1.21$$

$$\text{Required probability} = (\text{area under normal curve to right of } z = 1.21)$$
$$= 0.5000 - 0.3869 = 0.1131$$

(*b*)
$$\mu_P = p = 0.46 \qquad \text{and} \qquad \sigma_P = \sqrt{\frac{pq}{N}} = \sqrt{\frac{(0.46)(0.54)}{1000}} = 0.0158$$

$$0.5025 \text{ in standard units} = \frac{0.5025 - 0.46}{0.0158} = 2.69$$

$$\text{Required probability} = (\text{area under normal curve to right of } z = 2.69)$$
$$= 0.5000 - 0.4964 = 0.0036$$

SAMPLING DISTRIBUTIONS OF DIFFERENCES AND SUMS

8.11 Let U_1 be a variable that stands for any of the elements of the population 3, 7, 8 and U_2 be a variable that stands for any of the elements of the population 2, 4. Compute (*a*) μ_{U1}, (*b*) μ_{U2}, (*c*) μ_{U1-U2}, (*d*) σ_{U1}, (*e*) σ_{U2}, and (*f*) σ_{U1-U2}.

SOLUTION

(*a*) μ_{U1} = mean of population $U_1 = \frac{1}{3}(3 + 7 + 8) = 6$

(*b*) μ_{U2} = mean of population $U_2 = \frac{1}{2}(2 + 4) = 3$

(*c*) The population consisting of the differences of any member of U_1 and any member of U_2 is

$$\begin{matrix} 3-2 & 7-2 & 8-2 \\ 3-4 & 7-4 & 8-4 \end{matrix} \quad \text{or} \quad \begin{matrix} 1 & 5 & 6 \\ -1 & 3 & 4 \end{matrix}$$

Thus $$\mu_{U1-U2} = \text{mean of } (U_1 - U_2) = \frac{1+5+6+(-1)+3+4}{6} = 3$$

This illustrates the general result $\mu_{U1-U2} = \mu_{U1} - \mu_{U2}$, as seen from parts (*a*) and (*b*).

(*d*) $$\sigma^2_{U1} = \text{variance of population } U_1 = \frac{(3-6)^2+(7-6)^2+(8-6)^2}{3} = \frac{14}{3}$$

or $$\sigma_{U1} = \sqrt{\frac{14}{3}}$$

(*e*) $$\sigma^2_{U2} = \text{variance of population } U_2 = \frac{(2-3)^2+(4-3)^2}{2} = 1 \quad \text{or} \quad \sigma_{U2} = 1$$

(*f*) $$\sigma^2_{U1-U2} = \text{variance of population } (U_1 - U_2)$$
$$= \frac{(1-3)^2+(5-3)^2+(6-3)^2+(-1-3)+(3-3)^2+(4-3)^2}{6} = \frac{17}{3}$$

or $$\sigma_{U1-U2} = \sqrt{\frac{17}{3}}$$

This illustrates the general result for independent samples, $\sigma_{U1-U2} = \sqrt{\sigma^2_{U1} + \sigma^2_{U2}}$, as seen from parts (*d*) and (*e*).

Mathcad **8.12** The electric light bulbs of manufacturer *A* have a mean lifetime of 1400 hours (h) with a standard deviation of 200 h, while those of manufacturer *B* have a mean lifetime of 1200 h with a standard deviation of 100 h. If random samples of 125 bulbs of each brand are tested, what is the probability that the brand *A* bulbs will have a mean lifetime that is at least (*a*) 160 h and (*b*) 250 h more than the brand *B* bulbs?

SOLUTION

Let $\bar{X}_A$ and $\bar{X}_B$ denote the mean lifetimes of samples *A* and *B*, respectively. Then

$$\mu_{\bar{X}_A - \bar{X}_B} = \mu_{\bar{X}_A} - \mu_{\bar{X}_B} = 1400 - 1200 = 200 \text{ h}$$

and $$\sigma_{\bar{X}_A - \bar{X}_B} = \sqrt{\frac{\sigma_A^2}{N_A} + \frac{\sigma_B^2}{N_B}} = \sqrt{\frac{(100)^2}{125} + \frac{(200)^2}{125}} = 20 \text{ h}$$

The standardized variable for the difference in means is

$$z = \frac{(\bar{X}_A - \bar{X}_B) - (\mu_{\bar{X}_A - \bar{X}_B})}{\sigma_{\bar{X}_A - \bar{X}_B}} = \frac{(\bar{X}_A - \bar{X}_B) - 200}{20}$$

and is very closely normally distributed.

(*a*) The difference 160 h in standard units is $(160 - 200)/20 = -2$. Thus

$$\text{Required probability} = (\text{area under normal curve to right of } z = -2)$$
$$= 0.5000 + 0.4772 = 0.9772$$

(*b*) The difference 250 h in standard units is $(250 - 200)/20 = 2.50$. Thus

$$\text{Required probability} = (\text{area under normal curve to right of } z = 2.50)$$
$$= 0.5000 - 0.4938 = 0.0062$$

8.13 Ball bearings of a given brand weigh 0.50 g with a standard deviation of 0.02 g. What is the probability that two lots of 1000 ball bearings each will differ in weight by more than 2 g?

SOLUTION

Let $\bar{X}_1$ and $\bar{X}_2$ denote the mean weights of ball bearings in the two lots. Then

$$\mu_{\bar{X}_1-\bar{X}_2}=\mu_{\bar{X}_1}-\mu_{\bar{X}_2}=0.50-0.50=0$$

and
$$\sigma_{\bar{X}_1-\bar{X}_2}=\sqrt{\frac{\sigma_1^2}{N_1}+\frac{\sigma_2^2}{N_2}}=\sqrt{\frac{(0.02)^2}{1000}+\frac{(0.02)^2}{1000}}=0.000895$$

The standardized variable for the difference in means is

$$z=\frac{(\bar{X}_1-\bar{X}_2)-0}{0.000895}$$

and is very closely normally distributed.

A difference of 2 g in the lots is equivalent to a difference of $2/1000=0.002$ g in the means. This can occur either if $\bar{X}_1-\bar{X}_2\geq 0.002$ or $\bar{X}_1-\bar{X}_2\leq -0.002$; that is,

$$z\geq\frac{0.002-0}{0.000895}=2.23 \qquad \text{or} \qquad z\leq\frac{-0.002-0}{0.00895}=-2.23$$

Then $\Pr\{z\geq 2.23 \text{ or } z\leq -2.23\}=\Pr\{z\geq 2.23\}+\Pr\{z\leq -2.23\}=2(0.5000-0.4871)=0.0258.$

8.14 *A* and *B* play a game of "heads and tails," each tossing 50 coins. *A* will win the game if she tosses 5 or more heads than *B*; otherwise, *B* wins. Determine the odds against *A* winning any particular game.

SOLUTION

Let P_A and P_B denote the proportion of heads obtained by *A* and *B*. If we assume that the coins are all fair, the probability p of heads is $\frac{1}{2}$. Then

$$\mu_{P_A-P_B}=\mu_{P_A}-\mu_{P_B}=0$$

and

$$\sigma_{P_A-P_B}=\sqrt{\sigma_{P_A}^2+\sigma_{P_B}^2}=\sqrt{\frac{pq}{N_A}+\frac{pq}{N_B}}=\sqrt{\frac{2(\frac{1}{2})(\frac{1}{2})}{50}}=0.10$$

The standardized variable for the difference in proportions is $z=(P_A-P_B-0)/0.10$.

On a continuous-variable basis, 5 or more heads means 4.5 or more heads, so that the difference in proportions should be $4.5/50=0.09$ or more; that is, z is greater than or equal to $(0.09-0)/0.10=0.9$ (or $z\geq 0.9$). The probability of this is the area under the normal curve to the right of $z=0.9$, which is $(0.5000-0.3159)=0.1841$.

Thus the odds against *A* winning are $(1-0.1841):0.1841=0.8159:0.1841$, or 4.43 to 1.

8.15 Two distances are measured as 27.3 centimeters (cm) and 15.6 cm with standard deviations (standard errors) of 0.16 cm and 0.08 cm, respectively. Determine the mean and standard deviation of (*a*) the sum and (*b*) the difference of the distances.

SOLUTION

If the distances are denoted by D_1 and D_2, then:

(*a*)
$$\mu_{D1+D2}=\mu_{D1}+\mu_{D2}=27.3+15.6=42.9 \text{ cm}$$
$$\sigma_{D1+D2}=\sqrt{\sigma_{D1}^2+\sigma_{D2}^2}=\sqrt{(0.16)^2+(0.08)^2}=0.18 \text{ cm}$$

(*b*)
$$\mu_{D1-D2}=\mu_{D1}-\mu_{D2}=27.3-15.6=11.7 \text{ cm}$$
$$\sigma_{D1-D2}=\sqrt{\sigma_{D1}^2+\sigma_{D2}^2}=\sqrt{(0.16)^2+(0.08)^2}=0.18 \text{ cm}$$

8.16 A certain type of electric light bulb has a mean lifetime of 1500 h and a standard deviation of 150 h. Three bulbs are connected so that when one burns out, another will go on. Assuming that the lifetimes are normally distributed, what is the probability that lighting will take place for (*a*) at least 5000 h and (*b*) at most 4200 h?

SOLUTION

Assume the lifetimes to be L_1, L_2, and L_3. Then

$$\mu_{L1+L2+L3} = \mu_{L1} + \mu_{L2} + \mu_{L3} = 1500 + 1500 + 1500 = 4500 \text{ h}$$

$$\sigma_{L1+L2+L3} = \sqrt{\sigma_{L1}^2 + \sigma_{L2}^2 + \sigma_{L3}^2} = \sqrt{3(150)^2} = 260 \text{ h}$$

(*a*)
$$5000 \text{ h in standard units} = \frac{5000 - 4500}{260} = 1.92$$

$$\text{Required probability} = (\text{area under normal curve to right of } z = 1.92)$$
$$= 0.5000 - 0.4726 = 0.0274$$

(*b*)
$$4200 \text{ h in standard units} = \frac{4200 - 4500}{260} = -1.15$$

$$\text{Required probability} = (\text{area under normal curve to left of } z = -1.15)$$
$$= 0.5000 - 0.3749 = 0.1251$$

MISCELLANEOUS PROBLEMS

8.17 With reference to Problem 8.1, find (*a*) the mean of the sampling distribution of variances and (*b*) the standard deviation of the sampling distribution of variances (i.e., the standard error of variances).

SOLUTION

(*a*) The sample variances corresponding to each of the 25 samples in Problem 8.1 are

0	0.25	4.00	9.00	20.25
0.25	0	2.25	6.25	16.00
4.00	2.25	0	1.00	6.25
9.00	6.25	1.00	0	2.25
20.25	16.00	6.25	2.25	0

The mean of the sampling distribution of variances is

$$\mu_{s^2} = \frac{\text{sum of all variances in the table above}}{25} = \frac{135}{25} = 5.40$$

This illustrates the fact that $\mu_{s^2} = (N-1)(\sigma^2)/N$, since for $N = 2$ and $\sigma^2 = 10.8$ [see Problem 8.1(*b*)], the right-hand side is $\frac{1}{2}(10.8) = 5.4$.

The result shows the desirability of defining a corrected variance for samples as

$$\hat{s}^2 = \frac{N}{N-1} s^2$$

It would then follow that $\mu_{\hat{s}^2} = \sigma^2$ (see also the remarks on page 88). It should be noted that the population variances would be defined the same as before and that only the sample variances would be corrected.

(*b*) The variance of the sampling distribution of variances $\sigma_{s^2}^2$ is obtained by subtracting the mean 5.40 from each of the 25 numbers in the above table, squaring these numbers, adding them, and then dividing the result by 25. Thus $\sigma_{s^2}^2 = 575.75/25 = 23.03$, or $\sigma_{s^2} = 4.80$.

8.18 Work Problem 8.17 if the sampling is without replacement.

SOLUTION

(*a*) There are 10 samples whose variances are given by the numbers above (or below) the diagonal of zeros in the table of Problem 8.17(*a*). Thus

$$\mu_{s^2} = \frac{0.25+4.00+9.00+20.25+2.25+6.25+16.00+1.00+6.25+2.25}{10} = 6.75$$

This is a special case of the general result

$$\mu_{s^2} = \left(\frac{N_p}{N_p-1}\right)\left(\frac{N-1}{N}\right)\sigma^2$$

as is verified by putting $N_p = 5$, $N = 2$, and $\sigma^2 = 10.8$ on the right-hand side to obtain $\mu_{s^2} = (\frac{5}{4})(\frac{1}{2})(10.8) = 6.75$.

(*b*) Subtracting 6.75 from each of the 10 numbers above the diagonal of zeros in the table of Problem 8.17(*a*), squaring these numbers, adding them, and dividing by 10, we find $\sigma^2_{s^2} = 39.675$, or $\sigma_{s^2} = 6.30$.

8.19 The standard deviation of the weights of a very large population of students is 10.0 pounds (lb). Samples of 200 students each are drawn from this population, and the standard deviations of the heights in each sample are computed. Find (*a*) the mean and (*b*) the standard deviation of the sampling distribution of standard deviations.

SOLUTION

We can consider that the sampling is either from an infinite population or with replacement from a finite population. From Table 8.1 we have:

(*a*) The mean of the sampling distribution of standard deviations is $\mu_s = \sigma = 10.0$ lb.

(*b*) The standard deviation of the sampling distribution of standard deviations is $\sigma_s = \sigma/\sqrt{2N} = 10/\sqrt{400} = 0.50$ lb.

8.20 What percentage of the samples in Problem 8.19 would have standard deviations (*a*) greater than 11.0 lb and (*b*) less than 8.8 lb?

SOLUTION

The sampling distribution of standard deviations is approximately normally distributed with mean 10.0 lb and standard deviation 0.50 lb.

(*a*) 11.0 lb in standard units is $(11.0 - 10.0)/0.50 = 2.0$. The area under the normal curve to the right of $z = 2.0$ is $(0.5 - 0.4772) = 0.0228$; hence the required percentage is 2.3%.

(*b*) 8.8 lb in standard units is $(8.8 - 10.0)/0.50 = -2.4$. The area under the normal curve to the left of $z = -2.4$ is $(0.5 - 0.4918) = 0.0082$; hence the required percentage is 0.8%.

Supplementary Problems

SAMPLING DISTRIBUTION OF MEANS

8.21 A population consists of the four numbers 3, 7, 11, and 15. Consider all possible samples of size 2 that can be drawn with replacement from this population. Find (*a*) the population mean, (*b*) the population standard deviation, (*c*) the mean of the sampling distribution of means, and (*d*) the standard deviation of the sampling distribution of means. Verify parts (*c*) and (*d*) directly from (*a*) and (*b*) by using suitable formulas.

8.22 Solve Problem 8.21 if the sampling is without replacement.

8.23 The masses of 1500 ball bearings are normally distributed, with a mean of 22.40 g and a standard deviation of 0.048 g. If 300 random samples of size 36 are drawn from this population, determine the expected mean and standard deviation of the sampling distribution of means if the sampling is done (*a*) with replacement and (*b*) without replacement.

8.24 Solve Problem 8.23 if the population consists of 72 ball bearings.

8.25 How many of the random samples in Problem 8.23 would have their means (*a*) between 22.39 and 22.41 g, (*b*) greater than 22.42 g, (*c*) less than 22.37 g, and (*d*) less than 22.38 g or more than 22.41 g?

8.26 Certain tubes manufactured by a company have a mean lifetime of 800 h and a standard deviation of 60 h. Find the probability that a random sample of 16 tubes taken from the group will have a mean lifetime of (*a*) between 790 and 810 h, (*b*) less than 785 h, (*c*) more than 820 h; and (*d*) between 770 and 830 h.

8.27 Work Problem 8.26 if a random sample of 64 tubes is taken. Explain the difference.

8.28 The weights of packages received by a department store have a mean of 300 lb and a standard deviation of 50 lb. What is the probability that 25 packages received at random and loaded on an elevator will exceed the specified safety limit of the elevator, listed as 8200 lb?

RANDOM NUMBERS

8.29 Work Problem 8.6 by using a different set of random numbers and selecting (*a*) 15, (*b*) 30, (*c*) 45, and (*d*) 60 samples of size 4 with replacement. Compare with the theoretical results in each case.

8.30 Work Problem 8.29 by selecting samples of size (*a*) 2 and (*b*) 8 with replacement, instead of size 4 with replacement.

8.31 Work Problem 8.6 if the sampling is without replacement. Compare with the theoretical results.

8.32 (*a*) Show how to select 30 samples of size 2 from the distribution in Problem 3.61.
(*b*) Compute the mean and standard deviation of the resulting sampling distribution of means, and compare with theoretical results.

8.33 Work Problem 8.32 by using samples of size 4.

SAMPLING DISTRIBUTION OF PROPORTIONS

8.34 Find the probability that of the next 200 children born, (*a*) less than 40% will be boys, (*b*) between 43% and 57% will be girls, and (*c*) more than 54% will be boys. Assume equal probabilities for the births of boys and girls.

8.35 Out of 1000 samples of 200 children each, in how many would you expect to find that (*a*) less than 40% are boys, (*b*) between 40% and 60% are girls, and (*c*) 53% or more are girls?

8.36 Work Problem 8.34 if 100 instead of 200 children are considered, and explain the differences in results.

8.37 An urn contains 80 marbles, of which 60% are red and 40% are white. Out of 50 samples of 20 marbles, each selected with replacement from the urn, how many samples can be expected to consist of (*a*) equal numbers of red and white marbles, (*b*) 12 red and 8 white marbles, (*c*) 8 red and 12 white marbles, and (*d*) 10 or more white marbles?

8.38 Design an experiment intended to illustrate the results of Problem 8.37. Instead of red and white marbles, you may use slips of paper on which R and W are written in the correct proportions. What errors might you introduce by using two different sets of coins?

8.39 A manufacturer sends out 1000 lots, each consisting of 100 electric bulbs. If 5% of the bulbs are normally defective, in how many of the lots should we expect (*a*) fewer than 90 good bulbs and (*b*) 98 or more good bulbs?

SAMPLING DISTRIBUTIONS OF DIFFERENCES AND SUMS

8.40 *A* and *B* manufacture two types of cables that have mean breaking strengths of 4000 lb and 4500 lb and standard deviations of 300 lb and 200 lb, respectively. If 100 cables of brand *A* and 50 cables of brand *B* are tested, what is the probability that the mean breaking strength of *B* will be (*a*) at least 600 lb more than *A* and (*b*) at least 450 lb more than *A*?

8.41 What are the probabilities in Problem 8.40 if 100 cables of both brands are tested? Account for the differences.

8.42 The mean score of students on an aptitude test is 72 points with a standard deviation of 8 points. What is the probability that two groups of students, consisting of 28 and 36 students, respectively, will differ in their mean scores by (*a*) 3 or more points, (*b*) 6 or more points, and (*c*) between 2 and 5 points?

8.43 An urn contains 60 red marbles and 40 white marbles. Two sets of 30 marbles each are drawn with replacement from the urn and their colors are noted. What is the probability that the two sets differ by 8 or more red marbles?

8.44 Solve Problem 8.43 if the sampling is without replacement in obtaining each set.

8.45 Election returns showed that a certain candidate received 65% of the votes. Find the probability that two random samples, each consisting of 200 voters, indicated more than a 10% difference in the proportions who voted for the candidate.

8.46 If U_1 and U_2 are the sets of numbers in Problem 8.11, verify that (*a*) $\mu_{U1+U2} = \mu_{U1} + \mu_{U2}$ and (*b*) $\sigma_{U1+U2} = \sqrt{\sigma^2_{U1} + \sigma^2_{U2}}$.

8.47 Three masses are measured as 20.48, 35.97, and 62.34 g, with standard deviations of 0.21, 0.46, and 0.54 g, respectively. Find the (*a*) mean and (*b*) standard deviation of the sum of the masses.

8.48 The mean voltage of a battery is 15.0 volts (V) and the standard deviation is 0.2 V. What is the probability that four such batteries connected in series will have a combined voltage of 60.8 V or more?

MISCELLANEOUS PROBLEMS

8.49 A population of seven numbers has a mean of 40 and a standard deviation of 3. If samples of size 5 are drawn from this population and the variance of each sample is computed, find the mean of the sampling distribution of variances if the sampling is (*a*) with replacement and (*b*) without replacement.

8.50 Certain tubes produced by a company have a mean lifetime of 900 h and a standard deviation of 80 h. The company sends out 1000 lots of 100 tubes each. In how many lots can we expect (*a*) the mean lifetimes to exceed 910 h and (*b*) the standard deviations of the lifetimes to exceed 95 h? What assumptions must be made?

8.51 If the median lifetime in Problem 8.50 is 900 h, in how many lots can we expect the median lifetimes to exceed 910 h? Compare your answer with Problem 8.50(*a*) and explain the results.

8.52 On a citywide examination, the grades were normally distributed with mean 72 and standard deviation 8.

(*a*) Find the minimum grade of the top 20% of the students.

(*b*) Find the probability that in a random sample of 100 students the minimum grade of the top 20% will be less than 76.

Chapter 9

Statistical Estimation Theory

ESTIMATION OF PARAMETERS

In the last chapter we saw how sampling theory can be employed to obtain information about samples drawn at random from a known population. From a practical viewpoint, however, it is often more important to be able to infer information about a population from samples drawn from it. Such problems are dealt with in *statistical inference*, which uses principles of sampling theory.

One important problem of statistical inference is the estimation of *population parameters*, or briefly *parameters* (such as population mean and variance), from the corresponding *sample statistics*, or briefly *statistics* (such as sample mean and variance). We consider this problem in this chapter.

UNBIASED ESTIMATES

If the mean of the sampling distribution of a statistic equals the corresponding population parameter, the statistic is called an *unbiased estimator* of the parameter; otherwise, it is called a *biased estimator*. The corresponding values of such statistics are called *unbiased* or *biased estimates*, respectively.

EXAMPLE 1. The mean of the sampling distribution of means $\mu_{\bar{X}}$ is μ, the population mean. Hence the sample mean $\bar{X}$ is an unbiased estimate of the population mean μ.

EXAMPLE 2. The mean of the sampling distribution of variances is

$$\mu_{s^2} = \frac{N-1}{N}\sigma^2$$

where σ^2 is the population variance and N is the sample size (see Table 8.1). Thus the sample variance s^2 is a biased estimate of the population variance σ^2. By using the modified variance

$$\hat{s}^2 = \frac{N}{N-1}s^2$$

we find $\mu_{\hat{s}^2} = \sigma^2$, so that $\hat{s}^2$ is an unbiased estimate of σ^2. However, $\hat{s}$ is a biased estimate of σ.

In the language of expectation (see Chapter 6) we could say that a statistic is unbiased if its expectation equals the corresponding population parameter. Thus $\bar{X}$ and $\hat{s}^2$ are unbiased since $E\{\bar{X}\} = \mu$ and $E\{\hat{s}^2\} = \sigma^2$.

EFFICIENT ESTIMATES

If the sampling distributions of two statistics have the same mean (or expectation), then the statistic with the smaller variance is called an *efficient estimator* of the mean, while the other statistic is called an *inefficient estimator*. The corresponding values of the statistics are called *efficient estimates*, respectively.

If we consider all possible statistics whose sampling distributions have the same mean, the one with the smallest variance is sometimes called the *most efficient*, or *best*, *estimator* of this mean.

EXAMPLE 3. The sampling distributions of the mean and median both have the same mean, namely, the population mean. However, the variance of the sampling distribution of means is smaller than the variance of the sampling distribution of medians (see Table 8.1). Hence the sample mean gives an efficient estimate of the population mean, while the sample median gives an inefficient estimate of it.

Of all statistics estimating the population mean, the sample mean provides the best (or most efficient) estimate.

In practice, inefficient estimates are often used because of the relative ease with which some of them can be obtained.

POINT ESTIMATES AND INTERVAL ESTIMATES; THEIR RELIABILITY

An estimate of a population parameter given by a single number is called a *point estimate* of the parameter. An estimate of a population parameter given by two numbers between which the parameter may be considered to lie is called an *interval estimate* of the parameter.

Interval estimates indicate the precision, or accuracy, of an estimate and are therefore preferable to point estimates.

EXAMPLE 4. If we say that a distance is measured as 5.28 meters (m), we are giving a point estimate. If, on the other hand, we say that the distance is 5.28 ± 0.03 m (i.e., the distance lies between 5.25 and 5.31 m), we are giving an interval estimate.

A statement of the error (or precision) of an estimate is often called its *reliability.*

CONFIDENCE-INTERVAL ESTIMATES OF POPULATION PARAMETERS

Let μ_S and σ_S be the mean and standard deviation (standard error), respectively, of the sampling distribution of a statistic S. Then if the sampling distribution of S is approximately normal (which as we have seen is true for many statistics if the sample size $N \geq 30$), we can expect to find an actual sample statistic S lying in the intervals $\mu_S - \sigma_S$ to $\mu_S + \sigma_S$, $\mu_S - 2\sigma_S$ to $\mu_S + 2\sigma_S$, or $\mu_S - 3\sigma_S$ to $\mu_S + 3\sigma_S$ about 68.27%, 95.45%, and 99.73% of the time, respectively.

Equivalently, we can expect to find (or we can be *confident* of finding) μ_S in the intervals $S - \sigma_S$ to $S + \sigma_S$, $S - 2\sigma_S$ to $S + 2\sigma_S$, or $S - 3\sigma_S$ to $S + 3\sigma_S$ about 68.27%, 95.45%, and 99.73% of the time, respectively. Because of this, we call these respective intervals the 68.27%, 95.45%, and 99.73% *confidence intervals* for estimating μ_S. The end numbers of these intervals ($S \pm \sigma_S$, $S \pm 2\sigma_S$, and $S \pm 3\sigma_S$) are then called the 68.27%, 95.45%, and 99.73% *confidence limits,* or *fiducial limits.*

Similarly, $S \pm 1.96\sigma_S$ and $S \pm 2.58\sigma_S$ are the 95% and 99% (or 0.95 and 0.99) confidence limits for S. The percentage confidence is often called the *confidence level.* The numbers 1.96, 2.58, etc., in the confidence limits are called *confidence coefficients,* or *critical values,* and are denoted by z_c. From confidence levels we can find confidence coefficients, and vice versa.

Table 9.1 shows the values of z_c corresponding to various confidence levels used in practice. For confidence levels not presented in the table, the values of z_c can be found from the normal-curve area tables (see Appendix II).

Table 9.1

Confidence level	99.73%	99%	98%	96%	95.45%	95%	90%	80%	68.27%	50%
z_c	3.00	2.58	2.33	2.05	2.00	1.96	1.645	1.28	1.00	0.6745

Confidence Intervals for Means

If the statistic S is the sample mean $\bar{X}$, then the 95% and 99% confidence limits for estimating the population mean μ are given by $\bar{X} \pm 1.96\sigma_{\bar{X}}$ and $\bar{X} \pm 2.58\sigma_{\bar{X}}$, respectively. More generally, the confidence limits are given by $\bar{X} \pm z_c\sigma_{\bar{X}}$, where z_c (which depends on the particular level of confidence desired) can be read from Table 9.1. Using the values of $\sigma_{\bar{X}}$ obtained in Chapter 8, we see that the confidence limits for the population mean are given by

$$\bar{X} \pm z_c \frac{\sigma}{\sqrt{N}} \tag{1}$$

if the sampling is either from an infinite population or with replacement from a finite population and are given by

$$\bar{X} \pm z_c \frac{\sigma}{\sqrt{N}} \sqrt{\frac{N_p - N}{N_p - 1}} \tag{2}$$

if the sampling is without replacement from a population of finite size N_p.

Generally, the population standard deviation σ is unknown; thus, to obtain the above confidence limits, we use the sample estimate $\hat{s}$ or s. This will prove satisfactory when $N \geq 30$. For $N < 30$, the approximation is poor and small sampling theory must be employed (see Chapter 11).

Confidence Intervals for Proportions

If the statistic S is the proportion of "successes" in a sample of size N drawn from a binomial population in which p is the proportion of successes (i.e., the probability of success), then the confidence limits for p are given by $P \pm z_c\sigma_P$, where P is the proportion of successes in the sample of size N. Using the values of σ_P obtained in Chapter 8, we see that the confidence limits for the population proportion are given by

$$P \pm z_c \sqrt{\frac{pq}{N}} = P \pm z_c \sqrt{\frac{p(1-p)}{N}} \tag{3}$$

if the sampling is either from an infinite population or with replacement from a finite population and are given by

$$P \pm z_c \sqrt{\frac{pq}{N}} \sqrt{\frac{N_p - N}{N_p - 1}} \tag{4}$$

if the sampling is without replacement from a population of finite size N_p.

To compute these confidence limits, we can use the sample estimate P for p, which will generally prove satisfactory if $N \geq 30$. A more exact method for obtaining these confidence limits is given in Problem 9.12.

Confidence Intervals for Differences and Sums

If S_1 and S_2 are two sample statistics with approximately normal sampling distributions, confidence limits for the difference of the population parameters corresponding to S_1 and S_2 are given by

$$S_1 - S_2 \pm z_c\sigma_{S1-S2} = S_1 - S_2 \pm z_c\sqrt{\sigma_{S1}^2 + \sigma_{S2}^2} \tag{5}$$

while confidence limits for the sum of the population parameters are given by

$$S_1 + S_2 \pm z_c\sigma_{S1+S2} = S_1 + S_2 \pm z_c\sqrt{\sigma_{S1}^2 + \sigma_{S2}^2} \tag{6}$$

provided that the samples are independent (see Chapter 8).

For example, confidence limits for the difference of two population means, in the case where the populations are infinite, are given by

$$\bar{X}_1 - \bar{X}_2 \pm z_c\sigma_{\bar{X}1-\bar{X}2} = \bar{X}_1 - \bar{X}_2 \pm z_c \sqrt{\frac{\sigma_1^2}{N_1} + \frac{\sigma_2^2}{N_2}} \tag{7}$$

where $\bar{X}_1$, σ_1, N_1 and $\bar{X}_2$, σ_2, N_2 are the respective means, standard deviations, and sizes of the two samples drawn from the populations.

Similarly, confidence limits for the difference of two population proportions, where the populations are infinite, are given by

$$P_1 - P_2 \pm z_c \sigma_{P_1 - P_2} = P_1 - P_2 \pm z_c \sqrt{\frac{p_1(1-p_1)}{N_1} + \frac{p_2(1-p_2)}{N_2}} \tag{8}$$

where P_1 and P_2 are the two sample proportions, N_1 and N_2 are the sizes of the two samples drawn from the populations, and p_1 and p_2 are the proportions in the two populations (estimated by P_1 and P_2).

Confidence Intervals for Standard Deviations

The confidence limits for the standard deviation σ of a normally distributed population, as estimated from a sample with standard deviation s, are given by

$$s \pm z_c \sigma_s = s \pm z_c \frac{\sigma}{\sqrt{2N}} \tag{9}$$

using Table 8.1. In computing these confidence limits, we use s or $\hat{s}$ to estimate σ.

PROBABLE ERROR

The 50% confidence limits of the population parameters corresponding to a statistic S are given by $S \pm 0.6745\sigma_S$. The quantity $0.6745\sigma_S$ is known as the *probable error* of the estimate.

Solved Problems

UNBIASED AND EFFICIENT ESTIMATES

9.1 Give an example of estimators (or estimates) that are (*a*) unbiased and efficient, (*b*) unbiased and inefficient, and (*c*) biased and inefficient.

SOLUTION

(*a*) The sample mean $\bar{X}$ and the modified sample variance

$$\hat{s}^2 = \frac{N}{N-1} s^2$$

are two such examples.

(*b*) The sample median and the sample statistic $\frac{1}{2}(Q_1 + Q_3)$, where Q_1 and Q_3 are the lower and upper sample quartiles, are two such examples. Both statistics are unbiased estimates of the population mean, since the mean of their sampling distributions is the population mean.

(*c*) The sample standard deviation s, the modified standard deviation $\hat{s}$, the mean deviation, and the semi-interquartile range are four such examples.

9.2 In a sample of five measurements, the diameter of a sphere was recorded by a scientist as 6.33, 6.37, 6.36, 6.32, and 6.37 centimeters (cm). Determine unbiased and efficient estimates of (*a*) the true mean and (*b*) the true variance.

SOLUTION

(*a*) The unbiased and efficient estimate of the true mean (i.e., the populations mean) is

$$\bar{X} = \frac{\sum X}{N} = \frac{6.33 + 6.37 + 6.36 + 6.32 + 6.37}{5} = 6.35 \text{ cm}$$

(*b*) The unbiased and efficient estimate of the true variance (i.e., the population variance) is

$$\hat{s}^2 = \frac{N}{N-1} s^2 = \frac{\sum (X - \bar{X})^2}{N-1}$$

$$= \frac{(6.33-6.35)^2 + (6.37-6.35)^2 + (6.36-6.35)^2 + (6.32-6.35)^2 + (6.37-6.35)^2}{5-1}$$

$$= 0.00055 \text{ cm}^2$$

Note that although $\hat{s} = \sqrt{0.00055} = 0.023$ cm is an estimate of the true standard deviation, this estimate is neither unbiased nor efficient.

9.3 Suppose that the heights of 100 male students at XYZ University represent a random sample of the heights of all 1546 students at the university. Determine unbiased and efficient estimates of (*a*) the true mean and (*b*) the true variance.

SOLUTION

(*a*) From Problem 3.22, the unbiased and efficient estimate of the true mean height is $\bar{X} = 67.45$ inches (in).

(*b*) From Problem 4.17, the unbiased and efficient estimate of the true variance is

$$\hat{s}^2 = \frac{N}{N-1} s^2 = \frac{100}{99}(8.5275) = 8.6136$$

Thus $\hat{s} = \sqrt{8.6136} = 2.93$ in. Note that since N is large, there is essentially no difference between s^2 and $\hat{s}^2$ or between s and $\hat{s}$.

Note that we have not used Sheppard's correction for grouping. To take this into account, we would use $s = 2.79$ in (see Problem 4.21).

9.4 Give an unbiased and inefficient estimate of the true mean diameter of the sphere of Problem 9.2.

SOLUTION

The median is one example of an unbiased and inefficient estimate of the population mean. For the five measurements arranged in order of magnitude, the median is 6.36 cm.

CONFIDENCE INTERVALS FOR MEANS

9.5 Find the (*a*) 95% and (*b*) 99% confidence intervals for estimating the mean height of the XYZ University students in Problem 9.3.

SOLUTION

(*a*) The 95% confidence limits are $\bar{X} \pm 1.96\sigma/\sqrt{N}$. Using $\bar{X} = 67.45$ in, and $\hat{s} = 2.93$ in as an estimate of σ (see Problem 9.3), the confidence limits are $67.45 \pm 1.96(2.93/\sqrt{100})$, or 67.45 ± 0.57 in. Thus the 95% confidence interval for the population mean μ is 66.88 to 68.02 in, which can be denoted by $66.88 < \mu < 68.02$.

We can therefore say that the probability that the population mean height lies between 66.88 and 68.02 in is about 95%, or 0.95. In symbols we write $\Pr\{66.88 < \mu < 68.02\} = 0.95$. This is equivalent to saying that we are 95% *confident* that the population mean (or true mean) lies between 66.88 and 68.02 in.

(*b*) The 99% confidence limits are $\bar{X} \pm 2.58\sigma/\sqrt{N} = \bar{X} \pm 2.58\hat{s}/\sqrt{N} = 67.45 \pm 2.58(2.93/\sqrt{100}) = 67.45 \pm 0.76$ in. Thus the 99% confidence interval for the population mean μ is 66.69 to 68.21 in, which can be denoted by $66.69 < \mu < 68.21$.

In obtaining the above confidence intervals, we assumed that the population was infinite or so large that we could consider conditions to be the same as sampling with replacement. For finite populations where sampling is without replacement, we should use

$$\frac{\sigma}{\sqrt{N}}\sqrt{\frac{N_p - N}{N_p - 1}} \quad \text{in place of} \quad \frac{\sigma}{\sqrt{N}}$$

However, we can consider the factor

$$\sqrt{\frac{N_p - N}{N_p - 1}} = \sqrt{\frac{1546 - 100}{1546 - 1}} = 0.967$$

to be essentially 1.0, and thus it need not be used. If it is used, the above confidence limits become 67.45 ± 0.56 in and 67.45 ± 0.73 in, respectively.

9.6 Measurements of the diameters of a random sample of 200 ball bearings made by a certain machine during 1 week showed a mean of 0.824 cm and a standard deviation of 0.042 cm. Find the (*a*) 95% and (*b*) 99% confidence limits for the mean diameter of all the ball bearings.

SOLUTION

(*a*) The 95% confidence limits are

$$\bar{X} \pm \frac{1.96\sigma}{\sqrt{N}} = \bar{X} \pm \frac{1.96\hat{s}}{\sqrt{N}} = 0.824 \pm 1.96\frac{0.042}{\sqrt{200}} = 0.824 \pm 0.0058 \text{ cm} \quad \text{or} \quad 0.824 \pm 0.006 \text{ cm}$$

(*b*) The 99% confidence limits are

$$\bar{X} \pm \frac{2.58\sigma}{\sqrt{N}} = \bar{X} \pm \frac{2.58\hat{s}}{\sqrt{N}} = 0.824 \pm 2.58\frac{0.042}{\sqrt{200}} = 0.824 \pm 0.0077 \text{ cm} \quad \text{or} \quad 0.824 \pm 0.008 \text{ cm}$$

Note that we have assumed the reported standard deviation to be the *modified* standard deviation $\hat{s}$. If the standard deviation had been s, we would have used $\hat{s} = \sqrt{N/(N-1)}s = \sqrt{200/199}s$, which can be taken as s for all practical purposes. In general, for $N \geq 30$ we may assume that s and $\hat{s}$ are practically equal.

9.7 Find the (*a*) 98%, (*b*) 90%, and (*c*) 99.73% confidence limits for the mean diameter of the ball bearings in Problem 9.6.

SOLUTION

(*a*) Let $z = z_c$ be such that the area under the normal curve to the right is 1%. Then by symmetry the area to the left of $z = -z_c$ is also 1%, so that the shaded area is 98% of the total area; see Fig. 9-1(*a*). Since the total area under the curve is 1, the area from $z = 0$ to $z = z_c$ is 0.49; hence $z_c = 2.33$. Thus the 98% confidence limits are $\bar{X} \pm 2.33\sigma/\sqrt{N} = 0.824 \pm 2.33(0.042/\sqrt{200}) = 0.824 \pm 0.0069$ cm.

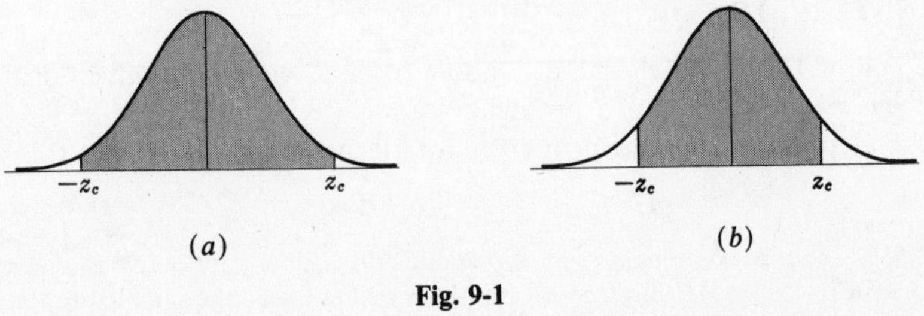

Fig. 9-1

(*b*) We require z_c such that the area from $z=0$ to $z=z_c$ is 0.45, as shown in Fig. 9.1(*b*); then $z_c = 1.645$. Thus, 90% confidence limits are $\bar{X} \pm 1.645\sigma/\sqrt{N} = 0.824 \pm 1.645(0.042/\sqrt{200}) = 0.824 \pm 0.0049$ cm.

(*c*) The 99.73% confidence limits are

$$\bar{X} \pm 3\sigma/\sqrt{N} = 0.824 \pm 3(0.042/\sqrt{200}) = 0.824 \pm 0.0089 \text{ cm}$$

Mathcad **9.8** In measuring reaction time, a psychologist estimates that the standard deviation is 0.05 second (s). How large a sample of measurements must he take in order to be (*a*) 95% and (*b*) 99% confident that the error of his estimate will not exceed 0.01 s?

SOLUTION

(*a*) The 95% confidence limits are $\bar{X} \pm 1.96\sigma/\sqrt{N}$, the error of the estimate being $1.96\sigma/\sqrt{N}$. Taking $\sigma = s = 0.05$ s, we see that this error will be equal to 0.01 s if $(1.96)(0.05)/\sqrt{N} = 0.01$; that is, $\sqrt{N} = (1.96)(0.05)/0.01 = 9.8$, or $N = 96.04$. Thus we can be 95% confident that the error of the estimate will be less than 0.01 s if N is 97 or larger.

Another method

$$\frac{(1.96)(0.05)}{\sqrt{N}} \le 0.01 \quad \text{if} \quad \frac{\sqrt{N}}{(1.96)(0.05)} \ge \frac{1}{0.01} \quad \text{or} \quad \sqrt{N} \ge \frac{(1.96)(0.05)}{0.01} = 9.8$$

Then $N \ge 96.04$, or $N \ge 97$.

(*b*) The 99% confidence limits are $\bar{X} \pm 2.58\sigma/\sqrt{N}$. Then $(2.58)(0.05)/\sqrt{N} = 0.01$, or $N = 166.4$. Thus we can be 99% confident that the error of the estimate will be less than 0.01 s only if N is 167 or larger.

9.9 A random sample of 50 mathematics grades out of a total of 200 showed a mean of 75 and a standard deviation of 10.

(*a*) What are the 95% confidence limits for estimates of the mean of the 200 grades?

(*b*) With what degree of confidence could we say that the mean of all 200 grades is 75 ± 1?

SOLUTION

(*a*) Since the population size is not very large compared with the sample size, we must adjust for it. Then the 95% confidence limits are

$$\bar{X} \pm 1.96\sigma_{\bar{X}} = \bar{X} \pm 1.96\frac{\sigma}{\sqrt{N}}\sqrt{\frac{N_p - N}{N_p - 1}} = 75 \pm 1.96\frac{10}{\sqrt{50}}\sqrt{\frac{200-50}{200-1}} = 75 \pm 2.4$$

(*b*) The confidence limits can be represented by

$$\bar{X} \pm z_c\sigma_{\bar{X}} = \bar{X} \pm z_c\frac{\sigma}{\sqrt{N}}\sqrt{\frac{N_p - N}{N_p - 1}} = 75 \pm z_c\frac{10}{\sqrt{50}}\sqrt{\frac{200-50}{200-1}} = 75 \pm 1.23z_c$$

Since this must equal 75 ± 1, we have $1.23z_c = 1$, or $z_c = 0.81$. The area under the normal curve from $z=0$ to $z=0.81$ is 0.2910; hence the required degree of confidence is $2(0.2910) = 0.582$, or 58.2%.

CONFIDENCE INTERVALS FOR PROPORTIONS

9.10 A sample poll of 100 voters chosen at random from all voters in a given district indicated that 55% of them were in favor of a particular candidate. Find the (*a*) 95%, (*b*) 99%, and (*c*) 99.73% confidence limits for the proportion of all the voters in favor of this candidate.

SOLUTION

(*a*) The 95% confidence limits for the population p are $P \pm 1.96\sigma_P = P \pm 1.96\sqrt{p(1-p)/N} = 0.55 \pm 1.96\sqrt{(0.55)(0.45)/100} = 0.55 \pm 0.10$, where we have used the sample proportion P to estimate p.

(*b*) The 99% confidence limits for p are $0.55 \pm 2.58\sqrt{(0.55)(0.45)/100} = 0.55 \pm 0.13$.

(*c*) The 99.73% confidence limits for p are $0.55 \pm 3\sqrt{(0.55)(0.45)/100} = 0.55 \pm 0.15$.

For a more exact method of working this problem, see Problem 9.12.

9.11 How large a sample of voters should we take in Problem 9.10 in order to be (*a*) 95% and (*b*) 99.73% confident that the candidate will be elected?

SOLUTION

The confidence limits for p are $P \pm z_c\sqrt{p(1-p)/N} = 0.55 \pm z_c\sqrt{(0.55)(0.45)/N} = 0.55 \pm 0.50z_c/\sqrt{N}$, where we have used the estimate $P = p = 0.55$ on the basis of Problem 9.10. Since the candidate will win only if she receives more than 50% of the population's votes, we require that $0.50z_c/\sqrt{N}$ be less than 0.05.

(*a*) For 95% confidence, $0.50z_c/\sqrt{N} = 0.50(1.96)/\sqrt{N} = 0.05$ when $N = 384.2$. Thus N should be at least 385.

(*b*) For 99.73% confidence, $0.50z_c/\sqrt{N} = 0.50(3)/\sqrt{N} = 0.05$ when $N = 900$. Thus N should be at least 901.

Another method

$1.50/\sqrt{N} < 0.05$ when $\sqrt{N}/1.50 > 1/0.05$ or $\sqrt{N} > 1.50/0.05$. Then $\sqrt{N} > 30$ or $N > 900$, so that N should be at least 901.

9.12 (*a*) If P is the observed proportion of successes in a sample of size N, show that the confidence limits for estimating the population proportion of successes p at the level of confidence determined by z_c are given by

$$p = \frac{P + \dfrac{z_c^2}{2N} \pm z_c\sqrt{\dfrac{P(1-P)}{N} + \dfrac{z_c^2}{4N^2}}}{1 + \dfrac{z_c^2}{N}}$$

(*b*) Use the formula derived in part (*a*) to obtain the 99.73% confidence limits of Problem 9.10.

(*c*) Show that for large N the formula in part (*a*) reduces to $p = P \pm z_c\sqrt{P(1-P)/N}$, as used in Problem 9.10.

SOLUTION

(*a*) The sample proportion P in standard units is

$$\frac{P-p}{\sigma_P} = \frac{P-p}{\sqrt{p(1-p)/N}}$$

The largest and smallest values of this standardized variable are $\pm z_c$, where z_c determines the level of confidence. At these extreme values we must therefore have

$$P - p = \pm z_c\sqrt{\frac{p(1-p)}{N}}$$

Squaring both sides, $$P^2 - 2pP + p^2 = \frac{z_c^2 p(1-p)}{N}$$

Multiplying both sizes by N and simplifying, we find

$$(N + z_c^2)p^2 - (2NP + z_c^2)p + NP^2 = 0$$

If $a = N + z_c^2$, $b = -(2NP + z_c^2)$, and $c = NP^2$, this equation becomes $ap^2 + bp + c = 0$ whose solution for p is given by the quadratic formula

$$p = \frac{-b \pm \sqrt{b^2 - 4ac}}{2a} = \frac{2NP + z_c^2 \pm \sqrt{(2NP + z_c^2)^2 - 4(N + z_c^2)(NP^2)}}{2(N + z_c^2)}$$

$$= \frac{2NP + z_c^2 \pm z_c\sqrt{4NP(1-P) + z_c^2}}{2(N + z_c^2)}$$

Dividing the numerator and denominator by $2N$, this becomes

$$p = \frac{P + \dfrac{z_c^2}{2N} \pm z_c \sqrt{\dfrac{P(1-P)}{N} + \dfrac{z_c^2}{4N^2}}}{1 + \dfrac{z_c^2}{N}}$$

(*b*) For 99.73% confidence limits, $z_c = 3$. Then using $P = 0.55$ and $N = 100$ in the formula derived in part (*a*), we find $p = 0.40$ and 0.69, agreeing with Problem 9.10(*c*).

(*c*) If N is large, then $z_c^2/(2N)$, $z_c^2/(4N^2)$, and z_c^2/N are all negligibly small and can essentially be replaced by zero, so that the required result is obtained.

9.13 In 40 tosses of a coin, 24 heads were obtained. Find the (*a*) 95% and (*b*) 99.73% confidence limits for the proportion of heads that would be obtained in an unlimited number of tosses of the coin.

SOLUTION

(*a*) At the 95% level, $z_c = 1.96$. Putting $P = 24/40 = 0.6$ and $N = 40$ in the formula of Problem 9.12(*a*), we find $p = 0.45$ and 0.74. Thus we can say with 95% confidence that p lies between 0.45 and 0.74.

Using the approximate formula $p = P \pm z_c\sqrt{P(1-P)/N}$, we find $p = 0.60 \pm 0.15$, yielding the interval 0.45 to 0.75.

(*b*) At the 99.73% level, $z_c = 3$. Using the formula of Problem 9.12(*a*), we find that $p = 0.37$ and 0.79.

Using the approximate formula $p = P \pm z_c\sqrt{P(1-P)/N}$, we find $p = 0.60 \pm 0.23$, yielding the interval 0.37 to 0.83.

CONFIDENCE INTERVALS FOR DIFFERENCES AND SUMS

9.14 A sample of 150 brand A light bulbs showed a mean lifetime of 1400 hours (h) and a standard deviation of 120 h. A sample of 200 brand B light bulbs showed a mean lifetime of 1200 h and a standard deviation of 80 h. Find the (*a*) 95% and (*b*) 99% confidence limits for the difference of the mean lifetimes of the populations of brands A and B.

SOLUTION

Confidence limits for the difference in means of brands A and B are given by

$$\bar{X}_A - \bar{X}_B \pm z_c\sqrt{\sigma_A^2/N_A + \sigma_B^2/N_B}$$

(*a*) The 95% confidence limits are $1400 - 1200 \pm 1.96\sqrt{(120)^2/150 + (80)^2/100} = 200 \pm 24.8$. Thus we can be 95% confident that the difference of population means lies between 175 and 225 h.

(*b*) The 99% confidence limits are $1400 - 1200 \pm 2.58\sqrt{(120)^2/150 + (80)^2/100} = 200 \pm 32.6$. Thus we can be 99% confident that the difference of population means lies between 167 and 233 h.

9.15 In a random sample of 400 adults and 600 teenagers who watched a certain television program, 100 adults and 300 teenagers indicated that they liked it. Construct (*a*) 95% and (*b*) 99% confidence limits for the difference in proportions of all adults and all teenagers who watched the program and liked it.

SOLUTION

Confidence limits for the differences in proportions of the two groups are given by

$$P_1 - P_2 \pm z_c\sqrt{p_1q_1/N_1 + p_2q_2/N_2}$$

where the subscripts 1 and 2 refer to teenagers and adults, respectively. Here, $P_1 = 300/600 = 0.50$ and $P_2 = 100/400 = 0.25$ are, respectively, the proportions of teenagers and adults who liked the program.

(*a*) The 95% confidence limits are $0.50 - 0.25 \pm 1.96\sqrt{(0.50)(0.50)/600 + (0.25)(0.75)/400} = 0.25 \pm 0.06$. Thus we can be 95% confident that the true difference in proportion lies between 0.19 and 0.31.

(*b*) The 99% confidence limits are $0.50 - 0.25 \pm 2.58\sqrt{(0.50)(0.50)/600 + (0.25)(0.75)/400} = 0.25 \pm 0.08$. Thus we can be 99% confident that the true difference in proportion lies between 0.17 and 0.33.

9.16 The mean electromotive force (emf) of batteries produced by a company is 45.1 volts (V), and the standard deviation is 0.04 V. If four such batteries are connected in series, find the (*a*) 95%, (*b*) 99%, (*c*) 99.73%, and (*d*) 50% confidence limits for the total emf.

SOLUTION

If E_1, E_2, E_3, and E_4 represent the emf's of the four batteries, we have

$$u_{E1+E2+E3+E4} = \mu_{E1} + \mu_{E2} + \mu_{E3} + \mu_{E4} \quad \text{and} \quad \sigma_{E1+E2+E3+E4} = \sqrt{\sigma_{E1}^2 + \sigma_{E2}^2 + \sigma_{E3}^2 + \sigma_{E4}^2}$$

Then since $\mu_{E1} = \mu_{E2} = \mu_{E3} = \mu_{E4} = 45.1$ V and $\sigma_{E1} = \sigma_{E2} = \sigma_{E3} = \sigma_{E4} = 0.04$ V, we have $\mu_{E1+E2+E3+E4} = 4(45.1) = 180.4$ and $\sigma_{E1+E2+E3+E4} = \sqrt{4(0.04)^2} = 0.08$.

(*a*) The 95% confidence limits are $180.4 \pm 1.96(0.08) = 180.4 \pm 0.16$ V.

(*b*) The 99% confidence limits are $180.4 \pm 2.58(0.08) = 180.4 \pm 0.21$ V.

(*c*) The 99.73% confidence limits are $180.4 \pm 3(0.08) = 180.4 \pm 0.24$ V.

(*d*) The 50% confidence limits are $180.4 \pm 0.6745(0.08) = 180.4 \pm 0.054$ V. The value 0.054 V is called the *probable error.*

CONFIDENCE INTERVALS FOR STANDARD DEVIATIONS

9.17 The standard deviation of the lifetimes of a sample of 200 electric light bulbs was computed to be 100 h. Find the (*a*) 95% and (*b*) 99% confidence limits for the standard deviation of all such electric light bulbs.

SOLUTION

Confidence limits for the population standard deviation σ are given by $s \pm z_c\sigma/\sqrt{2N}$, where z_c indicates the level of confidence. We use the sample standard deviation to estimate σ.

(*a*) The 95% confidence limits are $100 \pm 1.96(100)/\sqrt{400} = 100 \pm 9.8$. Thus we can be 95% confident that the population standard deviation will lie between 90.2 and 109.8 h.

(*b*) The 99% confidence limits are $100 \pm 2.58(100)/\sqrt{400} = 100 \pm 12.9$. Thus we can be 99% confident that the population standard deviation will lie between 87.1 and 112.9 h.

9.18 How large a sample of the light bulbs in Problem 9.17 must we take in order to be 99.73% confident that the true population standard deviation will not differ from the sample standard deviation by more than (*a*) 5% and (*b*) 10%?

SOLUTION

The 99% confidence limits for σ are $s \pm 3\sigma/\sqrt{2N} = s \pm 3s/\sqrt{2N}$, using s as an estimate of σ. Thus the percentage error in the standard deviation is

$$\frac{3s/\sqrt{2N}}{s} = \frac{300}{\sqrt{2N}}\%$$

(a) If $300/\sqrt{2N} = 5$, then $N = 1800$. Thus the sample size should be 1800 or more.

(b) If $300/\sqrt{2N} = 10$, then $N = 450$. Thus the sample size should be 450 or more.

PROBABLE ERROR

9.19 The voltages of 50 batteries of the same type have a mean of 18.2 V and a standard deviation of 0.5 V. Find (a) the probable error of the mean and (b) the 50% confidence limits.

SOLUTION

(a)
$$\text{Probable error of the mean} = 0.674\sigma_{\bar{X}} = 0.6745\frac{\sigma}{\sqrt{N}} = 0.6745\frac{\hat{s}}{\sqrt{N}}$$
$$= 0.6745\frac{s}{\sqrt{N-1}} = 0.6745\frac{0.5}{\sqrt{49}} = 0.048 \text{ V}$$

Note that if the standard deviation of 0.5 V is computed as $\hat{s}$, the probable error is $0.6745(0.5/\sqrt{50}) = 0.048$ also, so that either estimate can be used if N is large enough.

(b) The 50% confidence limits are 18 ± 0.048 V.

9.20 A measurement was recorded as 216.480 grams (g) with a probable error of 0.272 g. What are the 95% confidence limits for the measurement?

SOLUTION

The probable error is $0.272 = 0.6745\sigma_{\bar{X}}$, or $\sigma_{\bar{X}} = 0.272/0.6745$. Thus the 95% confidence limits are $\bar{X} \pm 1.96\sigma_{\bar{X}} = 216.480 \pm 1.96(0.272/0.6745) = 216.480 \pm 0.790$ g.

Supplementary Problems

UNBIASED AND EFFICIENT ESTIMATES

9.21 Measurements of a sample of masses were determined to be 8.3, 10.6, 9.7, 8.8, 10.2, and 9.4 kilograms (kg), respectively. Determine unbiased and efficient estimates of (a) the population mean and (b) the population variance, and (c) compare the sample standard deviation with the estimated population standard deviation.

9.22 A sample of 10 television tubes produced by a company showed a mean lifetime of 1200 h and a standard deviation of 100 h. Estimate (a) the mean and (b) the standard deviation of the population of all television tubes produced by this company.

9.23 (a) Work Problem 9.22 if the same results are obtained for 30, 50, and 100 television tubes.

(b) What can you conclude about the relation between sample standard deviations and estimates of population standard deviations for different sample sizes?

CONFIDENCE INTERVALS FOR MEANS

9.24 The mean and standard deviation of the maximum loads supported by 60 cables (see Problem 3.59) are given by 11.09 tons and 0.73 ton, respectively. Find the (a) 95% and (b) 99% confidence limits for the mean of the maximum loads of all cables produced by the company.

9.25 The mean and standard deviation of the diameters of a sample of 250 rivet heads manufactured by a company are 0.72642 in and 0.00058 in, respectively (see Problem 3.61). Find the (a) 99%, (b) 98%, (c) 95%, and (d) 90% confidence limits for the mean diameter of all the rivet heads manufactured by the company.

9.26 Find (*a*) the 50% confidence limits and (*b*) the probable error for the mean diameters in Problem 9.25.

9.27 If the standard deviation of the lifetimes of television tubes is estimated to be 100 h, how large a sample must we take in order to be (*a*) 95%, (*b*) 90%, (*c*) 99%, and (*d*) 99.73% confident that the error in the estimated mean lifetime will not exceed 20 h?

9.28 What are the sample sizes in Problem 9.27 if the error in the estimated mean lifetime must not exceed 10 h?

9.29 A company has 500 cables. A test of 40 cables selected at random showed a mean breaking strength of 2400 pounds (lb) and a standard deviation of 150 lb.

(*a*) What are the 95% and 99% confidence limits for estimating the mean breaking strength of the remaining 460 cables?

(*b*) With what degree of confidence could we say that the mean breaking strength of the remaining 460 cables is 2400 ± 35 lb?

CONFIDENCE INTERVALS FOR PROPORTIONS

9.30 An urn contains an unknown proportion of red and white marbles. A random sample of 60 marbles selected with replacement from the urn showed that 70% were red. Find the (*a*) 95%, (*b*) 99%, and (*c*) 99.73% confidence limits for the actual proportion of red marbles in the urn. Present the results from using both the approximate formula and the more exact formula of Problem 9.12.

9.31 How large a sample of marbles should one take in Problem 9.30 in order to be (*a*) 95%, (*b*) 99%, and (*c*) 99.73% confident that the true proportion does not differ from the sample proportion by more than 5%?

9.32 It is believed that an election will result in a very close vote between two candidates. What is the least number of voters that one should poll in order to be (*a*) 80%, (*b*) 90%, (*c*) 95%, and (*d*) 99% confident of a decision in favor of either one of the candidates?

CONFIDENCE INTERVALS FOR DIFFERENCES AND SUMS

9.33 Of two similar groups of patients, *A* and *B*, consisting of 50 and 100 individuals, respectively, the first was given a new type of sleeping pill and the second was given a conventional type. For the patients in group *A*, the mean number of hours of sleep was 7.82 with a standard deviation of 0.24 h. For the patients in group *B*, the mean number of hours of sleep was 6.75 with a standard deviation of 0.30 h. Find the (*a*) 95% and (*b*) 99% confidence limits for the difference in the mean number of hours of sleep induced by the two types of sleeping pills.

9.34 A sample of 200 bolts from one machine showed that 15 were defective, while a sample of 100 bolts from another machine showed that 12 were defective. Find the (*a*) 95%, (*b*) 99%, and (*c*) 99.73% confidence limits for the difference in proportions of defective bolts from the two machines. Discuss the results obtained.

9.35 A company manufactures ball bearings having a mean weight of 0.638 lb and a standard deviation of 0.012 lb. Find the (*a*) 95% and (*b*) 99% confidence limits for the weights of lots consisting of 100 ball bearings each.

CONFIDENCE INTERVALS FOR STANDARD DEVIATIONS

9.36 The standard deviation of the breaking strengths of 100 cables tested by a company was 180 lb. Find the (*a*) 95%, (*b*) 99%, and (*c*) 99.73% confidence limits for the standard deviation of all cables produced by the company.

9.37 Find the probable error of the standard deviation in Problem 9.36.

9.38 How large a sample should one take in order to be (*a*) 95%, (*b*) 99%, and (*c*) 99.73% confident that a population standard deviation will not differ from a sample standard deviation by more than 2%?

Chapter 10

Statistical Decision Theory

STATISTICAL DECISIONS

Very often in practice we are called upon to make decisions about populations on the basis of sample information. Such decisions are called *statistical decisions.* For example, we may wish to decide on the basis of sample data whether a new serum is really effective in curing a disease, whether one educational procedure is better than another, or whether a given coin is loaded.

STATISTICAL HYPOTHESES

In attempting to reach decisions, it is useful to make assumptions (or guesses) about the populations involved. Such assumptions, which may or may not be true, are called *statistical hypotheses.* They are generally statements about the probability distributions of the populations.

Null Hypotheses

In many instances we formulate a statistical hypothesis for the sole purpose of rejecting or nullifying it. For example, if we want to decide whether a given coin is loaded, we formulate the hypothesis that the coin is fair (i.e., $p = 0.5$, where p is the probability of heads). Similarly, if we want to decide whether one procedure is better than another, we formulate the hypothesis that there is *no difference* between the procedures (i.e., any observed differences are due merely to fluctuations in sampling from the *same* population). Such hypotheses are often called *null hypotheses* and are denoted by H_0.

Alternative Hypotheses

Any hypothesis that differs from a given hypothesis is called an *alternative hypothesis.* For example, if one hypothesis is $p = 0.5$, alternative hypotheses might be $p = 0.7$, $p \neq 0.5$, or $p > 0.5$. A hypothesis alternative to the null hypothesis is denoted by H_1.

TESTS OF HYPOTHESES AND SIGNIFICANCE, OR DECISION RULES

If we suppose that a particular hypothesis is true but find that the results observed in a random sample differ markedly from the results expected under the hypothesis (i.e., expected on the basis of pure chance, using sampling theory), then we would say that the observed differences are *significant* and would thus be inclined to reject the hypothesis (or at least not accept it on the basis of the evidence obtained). For example, if 20 tosses of a coin yield 16 heads, we would be inclined to reject the hypothesis that the coin is fair, although it is conceivable that we might be wrong.

Procedures that enable us to determine whether observed samples differ significantly from the results expected, and thus help us decide whether to accept or reject hypotheses, are called *tests of hypotheses, tests of significance, rules of decision,* or simply *decision rules.*

TYPE I AND TYPE II ERRORS

If we reject a hypothesis when it should be accepted, we say that a *Type I error* has been made. If, on the other hand, we accept a hypothesis when it should be rejected, we say that a *Type II error* has been made. In either case, a wrong decision or error in judgment has occurred.

In order for decision rules (or tests of hypotheses) to be good, they must be designed so as to minimize errors of decision. This is not a simple matter, because for any given sample size, an attempt to decrease one type of error is generally accompanied by an increase in the other type of error. In practice, one type of error may be more serious than the other, and so a compromise should be reached in favor of limiting the more serious error. The only way to reduce both types of error is to increase the sample size, which may or may not be possible.

LEVEL OF SIGNIFICANCE

In testing a given hypothesis, the maximum probability with which we would be willing to risk a Type I error is called the *level of significance*, or *significance level*, of the test. This probability, often denoted by α, is generally specified before any samples are drawn so that the results obtained will not influence our choice.

In practice, a significance level of 0.05 or 0.01 is customary, although other values are used. If, for example, the 0.05 (or 5%) significance level is chosen in designing a decision rule, then there are about 5 chances in 100 that we would reject the hypothesis when it should be accepted; that is, we are about 95% *confident* that we have made the right decision. In such case we say that the hypothesis has been rejected at the 0.05 significance level, which means that the hypothesis has a 0.05 probability of being wrong.

TESTS INVOLVING NORMAL DISTRIBUTIONS

To illustrate the ideas presented above, suppose that under a given hypothesis the sampling distribution of a statistic S is a normal distribution with mean μ_S and standard deviation σ_S. Thus the distribution of the standardized variable (or z score), given by $z=(S-\mu_S)/\sigma_S$, is the standardized normal distribution (mean 0, variance 1), as shown in Fig. 10-1.

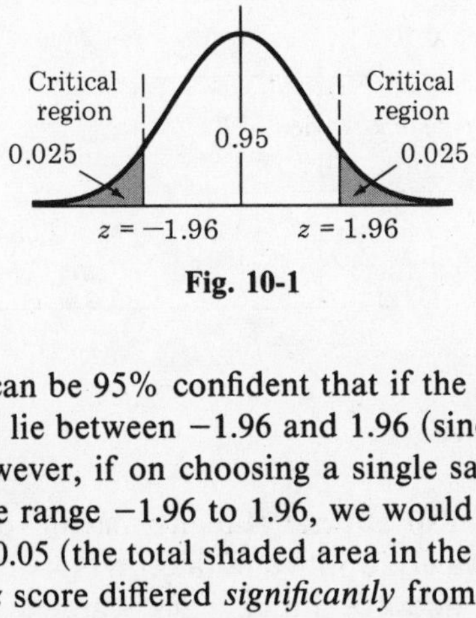

Fig. 10-1

As indicated in Fig. 10-1, we can be 95% confident that if the hypothesis is true, then the z score of an actual sample statistic S will lie between -1.96 and 1.96 (since the area under the normal curve between these values is 0.95). However, if on choosing a single sample at random we find that the z score of its statistic lies *outside* the range -1.96 to 1.96, we would conclude that such an event could happen with a probability of only 0.05 (the total shaded area in the figure) if the given hypothesis were true. We would then say that this z score differed *significantly* from what would be expected under the hypothesis, and we would then be inclined to reject the hypothesis.

The total shaded area 0.05 is the significance level of the test. It represents the probability of our being wrong in rejecting the hypothesis (i.e., the probability of making a Type I error). Thus we say that the hypothesis is *rejected at 0.05 the significance level* or that the z score of the given sample statistic is *significant at the 0.05 level.*

The set of z scores outside the range -1.96 to 1.96 constitutes what is called *the critical region of the hypothesis, the region of rejection of the hypothesis,* or *the region of significance.* The set of z scores inside the range -1.96 to 1.96 is thus called the *region of acceptance of the hypothesis,* or the *region of nonsignificance.*

On the basis of the above remarks, we can formulate the following decision rule (or test of hypothesis or significance):

Reject the hypothesis at the 0.05 significance level if the z score of the statistic S lies outside the range -1.96 to 1.96 (i.e., either $z > 1.96$ or $z < -1.96$). This is equivalent to saying that the observed sample statistic is significant at the 0.05 level.

Accept the hypothesis otherwise (or, if desired, make no decision at all).

Because the z score plays such an important part in tests of hypotheses, it is also called a *test statistic.*

It should be noted that other significance levels could have been used. For example, if the 0.01 level were used, we would replace 1.96 everywhere above with 2.58 (see Table 10.1). Table 9.1 can also be used, since the sum of the significance and confidence levels is 100%.

TWO-TAILED AND ONE-TAILED TESTS

In the above test we were interested in extreme values of the statistic S or its corresponding z score on *both* sides of the mean (i.e., in both tails of the distribution). Such tests are thus called *two-sided tests*, or *two-tailed tests.*

Often, however, we may be interested only in extreme values to one side of the mean (i.e., in one tail of the distribution), such as when we are testing the hypothesis that one process is better than another (which is different from testing whether one process is better or worse than the other). Such tests are called *one-sided tests*, or *one-tailed tests.* In such cases the critical region is a region to one side of the distribution, with area equal to the level of significance.

Table 10.1, which gives critical values of z for both one-tailed and two-tailed tests at various levels of significance, will be found useful for reference purposes. Critical values of z for other levels of significance are found from the table of normal-curve areas (Appendix II).

Table 10.1

Level of significance, α	0.10	0.05	0.01	0.005	0.002
Critical values of z for one-tailed tests	-1.28 *or* 1.28	-1.645 *or* 1.645	-2.33 *or* 2.33	-2.58 *or* 2.58	-2.88 *or* 2.88
Critical values of z for two-tailed tests	-1.645 *and* 1.645	-1.96 *and* 1.96	-2.58 *and* 2.58	-2.81 *and* 2.81	-3.08 *and* 3.08

SPECIAL TESTS

For large samples, the sampling distributions of many statistics are normal distributions (or at least nearly normal), and the above tests can be applied to the corresponding z scores. The following special cases, taken from Table 8.1, are just a few of the statistics of practical interest. In each case the results hold for infinite populations or for sampling with replacement. For sampling without replacement from finite populations, the results must be modified. See page 176.

1. **Means.** Here $S = \bar{X}$, the sample mean; $\mu_S = \mu_{\bar{X}} = \mu$, the population mean; and $\sigma_S = \sigma_{\bar{X}} = \sigma/\sqrt{N}$, where σ is the population standard deviation and N is the sample size. The z score is given by

$$z = \frac{\bar{X} - \mu}{\sigma/\sqrt{N}}$$

   When necessary, the sample deviation s or $\hat{s}$ is used to estimate σ.

2. **Proportions.** Here $S = P$, the proportion of "successes" in a sample; $\mu_S = \mu_P = p$, where p is the population proportion of successes and N is the sample size; and $\sigma_S = \sigma_P = \sqrt{pq/N}$, where $q = 1 - p$.

The z score is given by

$$z = \frac{P - p}{\sqrt{pq/N}}$$

In case $P = X/N$, where X is the actual number of successes in a sample, the z score becomes

$$z = \frac{X - Np}{\sqrt{Npq}}$$

That is, $\mu_X = \mu = Np$, $\sigma_X = \sigma = \sqrt{Npq}$, and $S = X$.

The results for other statistics can be obtained similarly.

OPERATING-CHARACTERISTIC CURVES; THE POWER OF A TEST

We have seen how the Type I error can be limited by choosing the significance level properly. It is possible to avoid risking Type II errors altogether simply by not making them, which amounts to never accepting hypotheses. In many practical cases, however, this cannot be done. In such cases, use is often made of *operating-characteristic curves*, or *OC curves*, which are graphs showing the probabilities of Type II errors under various hypotheses. These provide indications of how well a given test will enable us to minimize Type II errors; that is, they indicate the *power of a test* to prevent us from making wrong decisions. They are useful in designing experiments because they show such things as what sample sizes to use.

CONTROL CHARTS

It is often important in practice to know when a process has changed sufficiently that steps should be taken to remedy the situation. Such problems arise, for example, in quality control. Quality control supervisors must often decide whether observed changes are due simply to chance fluctuations or are due to actual changes in a manufacturing process because of deteriorating machine parts, employees' mistakes, etc. *Control charts* provide a useful and simple method for dealing with such problems (see Problem 10.16).

TESTS INVOLVING SAMPLE DIFFERENCES

Differences of Means

Let $\bar{X}_1$ and $\bar{X}_2$ be the sample means obtained in large samples of sizes N_1 and N_2 drawn from respective populations having means μ_1 and μ_2 and standard deviations σ_1 and σ_2. Consider the null hypothesis that there is *no difference* between the population means (i.e., $\mu_1 = \mu_2$), which is to say that the samples are drawn from two populations having the same mean.

Placing $\mu_1 = \mu_2$ in equation (*5*) of Chapter 8, we see that the sampling distribution of differences in means is approximately normally distributed, with its mean and standard deviation given by

$$\mu_{\bar{X}1-\bar{X}2} = 0 \qquad \text{and} \qquad \sigma_{\bar{X}1-\bar{X}2} = \sqrt{\frac{\sigma_1^2}{N_1} + \frac{\sigma_2^2}{N_2}} \tag{1}$$

where we can, if necessary, use the sample standard deviations s_1 and s_2 (or $\hat{s}_1$ and $\hat{s}_2$) as estimates of σ_1 and σ_2.

By using the standardized variable, or z score, given by

$$z = \frac{\bar{X}_1 - \bar{X}_2 - 0}{\sigma_{\bar{X}1-\bar{X}2}} = \frac{\bar{X}_1 - \bar{X}_2}{\sigma_{\bar{X}1-\bar{X}2}} \tag{2}$$

we can test the null hypothesis against alternative hypotheses (or the significance of an observed difference) at an appropriate level of significance.

Differences of Proportions

Let P_1 and P_2 be the sample proportions obtained in large samples of sizes N_1 and N_2 drawn from respective populations having proportions p_1 and p_2. Consider the null hypothesis that there is *no difference* between the population parameters (i.e., $p_1 = p_2$) and thus that the samples are really drawn from the same population.

Placing $p_1 = p_2 = p$ in equation (*6*) of Chapter 8, we see that the sampling distribution of differences in proportions is approximately normally distributed, with its mean and standard deviation given by

$$\mu_{P1-P2} = 0 \qquad \text{and} \qquad \sigma_{P1-P2} = \sqrt{pq\left(\frac{1}{N_1} + \frac{1}{N_2}\right)} \tag{3}$$

where

$$p = \frac{N_1P_1 + N_2P_2}{N_1 + N_2}$$

is used as an estimate of the population proportion and where $q = 1 - p$.

By using the standardized variable

$$z = \frac{P_1 - P_2 - 0}{\sigma_{P1-P2}} = \frac{P_1 - P_2}{\sigma_{P1-P2}} \tag{4}$$

we can test observed differences at an appropriate level of significance and thereby test the null hypothesis.

Tests involving other statistics can be designed similarly.

TESTS INVOLVING BINOMIAL DISTRIBUTIONS

Tests involving binomial distributions (as well as other distributions) can be designed in a manner analogous to those using normal distributions; the basic principles are essentially the same. See Problems 10.23 to 10.28.

Solved Problems

TESTS OF MEANS AND PROPORTIONS, USING NORMAL DISTRIBUTIONS

10.1 Find the probability of getting between 40 and 60 heads inclusive in 100 tosses of a fair coin.

SOLUTION

According to the binomial distribution, the required probability is

$$\binom{100}{40}\left(\frac{1}{2}\right)^{40}\left(\frac{1}{2}\right)^{60} + \binom{100}{41}\left(\frac{1}{2}\right)^{41}\left(\frac{1}{2}\right)^{59} + \cdots + \binom{100}{60}\left(\frac{1}{2}\right)^{60}\left(\frac{1}{2}\right)^{40}$$

Since $Np = 100(\frac{1}{2})$ and $Nq = 100(\frac{1}{2})$ are both greater than 5, the normal approximation to the binomial distribution can be used in evaluating this sum. The mean and standard deviation of the number of heads in 100 tosses are given by

$$\mu = Np = 100(\tfrac{1}{2}) = 50 \qquad \text{and} \qquad \sigma = \sqrt{Npq} = \sqrt{(100)(\tfrac{1}{2})(\tfrac{1}{2})} = 5$$

On a continuous scale, between 40 and 60 heads inclusive is the same as between 39.5 and 60.5 heads. We thus have

$$39.5 \text{ in standard units} = \frac{39.5-50}{5} = -2.10 \qquad 60.5 \text{ in standard units} = \frac{60.5-50}{5} = 2.10$$

$$\begin{aligned}\text{Required probability} &= \text{area under normal curve between } z=-2.10 \text{ and } z=2.10\\ &= 2(\text{area between } z=0 \text{ and } z=2.10) = 2(0.4821) = 0.9642\end{aligned}$$

10.2 To test the hypothesis that a coin is fair, adopt the following decision rule:

Accept the hypothesis if the number of heads in a single sample of 100 tosses is between 40 and 60 inclusive.

Reject the hypothesis otherwise.

(*a*) Find the probability of rejecting the hypothesis when it is actually correct.

(*b*) Graph the decision rule and the result of part (*a*).

(*c*) What conclusions would you draw if the sample of 100 tosses yielded 53 heads? And if it yielded 60 heads?

(*d*) Could you be wrong in your conclusions about part (*c*)? Explain.

SOLUTION

(*a*) From Problem 10.1, the probability of not getting between 40 and 60 heads inclusive if the coin is fair is $1-0.9642=0.0358$. Thus the probability of rejecting the hypothesis when it is correct is 0.0358.

(*b*) The decision rule is illustrated in Fig. 10-2, which shows the probability distribution of heads in 100 tosses of a fair coin. If a single sample of 100 tosses yields a z score between -2.10 and 2.10, we accept the hypothesis; otherwise, we reject the hypothesis and decide that the coin is not fair.

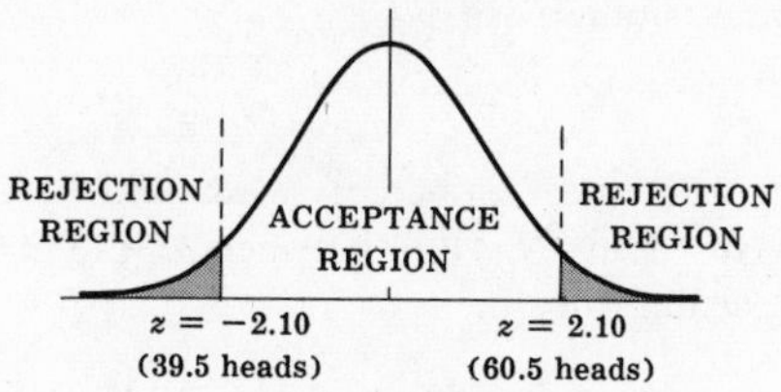

Fig. 10-2

The error made in rejecting the hypothesis when it should be accepted is the *Type I error* of the decision rule; and the probability of making this error, equal to 0.0358 from part (*a*), is represented by the total shaded area of the figure. If a single sample of 100 tosses yields a number of heads whose z score (or z statistic) lies in the shaded regions, we would say that this z score differed *significantly* from what would be expected if the hypothesis were true. For this reason, the total shaded area (i.e., the probability of a Type I error) is called the *significance level* of the decision rule and equals 0.0358 in this case. Thus we speak of rejecting the hypothesis at the 0.0358 (or 3.58%) significance level.

(*c*) According to the decision rule, we would have to accept the hypothesis that the coin is fair in both cases. One might argue that if only one more head had been obtained, we would have rejected the hypothesis. This is what one must face when any sharp line of division is used in making decisions.

(*d*) Yes. We could accept the hypothesis when it actually should be rejected—as would be the case, for example, when the probability of heads is really 0.7 instead of 0.5. The error made in accepting the hypothesis when it should be rejected is the *Type II error* of the decision. (For further discussion, see Problems 10.10 to 10.12.)

10.3 Design a decision rule to test the hypothesis that a coin is fair if we take a sample of 64 tosses of the coin and use significance levels of (*a*) 0.05 and (*b*) 0.01.

SOLUTION

(*a*) **First method**

If the significance level is 0.05, each shaded area in Fig. 10-3 is 0.025 by symmetry. Then the area between 0 and z_1 is $0.5000-0.0250=0.4750$, and $z_1=1.96$; the critical values -1.96 and 1.96 can also be read from Table 10.1. Thus a possible decision rule is:

Accept the hypothesis that the coin is fair if z is between -1.96 and 1.96.

Reject the hypothesis otherwise.

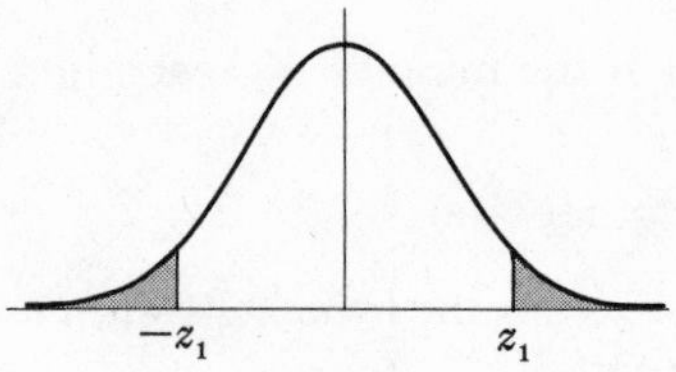

Fig. 10-3

To express this decision rule in terms of the number of heads to be obtained in 64 tosses of the coin, note that the mean and standard deviation of the distribution of heads are given by:

$$\mu = Np = 64(0.5) = 32 \qquad \text{and} \qquad \sigma = \sqrt{Npq} = \sqrt{64(0.5)(0.5)} = 4$$

under the hypothesis that the coin is fair. Then $z=(X-\mu)/\sigma=(X-32)/4$. If $z=1.96$, then $(X-32)/4=1.96$ and $X=39.84$; if $z=-1.96$, then $(X-32)/4=-1.96$ and $X=24.16$. Thus the decision rule becomes:

Accept the hypothesis that the coin is fair if the number of heads is between 24.16 and 39.84 (i.e., between 25 and 39 inclusive).

Reject the hypothesis otherwise.

Second method

With probability 0.95, the number of heads will lie bettween $\mu-1.96\sigma$ and $\mu+1.96\sigma$ (i.e., $Np-1.96\sqrt{Npq}$ and $Np+1.96\sqrt{Npq}$), or between $32-1.96(4)=24.16$ and $32+1.96(4)=39.84$, which leads to the above decision rule.

Third method

Since $-1.96<z<1.96$ is equivalent to $-1.96<\frac{1}{4}(X-32)<1.96$, then $-1.96(4)<(X-32)<1.96(4)$, or $32-1.96(4)<X<32+1.96(4)$ (i.e., $24.16<X<39.84$), which also leads to the above decision rule.

(*b*) If the significance level is 0.01, each shaded area in Fig. 10-3 is 0.005. Thus the area between 0 and z_1 is $0.5000-0.0050=0.4950$, and $z_1=2.58$ (more exactly 2.575); this can also be read from Table 10.1. Following the procedure in the second method of part (*a*), we see that with probability 0.99 the number of heads will lie between $\mu-2.58\sigma$ and $\mu+2.58\sigma$, which are $32-2.58(4)=21.68$ and $32+2.58(4)=42.32$. Thus the decision rule becomes:

Accept the hypothesis if the number of heads is between 22 and 42 inclusive.

Reject the hypothesis otherwise.

10.4 How could you design a decision rule in Problem 10.3 so as to avoid a Type II error?

SOLUTION

A Type II error is made by accepting a hypothesis when it should be rejected. We can avoid this error as follows: Instead of accepting the hypothesis, we simply do not reject it, which could mean that we are withholding any decision in this case. Thus, for example, we could word the decision rule of Problem 10.3(*b*) as:

Do not reject the hypothesis if the number of heads is between 22 and 42 inclusive.

Reject the hypothesis otherwise.

In many practical instances, however, it is important to decide whether a hypothesis should be accepted or rejected. A complete discussion of such cases requires consideration of Type II errors (see Problems 10.10 to 10.12).

10.5 In an experiment on extrasensory perception (ESP), an individual (subject) in one room is asked to state the color (red or blue) of a card chosen from a deck of 50 well-shuffled cards by an individual in another room. It is unknown to the subject how many red or blue cards are in the deck. If the subject identifies 32 cards correctly, determine whether the results are significant at the (*a*) 0.05 and (*b*) 0.01 levels.

SOLUTION

If p is the probability of the subject choosing the color of a card correctly, then we have to decide between two hypotheses:

$H_0: p = 0.5$, and the subject is simply guessing (i.e., the results are due to chance).

$H_1: p > 0.5$, and the subject has powers of ESP.

Since we are not interested in the subject's ability to obtain extremely low scores, but only in the ability to obtain high scores, we choose a one-tailed test. If hypothesis H_0 is true, then the mean and standard deviation of the number of cards identified correctly are given by

$$\mu = Np = 50(0.5) = 25 \quad \text{and} \quad \sigma = \sqrt{Npq} = \sqrt{50(0.5)(0.5)} = \sqrt{12.5} = 3.54$$

(*a*) For a one-tailed test at the 0.05 significance level, we must choose z_1 in Fig. 10-4 so that the shaded area in the critical region of high scores is 0.05. Then the area between 0 and z_1 is 0.4500, and $z_1 = 1.645$; this can also be read from Table 10.1. Thus our decision rule (or test of significance) is:

If the z score observed is greater than 1.645, the results are significant at the 0.05 level and the individual has powers of ESP.

If the z score is less than 1.645, the results are due to chance (i.e., not significant at the 0.05 level).

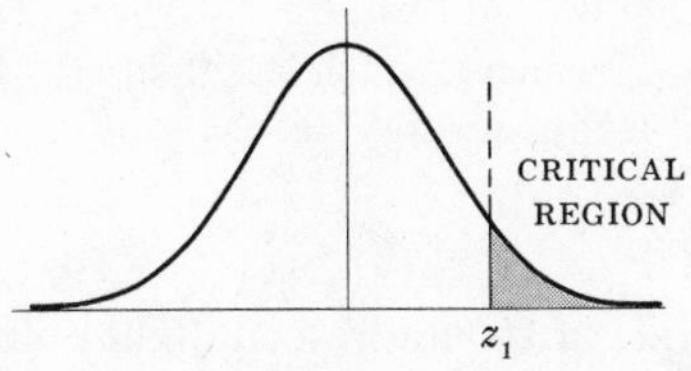

Fig. 10-4

Since 32 in standard units is $(32 - 25)/3.54 = 1.98$, which is greater than 1.645, we conclude at the 0.05 level that the individual has powers of ESP.

Note that we should really apply a continuity correction, since 32 on a continuous scale is between 31.5 and 32.5. However, 31.5 has a standard score of $(31.5 - 25)/3.54 = 1.84$, and so the same conclusion is reached.

(*b*) If the significance level is 0.01, then the area between 0 and z_1 is 0.4900, and $z_1 = 2.33$. Since 32 (or 31.5) in standard units is 1.98 (or 1.84), which is less than 2.33, we conclude that the results are *not significant* at the 0.01 level.

Some statisticians adopt the terminology that results significant at the 0.01 level are *highly significant*, that results significant at the 0.05 level but not at the 0.01 level are *probably significant*, and that results significant at levels larger than 0.05 are *not significant*. According to this terminology, we would conclude that the above experimental results are *probably significant*, so that further investigations of the phenomena are probably warranted.

Since significance levels serve as guides in making decisions, some statisticians quote the actual probabilities involved. For instance, since $\Pr\{z \geq 1.84\} = 0.0322$, in this problem, the statistician could say that on the basis of the experiment the chances of being wrong in concluding that the individual has powers of ESP are about 3 in 100. The quoted probability (0.0322 in this case) is sometimes called an *experimental*, or *descriptive*, *significance level*.

10.6 The manufacturer of a patent medicine claims that it is 90% effective in relieving an allergy for a period of 8 hours. In a sample of 200 people who had the allergy, the medicine provided relief for 160 people. Determine whether the manufacturer's claim is legitimate.

SOLUTION

Let p denote the probability of obtaining relief from the allergy by using the medicine. Then we must decide between two hypotheses:

$H_0: p = 0.9$, and the claim is correct.

$H_1: p < 0.9$, and the claim is false.

Since we are interested in determining whether the proportion of people relieved by the medicine is too low, we choose a one-tailed test. If the significance level is taken to be 0.01 (i.e., if the shaded area in Fig. 10-5 is 0.01), then $z_1 = -2.33$, as can be seen either from Problem 10.5(b) by using the symmetry of the curve or from Table 10.1. We thus take as our decision rule:

The claim is not legitimate if z is less than -2.33 (in which case we reject H_0).

Otherwise, the claim is legitimate and the observed results are due to chance (in which case we accept H_0).

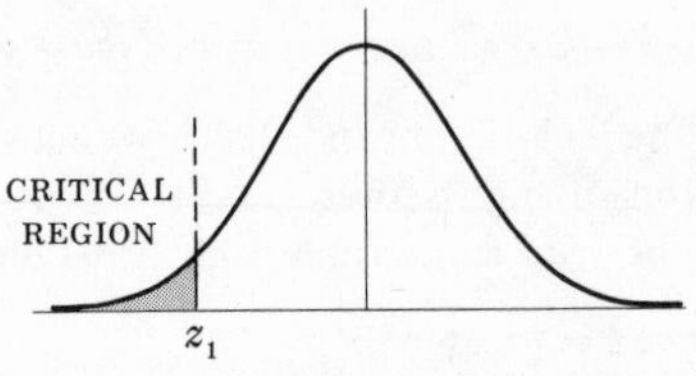

Fig. 10-5

If H_0 is true, then $\mu = Np = 200(0.9) = 180$ and $\sigma = \sqrt{Npq} = \sqrt{(200)(0.9)(0.1)} = 4.24$. Now 160 in standard units is $(160-180)/4.24 = -4.72$, which is much less than -2.33. Thus, according to our decision rule, we conclude that the claim is not legitimate and that the sample results are *highly significant* (see the end of Problem 10.5).

10.7 The mean lifetime of a sample of 100 fluorescent light bulbs produced by a company is computed to be 1570 hours (h) with a standard deviation of 120 h. If μ is the mean lifetime of all the bulbs produced by the company, test the hypothesis $\mu = 1600$ h against the alternative hypothesis $\mu \neq 1600$ h, using significance levels of (a) 0.05 and (b) 0.01.

SOLUTION

We must decide between two hypotheses:

$$H_0: \mu = 1600 \text{ h}$$
$$H_1: \mu \neq 1600 \text{ h}$$

Since $\mu \neq 1600$ includes values both larger and smaller than 1600, a two-tailed test should be used.

(a) For a two-tailed test at the 0.05 significance level, we have the following decision rule:

Reject H_0 if the z score of the sample mean is outside the range -1.96 to 1.96.

Accept H_0 otherwise (or withhold any decision).

The statistic under consideration is the sample mean $\bar{X}$. The sampling distribution of $\bar{X}$ has mean $\mu_{\bar{X}} = \mu$ and standard deviation $\sigma_{\bar{X}} = \sigma/\sqrt{N}$, where μ and σ are the mean and standard deviation of the population of all bulbs produced by the company. Under hypothesis H_0, we have $\mu = 1600$ and $\sigma_{\bar{X}} = \sigma/\sqrt{N} = 120/\sqrt{100} = 12$, using the sample standard deviation as an estimate of σ. Since $z = (\bar{X} - 1600)/12 = (1570 - 1600)/12 = -2.50$ lies outside the range -1.96 to 1.96, we reject H_0 at the 0.05 significance level.

(*b*) If the significance level is 0.01, the range -1.96 to 1.96 in the decision rule of part (*a*) is replaced by -2.58 to 2.58. Thus, since the z score of -2.50 lies inside this range, we accept H_0 (or withhold any decision) at the 0.01 significance level.

10.8 In Problem 10.7, test the hypothesis $\mu = 1600$ h against the alternative hypothesis $\mu < 1600$ h, using significance levels of (*a*) 0.05 and (*b*) 0.01.

SOLUTION

We must decide between two hypotheses:

$$H_0: \mu = 1600 \text{ h}$$
$$H_1: \mu < 1600 \text{ h}$$

A one-tailed test should be used here, for the corresponding figure is identical to Fig. 10-5 of Problem 10.6.

(*a*) If the significance level is 0.05, the shaded region of Fig. 10-5 has an area of 0.05, and we find that $z_1 = -1.645$. We therefore adopt the decision rule:

Reject H_0 if z is less than -1.645.

Accept H_0 otherwise (or withhold any decision).

Since [as in Problem 10.7(*a*)] the z score is -2.50, which is less than -1.645, we reject H_0 at the 0.05 significance level. Note that this decision is identical with that reached in Problem 10.7(*a*) by using a two-tailed test.

(*b*) If the significance level is 0.01, the z_1 value in Fig. 10-5 is -2.33. Hence we adopt the decision rule:

Reject H_0 if z is less than -2.33.

Accept H_0 otherwise (or withhold any decision).

Since [as in Problem 10.7(*a*)] the z score is -2.50, which is less than -2.33, we reject H_0 at the 0.01 significance level. Note that this decision is not the same as that reached in Problem 10.7(*b*) by using a two-tailed test.

It follows that decisions concerning a given hypothesis H_0 that are based on one-tailed and two-tailed tests are not always in agreement. This is to be expected, of course, since we are testing H_0 against a different alternative in each case.

10.9 The breaking strengths of cables produced by a manufacturer have a mean of 1800 pounds (lb) and a standard deviation of 100 lb. By a new technique in the manufacturing process, it is claimed that the breaking strength can be increased. To test this claim, a sample of 50 cables is tested and it is found that the mean breaking strength is 1850 lb. Can we support the claim at the 0.01 significance level?

SOLUTION

We have to decide between the two hypotheses:

$H_0: \mu = 1800$ lb, and there is really no change in breaking strength.

$H_1: \mu > 1800$ lb, and there is a change in breaking strength.

A one-tailed test should be used here; the diagram associated with this test is identical with Fig. 10-4 of Problem 10.5(*a*). At the 0.01 significance level, the decision rule is:

If the z score observed is greater than 2.33, the results are significant at the 0.01 level and H_0 is rejected.

Otherwise, H_0 is accepted (or the decision is withheld).

Under the hypothesis that H_0 is true, we find that

$$z = \frac{\bar{X} - \mu}{\sigma/\sqrt{N}} = \frac{1850 - 1800}{100/\sqrt{50}} = 3.55$$

which is greater than 2.33. Hence we conclude that the results are *highly significant* and that the claim should thus be supported.

OPERATING-CHARACTERISTIC CURVES

10.10 Referring to Problem 10.2, what is the probability of accepting the hypothesis that the coin is fair when the actual probability of heads is $p = 0.7$?

SOLUTION

The hypothesis H_0 that the coin is fair (i.e., $p = 0.5$) is accepted when the number of heads in 100 tosses lies between 39.5 and 60.5. The probability of rejecting H_0 when it should be accepted (i.e., the probability of a Type I error) is represented by the total area α of the shaded region under the normal curve to the left in Fig. 10-6. As computed in Problem 10.2(a), this area α, which represents the significance level of the test of H_0, is equal to 0.0358.

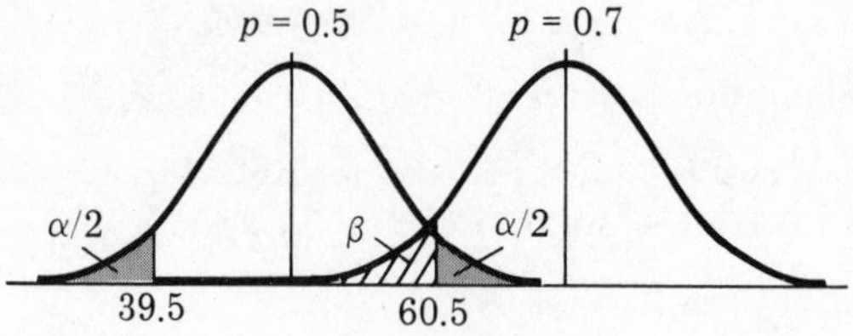

Fig. 10-6

If the probability of heads is $p = 0.7$, then the distribution of heads in 100 tosses is represented by the normal curve to the right in Fig. 10-6. From the diagram it is clear that the probability of accepting H_0 when actually $p = 0.7$ (i.e., the probability of a Type II error) is given by the cross-hatched area β of the figure. To compute this area, we observe that the distribution under the hypothesis $p = 0.7$ has its mean and standard deviation given by

$$\mu = Np = (100)(0.7) = 70 \qquad \text{and} \qquad \sigma = \sqrt{Npq} = \sqrt{(100)(0.7)(0.3)} = 4.58$$

$$60.5 \text{ in standard units} = \frac{60.5 - 70}{4.58} = -2.07$$

$$39.5 \text{ in standard units} = \frac{39.5 - 70}{4.58} = -6.66$$

Then $\qquad \beta = (\text{area under normal curve between } z = -6.66 \text{ and } z = -2.07) = 0.0192$

Thus with the given decision rule there is very little chance of accepting the hypothesis that the coin is fair when actually $p = 0.7$.

Note that in this problem we were given the decision rule from which we computed α and β. In practice, two other possibilities may arise:

(1) We decide on α (such as 0.05 or 0.01), arrive at a decision rule, and then compute β.

(2) We decide on α and β and then arrive at a decision rule.

10.11 Work Problem 10.10 if (a) $p = 0.6$, (b) $p = 0.8$, (c) $p = 0.9$, and (d) $p = 0.4$.

SOLUTION

(a) If $p = 0.6$, the distribution of heads has its mean and standard deviation given by

$$\mu = Np = (100)(0.6) = 60 \qquad \text{and} \qquad \sigma = \sqrt{Npq} = \sqrt{(100)(0.6)(0.4)} = 4.90$$

$$60.5 \text{ in standard units} = \frac{60.5 - 60}{4.90} = 0.102$$

$$39.5 \text{ in standard units} = \frac{39.5 - 60}{4.90} = -4.18$$

Then $\qquad \beta = (\text{area under normal curve between } z = -4.18 \text{ and } z = 0.102) = 0.5406$

Thus with the given decision rule there is a large chance of accepting the hypothesis that the coin is fair when actually $p = 0.6$.

(*b*) If $p = 0.8$, then

$$\mu = Np = (100)(0.8) = 80 \qquad \text{and} \qquad \sigma = \sqrt{Npq} = \sqrt{(100)(0.8)(0.2)} = 4$$

$$60.5 \text{ in standard units} = \frac{60.5 - 80}{4} = -4.88$$

$$39.5 \text{ in standard units} = \frac{39.5 - 80}{4} = -10.12$$

Then β = (area under normal curve between $z = -10.12$ and $z = -4.88$) = 0.0000 very closely.

(*c*) From comparison with part (*b*) or by calculation, we see that if $p = 0.9$, then $\beta = 0$ for all practical purposes.

(*d*) By symmetry, $p = 0.4$ yields the same value of β as $p = 0.6$ (i.e., $\beta = 0.5040$).

10.12 Graph the results of Problems 10.10 and 10.11 by constructing a graph of (*a*) β versus p and (*b*) $(1 - \beta)$ versus p. Interpret the graphs obtained.

SOLUTION

Table 10.2 shows the values of β corresponding to given values of p as obtained in Problems 10.10 and 10.11. Note that β represents the probability of accepting the hypothesis $p = 0.5$ when actually p is a value other than 0.5; however, if it is actually true that $p = 0.5$, then we can interpret β as the probability of accepting $p = 0.5$ when it should be accepted. This probability is $1 - 0.0358 = 0.9642$ and has been entered into Table 10.2.

Table 10.2

p	0.1	0.2	0.3	0.4	0.5	0.6	0.7	0.8	0.9
β	0.0000	0.0000	0.0192	0.5040	0.9642	0.5040	0.0192	0.0000	0.0000

(*a*) The graph of β versus p, shown in Fig. 10-7(*a*), is called the *operating-characteristic curve*, or *OC curve*, of the decision rule (or test of hypothesis). The distance from the maximum point of the OC curve to the line $\beta = 1$ is equal to $\alpha = 0.0358$, the significance level of the test.

In general, the sharper the peak of the OC curve, the better is the decision rule for rejecting invalid hypotheses.

(*b*) The graph of $(1 - \beta)$ versus p, shown in Fig. 10-7(*b*), is called the *power curve* of the decision rule. This curve is obtained simply by inverting the OC curve; thus both graphs are actually equivalent.

The quantity $(1 - \beta)$ is often called a *power function* since it indicates the *power of a test* to reject hypotheses which are false and which should thus be rejected. The quantity β is also called the *operating-characteristic function* of a test.

Mathcad **10.13** A company manufactures rope whose breaking strengths have a mean of 300 lb and a standard deviation of 24 lb. It is believed that by a newly developed process the mean breaking strength can be increased.

(*a*) Design a decision rule for rejecting the old process at the 0.01 significance level if it is agreed to test 64 ropes.

(*b*) Under the decision rule adopted in part (*a*), what is the probability of accepting the old process when in fact the new process has increased the mean breaking strength to 310 lb? Assume that the standard deviation is still 24 lb.

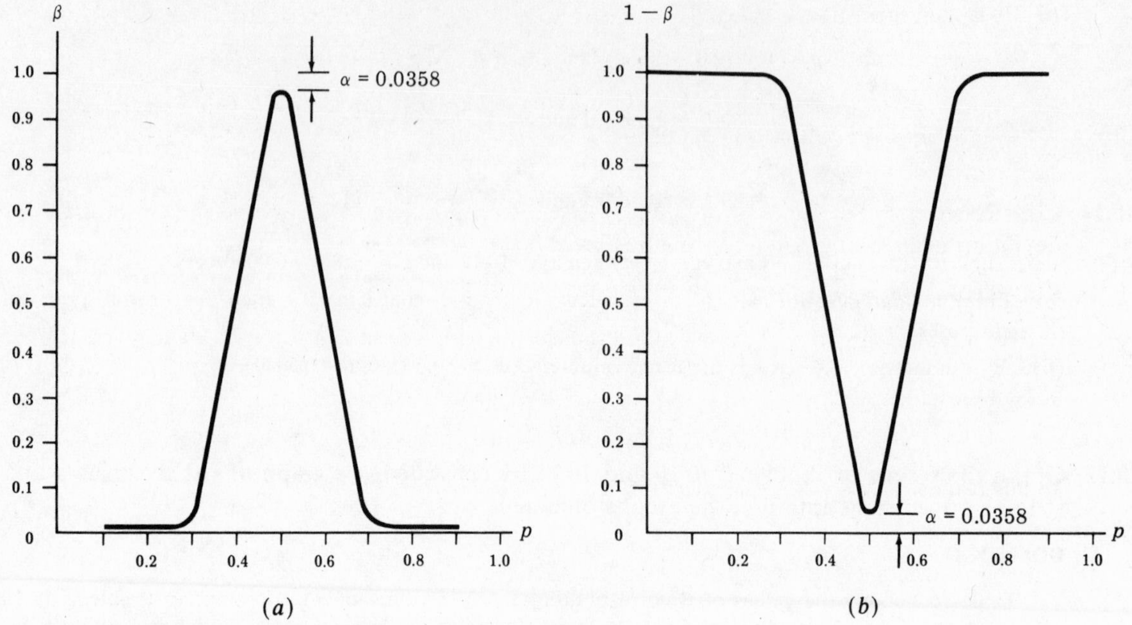

Fig. 10-7

SOLUTION

(*a*) If μ is the mean breaking strength, we wish to decide between two hypotheses:

H_0: $\mu = 300$ lb, and the new process is the same as the old one.

H_1: $\mu > 300$ lb, and the new process is better than the old one.

For a one-tailed test at the 0.01 significance level, we have the following decision rule [refer to Fig. 10-8(*a*)]:

Reject H_0 if the z score of the sample mean breaking strength is greater than 2.33.

Accept H_0 otherwise.

Since
$$z = \frac{\bar{X} - \mu}{\sigma/\sqrt{N}} = \frac{\bar{X} - 300}{24/\sqrt{64}}$$

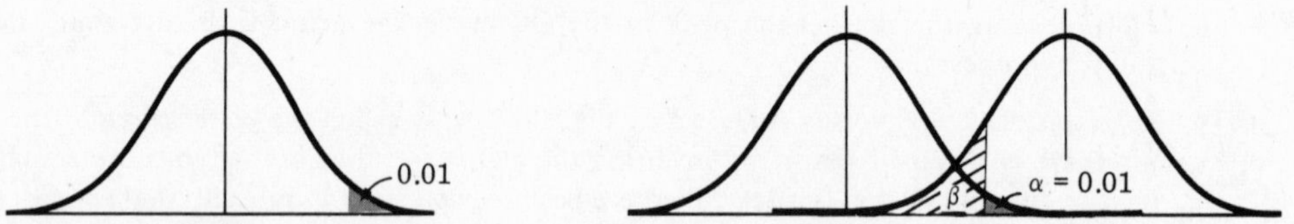

Fig. 10-8

we have $\bar{X} = 300 + 3z$. Then if $z > 2.33$, we have $\bar{X} > 300 + 3(2.33) = 307.7$ lb. Thus the above decision rule becomes:

Reject H_0 if the mean breaking strength of 64 ropes exceeds 307.0 lb.

Accept H_0 otherwise.

(*b*) Consider the two hypotheses H_0: $\mu = 300$ lb and H_1: $\mu = 310$ lb. The distributions of mean breaking strengths corresponding to these two hypotheses are represented, respectively, by the left and right normal distributions of Fig. 10-8(*b*). The probability of accepting the old process when the new mean breaking strength is actually 310 lb is represented by the region of area β in Fig. 10-8(*b*). To find this, note that 307.0 lb in standard units is $(307.0-310)/3=-1.00$, hence

$$\beta = (\text{area under right-hand normal curve to left of } z=-1.00)=0.1587$$

This is the probability of accepting $H_0: \mu=300$ lb when actually $H_1: \mu=310$ lb is true (i.e., it is the probability of making a Type II error).

10.14 Construct (*a*) an OC curve and (*b*) a power curve for Problem 10.13, assuming that the standard deviation of breaking strengths remains at 24 lb.

SOLUTION

By a reasoning similar to that used in Problem 10.13(*b*), we can find β for the cases where the new process yields mean breaking strengths μ equal to 305 lb, 315 lb, etc. For example, if $\mu=305$ lb, then 307.0 lb in standard units is $(307.0-305)/3=0.67$, and hence

$$\beta = (\text{area under right-hand normal curve to left of } z=0.67)=0.7486$$

In this manner Table 10.3 is obtained.

Table 10.3

μ	290	295	300	305	310	315	320
β	1.0000	1.0000	0.9900	0.7486	0.1587	0.0038	0.0000

(*a*) The OC curve is shown in Fig. 10-9(*a*). From this curve we see that the probability of keeping the old process if the new breaking strength is less than 300 lb is practically 1 (except for the significance level of 0.01 when the new process gives a mean of 300 lb). It then drops rather sharply to zero, which means that there is practically no chance of keeping the old process when the mean breaking strength is greater than 315 lb.

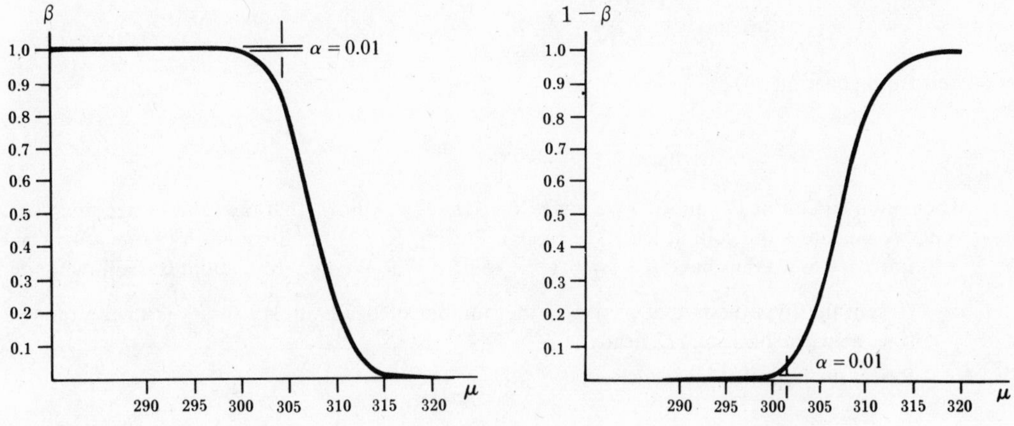

(*a*) (*b*)

Fig. 10-9

(*b*) The power curve shown in Fig. 10-9(*b*) is capable of exactly the same interpretation as that for the OC curve. In fact, the two curves are essentially equivalent.

10.15 To test the hypothesis that a coin is fair (i.e., $p=0.5$) by a number of tosses of the coin, we wish to impose the following restrictions:

(1) The probability of rejecting the hypothesis when it is actually correct must be 0.05 at most.

(2) The probability of accepting the hypothesis when actually p differs from 0.5 by 0.1 or more (i.e., $p \geq 0.6$ or $p \leq 0.4$) must be 0.05 at most.

Determine the minimum sample size that is necessary, and state the resulting decision rule.

SOLUTION

Here we have placed limits on the risks of Type I and Type II errors. For example, restriction (1) requires that the probability of a Type I error be $\alpha = 0.05$ at most, while restriction (2) requires that the probability of a Type II error be $\beta = 0.05$ at most. The situation is graphed in Fig. 10-10.

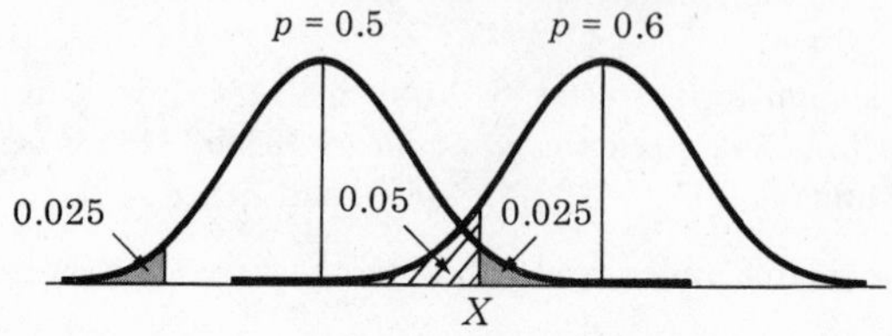

Fig. 10-10

Let N denote the required sample size and let X denote the number of heads in N tosses, above which we reject the hypothesis that $p = 0.5$. From Fig. 10-10 the area under the normal curve $p = 0.5$ is 0.025 to the right of

$$\frac{X - Np}{\sqrt{Npq}} = \frac{X - 0.5N}{\sqrt{N(0.5)(0.5)}} = \frac{X - 0.5N}{0.5\sqrt{N}} \tag{5}$$

and the area under the normal curve $p = 0.6$ is 0.05 to the left of

$$\frac{X - Np}{\sqrt{Npq}} = \frac{X - 0.6N}{\sqrt{N(0.6)(0.4)}} = \frac{X - 0.6N}{0.49\sqrt{N}} \tag{6}$$

{Actually, the area between $(X - 0.6N)/0.49\sqrt{N}$ and $[(N - X) - 0.6N]/0.49\sqrt{N}$ is 0.05; equation (*5*) is a close approximation.} From equation (*6*)

$$\frac{X - 0.5N}{0.5\sqrt{N}} = 1.96 \qquad \text{or} \qquad X = 0.5N + 0.980\sqrt{N} \tag{7}$$

and from equation (*6*)

$$\frac{X - 0.6N}{0.49\sqrt{N}} = -1.645 \qquad \text{or} \qquad X = 0.6N - 0.806\sqrt{N} \tag{8}$$

Then from equations (*7*) and (*8*) we have $N = 318.98$. It follows that the sample size must be at least 319 (i.e., we must toss the coin at least 319 times). Putting $N = 319$ into equation (*7*) or (*8*), $X = 177$.

For $p = 0.5$, we thus have $X - Np = 177 - 159.5 = 17.5$. We therefore adopt the following decision rule:

Accept the hypothesis that $p = 0.5$ if the number of heads in 319 tosses is in the range 159.5 ± 17.5 (i.e., between 142 and 177 heads).

Reject the hypothesis otherwise.

CONTROL CHARTS

10.16 A machine is constructed to produce ball bearings having a mean diameter of 0.574 centimeter (cm) and a standard deviation of 0.008 cm. To determine whether the machine is in proper working order, a sample of six ball bearings is taken every 2 hours (for example), and the mean diameter is computed from this sample.

(*a*) Design a decision rule whereby one can be fairly certain that the quality of the products is conforming to the required standards.

(*b*) Show how to graph the decision rule in part (*a*).

SOLUTION

(*a*) With 99.73% confidence we can say that the sample mean $\bar{X}$ must lie in the range $\mu_{\bar{X}} - 3\sigma_{\bar{X}}$ to $\mu_{\bar{X}} + 3\sigma_{\bar{X}}$, or $\mu - 3\sigma/\sqrt{N}$ to $\mu + 3\sigma/\sqrt{N}$. Since $\mu = 0.574$, $\sigma = 0.008$, and $N = 6$, it follows that with 99.73% confidence the sample mean should lie between $0.574 - 0.024/\sqrt{6}$ and $0.574 + 0.024/\sqrt{6}$, or between 0.564 and 0.584 cm. Hence our decision rule is as follows:

> If a sample mean falls inside the range 0.564 to 0.584 cm, assume that the machine is in proper working order.
>
> Otherwise, conclude that the machine is not in proper working order and seek to determine the reasons.

(*b*) A record of the sample means can be kept by means of a chart such as shown in Fig. 10-11, called a *quality control chart.* Each time a sample mean is computed, it is represented by a particular point. As long as the points lie between the lower limit (0.564 cm) and the upper limit (0.584 cm), the process is under control. When a point goes outside these control limits (such as in the third sample taken on Thursday), there is a possibility that something is wrong, and investigation is warranted.

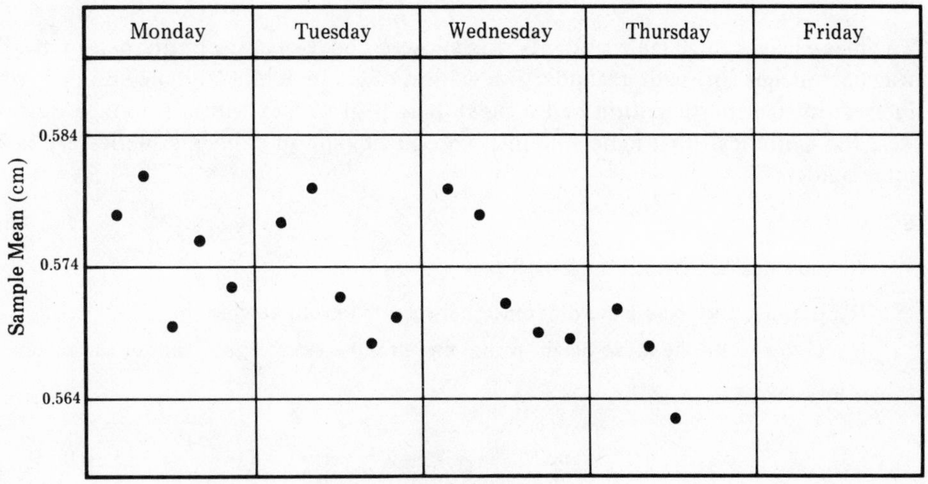

Fig. 10-11

The control limits specified above are called the 99.73% confidence limits, or briefly the 3σ limits. Other confidence limits (such as 99% or 95% limits) could be determined as well. The choice in each case depends on the particular circumstances.

TESTS INVOLVING DIFFERENCES OF MEANS AND PROPORTIONS

10.17 An examination was given to two classes consisting of 40 and 50 students, respectively. In the first class the mean grade was 74 with a standard deviation of 8, while in the second class the mean grade was 78 with a standard deviation of 7. Is there a significant difference between the performance of the two classes at the (*a*) 0.05 and (*b*) 0.01 levels?

SOLUTION

Suppose that the two classes come from two populations having the respective means μ_1 and μ_2. We thus need to decide between the hypotheses:

$H_0: \mu_1 = \mu_2$, and the difference is due merely to chance.

$H_1: \mu_1 \neq \mu_2$, and there is a significant difference between the classes.

Under hypothesis H_0, both classes come from the same population. The mean and standard deviation of the difference in means are given by

$$\mu_{\bar{X}_1-\bar{X}_2}=0 \qquad \text{and} \qquad \sigma_{\bar{X}_1-\bar{X}_2}=\sqrt{\frac{\sigma_1^2}{N_1}+\frac{\sigma_2^2}{N_2}}=\sqrt{\frac{8^2}{40}+\frac{7^2}{50}}=1.606$$

where we have used the sample standard deviations as estimates of σ_1 and σ_2. Thus

$$z=\frac{\bar{X}_1-\bar{X}_2}{\sigma_{\bar{X}_1-\bar{X}_2}}=\frac{74-78}{1.606}=-2.49$$

(*a*) For a two-tailed test, the results are significant at the 0.05 level if z lies outside the range -1.96 to 1.96. Hence we conclude that at the 0.05 level there is a significant difference in performance between the two classes and that the second class is probably better.

(*b*) For a two-tailed test, the results are significant at the 0.01 level if z lies outside the range -2.58 and 2.58. Hence we conclude that at the 0.01 level there is no significant difference between the classes.

Since the results are significant at the 0.05 level but not at the 0.01 level, we conclude that the results are *probably significant* (according to the terminology used at the end of Problem 10.5).

10.18 The mean height of 50 male students who showed above-average participation in college athletics was 68.2 inches (in) with a standard deviation of 2.5 in, while 50 male students who showed no interest in such participation had a mean height of 67.5 in with a standard deviation of 2.8 in. Test the hypothesis that male students who participate in college athletics are taller than other male students.

SOLUTION

We must decide between the hypotheses:

H_0: $\mu_1=\mu_2$, and there is no difference between the mean heights.

H_1: $\mu_1>\mu_2$, and the mean height of the first group is greater than that of the second group.

Under hypothesis H_0,

$$\mu_{\bar{X}_1-\bar{X}_2}=0 \qquad \text{and} \qquad \sigma_{\bar{X}_1-\bar{X}_2}=\sqrt{\frac{\sigma_1^2}{N_1}+\frac{\sigma_2^2}{N_2}}=\sqrt{\frac{(2.5)^2}{50}+\frac{(2.8)^2}{50}}=0.53$$

where we have used the sample standard deviations as estimates of σ_1 and σ_2. Thus

$$z=\frac{\bar{X}_1-\bar{X}_2}{\sigma_{\bar{X}_1-\bar{X}_2}}=\frac{68.2-67.5}{0.53}=1.32$$

Using a one-tailed test at the 0.05 significance level, we would reject hypothesis H_0 if the z score were greater than 1.645. Thus we cannot reject the hypothesis at this level of significance.

It should be noted, however, that the hypothesis can be rejected at the 0.10 level if we are willing to take the risk of being wrong with a probability of 0.10 (i.e., 1 chance in 10).

10.19 By how much should the sample size of each of the two groups in Problem 10.18 be increased in order that the observed difference of 0.7 in in the mean heights be significant at the (*a*) 0.05 and (*b*) 0.01 levels?

SOLUTION

Suppose that the sample size of each group is N and that the standard deviations for the two groups remain the same. Then under hypothesis H_0 we have

$$\mu_{\bar{X}_1-\bar{X}_2}=0 \qquad \text{and} \qquad \sigma_{\bar{X}_1-\bar{X}_2}=\sqrt{\frac{\sigma_1^2}{N}+\frac{\sigma_2^2}{N}}=\sqrt{\frac{(2.5)^2+(2.8)^2}{N}}=\sqrt{\frac{14.09}{N}}=\frac{3.75}{\sqrt{N}}$$

For an observed difference in mean heights of 0.7 in, we thus have

$$z = \frac{\bar{X}_1 - \bar{X}_2}{\sigma_{\bar{X}_1 - \bar{X}_2}} = \frac{0.7}{3.75/\sqrt{N}} = \frac{0.7\sqrt{N}}{3.75}$$

(*a*) The observed difference will be significant at the 0.05 level if $0.7\sqrt{N}/3.75 = 1.645$ at least, so that N must be 78 at least. Thus we must increase the sample size in each group by at least $(78 - 50) = 28$.

Another method

$$\frac{0.7\sqrt{N}}{3.75} \geq 1.645 \qquad \sqrt{N} \geq \frac{(3.75)(1.645)}{0.7} \qquad \sqrt{N} \geq 8.8 \qquad N \geq 77.4 \quad \text{or} \quad N \geq 78$$

(*b*) The observed difference will be significant at the 0.01 level if

$$\frac{0.7\sqrt{N}}{3.75} \geq 2.33 \qquad \sqrt{N} \geq \frac{(3.75)(2.33)}{0.7} \qquad \sqrt{N} \geq 12.5 \qquad N \geq 156.3 \quad \text{or} \quad N \geq 157$$

Hence we must increase the sample size in each group by at least $(157 - 50) = 107$.

10.20 Two groups, A and B, consist of 100 people each who have a disease. A serum is given to group A but not to group B (which is called the *control*); otherwise, the two groups are treated identically. It is found that in groups A and B, 75 and 65 people, respectively, recover from the disease. At significance levels of (*a*) 0.01, (*b*) 0.05, and (*c*) 0.10, test the hypothesis that the serum helps cure the disease.

SOLUTION

Let p_1 and p_2 denote the population proportions cured by (1) using the serum and (2) not using the serum, respectively. We must decide between two hypotheses:

$H_0: p_1 = p_2$, and the observed differences are due to chance (i.e. the serum is ineffective).

$H_1: p_1 > p_2$, and the serum is effective.

Under hypothesis H_0,

$$\mu_{P_1 - P_2} = 0 \qquad \text{and} \qquad \sigma_{P_1 - P_2} = \sqrt{pq\left(\frac{1}{N_1} + \frac{1}{N_2}\right)} = \sqrt{(0.70)(0.30)\left(\frac{1}{100} + \frac{1}{100}\right)} = 0.0648$$

where we have used as an estimate of p the average proportion of cures in the two sample groups given by $(75 + 65)/200 = 0.70$, and where $q = 1 - p = 0.30$. Thus

$$z = \frac{P_1 - P_2}{\sigma_{P_1 - P_2}} = \frac{0.750 - 0.650}{0.0648} = 1.54$$

(*a*) Using a one-tailed test at the 0.01 significance level, we would reject hypothesis H_0 only if the z score were greater than 2.33. Since the z score is only 1.54, we must conclude that the results are due to chance at this level of significance.

(*b*) Using a one-tailed test at the 0.05 significance level, we would reject H_0 only if the z score were greater than 1.645. Hence we must conclude that the results are due to chance at this level also.

(*c*) If a one-tailed test at the 0.10 significance level were used, we would reject H_0 only if the z score were greater than 1.28. Since this condition is satisfied, we conclude that the serum is effective at the 0.10 level.

Note that these conclusions have depended on how much we are willing to risk being wrong. If the results are actually due to chance, but we conclude that they are due to the serum (Type I error), we might proceed to give the serum to large groups of people—only to find that it is actually ineffective. This is a risk that we are not always willing to assume.

On the other hand, we could conclude that the serum does not help, whereas it actually does help (Type II error). Such a conclusion is very dangerous, especially if human lives are at stake.

10.21 Work Problem 10.20 if each group consists of 300 people and if 225 people in group A and 195 people in group B are cured.

SOLUTION

Note that in this case the proportions of people cured in the two groups are $225/300 = 0.750$ and $195/300 = 0.650$, respectively, which are the same as in Problem 10.20. Under hypothesis H_0,

$$\mu_{P1-P2} = 0 \quad \text{and} \quad \sigma_{P1-P2} = \sqrt{pq\left(\frac{1}{N_1} + \frac{1}{N_2}\right)} = \sqrt{(0.70)(0.30)\left(\frac{1}{300} + \frac{1}{300}\right)} = 0.0374$$

where $(225 + 195)/600 = 0.70$ is used as an estimate of p. Thus

$$z = \frac{P_1 - P_2}{\sigma_{P1-P2}} = \frac{0.750 - 0.650}{0.0374} = 2.67$$

Since this value of z is greater than 2.33, we can reject the hypothesis at the 0.01 significance level; that is, we can conclude that the serum is effective with only a 0.01 probability of being wrong.

This shows how increasing the sample size can increase the reliability of decisions. In many cases, however, it may be impractical to increase sample sizes. In such cases we are forced to make decisions on the basis of available information and must therefore contend with greater risks of incorrect decisions.

10.22 A sample poll of 300 voters from district A and 200 voters from district B showed that 56% and 48%, respectively, were in favor of a given candidate. At a significance level of 0.05, test the hypotheses (a) that there is a difference between the districts and (b) that the candidate is preferred in district A.

SOLUTION

Let p_1 and p_2 denote the proportions of all voters from districts A and B, respectively, who are in favor of the candidate. Under the hypothesis $H_0: p_1 = p_2$, we have

$$\mu_{P1-P2} = 0 \quad \text{and} \quad \sigma_{P1-P2} = \sqrt{pq\left(\frac{1}{N_1} + \frac{1}{N_2}\right)} = \sqrt{(0.528)(0.472)\left(\frac{1}{300} + \frac{1}{200}\right)} = 0.0456$$

where we have used as estimates of p and q the values $[(0.56)(300) + (0.48)(200)]/500 = 0.528$ and $(1 - 0.528) = 0.472$, respectively. Thus

$$z = \frac{P_1 - P_2}{\sigma_{P1-P2}} = \frac{0.560 - 0.480}{0.0456} = 1.75$$

(a) If we wish only to determine whether there is a difference between the districts, we must decide between the hypotheses $H_0: p_1 = p_2$ and $H_1: p_1 \neq p_2$, which involves a two-tailed test. Using a two-tailed test at the 0.05 significance level, we would reject H_0 if z were outside the interval -1.96 to 1.96. Since $z = 1.75$ lies inside this interval, we cannot reject H_0 at this level; that is, there is no significant difference between the districts.

(b) If we wish to determine whether the candidate is preferred in district A, we must decide between the hypotheses $H_0: p_1 = p_2$ and $H_1: p_1 > p_2$, which involves a one-tailed test. Using a one-tailed test at the 0.05 significance level, we would reject H_0 if z were greater than 1.645. Since this is the case, we can reject H_0 at this level and conclude that the candidate is preferred in district A.

TESTS INVOLVING BINOMIAL DISTRIBUTIONS

Mathcad **10.23** An instructor gives a short quiz involving 10 true–false questions. To test the hypothesis that students are guessing, the instructor adopts the following decision rule:

If seven or more answers are correct, the student is not guessing.

If less than seven answers are correct, the student is guessing.

Find the probability of rejecting the hypothesis when it is correct.

SOLUTION

Let p be the probability that a question is answered correctly. The probability of getting X problems out of 10 correct is $\binom{10}{X}p^X q^{10-X}$, where $q = 1 - p$. Then under the hypothesis $p = 0.5$ (i.e., the student is guessing),

$$\Pr\{7 \text{ or more correct}\} = \Pr\{7 \text{ correct}\} + \Pr\{8 \text{ correct}\} + \Pr\{9 \text{ correct}\} + \Pr\{10 \text{ correct}\}$$

$$= \binom{10}{7}\left(\frac{1}{2}\right)^7\left(\frac{1}{2}\right)^3 + \binom{10}{8}\left(\frac{1}{2}\right)^8\left(\frac{1}{2}\right)^2 + \binom{10}{9}\left(\frac{1}{2}\right)^9\left(\frac{1}{2}\right) + \binom{10}{10}\left(\frac{1}{2}\right)^{10} = 0.1719$$

Thus the probability of concluding that students are not guessing when in fact they are guessing is 0.1719. Note that this is the probability of a Type I error.

10.24 In Problem 10.23, find the probability of accepting the hypothesis $p = 0.5$ when actually $p = 0.7$.

SOLUTION

Under the hypothesis $p = 0.7$,

$$\Pr\{\text{less than 7 correct}\} = 1 - \Pr\{7 \text{ or more correct}\}$$

$$= 1 - \left[\binom{10}{7}(0.7)^7(0.3)^3 + \binom{10}{8}(0.7)^8(0.3)^2 + \binom{10}{9}(0.7)^9(0.3) + \binom{10}{10}(0.3)^{10}\right]$$

$$= 0.3504$$

10.25 In Problem 10.23, find the probability of accepting the hypothesis $p = 0.5$ when actually (a) $p = 0.6$, (b) $p = 0.8$, (c) $p = 0.9$, (d) $p = 0.4$, (e) $p = 0.3$), (f) $p = 0.2$, and (g) $p = 0.1$.

SOLUTION

(a) If $p = 0.6$,

$$\text{Required probability} = 1 - [\Pr\{7 \text{ correct}\} + \Pr\{8 \text{ correct}\} + \Pr\{9 \text{ correct}\} + \Pr\{10 \text{ correct}\}]$$

$$= 1 - \left[\binom{10}{7}(0.6)^7(0.4)^3 + \binom{10}{8}(0.6)^8(0.4)^2 + \binom{10}{9}(0.6)^9(0.4) + \binom{10}{10}(0.6)^{10}\right] = 0.618$$

The results for parts (b) through (g) can be found similarly and are shown in Table 10.4, together with the values corresponding to $p = 0.5$ and to $p = 0.7$. Note that the probability is denoted in Table 10.4 by β (probability of a Type II error); the β entry for $p = 0.5$ is given by $\beta = 1 - 0.1719 = 0.828$ (from Problem 10.23), and the β entry for $p = 0.7$ is from Problem 10.24.

Table 10.4

p	0.1	0.2	0.3	0.4	0.5	0.6	0.7	0.8	0.9
β	1.000	0.999	0.989	0.945	0.828	0.618	0.350	0.121	0.013

10.26 Use Problem 10.25 to construct the graph of β versus p, thus obtaining the operating-characteristic curve of the decision rule in Problem 10.23.

SOLUTION

The required graph is shown in Fig. 10-12; note the similarity with the OC curve of Problem 10.14. If we had plotted $(1 - \beta)$ versus p, the *power curve* of the decision rule would have been obtained. The graph indicates that the given decision rule is *powerful* for rejecting $p = 0.5$ when actually $p \leq 0.4$ or $p \geq 0.8$.

10.27 A coin that is tossed six times comes up heads six times. Can we conclude at significance levels of (a) 0.05 and (b) 0.01 that the coin is not fair? Consider both a one-tailed and a two-tailed test.

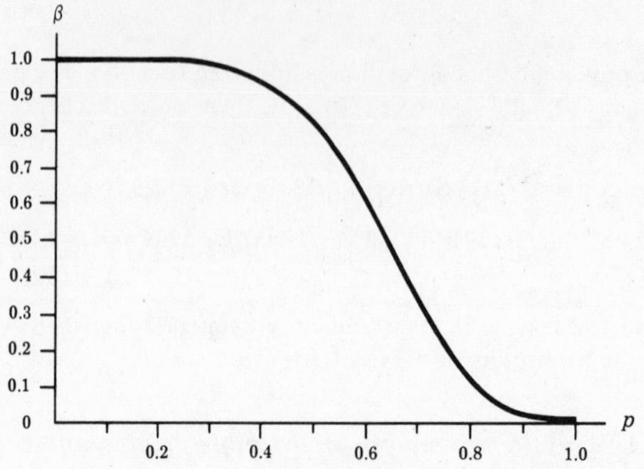

Fig. 10-12

SOLUTION

Let p be the probability of heads in a single toss of the coin. Under the hypothesis $H_0: p = 0.5$ (i.e., the coin is fair),

$$p(X) = \Pr\{X \text{ heads in 6 tosses}\} = \binom{6}{X}\left(\frac{1}{2}\right)^X\left(\frac{1}{2}\right)^{6-X} = \binom{6}{X}\left(\frac{1}{64}\right)$$

Thus the probabilities of 0, 1, 2, 3, 4, 5, and 6 heads are given, respectively, by $\frac{1}{64}$, $\frac{6}{64}$, $\frac{15}{64}$, $\frac{20}{64}$, $\frac{15}{64}$, $\frac{6}{64}$, and $\frac{1}{64}$, as graphed in the probability distribution of Fig. 10-13.

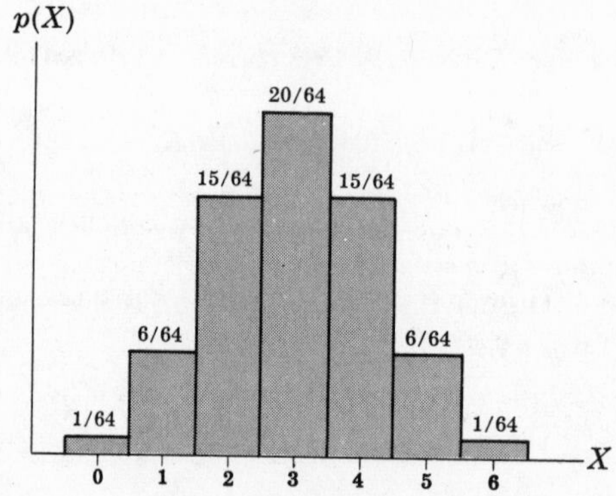

Fig. 10-13

One-tailed test

Here we wish to decide between the hypotheses $H_0: p = 0.5$ and $H_1: p > 0.5$. Since $\Pr\{6 \text{ heads}\} = \frac{1}{64} = 0.01562$ and $\Pr\{5 \text{ or } 6 \text{ heads}\} = \frac{6}{64} + \frac{1}{64} = 0.1094$, we can reject H_0 at the 0.05 level, but not at the 0.01 level (i.e., the result observed is significant at the 0.05 level, but not at the 0.01 level).

Two-tailed test

Here we wish to decide between the hypotheses $H_0: p = 0.5$ and $H_1: p \neq 0.5$. Since $\Pr\{0 \text{ or } 6 \text{ heads}\} = \frac{1}{64} + \frac{1}{64} = 0.03125$, we can reject H_0 at the 0.05 level, but not at the 0.01 level.

10.28 Work Problem 10.27 if the coin comes up heads five times.

SOLUTION

One-tailed test

Since Pr{5 or 6 heads} $= \frac{6}{64} + \frac{1}{64} = \frac{7}{64} = 0.1094$, we cannot reject H_0 at the 0.05 or 0.01 levels.

Two-tailed test

Since Pr{0 or 1 or 5 or 6 heads} $= 2(\frac{7}{64}) = 0.2188$, we cannot reject H_0 at the 0.05 or 0.01 levels.

Supplementary Problems

TESTS OF MEANS AND PROPORTIONS, USING NORMAL DISTRIBUTIONS

10.29 An urn contains marbles that are either red or blue. To test the hypothesis of equal proportions of these colors, we agree to sample 64 marbles with replacement, noting the colors drawn, and to adopt the following decision rule:

Accept the hypothesis if between 28 and 36 red marbles are drawn.

Reject the hypothesis otherwise.

(*a*) Find the probability of rejecting the hypothesis when it is actually correct.

(*b*) Graph the decision rule and the result obtained in part (*a*).

10.30 (*a*) What decision rule would you adopt in Problem 10.29 if you require that the probability of rejecting the hypothesis when it is actually correct be no more than 0.01 (i.e., you want a 0.01 significance level)?

(*b*) At what level of confidence would you accept the hypothesis?

(*c*) What would the decision rule be if the 0.05 significance level were adopted?

10.31 Suppose that in Problem 10.29 we wish to test the hypothesis that there is a *greater proportion* of red than blue marbles.

(*a*) What would you take as the null hypothesis, and what would be the alternative hypothesis?

(*b*) Should you use a one- or a two-tailed test? Why?

(*c*) What decision rule should you adopt if the significance level is 0.05?

(*d*) What is the decision rule if the significance level is 0.01?

10.32 A pair of dice is tossed 100 times and it is observed that 7's appear 23 times. Test the hypothesis that the dice are fair (i.e., not loaded) at the 0.05 significance level by using (*a*) a two-tailed test and (*b*) a one-tailed test. Discuss your reasons, if any, for preferring one of these tests over the other.

10.33 Work Problem 10.32 if the significance level is 0.01.

10.34 A manufacturer claimed that at least 95% of the equipment that she supplied to a factory conformed to specifications. An examination of a sample of 200 pieces of equipment revealed that 18 were faulty. Test her claim at significance levels of (*a*) 0.01 and (*b*) 0.05.

10.35 The percentage of A's given in a physics course at a certain university over a long period of time was 10%. During one particular term there were 40 A's in a group of 300 students. Test the significance of this result at the (*a*) 0.05 and (*b*) 0.01 levels.

10.36 It has been found from experience that the mean breaking strength of a particular brand of thread is 9.72 ounces (oz) with a standard deviation of 1.40 oz. Recently a sample of 36 pieces of thread showed a mean breaking strength of 8.93 oz. Can one conclude at the (*a*) 0.05 and (*b*) 0.01 significance levels that the thread has become inferior?

10.37 On an examination given to students at a large number of different schools, the mean grade was 74.5 and the standard deviation was 8.0. At one particular school where 200 students took the examination, the mean grade was 75.9. Discuss the significance of this result at the 0.05 level from the viewpoint of (*a*) a one-tailed test and (*b*) a two-tailed test, carefully explaining what conclusions you draw from these tests.

10.38 Answer Problem 10.37 if the significance level is 0.01.

OPERATING-CHARACTERISTIC CURVES

10.39 Referring to Problem 10.29, determine the probability of accepting the hypothesis that there are equal proportions of red and blue marbles when the actual proportion p of red marbles is (*a*) 0.6, (*b*) 0.7, (*c*) 0.8, (*d*) 0.9, and (*e*) 0.3.

10.40 Graph the results of Problem 10.39 by constructing a graph of (*a*) β versus p and (*b*) $1-\beta$ versus p. Compare these graphs with those of Problem 10.12 by considering the analogy of red and blue marbles to heads and tails, respectively.

10.41 (*a*) Work Problems 10.13 and 10.14 if it is agreed to test 400 ropes.

(*b*) What conclusions can you draw regarding the risks of Type II errors when the sample sizes are increased?

10.42 Construct (*a*) an OC curve and (*b*) a power curve corresponding to Problem 10.31. Compare these curves with those of Problem 10.14.

QUALITY CONTROL CHARTS

10.43 In the past a certain type of thread produced by a manufacturer has had a mean breaking strength of 8.64 oz and a standard deviation of 1.28 oz. To determine whether the product is conforming to standards, a sample of 16 pieces of thread is taken every 3 hours and the mean breaking strength is determined. Record the (*a*) 99.73 (or 3σ), (*b*) 99%, and (*c*) 95% control limits on a quality control chart and explain their applications.

10.44 On average, about 3% of the bolts produced by a company are defective. To maintain this quality of performance, a sample of 200 bolts produced is examined every 4 hours. Determine the (*a*) 99% and (*b*) 95% control limits for the number of defective bolts in each sample. Note that only *upper control limits* are needed in this case.

TESTS INVOLVING DIFFERENCES OF MEANS AND PROPORTIONS

10.45 A sample of 100 electric light bulbs produced by manufacturer *A* showed a mean lifetime of 1190 h and a standard deviation of 90 h. A sample of 75 bulbs produced by manufacturer *B* showed a mean lifetime of 1230 h and a standard deviation of 120 h. Is there a difference between the mean lifetimes of the two brands of bulbs at significance levels of (*a*) 0.05 and (*b*) 0.01?

10.46 In Problem 10.45, test the hypothesis that the bulbs of manufacturer *B* are superior to those of manufacturer *A* by using significance levels of (*a*) 0.05 and (*b*) 0.01. Explain the differences between these results and those called for in the last sentence of Problem 10.45. Do the results here contradict those of Problem 10.45?

10.47 On an elementary school examination in spelling, the mean grade of 32 boys was 72 with a standard deviation of 8, while the mean grade of 36 girls was 75 with a standard deviation of 6. Test the hypothesis at the (*a*) 0.05 and (*b*) 0.01 significance levels that the girls are better in spelling than the boys.

10.48 To test the effects of a new fertilizer on wheat production, a tract of land was divided into 60 squares of equal areas, all portions having identical qualities in terms of soil, exposure to sunlight, etc. The new fertilizer was applied to 30 squares and the old fertilizer was applied to the remaining squares. The mean number of bushels of wheat harvested per square of land using the new fertilizer was 18.2 bushels (bu) with a standard deviation of 0.63 bu. The corresponding mean and standard deviation for the squares using the old fertilizer were 17.8 and 0.54 bu, respectively. Using significance levels of (*a*) 0.05 and (*b*) 0.01, test the hypothesis that the new fertilizer is better than the old one.

10.49 Random samples of 200 bolts manufactured by machine *A* and of 100 bolts manufactured by machine *B* showed 19 and 5 defective bolts, respectively. Test the hypotheses (*a*) that the two machines are showing different qualities of performance and (*b*) that machine *B* is performing better than *A*. Use the 0.05 significance level.

10.50 Two urns, *A* and *B*, contain equal numbers of marbles, but the proportions of red and white marbles in each of the urns is unknown. A sample of 50 marbles selected with replacement from each of the urns revealed 32 red marbles from *A* and 23 red marbles from *B*. Using a significance level of 0.05, test the hypotheses (*a*) that the two urns have equal proportions of red marbles and (*b*) that *A* has a greater proportion of red marbles than does *B*.

TESTS INVOLVING BINOMIAL DISTRIBUTIONS

10.51 Referring to Problem 10.23, find the least number of questions that a student must answer correctly before the instructor is sure at significance levels of (*a*) 0.05, (*b*) 0.01, (*c*) 0.001, and (*d*) 0.06 that the student is not merely guessing. Discuss the results.

10.52 Construct graphs similar to those of Problem 10.10 for Problem 10.24.

10.53 Work Problems 10.23 to 10.25 if the 7 in the decision rule of Problem 10.23 is changed to 8.

10.54 A coin that is tossed eight times comes up heads seven times. Can we reject the hypothesis that the coin is fair at significance levels of (*a*) 0.05, (*b*) 0.10, and (*c*) 0.01? Use a two-tailed test.

10.55 Work Problem 10.54 if a one-tailed test is used.

10.56 Work Problem 10.54 if the coin comes up heads eight times.

10.57 Work Problem 10.54 if the coin comes up heads six times.

10.58 An urn contains a large number of red and white marbles. A random sample of 8 marbles revealed 6 white and 2 red. Using appropriate tests and levels of significance, discuss the proportions of red and white marbles in the urn.

10.59 Discuss how sampling theory can be used to investigate the proportions of different types of fish present in a lake.

Chapter 11

Small Sampling Theory

SMALL SAMPLES

In previous chapters we often made use of the fact that for samples of size $N > 30$, called *large samples*, the sampling distributions of many statistics are approximately normal, the approximation becoming better with increasing N. For samples of size $N < 30$, called *small samples*, this approximation is not good and becomes worse with decreasing N, so that appropriate modifications must be made.

A study of sampling distributions of statistics for small samples is called *small sampling theory*. However, a more suitable name would be *exact sampling theory*, since the results obtained hold for large as well as for small samples. In this chapter we study three important distributions: Student's t distribution, the chi-square distribution, and the F distribution.

STUDENT'S *t* DISTRIBUTION

Let us define the statistic

$$t = \frac{\bar{X} - \mu}{s}\sqrt{N-1} = \frac{\bar{X} - \mu}{\hat{s}/\sqrt{N}} \tag{1}$$

which is analogous to the z statistic given by

$$z = \frac{\bar{X} - \mu}{\sigma/\sqrt{N}}$$

(see page 208).

If we consider samples of size N drawn from a normal (or approximately normal) population with mean μ and if for each sample we compute t, using the sample mean $\bar{X}$ and sample standard deviation s or $\hat{s}$, the sampling distribution for t can be obtained. This distribution (see Fig. 11-1) is given by

$$Y = \frac{Y_0}{\left(1 + \dfrac{t^2}{N-1}\right)^{N/2}} = \frac{Y_0}{\left(1 + \dfrac{t^2}{\nu}\right)^{(\nu+1)/2}} \tag{2}$$

where Y_0 is a constant depending on N such that the total area under the curve is 1, and where the constant $\nu = (N-1)$ is called the *number of degrees of freedom* (ν is the Greek letter *nu*). For a definition of degrees of freedom, see page 233.

Distribution (*2*) is called *Student's t distribution* after its discoverer, W. S. Gossett, who published his works under the pseudonym "Student" during the early part of the twentieth century.

For large values of ν or N (certainly $N \geq 30$) the curves (*2*) closely approximate the standardized normal curve

$$Y = \frac{1}{\sqrt{2\pi}} e^{-\frac{1}{2}t^2}$$

as shown in Fig. 11-1.

CONFIDENCE INTERVALS

As done with normal distributions in Chapter 9, we can define 95%, 99%, or other confidence intervals by using the table of the t distribution in Appendix III. In this manner we can estimate within specified limits of confidence the population mean μ.

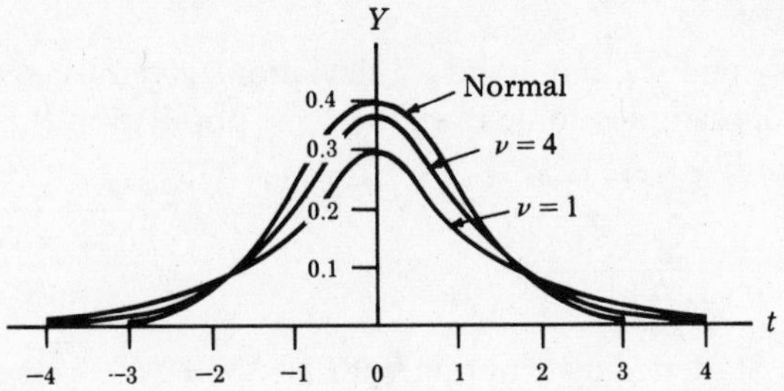

Fig. 11-1 Student's t distributions for various values of ν.

For example, if $-t_{.975}$ and $t_{.975}$ are the values of t for which 2.5% of the area lies in each tail of the t distribution, then the 95% confidence interval for t is

$$-t_{.975} < \frac{\bar{X} - \mu}{s}\sqrt{N-1} < t_{.975} \tag{3}$$

from which we see that μ is estimated to lie in the interval

$$\bar{X} - t_{.975}\frac{s}{\sqrt{N-1}} < \mu < \bar{X} + t_{.975}\frac{s}{\sqrt{N-1}} \tag{4}$$

with 95% confidence (i.e. probability 0.95). Note that $t_{.975}$ represents the 97.5 percentile value, while $t_{.025} = -t_{.975}$ represents the 2.5 percentile value.

In general, we can represent confidence limits for population means by

$$\bar{X} \pm t_c \frac{s}{\sqrt{N-1}} \tag{5}$$

where the values $\pm t_c$, called *critical values* or *confidence coefficients*, depend on the level of confidence desired and on the sample size. They can be read from Appendix III.

A comparison of equation (5) with the confidence limits $(\bar{X} \pm z_c\sigma/\sqrt{N})$ of Chapter 9, page 196, shows that for small samples we replace z_c (obtained from the normal distribution) with t_c (obtained from the t distribution) and that we replace σ with $\sqrt{N/(N-1)}s = \hat{s}$, which is the sample estimate of σ. As N increases, both methods tend toward agreement.

TESTS OF HYPOTHESES AND SIGNIFICANCE

Tests of hypotheses and significance, or decision rules (as discussed in Chapter 10), are easily extended to problems involving small samples, the only difference being that the *z score*, or *z statistic*, is replaced by a suitable *t score*, or *t statistic*.

1. **Means.** To test the hypothesis H_0 that a normal population has mean μ, we use the t score (or t statistic)

$$t = \frac{\bar{X} - \mu}{s}\sqrt{N-1} = \frac{\bar{X} - \mu}{\hat{s}}\sqrt{N} \tag{6}$$

where $\bar{X}$ is the mean of a sample of size N. This is analogous to using the z score

$$z = \frac{\bar{X} - \mu}{\sigma/\sqrt{N}}$$

for large N, except that $\hat{s} = \sqrt{N/(N-1)}s$ is used in place of σ. The difference is that while z is normally distributed, t follows Student's distribution. As N increases, these tend toward agreement.

2. **Differences of Means.** Suppose that two random samples of sizes N_1 and N_2 are drawn from normal populations whose standard deviations are equal ($\sigma_1 = \sigma_2$). Suppose further that these two samples

have means given by $\bar{X}_1$ and $\bar{X}_2$ and standard deviations given by s_1 and s_2, respectively. To test the hypothesis H_0 that the samples come from the same population (i.e., $\mu_1 = \mu_2$ as well as $\sigma_1 = \sigma_2$), we use the t score given by

$$t = \frac{\bar{X}_1 - \bar{X}_2}{\sigma\sqrt{1/N_1 + 1/N_2}} \quad \text{where} \quad \sigma = \sqrt{\frac{N_1 s_1^2 + N_2 s_2^2}{N_1 + N_2 - 2}} \tag{7}$$

The distribution of t is Student's distribution with $\nu = N_1 + N_2 - 2$ degrees of freedom. The use of equation (7) is made plausible on placing $\sigma_1 = \sigma_2 = \sigma$ in the z score of equation (2) of Chapter 10 and then using as an estimate of σ^2 the weighted mean

$$\frac{(N_1 - 1)\hat{s}_1^2 + (N_2 - 1)\hat{s}_2^2}{(N_1 - 1) + (N_2 - 1)} = \frac{N_1 s_1^2 + N_2 s_2^2}{N_1 + N_2 - 2}$$

where $\hat{s}_1^2$ and $\hat{s}_2^2$ are the unbiased estimates of σ_1^2 and σ_2^2 (see Property 3 on page 90).

THE CHI-SQUARE DISTRIBUTION

Let us define the statistic

$$\chi^2 = \frac{Ns^2}{\sigma^2} = \frac{(X_1 - \bar{X})^2 + (X_2 - \bar{X})^2 + \cdots + (X_N - \bar{X})^2}{\sigma^2} \tag{8}$$

where χ is the Greek letter *chi* and χ^2 is read "chi-square."

If we consider samples of size N drawn from a normal population with standard deviation σ, and if for each sample we compute χ^2, a sampling distribution for χ^2 can be obtained. This distribution, called the *chi-square distribution*, is given by

$$Y = Y_0(\chi^2)^{\frac{1}{2}(\nu-2)}\, e^{-\frac{1}{2}\chi^2} = Y_0\chi^{\nu-2}\, e^{-\frac{1}{2}\chi^2} \tag{9}$$

where $\nu = N - 1$ is the *number of degrees of freedom*, and Y_0 is a constant depending on ν such that the total area under the curve is 1. The chi-square distributions corresponding to various values of ν are shown in Fig. 11-2. The maximum value of Y occurs at $\chi^2 = \nu - 2$ for $\nu \geq 2$.

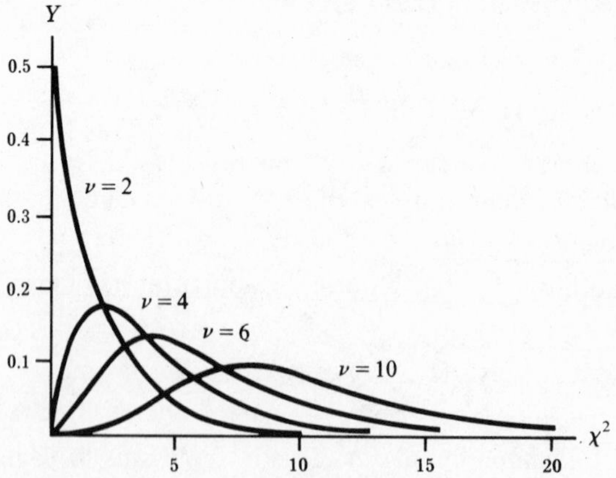

Fig. 11-2 Chi-square distributions for various values of ν.

CONFIDENCE INTERVALS FOR χ^2

As done with the normal and t distribution, we can define 95%, 99%, or other confidence limits and intervals χ^2 by using the table of the χ^2 distribution in Appendix IV. In this manner we can estimate within specified limits of confidence the population standard deviation σ in terms of a sample standard deviation s.

For example, if $\chi^2_{.025}$ and $\chi^2_{.975}$ are the values of χ^2 (called *critical values*) for which 2.5% of the area lies in each tail of the distribution, then the 95% confidence interval is

$$\chi^2_{.025} < \frac{Ns^2}{\sigma^2} < \chi^2_{.975} \tag{10}$$

from which we see that σ is estimated to lie in the interval

$$\frac{s\sqrt{N}}{\chi_{.975}} < \sigma < \frac{s\sqrt{N}}{\chi_{.025}} \tag{11}$$

with 95% confidence. Other confidence intervals can be found similarly. The values $\chi_{.025}$ and $\chi_{.975}$ represent, respectively, the 2.5 and 97.5 percentile values.

Appendix IV gives percentile values corresponding to the number of degrees of freedom ν. For large values of ν ($\nu \geq 30$), we can use the fact that $(\sqrt{2\chi^2} - \sqrt{2\nu - 1})$ is very nearly normally distributed with mean 0 and standard deviation 1; thus normal distribution tables can be used if $\nu \geq 30$. Then if χ^2_p and z_p are the pth percentiles of the chi-square and normal distributions, respectively, we have

$$\chi^2_p = \tfrac{1}{2}(z_p + \sqrt{2\nu - 1})^2 \tag{12}$$

In these cases, agreement is close to the results obtained in Chapters 8 and 9.

For further applications of the chi-square distribution, see Chapter 12.

DEGREES OF FREEDOM

In order to compute a statistic such as (*1*) or (*8*), it is necessary to use observations obtained from a sample as well as certain population parameters. If these parameters are unknown, they must be estimated from the sample.

The *number of degrees of freedom* of a statistic, generally denoted by ν, is defined as the number N of independent observations in the sample (i.e., the sample size) minus the number k of population parameters, which must be estimated from sample observations. In symbols, $\nu = N - k$.

In the case of statistic (*1*), the number of independent observations in the sample is N, from which we can compute $\bar{X}$ and s. However, since we must estimate μ, $k = 1$ and so $\nu = N - 1$.

In the case of statistic (*8*), the number of independent observations in the sample is N, from which we can compute s. However, since we must estimate σ, $k = 1$ and so $\nu = N - 1$.

THE *F* DISTRIBUTION

As we have seen, it is important in some applications to know the sampling distribution of the difference in means $(\bar{X}_1 - \bar{X}_2)$ of two samples. Similarly, we may need the sampling distribution of the difference in variances $(S_1^2 - S_2^2)$. It turns out, however, that this distribution is rather complicated. Because of this, we consider instead the statistic S_1^2/S_2^2, since a large or small ratio would indicate a large difference, while a ratio nearly equal to 1 would indicate a small difference. The sampling distribution in such a case can be found and is called the *F distribution*, named after R. A. Fisher.

More precisely, suppose that we have two samples, 1 and 2, of sizes N_1 and N_2, respectively, drawn from two normal (or nearly normal) populations having variances σ_1^2 and σ_2^2. Let us define the statistic

$$F = \frac{\hat{S}_1^2/\sigma_1^2}{\hat{S}_2^2/\sigma_2^2} = \frac{N_1S_1^2/(N_1-1)\sigma_1^2}{N_2S_2^2/(N_2-1)\sigma_2^2} \tag{13}$$

where

$$\hat{S}_1^2 = \frac{N_1S_1^2}{N_1 - 1} \qquad \hat{S}_2^2 = \frac{N_2S_2^2}{N_2 - 1} \tag{14}$$

(see page 194). Then the sampling distribution of F is called Fisher's F distribution, or briefly the F distribution, with $\nu_1 = N_1 - 1$ and $\nu_2 = N_2 - 1$ degrees of freedom. This distribution is given by

$$Y = \frac{CF^{(\nu_1/2)-1}}{(\nu_1 F + \nu_2)^{(\nu_1+\nu_2)/2}} \tag{15}$$

where C is a constant depending on ν_1 and ν_2 such that the total area under the curve is 1. The curve has a shape similar to that shown in Fig. 11-3, although this shape can vary considerably for different values of ν_1 and ν_2.

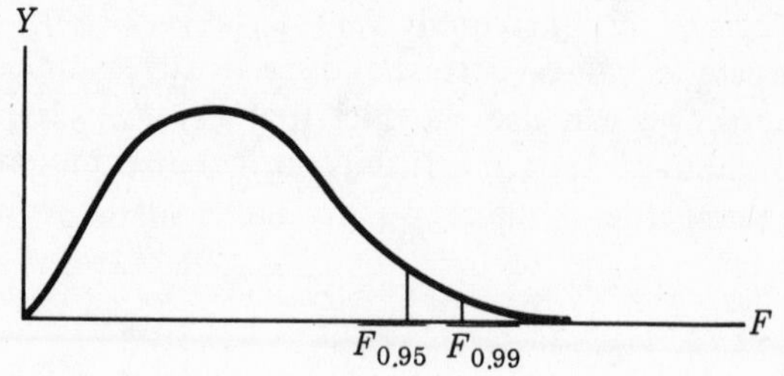

Fig. 11-3

Appendixes V and VI give percentile values of F for which the areas in the right-hand tail are 0.05 and 0.01, denoted by $F_{.95}$ and $F_{.99}$, respectively. Representing the 5% and 1% significance levels, these can be used to determine whether or not the variance S_1^2 is significantly larger than S_2^2. In practice, the sample with the larger variance is chosen as sample 1.

Solved Problems

STUDENT'S t DISTRIBUTION

11.1 The graph of Student's t distribution with 9 degrees of freedom is shown in Fig. 11-4. Find the value of t_1 for which (*a*) the shaded area on the right is 0.05, (*b*) the total shaded area is 0.05, (*c*) the total unshaded area is 0.99, (*d*) the shaded area on the left is 0.01, and (*e*) the area to the left of t_1 is 0.90.

SOLUTION

(*a*) If the shaded area on the right is 0.05, then the area to the left of t_1 is $(1-0.05) = 0.95$ and t_1 represents the 95th percentile, $t_{.95}$. Referring to Appendix III, proceed downward under the column headed ν until reaching entry 9, and then proceed right to the column headed $t_{.95}$; the result, 1.83, is the required value of t.

(*b*) If the total shaded area is 0.05, then the shaded area on the right is 0.025 by symmetry. Thus the area to the left of t_1 is $(1-0.025) = 0.975$ and t_1 represents the 97.5th percentile, $t_{.975}$. From Appendix III we find 2.26 to be the required value of t.

(*c*) If the total unshaded area is 0.99, then the total shaded area is $(1-0.99) = 0.01$ and the shaded area to the right is $0.01/2 = 0.005$. From Appendix III we find that $t_{.995} = 3.25$.

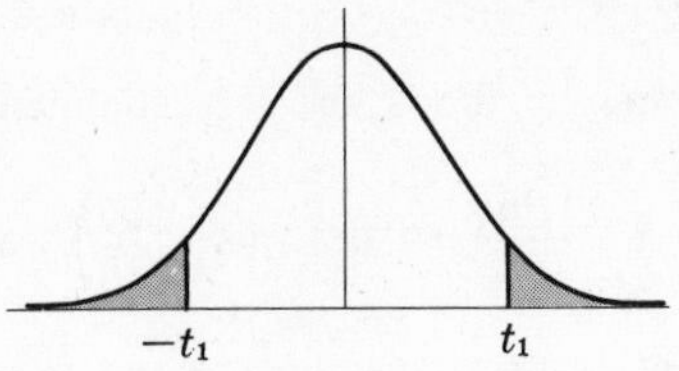

Fig. 11-4

(*d*) If the shaded area on the left is 0.01, then by symmetry the shaded area on the right is 0.01. From Appendix III, $t_{.99} = 2.82$. Thus the critical value of t for which the shaded area on the left is 0.01 equals -2.82.

(*e*) If the area to the left of t_1 is 0.90, then t_1 corresponds to the 90th percentile, $t_{.90}$, which from Appendix III equals 1.38.

11.2 Find the critical values of t for which the area of the right-hand tail of the t distribution is 0.05 if the number of degrees of freedom, ν, is equal to (*a*) 16, (*b*) 27, and (*c*) 200.

SOLUTION

Using Appendix III, we find in the column headed $t_{.95}$ the values (*a*) 1.75, corresponding to $\nu = 16$; (*b*) 1.70, corresponding to $\nu = 27$; and (*c*) 1.645, corresponding to $\nu = 200$. (The latter is the value that would be obtained by using the normal curve; in Appendix III it corresponds to the entry in the last row marked ∞, or infinity.)

11.3 The 95% confidence coefficients (two-tailed) for the normal distribution are given by ± 1.96. What are the corresponding coefficients for the t distribution if (*a*) $\nu = 9$, (*b*) $\nu = 20$, (*c*) $\nu = 30$, and (*d*) $\nu = 60$?

SOLUTION

For the 95% confidence coefficients (two-tailed), the total shaded area in Fig. 11-4 must be 0.05. Thus the shaded area in the right tail is 0.025 and the corresponding critical value of t is $t_{.975}$. Then the required confidence coefficients are $\pm t_{.975}$; for the given values of ν, these are (*a*) ± 2.26, (*b*) ± 2.09, (*c*) ± 2.04, and (*d*) ± 2.00.

11.4 A sample of 10 measurements of the diameter of a sphere gave a mean $\bar{X} = 4.38$ centimeters (cm) and a standard deviation $s = 0.06$ cm. Find the (*a*) 95% and (*b*) 99% confidence limits for the actual diameter.

SOLUTION

(*a*) The 95% confidence limits are given by $\bar{X} \pm t_{.975}(s/\sqrt{N-1})$.

Since $\nu = N - 1 = 10 - 1 = 9$, we find $t_{.975} = 2.26$ [see also Problem 11.3(*a*)]. Then, using $\bar{X} = 4.38$ and $s = 0.06$, the required 95% confidence limits are $4.38 \pm 2.26(0.06/\sqrt{10-1}) = 4.38 \pm 0.0452$ cm. Thus we can be 95% confident that the true mean lies between $(4.38 - 0.045) = 4.335$ cm and $(4.38 + 0.045) = 4.425$ cm.

(*b*) The 99% confidence limits are given by $\bar{X} \pm t_{.995}(s/\sqrt{N-1})$.

For $\nu = 9$, $t_{.995} = 3.25$. Then the 99% confidence limits are $4.38 \pm 3.25(0.06/\sqrt{10-1}) = 4.38 \pm 0.0650$ cm, and the 99% confidence interval is 4.315 to 4.445 cm.

11.5 (*a*) Work Problem 11.4, assuming that the methods of large sampling theory are valid.

(*b*) Compare the results of the two methods.

SOLUTION

(*a*) Using large-sampling-theory methods, the 95% confidence limits are

$$\bar{X} \pm \frac{1.96\sigma}{\sqrt{N}} = 4.38 \pm 1.96\left(\frac{0.06}{\sqrt{10}}\right) = 4.38 \pm 0.037 \text{ cm}$$

where we have used the sample standard deviation 0.06 as the estimate of σ. Similarly, the 99% confidence limits are

$$\bar{X} \pm \frac{2.58\sigma}{\sqrt{N}} = 4.38 \pm 2.58\left(\frac{0.06}{\sqrt{10}}\right) = 4.38 \pm 0.049 \text{ cm}$$

(*b*) In each case the confidence intervals obtained by using the small (or exact) sampling methods are wider than those obtained by using the large sampling methods. This is to be expected, since less precision is available with small samples than with large samples.

Mathcad **11.6** In the past, a machine has produced washers having a thickness of 0.050 inch (in). To determine whether the machine is in proper working order, a sample of 10 washers is chosen, for which the mean thickness is 0.053 in and the standard deviation is 0.003 in. Test the hypothesis that the machine is in proper working order, using significance levels of (*a*) 0.05 and (*b*) 0.01.

SOLUTION

We wish to decide between the hypotheses:

H_0: $\mu = 0.050$, and the machine is in proper working order

H_1: $\mu \neq 0.050$, and the machine is not in proper working order

Thus a two-tailed test is required. Under hypothesis H_0, we have

$$t = \frac{\bar{X} - \mu}{s}\sqrt{N-1} = \frac{0.053 - 0.050}{0.003}\sqrt{10-1} = 3.00$$

(*a*) For a two-tailed test at the 0.05 significance level, we adopt the decision rule:

Accept H_0 if t lies inside the interval $-t_{.975}$ to $t_{.975}$, which for $10-1=9$ degrees of freedom is the interval -2.26 to 2.26.

Reject H_0 otherwise

Since $t = 3.00$, we reject H_0 at the 0.05 level.

(*b*) For a two-tailed test at the 0.01 significance level, we adopt the decision rule:

Accept H_0 if t lies inside the interval $-t_{.995}$ to $t_{.995}$, which for $10-1=9$ degrees of freedom is the interval -3.25 to 3.25.

Reject H_0 otherwise

Since $t = 3.00$, we accept H_0 at the 0.01 level.

Because we can reject H_0 at the 0.05 level but not at the 0.01 level, we say that the sample result is *probably significant* (see the terminology at the end of Problem 10.5). It would thus be advisable to check the machine or at least to take another sample.

11.7 A test of the breaking strengths of six ropes manufactured by a company showed a mean breaking strength of 7750 pounds (lb) and a standard deviation of 145 lb, whereas the manufacturer claimed a mean breaking strength of 8000 lb. Can we support the manufacturer's claim at significance levels of (*a*) 0.05 and (*b*) 0.01?

SOLUTION

We must decide between the hypotheses:

H_0: $\mu = 8000$ lb, and the manufacturer's claim is justified

H_1: $\mu < 8000$ lb, and the manufacturer's claim is not justified

Thus a one-tailed test is required. Under hypothesis H_0, we have

$$t = \frac{\bar{X} - \mu}{s}\sqrt{N-1} = \frac{7750 - 8000}{145}\sqrt{6-1} = -3.86$$

(*a*) For a one-tailed test at the 0.05 significance level, we adopt the decision rule:

Accept H_0 if t is greater than $-t_{.95}$, which for $6-1=5$ degrees of freedom means $t > -2.01$.
Reject H_0 otherwise.

Since $t = -3.86$, we reject H_0.

(*b*) For a one-tailed test at the 0.01 significance level, we adopt the decision rule:

Accept H_0 if t is greater than $-t_{.99}$, which for 5 degrees of freedom means $t > -3.36$.
Reject H_0 otherwise.

Since $t = -3.86$, we reject H_0.

We conclude that it is extremely unlikely that the manufacturer's claim is justified.

11.8 The intelligence quotients (IQs) of 16 students from one area of a city showed a mean of 107 and a standard deviation of 10, while the IQs of 14 students from another area of the city showed a mean of 112 and a standard deviation of 8. Is there a significant difference between the IQs of the two groups at significance levels of (*a*) 0.01 and (*b*) 0.05?

SOLUTION

If μ_1 and μ_2 denote the population mean IQs of students from the two areas, respectively, we have to decide between the hypotheses:

H_0: $\mu_1 = \mu_2$, and there is essentially no difference between the groups.

H_1: $\mu_1 \neq \mu_2$, and there is a significant difference between the groups.

Under hypothesis H_0,

$$t = \frac{\bar{X}_1 - \bar{X}_2}{\sigma\sqrt{1/N_1 + 1/N_2}} \qquad \text{where} \qquad \sigma = \sqrt{\frac{N_1 s_1^2 + N_2 s_2^2}{N_1 + N_2 - 2}}$$

Thus

$$\sigma = \sqrt{\frac{16(10)^2 + 14(8)^2}{16+14-2}} = 9.44 \qquad \text{and} \qquad t = \frac{112-107}{9.44\sqrt{1/16+1/14}} = 1.45$$

(*a*) Using a two-tailed test at the 0.01 significance level, we would reject H_0 if t were outside the range $-t_{.995}$ to $t_{.995}$, which for $(N_1 + N_2 - 2) = (16+14-2) = 28$ degrees of freedom is the range -2.76 to 2.76. Thus we cannot reject H_0 at the 0.01 significance level.

(*b*) Using a two-tailed test at the 0.05 significance level, we would reject H_0 if t were outside the range $-t_{.975}$ to $t_{.975}$, which for 28 degrees of freedom is the range -2.05 to 2.05. Thus we cannot reject H_0 at the 0.05 significance levels.

We conclude that there is no significant difference between the IQs of the two groups.

11.9 At an agricultural station it was desired to test the effect of a given fertilizer on wheat production. To accomplish this, 24 plots of land having equal areas were chosen. Half of these were treated with fertilizer, and the other half were untreated (as a control group); otherwise, the conditions were the same. The mean yield of wheat on the untreated plots was 4.8 bushels (bu) with a standard deviation of 0.40 bu, while the mean yield on the treated plots was 5.1 bu with a standard deviation of 0.36 bu. Can we conclude at significance levels of (*a*) 1% and (*b*) 5% that there is a significant improvement in wheat production because of the fertilizer?

SOLUTION

If μ_1 and μ_2 denote the population mean yields of wheat on treated and untreated land, respectively, we have to decide between the hypotheses:

H_0: $\mu_1 = \mu_2$, and the difference is due to chance.

H_1: $\mu_1 > \mu_2$, and the fertilizer improves the yield.

Under hypothesis H_0,

$$t = \frac{\bar{X}_1 - \bar{X}_2}{\sigma\sqrt{1/N_1 + 1/N_2}} \qquad \text{where} \qquad \sigma = \sqrt{\frac{N_1 s_1^2 + N_2 s_2^2}{N_1 + N_2 - 2}}$$

Thus
$$\sigma = \sqrt{\frac{12(0.40)^2 + 12(0.36)^2}{12 + 12 - 2}} = 0.397 \qquad \text{and} \qquad t = \frac{5.1 - 4.8}{0.397\sqrt{1/12 + 1/12}} = 1.85$$

(*a*) Using a one-tailed test at the 0.01 significance level, we would reject H_0 if t were greater than $t_{.99}$, which for $(N_1 + N_2 - 2) = (12 + 12 - 2) = 22$ degrees of freedom is 2.51. Thus we cannot reject H_0 at the 0.01 significance level.

(*b*) Using a one-tailed test at the 0.05 significance level, we would reject H_0 if t were greater than $t_{.95}$, which for 22 degrees of freedom is 1.72. Thus we can reject H_0 at the 0.05 level of significance.

We conclude that the improvement in yield of wheat by use of the fertilizer is ***probably significant***. However, before definite conclusions are drawn concerning the usefulness of the fertilizer it may be desirable to have some further evidence.

THE CHI-SQUARE DISTRIBUTION

Mathcad **11.10** The graph of the chi-square distribution with 5 degrees of freedom is shown in Fig. 11-5. Find the critical values of χ^2 for which (*a*) the shaded area on the right is 0.05, (*b*) the total shaded area is 0.05, (*c*) the shaded area on the left is 0.10, and (*d*) the shaded area on the right is 0.01.

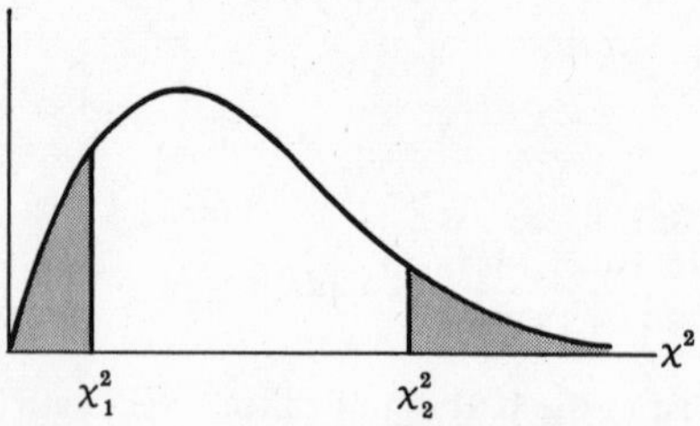

Fig. 11-5

SOLUTION

(*a*) If the shaded area on the right is 0.05, then the area to the left of χ_2^2 is $(1 - 0.05) = 0.95$ and χ_2^2 represents the 95th percentile, $\chi_{.95}^2$. Referring to Appendix IV, proceed downward under the column headed ν until reaching entry 5, and then proceed right to the column headed $\chi_{.95}^2$; the result, 11.1, is the required critical value of χ^2.

(*b*) Since the distribution is not symmetrical, there are many critical values for which the total shaded area is 0.05. For example, the right-hand shaded area could be 0.04 while the left-hand shaded area is 0.01. It is customary, however, unless otherwise specified, to choose the two areas to be equal. In this case, then, each area is 0.025.

If the shaded area on the right is 0.025, the area to the left of χ_2^2 is $1-0.025=0.975$ and χ_2^2 represents the 97.5th percentile, $\chi^2_{.975}$, which from Appendix IV is 12.8. Similarly, if the shaded area on the left is 0.025, the area to the left of χ_1^2 is 0.025 and χ_1^2 represents the 2.5th percentile, $\chi^2_{.025}$, which equals 0.831. Thus the critical values are 0.831 and 12.8.

(*c*) If the shaded area on the left is 0.10, χ_1^2 represents the 10th percentile, $\chi^2_{.10}$, which equals 1.61.

(*d*) If the shaded area on the right is 0.01, the area to the left of χ_2^2 is 0.99 and χ_2^2 represents the 99th percentile, $\chi^2_{.99}$, which equals 15.1.

11.11 Find the critical values of χ^2 for which the area of the right-hand tail of the χ^2 distribution is 0.05, if the number of degrees of freedom, ν, is equal to (*a*) 15, (*b*) 21, and (*c*) 50.

SOLUTION

Using Appendix IV, we find in the column headed $\chi^2_{.95}$ the values (*a*) 25.0, corresponding to $\nu=15$; (*b*) 32.7, corresponding to $\nu=21$; and (*c*) 67.5, corresponding to $\nu=50$.

11.12 Find the median value of χ^2 corresponding to (*a*) 9, (*b*) 28, and (*c*) 40 degrees of freedom.

SOLUTION

Using Appendix IV, we find in the column headed $\chi^2_{.50}$ (since the median is the 50th percentile) the value (*a*) 8.34, corresponding to $\nu=9$; (*b*) 27.3, corresponding to $\nu=28$; and (*c*) 39.3, corresponding to $\nu=40$.

It is of interest to note that the median values are very nearly equal to the number of degrees of freedom. In fact, for $\nu>10$ the median values are equal to $(\nu-0.7)$, as can be seen from the table.

11.13 The standard deviation of the heights of 16 male students chosen at random in a school of 1000 male students is 2.40 in. Find the (*a*) 95% and (*b*) 99% confidence limits of the standard deviation for all male students at the school.

SOLUTION

(*a*) The 95% confidence limits are given by $s\sqrt{N}/\chi_{.975}$ and $s\sqrt{N}/\chi_{.025}$.

For $\nu=16-1=15$ degrees of freedom, $\chi^2_{.975}=27.5$ (or $\chi_{.975}=5.24$) and $\chi^2_{.025}=6.26$ (or $\chi_{.025}=2.50$). Then the 95% confidence limits are $2.40\sqrt{16}/5.24$ and $2.40\sqrt{16}/2.50$ (i.e., 1.83 and 3.84 in). Thus we can be 95% confident that the population standard deviation lies between 1.83 and 3.84 in.

(*b*) The 99% confidence limits are given by $s\sqrt{N}/\chi_{.995}$ and $s\sqrt{N}/\chi_{.005}$.

For $\nu=16-1=15$ degrees of freedom, $x^2_{.995}=32.8$ (or $\chi_{.995}=5.73$) and $\chi^2_{.005}=4.60$ (or $\chi_{.005}=2.14$). Then the 99% confidence limits are $2.40\sqrt{16}/5.73$ and $2.40\sqrt{16}/2.14$ (i.e., 1.68 and 4.49 in). Thus we can be 99% confident that the population standard deviation lies between 1.68 and 4.49 in.

11.14 Find $\chi^2_{.95}$ for (*a*) $\nu=50$ and (*b*) $\nu=100$ degrees of freedom.

SOLUTION

For ν greater than 30, we can use the fact that $\sqrt{2\chi^2}-\sqrt{2\nu-1}$ is very closely normally distributed with mean 0 and standard deviation 1. Then if z_p is the z-score percentile of the standardized normal distribution, we can write, to a high degree of approximation,

$$\sqrt{2\chi_p^2}-\sqrt{2\nu-1}=z_p \qquad \text{or} \qquad \sqrt{2\chi_p^2}=z_p+\sqrt{2\nu-1}$$

from which $\chi_p^2=\frac{1}{2}(z_p+\sqrt{2\nu-1})^2$.

(*a*) If $\nu=50$, $\chi^2_{.95}=\frac{1}{2}(z_{.95}+\sqrt{2(50)-1})^2=\frac{1}{2}(1.64+\sqrt{99})^2=67.2$, which agrees very well with the value of 67.5 given in Appendix IV.

(*b*) If $\nu=100$, $\chi^2_{.95}=\frac{1}{2}(z_{.95}+\sqrt{2(100)-1})^2=\frac{1}{2}(1.64+\sqrt{199})^2=124.0$ (actual value $=124.3$).

Mathcad **11.15** The standard deviation of the lifetimes of a sample of 200 electric light bulbs is 100 hours (h). Find the (*a*) 95% and (*b*) 99% confidence limits for the standard deviation of all such electric light bulbs.

SOLUTION

(*a*) The 95% confidence limits are given by $s\sqrt{N}/\chi_{.975}$ and $s\sqrt{N}/\chi_{.025}$.

For $\nu = 200 - 1 = 199$ degrees of freedom, we find (as in Problem 11.14)

$$\chi^2_{.975} = \tfrac{1}{2}(z_{.975} + \sqrt{2(199) - 1})^2 = \tfrac{1}{2}(1.96 + 19.92)^2 = 239$$
$$\chi^2_{.025} = \tfrac{1}{2}(z_{.025} + \sqrt{2(199) - 1})^2 = \tfrac{1}{2}(-1.96 + 19.92)^2 = 161$$

from which $\chi_{.975} = 15.5$ and $\chi_{.025} = 12.7$. Then the 95% confidence limits are $100\sqrt{200}/15.5 = 91.2$ h and $100\sqrt{200}/12.7 = 111.3$ h, respectively. Thus we can be 95% confident that the population standard deviation will lie between 91.2 and 111.3 h.

This should be compared with Problem 9.17(*a*).

(*b*) The 99% confidence limits are given by $s\sqrt{N}/\chi_{.995}$ and $s\sqrt{N}/\chi_{.005}$.

For $\nu = 200 - 1 = 199$ degrees of freedom,

$$\chi^2_{.995} = \tfrac{1}{2}(z_{.995} + \sqrt{2(199) - 1})^2 = \tfrac{1}{2}(2.58 + 19.92)^2 = 253$$
$$\chi^2_{.005} = \tfrac{1}{2}(z_{.005} + \sqrt{2(199) - 1})^2 = \tfrac{1}{2}(-2.58 + 19.92)^2 = 150$$

from which $\chi_{.995} = 15.9$ and $\chi_{.005} = 12.2$. Then the 99% confidence limits are $100\sqrt{200}/15.9 = 88.9$ h and $100\sqrt{200}/12.2 = 115.9$ h, respectively. Thus we can be 99% confident that the population standard deviation will lie between 88.9 and 115.9 h.

This should be compared with Problem 9.17(*b*).

11.16 Is it possible to obtain a 95% confidence interval for the population standard deviation whose width is smaller than that found in Problem 11.15(*a*)?

SOLUTION

The 95% confidence limits for the population standard deviation found in Problem 11.15(*a*) were obtained by choosing critical values of χ^2 such that the area in each tail was 2.5%. It is possible to find other 95% confidence limits by choosing critical values of χ^2 for which the sum of the areas in the tails is 5%, or 0.05, but such that the areas in each tail are not equal.

In Table 11.1 several such critical values have been obtained (using the methods of Problem 11.14), and the corresponding 95% confidence intervals are shown. From this table it is seen that a 95% interval with a width of only 19.8 is 91.0 to 110.8. An interval with even smaller width can be found by continuing the same method of approach, using critical values such as $\chi_{.031}$ and $\chi_{.981}$, $\chi_{.032}$ and $\chi_{.982}$, etc. In general, however, the decrease in the interval that is thereby obtained is usually negligible and is not worth the labor involved.

Table 11.1

Critical Values	95% Confidence Interval	Width
$\chi_{.01} = 12.44$, $\chi_{.96} = 15.32$	92.3 to 113.7	21.4
$\chi_{.02} = 12.64$, $\chi_{.97} = 15.42$	91.7 to 111.9	20.2
$\chi_{.03} = 12.76$, $\chi_{.98} = 15.54$	91.0 to 110.8	19.8
$\chi_{.04} = 12.85$, $\chi_{.99} = 15.73$	89.9 to 110.0	20.1

11.17 In the past, the standard deviation of weights of certain 40.0-ounce packages filled by a machine was 0.25 ounce (oz). A random sample of 20 packages showed a standard deviation of 0.32 oz. Is the apparent increase in variability significant at the (*a*) 0.05 and (*b*) 0.01 levels?

SOLUTION

We have to decide between the hypotheses:

H_0: $\sigma = 0.25$ oz, and the observed result is due to chance.

H_1: $\sigma > 0.25$ oz, and the variability has increased.

The value of χ^2 for the sample is

$$\chi^2 = \frac{Ns^2}{\sigma^2} = \frac{20(0.32)^2}{(0.25)^2} = 32.8$$

(*a*) Using a one-tailed test, we would reject H_0 at the 0.05 significance level if the sample value of χ^2 were greater than $\chi^2_{.95}$, which equals 30.1 for $\nu = 20 - 1 = 19$ degrees of freedom. Thus we would reject H_0 at the 0.05 significance level.

(*b*) Using a one-tailed test, we would reject H_0 at the 0.01 significance level if the sample value of χ^2 were greater than $\chi^2_{.99}$, which equals 36.2 for 19 degrees of freedom. Thus we would not reject H_0 at the 0.01 significance level.

We conclude that the variability has probably increased. An examination of the machine should be made.

THE *F* DISTRIBUTION

11.18 Two samples of sizes 9 and 12 are drawn from two normally distributed populations having variances 16 and 25, respectively. If the sample variances are 20 and 8, determine whether the first sample has a significantly larger variance than the second sample at significance levels of (*a*) 0.05 and (*b*) 0.01.

SOLUTION

For the two samples, 1 and 2, we have $N_1 = 9$, $N_2 = 12$, $\sigma_1^2 = 16$, $\sigma_2^2 = 25$, $S_1^2 = 20$, and $S_2^2 = 8$. Thus

$$F = \frac{\hat{S}_1^2/\sigma_1^2}{\hat{S}_2^2/\sigma_2^2} = \frac{N_1 S_1^2/(N_1 - 1)\sigma_1^2}{N_2 S_2^2/(N_2 - 1)\sigma_2^2} = \frac{(9)(20)/(9-1)(16)}{(12)(8)/(12-1)(25)} = 4.03$$

(*a*) The degrees of freedom for the numerator and denominator of F are $\nu_1 = N_1 - 1 = 9 - 1 = 8$ and $\nu_2 = N_2 - 1 = 12 - 1 = 11$. Then from Appendix V we find that $F_{.95} = 2.95$. Since the calculated $F = 4.03$ is greater than 2.95, we conclude that the variance for sample 1 is significantly larger than that for sample 2 at the 0.05 significance level.

(*b*) For $\nu_1 = 8$ and $\nu_2 = 11$, we find from Appendix VI that $F_{.01} = 4.74$. In this case the calculated $F = 4.03$ is less than 4.74. Thus we cannot conclude that the sample 1 variance is larger than the sample 2 variance at the 0.01 significance level.

Mathcad **11.19** Two samples of sizes 8 and 10 are drawn from two normally distributed populations having variances 20 and 36, respectively. Find the probability that the variance of the first sample is more than twice the variance of the second sample.

SOLUTION

We have $N_1 = 8$, $N_2 = 10$, $\sigma_1^2 = 20$, and $\sigma_2^2 = 36$. Thus

$$F = \frac{8S_1^2/(7)(20)}{10S_2^2/(9)(36)} = 1.85\frac{S_1^2}{S_2^2}$$

The number of degrees of freedom for the numerator and denominator are $\nu_1 = N_1 - 1 = 8 - 1 = 7$ and $\nu_2 = N_2 - 1 = 10 - 1 = 9$. Now if S_1^2 is more than twice S_2^2, then

$$F = 1.85\frac{S_1^2}{S_2^2} > (1.85)(2) = 3.70$$

Looking up 3.70 in Appendixes V and VI, we find that the probability is less than 0.05 but greater than 0.01. For exact values, we need a more extensive tabulation of the F distribution.

Supplementary Problems

STUDENT'S t DISTRIBUTION

11.20 For a Student's distribution with 15 degrees of freedom, find the value of t_1 such that (*a*) the area to the right of t_1 is 0.01, (*b*) the area to the left of t_1 is 0.95, (*c*) the area to the right of t_1 is 0.10, (*d*) the combined area to the right of t_1 and to the left of $-t_1$ is 0.01, and (*e*) the area between $-t_1$ and t_1 is 0.95.

11.21 Find the critical values of t for which the area of the right-hand tail of the t distribution is 0.01 if the number of degrees of freedom, ν, is equal to (*a*) 4, (*b*) 12, (*c*) 25, (*d*) 60, and (*e*) 150.

11.22 Find the values of t_1 for Student's distribution that satisfy each of the following conditions:

(*a*) The area between $-t_1$ and t_1 is 0.90 and $\nu = 25$.

(*b*) The area to the left of $-t_1$ is 0.025 and $\nu = 20$.

(*c*) The combined area to the right of t_1 and left of $-t_1$ is 0.01 and $\nu = 5$.

(d) The area to the right of t_1 is 0.55 and $\nu = 16$.

11.23 If a variable U has a Student's distribution with $\nu = 10$, find the constant C such that (*a*) $\Pr\{U > C\} = 0.05$, (*b*) $\Pr\{-C \le U \le C\} = 0.98$, (*c*) $\Pr\{U \le C\} = 0.20$, and (*d*) $\Pr\{U \ge C) = 0.90$.

11.24 The 99% confidence coefficients (two-tailed) for the normal distribution are given by ± 2.58. What are the corresponding coefficients for the t distribution if (*a*) $\nu = 4$, (*b*) $\nu = 12$, (*c*) $\nu = 25$, (*d*) $\nu = 30$, and (*e*) $\nu = 40$?

11.25 A sample of 12 measurements of the breaking strengths of cotton threads gave a mean of 7.38 grams (g) and a standard deviation of 1.24 g. Find the (*a*) 95% and (*b*) 99% confidence limits for the actual breaking strength.

11.26 Work Problem 11.25 by assuming that the methods of large sampling theory are applicable, and compare the results obtained.

11.27 Five measurements of the reaction time of an individual to certain stimuli were recorded as 0.28, 0.30, 0.27, 0.33, and 0.31 second. Find the (*a*) 95% and (*b*) 99% confidence limits for the actual reaction time.

11.28 The mean lifetime of electric light bulbs produced by a company has in the past been 1120 h with a standard deviation of 125 h. A sample of eight electric light bulbs recently chosen from a supply of newly produced bulbs showed a mean lifetime of 1070 h. Test the hypothesis that the mean lifetime of the bulbs has not changed, using significance levels of (*a*) 0.05 and (*b*) 0.01.

11.29 In Problem 11.28, test the hypothesis $\mu = 1120$ h against the alternative hypothesis $\mu < 1120$ h, using significance levels of (*a*) 0.05 and (*b*) 0.01.

11.30 The specifications for the production of a certain alloy call for 23.2% copper. A sample of 10 analyses of the product showed a mean copper content of 23.5% and a standard deviation of 0.24%. Can we conclude at (*a*) 0.01 and (*b*) 0.05 significance levels that the product meets the required specifications?

11.31 In Problem 11.30, test the hypothesis that the mean copper content is higher than in the required specifications, using significance levels of (*a*) 0.01 and (*b*) 0.05.

11.32 An efficiency expert claims that by introducing a new type of machinery into a production process, he can substantially decrease the time required for production. Because of the expense involved in maintenance of the machines, management feels that unless the production time can be decreased by at least 8.0%, it cannot afford to introduce the process. Six resulting experiments show that the time for production is decreased by 8.4% with a standard deviation of 0.32%. Using significance levels of (*a*) 0.01 and (*b*) 0.05, test the hypothesis that the process should be introduced.

11.33 Using brand A gasoline, the mean number of miles per gallon traveled by five similar automobiles under identical conditions was 22.6 with a standard deviation of 0.48. Using brand B, the mean number was 21.4 with a standard deviation of 0.54. Using a significance level of 0.05, investigate whether brand A is really better than brand B in providing more mileage to the gallon.

11.34 Two types of chemical solutions, A and B, were tested for their pH (degree of acidity of the solution). Analysis of six samples of A showed a mean pH of 7.52 with a standard deviation of 0.024. Analysis of five samples of B showed a mean pH of 7.49 with a standard deviation of 0.032. Using the 0.05 significance level, determine whether the two types of solutions have different pH values.

11.35 On an examination in psychology, 12 students in one class had a mean grade of 78 with a standard deviation of 6, while 15 students in another class had a mean grade of 74 with a standard deviation of 8. Using a significance level of 0.05, determine whether the first group is superior to the second group.

THE CHI-SQUARE DISTRIBUTION

11.36 For a chi-square distribution with 12 degrees of freedom, find the value of χ_c^2 such that (*a*) the area to the right of χ_c^2 is 0.05, (*b*) the area to the left of χ_c^2 is 0.99, and (*c*) the area to the right of χ_c^2 is 0.025.

11.37 Find the critical values of χ^2 for which the area of the right-hand tail of the χ^2 distribution is 0.05 if the number of degrees of freedom, ν, is equal to (*a*) 8, (*b*) 19, (*c*) 28, and (*d*) 40.

11.38 Work Problem 11.37 if the area of the right-hand tail is 0.01.

11.39 (*a*) Find χ_1^2 and χ_2^2 such that the area under the χ^2 distribution corresponding to $\nu = 20$ between χ_1^2 and χ_2^2 is 0.95, assuming equal areas to the right of χ_2^2 and left of χ_1^2.

(*b*) Show that if the assumption of equal areas in part (*a*) is not made, the values χ_1^2 and χ_2^2 are not unique.

11.40 If the variable U is chi-square-distributed with $\nu = 7$, find χ_1^2 and χ_2^2 such that (*a*) $\Pr\{U > \chi_2^2\} = 0.025$, (*b*) $\Pr\{U < \chi_1^2\} = 0.50$, (*c*) $\Pr\{\chi_1^2 \leq U \leq \chi_2^2\} = 0.90$.

11.41 The standard deviation of the lifetimes of 10 electric light bulbs manufactured by a company is 120 h. Find the (*a*) 95% and (*b*) 99% confidence limits for the standard deviation of all bulbs manufactured by the company.

11.42 Work Problem 11.41 if 25 electric light bulbs show the same standard deviation of 120 h.

11.43 Find (*a*) $\chi_{.05}^2$ and (*b*) $\chi_{.95}^2$ for $\nu = 150$.

11.44 Find (*a*) $\chi_{.025}^2$ and (*b*) $\chi_{.975}^2$ for $\nu = 250$.

11.45 Show that for large values of ν, a good approximation to χ^2 is given by $(\nu + z_p\sqrt{2\nu})$, where z_p is the pth percentile of the standard normal distribution.

11.46 Work Problem 11.39 by using the χ^2 distributions if a sample of 100 electric bulbs shows the same standard deviation of 120 h. Compare the results with those obtained by the methods of Chapter 9.

11.47 What is the 95% confidence interval of Problem 11.44 that has the least width?

11.48 The standard deviation of the breaking strengths of certain cables produced by a company is given as 240 lb. After a change was introduced in the process of manufacture of these cables, the breaking strengths of a sample of eight cables showed a standard deviation of 300 lb. Investigate the significance of the apparent increase in variability, using significance levels of (*a*) 0.05 and (*b*) 0.01.

11.49 The standard deviation of the annual temperatures of a city over a period of 100 years was 16° Fahrenheit. Using the mean temperature on the 15th day of each month during the last 15 years, a standard deviation of annual temperatures was computed as 10° Fahrenheit. Test the hypothesis that the temperatures in the city have become less variable than in the past, using significance levels of (*a*) 0.05 and (*b*) 0.01.

THE *F* DISTRIBUTION

11.50 Find the values of F in each of the following cases:

(*a*) $F_{.95}$ with $\nu_1 = 8$ and $\nu_2 = 10$ (*c*) $F_{.95}$ with $N_1 = 16$ and $N_2 = 25$

(*b*) $F_{.99}$ with $\nu_1 = 24$ and $\nu_2 = 11$ (*d*) $F_{.99}$ with $N_1 = 21$ and $N_2 = 23$

11.51 Find $F_{.95}$ with $\nu_1 = 22$ and $\nu_2 = 27$.

11.52 Two samples of sizes 10 and 15 are drawn from two normally distributed populations having variances 40 and 60, respectively. If the sample variances are 90 and 50, determine whether the sample 1 variance is significantly greater than the sample 2 variance at significance levels of (*a*) 0.05 and (*b*) 0.01.

11.53 Two companies, *A* and *B*, manufacture electric light bulbs. The lifetimes for the *A* and *B* bulbs are very nearly normally distributed, with standard deviations of 20 h and 27 h, respectively. If we select 16 bulbs from company *A* and 20 bulbs from company *B* and determine the standard deviations of their lifetimes to be 15 h and 40 h, respectively, can we conclude at significance levels of (*a*) 0.05 and (*b*) 0.01 that the variability of the *A* bulbs is significantly less than that of the *B* bulbs?

Chapter 12

The Chi-Square Test

OBSERVED AND THEORETICAL FREQUENCIES

As we have already seen many times, the results obtained in samples do not always agree exactly with the theoretical results expected according to the rules of probability. For example, although theoretical considerations lead us to expect 50 heads and 50 tails when we toss a fair coin 100 times, it is rare that these results are obtained exactly.

Suppose that in a particular sample a set of possible events $E_1, E_2, E_3, \ldots, E_k$ (see Table 12.1) are observed to occur with frequencies $o_1, o_2, o_3, \ldots, o_k$, called *observed frequencies*, and that according to probability rules they are expected to occur with frequencies $e_1, e_2, e_3, \ldots, e_k$, called *expected*, or *theoretical, frequencies*.

Table 12.1

Event	E_1	E_2	E_3	$\cdots$	E_k
Observed frequency	o_1	o_2	o_3	$\cdots$	o_k
Expected frequency	e_1	e_2	e_3	$\cdots$	e_k

Often we wish to know whether the observed frequencies differ significantly from the expected frequencies. For the case where only two events E_1 and E_2 are possible (sometimes called a *dichotomy*, or *dichotomous classification*), as in the case of heads or tails, defective or nondefective bolts, etc., the problem is answered satisfactorily by the methods of previous chapters. In this chapter the general problem is considered.

DEFINITION OF χ^2

A measure of the discrepancy existing between the observed and expected frequencies is supplied by the statistic χ^2 (read chi-square) given by

$$\chi^2 = \frac{(o_1 - e_1)^2}{e_1} + \frac{(o_2 - e_2)^2}{e_2} + \cdots + \frac{(o_k - e_k)^2}{e_k} = \sum_{j=1}^{k} \frac{(o_j - e_j)^2}{e_j} \tag{1}$$

where if the total frequency is N,

$$\sum o_j = \sum e_j = N \tag{2}$$

An expression equivalent to formula (*1*) is (see Problem 12.11)

$$\chi^2 = \sum \frac{o_j^2}{e_j} - N \tag{3}$$

If $\chi^2 = 0$, the observed and theoretical frequencies agree exactly; while if $\chi^2 > 0$, they do not agree exactly. The larger the value of χ^2, the greater is the discrepancy between the observed and expected frequencies.

The sampling distribution of χ^2 is approximated very closely by the chi-square distribution

$$Y = Y_0(\chi^2)^{\frac{1}{2}(\nu-2)} e^{-\frac{1}{2}\chi^2} = Y_0\chi^{\nu-2} e^{-\frac{1}{2}\chi^2} \tag{4}$$

(already considered in Chapter 11) if the expected frequencies are at least equal to 5. The approximation improves for larger values.

The number of degrees of freedom, ν, is given by

(1) $\nu = k - 1$ if the expected frequencies can be computed without having to estimate the population parameters from sample statistics. Note that we subtract 1 from k because of constraint condition (*2*), which states that if we know $k-1$ of the expected frequencies, the remaining frequency can be determined.

(2) $\nu = k - 1 - m$ if the expected frequencies can be computed only by estimating m population parameters from sample statistics.

SIGNIFICANCE TESTS

In practice, expected frequencies are computed on the basis of a hypothesis H_0. If under this hypothesis the computed value of χ^2 given by equation (*1*) or (*3*) is greater than some critical value (such as $\chi^2_{.95}$ or $\chi^2_{.99}$, which are the critical values of the 0.05 and 0.01 significance levels, respectively), we would conclude that the observed frequencies differ *significantly* from the expected frequencies and would reject H_0 at the corresponding level of significance; otherwise, we would accept it (or at least not reject it). This procedure is called *the chi-square test* of hypothesis or significance.

It should be noted that we must look with suspicion upon circumstances where χ^2 is *too close to zero*, since it is rare that observed frequencies agree *too well* with expected frequencies. To examine such situations, we can determine whether the computed value of χ^2 is less than $\chi^2_{.05}$ or $\chi^2_{.01}$, in which cases we would decide that the agreement is *too good* at the 0.05 or 0.01 significance levels, respectively.

THE CHI-SQUARE TEST FOR GOODNESS OF FIT

The chi-square test can be used to determine how well theoretical distributions (such as the normal and binomial distributions) fit empirical distributions (i.e., those obtained from sample data). See Problems 12.12 and 12.13.

CONTINGENCY TABLES

Table 12.1, in which the observed frequencies occupy a single row, is called a *one-way classification table.* Since the number of columns is k, this is also called a $1 \times k$ (read "1 by k") *table.* By extending these ideas, we can arrive at *two-way classification tables*, or *$h \times k$ tables*, in which the observed frequencies occupy h rows and k columns. Such tables are often called *contingency tables.*

Corresponding to each observed frequency in an $h \times k$ contingency table, there is an *expected* (or *theoretical*) *frequency* that is computed subject to some hypothesis according to rules of probability. These frequencies, which occupy the *cells* of a contingency table, are called *cell frequencies.* The total frequency in each row or each column is called the *marginal frequency.*

To investigate agreement between the observed and expected frequencies, we compute the statistic

$$\chi^2 = \sum_j \frac{(o_j - e_j)^2}{e_j} \tag{5}$$

where the sum is taken over all cells in the contingenecy table and where the symbols o_j and e_j represent, respectively, the observed and expected frequencies in the jth cell. This sum, which is analogous to equation (*1*), contains hk terms. The sum of all observed frequencies is denoted by N and is equal to the sum of all expected frequencies [compare with equation (*2*)].

As before, statistic (*5*) has a sampiing distribution given very closely by (*4*), provided the expected frequencies are not too small. The number of degrees of freedom, ν, of this chi-square distribution is given for $h > 1$ and $k > 1$ by

(1) $\nu = (h-1)(k-1)$ if the expected frequencies can be computed without having to estimate population parameters from sample statistics. For a proof of this, see Problem 12.18.

(2) $\nu = (h-1)(k-1) - m$ if the expected frequencies can be computed only by estimating m population parameters from sample statistics.

Significance tests for $h \times k$ tables are similar to those for $1 \times k$ tables. The expected frequencies are found subject to a particular hypothesis H_0. A hypothesis commonly assumed is that the two classifications are independent of each other.

Contingency tables can be extended to higher dimensions. Thus, for example, we can have $h \times k \times l$ tables, where three classifications are present.

YATES' CORRECTION FOR CONTINUITY

When results for continuous distributions are applied to discrete data, certain corrections for continuity can be made, as we have seen in previous chapters. A similar correction is available when the chi-square distribution is used. The correction consists in rewriting equation (*1*) as

$$\chi^2 \text{ (corrected)} = \frac{(|o_1 - e_1| - 0.5)^2}{e_1} + \frac{(|o_2 - e_2| - 0.5)^2}{e_2} + \cdots + \frac{(|o_k - e_k| - 0.5)^2}{e_k} \tag{6}$$

and is often referred to as *Yates' correction.* An analogous modification of equation (*5*) also exists.

In general, the correction is made only when the number of degrees of freedom is $\nu = 1$. For large samples, this yields practically the same results as the uncorrected χ^2, but difficulties can arise near critical values (see Problem 12.8). For small samples where each expected frequency is between 5 and 10, it is perhaps best to compare both the corrected and uncorrected values of χ^2. If both values lead to the same conclusion regarding a hypothesis, such as rejection at the 0.05 level, difficulties are rarely encountered. If they lead to different conclusions, one can resort to increasing the sample sizes or, if this proves impractical, one can employ methods of probability involving the *multinomial distribution* of Chapter 6.

SIMPLE FORMULAS FOR COMPUTING χ^2

Simple formulas for computing χ^2 that involve only the observed frequencies can be derived. The following gives the results for 2×2 and 2×3 contingency tables (see Tables 12.2 and 12.3, respectively).

2×2 Tables

$$\chi^2 = \frac{N(a_1 b_2 - a_2 b_1)^2}{(a_1 + b_1)(a_2 + b_2)(a_1 + a_2)(b_1 + b_2)} = \frac{N\Delta^2}{N_1 N_2 N_A N_B} \tag{7}$$

Table 12.2

	I	II	Total
A	a_1	a_2	N_A
B	b_1	b_2	N_B
Total	N_1	N_2	N

Table 12.3

	I	II	III	Total
A	a_1	a_2	a_3	N_A
B	b_1	b_2	b_3	N_B
Total	N_1	N_2	N_3	N

where $\Delta = a_1b_2 - a_2b_1$, $N = a_1 + a_2 + b_1 + b_2$, $N_1 = a_1 + b_1$, $N_2 = a_2 + b_2$, $N_A = a_1 + a_2$, and $N_B = b_1 + b_2$ (see Problem 12.19). With Yates' correction, this becomes

$$\chi^2\,(\text{corrected}) = \frac{N(|a_1b_2 - a_2b_1| - \frac{1}{2}N)^2}{(a_1+b_1)(a_2+b_2)(a_1+a_2)(b_1+b_2)} = \frac{N(|\Delta| - \frac{1}{2}N)^2}{N_1N_2N_AN_B} \tag{8}$$

2 × 3 Tables

$$\chi^2 = \frac{N}{N_A}\left[\frac{a_1^2}{N_1} + \frac{a_2^2}{N_2} + \frac{a_3^2}{N_3}\right] + \frac{N}{N_B}\left[\frac{b_1^2}{N_1} + \frac{b_2^2}{N_2} + \frac{b_3^2}{N_3}\right] - N \tag{9}$$

where we have used the general result valid for all contingency tables (see Problem 12.43):

$$\chi^2 = \sum \frac{o_j^2}{e_j} - N \tag{10}$$

Result (*9*) for $2 \times k$ tables where $k > 3$ can be generalized (see Problem 12.46).

COEFFICIENT OF CONTINGENCY

A measure of the degree of relationship, association, or dependence of the classifications in a contingency table is given by

$$C = \sqrt{\frac{\chi^2}{\chi^2 + N}} \tag{11}$$

which is called the *coefficient of contingency*. The larger the value of C, the greater is the degree of association. The number of rows and columns in the contingency table determines the maximum value of C, which is never greater than 1. If the number of rows and columns of a contingency table is equal to k, the maximum value of C is given by $\sqrt{(k-1)/k}$ (see Problems 12.22, 12.52, and 12.53).

CORRELATION OF ATTRIBUTES

Because classifications in a contingency table often describe characteristics of individuals or objects, they are often referred to as *attributes*, and the degree of dependence, association, or relationship is called the *correlation* of attributes. For $k \times k$ tables, we define

$$r = \sqrt{\frac{\chi^2}{N(k-1)}} \tag{12}$$

as the correlation coefficient between attributes (or classifications). This coefficient lies between 0 and 1 (see Problem 12.24). For 2×2 tables in which $k = 2$, the correlation is often called *tetrachoric correlation.*

The general problem of correlation of numerical variables is considered in Chapter 14.

ADDITIVE PROPERTY OF χ^2

Suppose that the results of repeated experiments yield sample values of χ^2 given by $\chi_1^2, \chi_2^2, \chi_3^2, \ldots$ with ν_1, ν_2, $\nu_3, \ldots$ degrees of freedom, respectively. Then the result of all these experiments can be considered equivalent to a χ^2 value given by $\chi_1^2 + \chi_2^2 + \chi_3^2 + \cdots$ with $\nu_1 + \nu_2 + \nu_3 + \cdots$ degrees of freedom (see Problem 12.25).

Solved Problems

THE CHI-SQUARE TEST

12.1 In 200 tosses of a coin, 115 heads and 85 tails were observed. Test the hypothesis that the coin is fair, using significance levels of (*a*) 0.05 and (*b*) 0.01.

SOLUTION

The observed frequencies of heads and tails are $o_1 = 115$ and $o_2 = 85$, respectively, and the expected frequencies of heads and tails (if the coin is fair) are $e_1 = 100$ and $e_2 = 100$, respectively. Thus

$$\chi^2 = \frac{(o_1 - e_1)^2}{e_1} + \frac{(o_2 - e_2)^2}{e_2} = \frac{(115 - 100)^2}{100} + \frac{(85 - 100)^2}{100} = 4.50$$

Since the number of categories, or classes (heads, tails), is $k = 2$, $\nu = k - 1 = 2 - 1 = 1$.

(*a*) The critical value $\chi^2_{.95}$ for 1 degree of freedom is 3.84. Thus, since $4.50 > 3.84$, we reject the hypothesis that the coin is fair at the 0.05 significance level.

(*b*) The critical value $\chi^2_{.99}$ for 1 degree of freedom is 6.63. Thus, since $4.50 < 6.63$, we cannot reject the hypothesis that the coin is fair at the 0.01 significance level.

We conclude that the observed results are *probably significant* and that the coin is *probably not fair.* For a comparison of this method with previous methods used, see Problem 12.3.

12.2 Work Problem 12.1 by using Yates' correction.

SOLUTION

$$\chi^2\,(\text{corrected}) = \frac{(|o_1 - e_1| - 0.5)^2}{e_1} + \frac{(|o_2 - e_2| - 0.5)^2}{e_2} = \frac{(|115 - 100| - 0.5)^2}{100} + \frac{(|85 - 100| - 0.5)^2}{100}$$

$$= \frac{(14.5)^2}{100} + \frac{(14.5)^2}{100} = 4.205$$

Since $4.205 > 3.84$ and $4.205 < 6.63$, the conclusions reached in Problem 12.1 are valid. For a comparison with previous methods, see Problem 12.3.

12.3 Work Problem 12.1 by using the normal approximation to the binomial distribution.

SOLUTION

Under the hypothesis that the coin is fair, the mean and standard deviation of the number of heads expected in 200 tosses of a coin are $\mu = Np = (200)(0.5) = 100$ and $\sigma = \sqrt{Npq} = \sqrt{(200)(0.5)(0.5)} = 7.07$, respectively.

First method

$$115 \text{ heads in standard units} = \frac{115 - 100}{7.07} = 2.12$$

Using the 0.05 significance level and a two-tailed test, we would reject the hypothesis that the coin is fair if the z score were outside the interval -1.96 to 1.96. With the 0.01 level, the corresponding interval would be -2.58 to 2.58. It follows (as in Problem 12.1) that we can reject the hypothesis at the 0.05 level but cannot reject it at the 0.01 level.

Note that the square of the above standard score, $(2.12)^2 = 4.50$, is the same as the value of χ^2 obtained in Problem 12.1. This is always the case for a chi-square test involving two categories (see Problem 12.10).

Second method

Using the correction for continuity, 115 or more heads is equivalent to 114.5 or more heads. Then 114.5 in standard units $= (114.5 - 100)/7.07 = 2.05$. This leads to the same conclusions as in the first method.

Note that the square of this standard score is $(2.05)^2 = 4.20$, agreeing with the value of χ^2 corrected for continuity by using Yates' correction of Problem 12.2. This is always the case for a chi-square test involving two categories in which Yates' correction is applied.

12.4 Table 12.4 shows the observed and expected frequencies in tossing a die 120 times. Test the hypothesis that the die is fair, using a significance level of 0.05.

Table 12.4

Die face	1	2	3	4	5	6
Observed frequency	25	17	15	23	24	16
Expected frequency	20	20	20	20	20	20

SOLUTION

$$\chi^2 = \frac{(o_1 - e_1)^2}{e_1} + \frac{(o_2 - e_2)^2}{e_2} + \frac{(o_3 - e_3)^2}{e_3} + \frac{(o_4 - e_4)^2}{e_4} + \frac{(o_5 - e_5)^2}{e_5} + \frac{(o_6 - e_6)^2}{e_6}$$

$$= \frac{(25-20)^2}{20} + \frac{(17-20)^2}{20} + \frac{(15-20)^2}{20} + \frac{(23-20)^2}{20} + \frac{(24-20)^2}{20} + \frac{(16-20)^2}{20} = 5.00$$

Since the number of categories, or classes (faces 1, 2, 3, 4, 5, and 6), is $k = 6$, $\nu = k - 1 = 6 - 1 = 5$. The critical value $\chi^2_{.95}$ for 5 degrees of freedom is 11.1. Thus, since $5.00 < 11.1$, we cannot reject the hypothesis that the die is fair.

For 5 degrees of freedom, $\chi^2_{.05} = 1.15$, so that $\chi^2 = 5.00 > 1.15$. It follows that the agreement is not so exceptionally good that we would look upon it with suspicion.

Mathcad **12.5** Table 12.5 shows the distribution of the digits 0, 1, 2, ..., 9 in a random-number table of 250 digits. Does the observed distribution differ significantly from the expected distribution?

Table 12.5

Digit	0	1	2	3	4	5	6	7	8	9
Observed frequency	17	31	29	18	14	20	35	30	20	36
Expected frequency	25	25	25	25	25	25	25	25	25	25

SOLUTION

$$\chi^2 = \frac{(17-25)^2}{25} + \frac{(31-25)^2}{25} + \frac{(29-25)^2}{25} + \frac{(18-25)^2}{25} + \cdots + \frac{(36-25)^2}{25} = 23.3$$

The critical value $\chi^2_{.99}$ for $\nu = k - 1 = 9$ degrees of freedom is 21.7, and $23.3 > 21.7$. Hence we conclude that the observed distribution differs significantly from the expected distribution at the 0.01 significance level. It follows that some suspicion is cast upon the table of random numbers.

12.6 In his experiments with peas, Gregor Mendel observed that 315 were round and yellow, 108 were round and green, 101 were wrinkled and yellow, and 32 were wrinkled and green. According to his theory of heredity, the numbers should be in the proportion 9:3:3:1. Is there any evidence to doubt his theory at the (*a*) 0.01 and (*b*) 0.05 significance levels?

SOLUTION

The total number of peas is $315+108+101+32=556$. Since the expected numbers are in the proportion 9:3:3:1 (and $9+3+3+1=16$), we would expect

$\frac{9}{16}(556)=312.75$ round and yellow $\frac{3}{16}(556)=104.25$ wrinkled and yellow

$\frac{3}{16}(556)=104.25$ round and green $\frac{1}{16}(556)=34.75$ wrinkled and green

Thus
$$\chi^2=\frac{(315-312.75)^2}{312.75}+\frac{(108-104.25)^2}{104.25}+\frac{(101-104.25)^2}{104.25}+\frac{(32-34.75)^2}{34.75}=0.470$$

Since there are four categories, $k=4$ and the number of degrees of freedom is $\nu=4-1=3$.

(*a*) For $\nu=3$, $\chi^2_{.99}=11.3$, and thus we cannot reject the theory at the 0.01 level.

(*b*) For $\nu=3$, $\chi^2_{.95}=7.81$, and thus we cannot reject the theory at the 0.05 level.

We conclude that the theory and experiment are in agreement.

Note that for 3 degrees of freedom, $\chi^2_{.05}=0.352$ and $\chi^2=0.470>0.352$. Thus, although the agreement is good, the results obtained are subject to a reasonable amount of sampling error.

12.7 An urn contains a very large number of marbles of four different colors: red, orange, yellow, and green. A sample of 12 marbles drawn at random from the urn revealed 2 red, 5 orange, 4 yellow, and 1 green marble. Test the hypothesis that the urn contains equal proportions of the differently colored marbles.

SOLUTION

Under the hypothesis that the urn contains equal proportions of the differently colored marbles, we would expect 3 of each kind in a sample of 12 marbles. Since these expected numbers are less than 5, the chi-square approximation will be in error. To avoid this, we combine categories so that the expected number in each category is at least 5.

If we wish to reject the hypothesis, we should combine categories in such a way that the evidence against the hypothesis shows up best. This is achieved in our case by considering the categories "red or green" and "orange or yellow," for which the sample revealed 3 and 9 marbles, respectively. Since the expected number in each category under the hypothesis of equal proportions is 6, we have

$$\chi^2=\frac{(3-6)^2}{6}+\frac{(9-6)^2}{6}=3$$

For $\nu=2-1=1$, $\chi^2_{.95}=3.84$. Thus we cannot reject the hypothesis at the 0.05 significance level (although we can at the 0.10 level). Conceivably the observed results could arise on the basis of chance even when equal proportions of the colors are present.

Another method

Using Yates' correction, we find

$$\chi^2=\frac{(|3-6|-0.5)^2}{6}+\frac{(|9-6|-0.5)^2}{6}=\frac{(2.5)^2}{6}+\frac{(2.5)^2}{6}=2.1$$

which leads to the same conclusion given above. This is to be expected, of course, since Yates' correction always *reduces* the value of χ^2.

It should be noted that if the χ^2 approximation is used despite the fact that the frequencies are too small, we would obtain

$$\chi^2=\frac{(2-3)^2}{3}+\frac{(5-3)^2}{3}+\frac{(4-3)^2}{3}+\frac{(1-3)^2}{3}=3.33$$

Since for $\nu = 4 - 1 = 3$, $\chi^2_{.95} = 7.81$, we would arrive at the same conclusions as above. Unfortunately, the χ^2 approximation for small frequencies is poor; hence, when it is not advisable to combine frequencies, we must resort to the exact probability methods of Chapter 6.

12.8 In 360 tosses of a pair of dice, 74 sevens and 24 elevens are observed. Using the 0.05 significance level, test the hypothesis that the dice are fair.

SOLUTION

A pair of dice can fall in 36 ways. A seven can occur in 6 ways, an eleven in 2 ways. Then $\Pr\{\text{seven}\} = \frac{6}{36} = \frac{1}{6}$ and $\Pr\{\text{eleven}\} = \frac{2}{36} = \frac{1}{18}$. Thus in 360 tosses we would expect $\frac{1}{6}(360) = 60$ sevens and $\frac{1}{18}(360) = 20$ elevens, so that

$$\chi^2 = \frac{(74-60)^2}{60} + \frac{(24-20)^2}{20} = 4.07$$

For $\nu = 2 - 1 = 1$, $\chi^2_{.95} = 3.84$. Thus, since $4.07 > 3.84$, we would be inclined to reject the hypothesis that the dice are fair. Using Yates' correction, however, we find

$$\chi^2\,(\text{corrected}) = \frac{(|74-60|-0.5)^2}{60} + \frac{(|24-20|-0.5)^2}{20} = \frac{(13.5)^2}{60} + \frac{(3.5)^2}{20} = 3.65$$

Thus on the basis of the corrected χ^2 we could not reject the hypothesis at the 0.05 level.

In general, for large samples such as we have here, results using Yates' correction prove to be more reliable than uncorrected results. However, since even the corrected value of χ^2 lies so close to the critical value, we are hesitant about making decisions one way or the other. In such cases it is perhaps best to increase the sample size by taking more observations if we are interested especially in the 0.05 level for some reason; otherwise, we could reject the hypothesis at some other level (such as 0.10) if this is satisfactory.

12.9 A survey of 320 families with 5 children revealed the distribution shown in Table 12.6. Is the result consistent with the hypothesis that male and female births are equally probable?

Table 12.6

Number of boys and girls	5 boys 0 girls	4 boys 1 girl	3 boys 2 girls	2 boys 3 girls	1 boy 4 girls	0 boys 5 girls	Total
Number of families	18	56	110	88	40	8	320

SOLUTION

Let p = probability of a male birth, and let $q = 1 - p$ = probability of a female birth. Then the probabilities of (5 boys), (4 boys and 1 girl), ..., (5 girls) are given by the terms in the binomial expansion

$$(p+q)^5 = p^5 + 5p^4q + 10p^3q^2 + 10p^2q^3 + 5pq^4 + q^5$$

If $p = q = \frac{1}{2}$, we have

$\Pr\{5 \text{ boys and } 0 \text{ girls}\} = (\frac{1}{2})^5 = \frac{1}{32}$ $\Pr\{2 \text{ boys and } 3 \text{ girls}\} = 10(\frac{1}{2})^2(\frac{1}{2})^3 = \frac{10}{32}$

$\Pr\{4 \text{ boys and } 1 \text{ girl}\} = 5(\frac{1}{2})^4(\frac{1}{2}) = \frac{5}{32}$ $\Pr\{1 \text{ boy and } 4 \text{ girls}\} = 5(\frac{1}{2})(\frac{1}{2})^4 = \frac{5}{32}$

$\Pr\{3 \text{ boys and } 2 \text{ girls}\} = 10(\frac{1}{2})^3(\frac{1}{2})^2 = \frac{10}{32}$ $\Pr\{0 \text{ boys and } 5 \text{ girls}\} = (\frac{1}{2})^5 = \frac{1}{32}$

Then the expected number of families with 5, 4, 3, 2, 1, and 0 boys are obtained by multiplying the above probabilities by 320, and the results are 10, 50, 100, 100, 50, and 10, respectively. Hence

$$\chi^2 = \frac{(18-10)^2}{10} + \frac{(56-50)^2}{50} + \frac{(110-100)^2}{100} + \frac{(88-100)^2}{100} + \frac{(40-50)^2}{50} + \frac{(8-10)^2}{10} = 12.0$$

Since $\chi^2_{.95} = 11.1$ and $\chi^2_{.99} = 15.1$ for $\nu = 6 - 1 = 5$ degrees of freedom, we can reject the hypothesis at the 0.05 but not at the 0.01 significance level. Thus we conclude that the results are probably significant and male and female births are not equally probable.

12.10 Show that a chi-square test involving only two categories is equivalent to the significance test for proportions (i.e., test 2) on page 209.

SOLUTION

If P is the sample proportion for category I, if p is the population proportion, and if N is the total frequency, we can describe the situation by means of Table 12.7. Then, by definition,

$$\chi^2 = \frac{(NP - Np)^2}{Np} + \frac{[N(1-P) - N(1-p)]^2}{Nq} = \frac{N^2(P-p)^2}{Np} + \frac{N^2(P-p)^2}{Nq}$$

$$= N(P-p)^2\left(\frac{1}{p} + \frac{1}{q}\right) = \frac{N(P-p)^2}{pq} = \frac{(P-p)^2}{pq/N}$$

which is the square of the z statistic on page 209.

Table 12.7

	I	II	Total
Observed frequency	NP	$N(1-P)$	N
Expected frequency	Np	$N(1-p) = Nq$	N

12.11 (*a*) Prove that formula (*1*) of this chapter can be written

$$\chi^2 = \sum \frac{o_j^2}{e_j} - N$$

(*b*) Use the result of part (*a*) to verify the value of χ^2 computed in Problem 12.6.

SOLUTION

(*a*) By definition,

$$\chi^2 = \sum \frac{(o_j - e_j)^2}{e_j} = \sum \left(\frac{o_j^2 - 2o_j e_j + e_j^2}{e_j}\right)$$

$$= \sum \frac{o_j^2}{e_j} - 2\sum o_j + \sum e_j = \sum \frac{o_j^2}{e_j} - 2N + N = \sum \frac{o_j^2}{e_j} - N$$

where formula (*2*) of this chapter has been used.

(*b*)
$$\chi^2 = \sum \frac{o_j^2}{e_j} - N = \frac{(315)^2}{312.75} + \frac{(108)^2}{104.25} + \frac{(101)^2}{104.25} + \frac{(32)^2}{34.75} - 556 = 0.470$$

GOODNESS OF FIT

12.12 Use the chi-square test to determine the goodness of fit of the data in Table 7.4 of Problem 7.31.

SOLUTION

$$\chi^2 = \frac{(38 - 33.2)^2}{33.2} + \frac{(144 - 161.9)^2}{161.9} + \frac{(342 - 316.2)^2}{316.2} + \frac{(287 - 308.7)^2}{308.7} + \frac{(164 - 150.7)^2}{150.7} + \frac{(25 - 29.4)^2}{29.4}$$

$$= 7.54$$

Since the number of parameters used in estimating the expected frequencies is $m = 1$ (namely, the parameter p of the binomial distribution), $\nu = k - 1 - m = 6 - 1 - 1 = 4$.

For $\nu = 4$, $\chi^2_{.95} = 9.49$. Thus the fit of the data is good.

For $\nu = 4$, $\chi^2_{.05} = 0.711$. Thus, since $\chi^2 = 7.54 > 0.711$, the fit is not so good as to be unbelievable.

Mathcad **12.13** Determine the goodness of fit of the data in Table 7.6 of Problem 7.33.

SOLUTION

$$\chi^2 = \frac{(5-4.13)^2}{4.13} + \frac{(18-20.68)^2}{20.68} + \frac{(42-38.92)^2}{38.92} + \frac{(27-27.71)^2}{27.71} + \frac{(8-7.43)^2}{7.43} = 0.959$$

Since the number of parameters used in estimating the expected frequencies is $m = 2$ (namely, the mean μ and standard deviation σ of the normal distribution), $\nu = k - 1 - m = 5 - 1 - 2 = 2$.

For $\nu = 2$, $\chi^2_{.95} = 5.99$. Thus we conclude that the fit of the data is very good.

For $\nu = 2$, $\chi^2_{.05} = 0.103$. Thus, since $\chi^2 = 0.959 > 0.103$, the fit is not "too good."

CONTINGENCY TABLES

Mathcad **12.14** Work Problem 10.20 by using the chi-square test.

SOLUTION

The conditions of the problem are presented in Table 12.8(*a*), Under the null hypothesis H_0 that the serum has no effect, we would expect 70 people in each of the groups to recover and 30 in each group not to recover, as shown in Table 12.8(*b*). Note that H_0 is equivalent to the statement that recovery is *independent* of the use of the serum (i.e., the classifications are independent).

Table 12.8(*a*) Frequencies Observed

	Recover	Do Not Recover	Total
Group A (using serum)	75	25	100
Group B (not using serum)	65	35	100
Total	140	60	200

Table 12.8(*b*) Frequencies Expected under H_0

	Recover	Do Not Recover	Total
Group A (using serum)	70	30	100
Group B (not using serum)	70	30	100
Total	140	60	200

$$\chi^2 = \frac{(75-70)^2}{70} + \frac{(65-70)^2}{70} + \frac{(25-30)^2}{30} + \frac{(35-30)^2}{30} = 2.38$$

To determine the number of degrees of freedom, consider Table 12.9, which is the same as Table 12.8 except that only the totals are shown. It is clear that we have the freedom of placing only one number in any of the four empty cells, since once this is done the numbers in the remaining cells are uniquely determined from the indicated totals. Thus there is 1 degree of freedom.

Table 12.9

	Recover	Do Not Recover	Total
Group A			100
Group B			100
Total	140	60	200

Another method

By formula (see Problem 12.18), $\nu = (h-1)(k-1) = (2-1)(2-1) = 1$. Since $\chi^2_{.95} = 3.84$ for 1 degree of freedom and since $\chi^2 = 2.38 < 3.84$, we conclude that the results are *not significant* at the 0.05 level. We are thus unable to reject H_0 at this level, and we either conclude that the serum is not effective or withhold decision, pending further tests.

Note that $\chi^2 = 2.38$ is the square of the z score, $z = 1.54$, obtained in Problem 10.20. In general the chi-square test involving sample proportions in a 2×2 contingency table is equivalent to a test of significance of differences in proportions using the normal approximation, as on page 210. (See Problem 12.20.)

Note also that a one-tailed test using χ^2 is equivalent to a two-tailed test using χ since, for example, $\chi^2 > \chi^2_{.95}$ corresponds to $\chi > \chi_{.95}$ or $\chi < -\chi_{.95}$. Since for 2×2 tables χ^2 is the square of the z score, it follows that χ is the same as z for this case. Thus a rejection of a hypothesis at the 0.05 level using χ^2 is equivalent to a rejection in a two-tailed test at the 0.10 level using z.

12.15 Work Problem 12.14 by using Yates' correction.

SOLUTION

$$\chi^2\,(\text{corrected}) = \frac{(|75-70|-0.5)^2}{70} + \frac{(|65-70|-0.5)^2}{70} + \frac{(|25-30|-0.5)^2}{30} + \frac{(|35-30|-0.5)^2}{30} = 1.93$$

Thus the conclusions reached in Problem 12.14 are valid. This could have been realized at once by noting that Yates' correction always decreases the value of χ^2.

12.16 Table 12.10 shows the numbers of students passed and failed by three instructors: Mr. X, Mr. Y, and Mr. Z. Test the hypothesis that the proportions of students failed by the three instructors are equal.

Table 12.10 Frequencies Observed

	Mr. X	Mr. Y	Mr. Z	Total
Passed	50	47	56	153
Failed	5	14	8	27
Total	55	61	64	180

SOLUTION

Under the hypothesis H_0 that the proportions of students failed by the three instructors are the same, they would have failed $27/180 = 15\%$ of the students and thus passed 85% of the students. In this case Mr. X, for example, would have failed 15% of 55 students and passed 85% of 55 students. The frequencies expected under H_0 are shown in Table 12.11. We thus have

$$\chi^2 = \frac{(50-46.75)^2}{46.75} + \frac{(47-51.85)^2}{51.85} + \frac{(56-54.40)^2}{54.40} + \frac{(5-8.25)^2}{8.25} + \frac{(14-9.15)^2}{9.15} + \frac{(8-9.60)^2}{9.60} = 4.84$$

To determine the number of degrees of freedom, consider Table 12.12, which is the same as Tables 12.10 and 12.11 except that only the totals are shown. It is clear that we have the freedom of placing only one number into an empty cell of the first column and one number into an empty cell of the second or third column, after which all numbers in the remaining cells will be uniquely determined from the indicated totals. Thus there are 2 degrees of freedom in this case.

Table 12.11 Frequencies Expected under H_0

	Mr. X	Mr. Y	Mr. Z	Total
Passed	88% of 55 = 46.75	85% of 61 = 51.85	85% of 64 = 54.40	153
Failed	15% of 55 = 8.25	15% of 61 = 9.15	15% of 64 = 9.60	27
Total	55	61	64	180

Table 12.12

	Mr. X	Mr. Y	Mr. Z	Total
Passed				153
Failed				27
Total	55	61	64	180

Another method

By formula, $\nu = (h-1)(k-1) = (2-1)(3-1) = 2$. Since $\chi^2_{.95} = 5.99$, we cannot reject H_0 at the 0.05 level. Note, however, that since $\chi^2_{.90} = 4.61$, we can reject H_0 at the 0.10 level if we are willing to take the risk of 1 chance in 10 of being wrong.

12.17 Use formula (*9*) of this chapter to compute the value of χ^2 for Problem 12.16.

SOLUTION

We have $a_1 = 50$, $a_2 = 47$, $a_3 = 56$, $b_1 = 5$, $b_2 = 14$, $b_3 = 8$, $N_A = a_1 + a_2 + a_3 = 153$, $N_B = b_1 + b_2 + b_3 = 27$, $N_1 = a_1 + b_1 = 55$, $N_2 = a_2 + b_2 = 61$, $N_3 = a_3 + b_3 = 64$, and $N = N_A + N_B = N_1 + N_2 + N_3 = 180$. Thus

$$\chi^2 = \frac{N}{N_A}\left[\frac{a_1^2}{N_1} + \frac{a_2^2}{N_2} + \frac{a_3^2}{N_3}\right] + \frac{N}{N_B}\left[\frac{b_1^2}{N_1} + \frac{b_2^2}{N_2} + \frac{b_3^2}{N_3}\right] - N$$

$$= \frac{180}{153}\left[\frac{(50)^2}{55} + \frac{(47)^2}{61} + \frac{(56)^2}{64}\right] + \frac{180}{27}\left[\frac{(5)^2}{55} + \frac{(14)^2}{61} + \frac{(8)^2}{64}\right] - 180 = 4.84$$

12.18 Show that for an $h \times k$ contingency table the number of degrees of freedom is $(h-1)\times(k-1)$, where $h>1$ and $k>1$.

SOLUTION

In a table with h rows and k columns, we can leave out a single number in each row and column, since such numbers can easily be restored from a knowledge of the totals of each column and row. It follows that we have the freedom of placing only $(h-1)(k-1)$ numbers into the table, the others being then automatically determined uniquely. Thus the number of degrees of freedom is $(h-1)(k-1)$. Note that this result holds if the population parameters needed in obtaining the expected frequencies are known.

12.19 (*a*) Prove that for the 2×2 contingency table shown in Table 12.13(*a*),

$$\chi^2 = \frac{N(a_1 b_2 - a_2 b_1)^2}{N_1 N_2 N_A N_B}$$

(*b*) Illustrate the result in part (*a*) with reference to the data of Problem 12.14.

Table 12.13(*a*) Results Observed

	I	II	Total
A	a_1	a_2	N_A
B	b_1	b_2	N_B
Total	N_1	N_2	N

Table 12.13(*b*) Results Expected

	I	II	Total
A	$N_1 N_A/N$	$N_2 N_A/N$	N_A
B	$N_1 N_B/N$	$N_2 N_B/N$	N_B
Total	N_1	N_2	N

SOLUTION

(*a*) As in Problem 12.14, the results expected under a null hypothesis are shown in Table 12.13(*b*). Then

$$\chi^2 = \frac{(a_1 - N_1 N_A/N)^2}{N_1 N_A/N} + \frac{(a_2 - N_2 N_A/N)^2}{N_2 N_A/N} + \frac{(b_1 - N_1 N_B/N)^2}{N_1 N_B/N} + \frac{(b_2 - N_2 N_B/N)^2}{N_2 N_B/N}$$

But
$$a_1 - \frac{N_1 N_A}{N} = a_1 - \frac{(a_1+b_1)(a_1+a_2)}{a_1+b_1+a_2+b_2} = \frac{a_1 b_2 - a_2 b_1}{N}$$

Similarly,
$$a_2 - \frac{N_2 N_A}{N} \quad \text{and} \quad b_1 - \frac{N_1 N_B}{N} \quad \text{and} \quad b_2 - \frac{N_2 N_B}{N}$$

are also equal to
$$\frac{a_1 b_2 - a_2 b_1}{N}$$

Thus we can write

$$\chi^2 = \frac{N}{N_1 N_A}\left(\frac{a_1 b_2 - a_2 b_1}{N}\right)^2 + \frac{N}{N_2 N_A}\left(\frac{a_1 b_2 - a_2 b_1}{N}\right)^2 + \frac{N}{N_1 N_B}\left(\frac{a_1 b_2 - a_2 b_1}{N}\right)^2 + \frac{N}{N_2 N_B}\left(\frac{a_1 b_2 - a_2 b_1}{N}\right)^2$$

which simplifies to
$$\chi^2 = \frac{N(a_1 b_2 - a_2 b_1)^2}{N_1 N_2 N_A N_B}$$

(*b*) In Problem 12.14, $a_1 = 75$, $a_2 = 25$, $b_1 = 65$, $b_2 = 35$, $N_1 = 140$, $N_2 = 60$, $N_A = 100$, $N_B = 100$, and $N = 200$; then, as obtained before,

$$\chi^2 = \frac{200[(75)(35) - (25)(65)]^2}{(140)(60)(100)(100)} = 2.38$$

Using Yates' correction, the result is the same as in Problem 12.15:

$$\chi^2\,(\text{corrected}) = \frac{N(|a_1b_2 - a_2b_1| - \frac{1}{2}N)^2}{N_1N_2N_AN_B} = \frac{200[|(75)(35)-(25)(65)| - 100]^2}{(140)(60)(100)(100)} = 1.93$$

12.20 Show that a chi-square test involving two sample proportions is equivalent to a significance test of differences in proportions using the normal approximation (see page 210).

SOLUTION

Let P_1 and P_2 denote the two sample proportions, and let p denote the population proportion. With reference to Problem 12.19, we have

$$P_1 = \frac{a_1}{N_1} \qquad P_2 = \frac{a_2}{N_2} \qquad 1 - P_1 = \frac{b_1}{N_1} \qquad 1 - P_2 = \frac{b_2}{N_2} \tag{13}$$

and
$$p = \frac{N_A}{N} \qquad 1 - p = q = \frac{N_B}{N} \tag{14}$$

Thus
$$a_1 = N_1P_1 \qquad a_2 = N_2P_2 \qquad b_1 = N_1(1-P_1) \qquad b_2 = N_2(1-P_2) \tag{15}$$

and
$$N_A = Np \qquad N_B = Nq \tag{16}$$

Using equations (*15*) and (*16*), from Problem 12.19 we have

$$\chi^2 = \frac{N(a_1b_2 - a_2b_1)^2}{N_1N_2N_AN_B} = \frac{N[N_1P_1N_2(1-P_2) - N_2P_2N_1(1-P_1)]^2}{N_1N_2NpNq}$$

$$= \frac{N_1N_2(P_1-P_2)^2}{Npq} = \frac{(P_1-P_2)^2}{pq(1/N_1 + 1/N_2)} \qquad (\text{since } N = N_1 + N_2)$$

which is the square of the z statistic given on page 210.

COEFFICIENT OF CONTINGENCY

12.21 Find the coefficient of contingency for the data in the contingency table of Problem 12.14.

SOLUTION

$$C = \sqrt{\frac{\chi^2}{\chi^2 + N}} = \sqrt{\frac{2.38}{2.38 + 200}} = \sqrt{0.01176} = 0.1084$$

12.22 Find the maximum value of C for the 2×2 table of Problem 12.14.

SOLUTION

The maximum value of C occurs when the two classifications are perfectly dependent or associated. In such case all those who take the serum will recover, and all those who do not take the serum will not recover. The contingency table then appears as in Table 12.14.

Table 12.14

	Recover	Do Not Recover	Total
Group A (using serum)	100	0	100
Group B (not using serum)	0	100	100
Total	100	100	200

Since the expected cell frequencies, assuming complete independence, are all equal to 50,

$$\chi^2 = \frac{(100-50)^2}{50} + \frac{(0-50)^2}{50} + \frac{(0-50)^2}{50} + \frac{(100-50)^2}{50} = 200$$

Thus the maximum value of C is $\sqrt{\chi^2/(\chi^2+N)} = \sqrt{200/(200+200)} = 0.7071$.

In general, for perfect dependence in a contingency table where the number of rows and columns are both equal to k, the only nonzero cell frequencies occur in the diagonal from upper left to lower right of the contingency table. For such cases, $C_{\max} = \sqrt{(k-1)/k}$. (See Problems 12.52 and 12.53.)

CORRELATION OF ATTRIBUTES

12.23 For Table 12.8 of Problem 12.14, find the correlation coefficient (*a*) without and (*b*) with Yates' correction.

SOLUTION

(*a*) Since $\chi^2 = 2.38$, $N = 200$, and $k = 2$, we have

$$r = \sqrt{\frac{\chi^2}{N(k-1)}} = \sqrt{\frac{2.38}{200}} = 0.1091$$

indicating very little correlation between recovery and the use of the serum.

(*b*) From Problem 12.15, r (corrected) $= \sqrt{1.93/200} = 0.0982$.

12.24 Prove that the correlation coefficient for contingency tables, as defined by equation (*12*) of this chapter, lies between 0 and 1.

SOLUTION

By Problem 12.53, the maximum value of $\sqrt{\chi^2/(\chi^2+N)}$ is $\sqrt{(k-1)/k}$. Thus

$$\frac{\chi^2}{\chi^2+N} \le \frac{k-1}{k} \qquad k\chi^2 \le (k-1)(\chi^2+N) \qquad k\chi^2 \le k\chi^2 - \chi^2 + kN - N$$

$$\chi^2 \le (k-1)N \qquad \frac{\chi^2}{N(k-1)} \le 1 \qquad \text{and} \qquad r = \sqrt{\frac{\chi^2}{N(k-1)}} \le 1$$

Since $\chi^2 \ge 0$, $r \ge 0$. Thus $0 \le r \le 1$, as required.

ADDITIVE PROPERTY OF χ^2

12.25 To test a hypothesis H_0, an experiment is performed three times. The resulting values of χ^2 are 2.37, 2.86, and 3.54, each of which corresponds to 1 degree of freedom. Show that while H_0 cannot be rejected at the 0.05 level on the basis of any individual experiment, it can be rejected when the three experiments are combined.

SOLUTION

The value of χ^2 obtained by combining the results of the three experiments is, according to the *additive property*, $\chi^2 = 2.37 + 2.86 + 3.54 = 8.77$ with $1+1+1=3$ degrees of freedom. Since $\chi^2_{.95}$ for 3 degrees of freedom is 7.81, we can reject H_0 at the 0.05 significance level. But since $\chi^2_{.95} = 3.84$ for 1 degree of freedom, we cannot reject H_0 on the basis of any one experiment.

In combining experiments in which values of χ^2 corresponding to 1 degree of freedom are obtained, Yates' correction is omitted since it has a tendency to overcorrect.

Supplementary Problems

THE CHI-SQUARE TEST

12.26 In 60 tosses of a coin, 37 heads and 23 tails were observed. Using significance levels of (*a*) 0.05 and (*b*) 0.01, test the hypothesis that the coin is fair.

12.27 Work Problem 12.26 by using Yates' correction.

12.28 Over a long period of time the grades given by a group of instructors in a particular course have averaged 12% A's, 18% B's, 40% C's, 18% D's, and 12% F's. A new instructor gives 22 A's, 34 B's, 66 C's, 16 D's, and 12 F's during two semesters. Determine at the 0.05 significance level whether the new instructor is following the grade pattern set by the others.

12.29 Three coins were tossed a total of 240 times, and each time the number of heads turning up was observed. The results are shown in Table 12.15, together with the results expected under the hypothesis that the coins are fair. Test this hypothesis at a significance level of 0.05.

Table 12.15

	0 Heads	1 Head	2 Heads	3 Heads
Observed frequency	24	108	95	23
Expected frequency	30	90	90	30

12.30 The number of books borrowed from a public library during a particular week is given in Table 12.16. Test the hypothesis that the number of books borrowed does not depend on the day of the week, using significance levels of (*a*) 0.05 and (*b*) 0.01.

Table 12.16

	Mon	Tue	Wed	Thu	Fri
Number of books borrowed	135	108	120	114	146

12.31 An urn contains 6 red marbles and 3 white ones. Two marbles are selected at random from the urn, their colors are noted, and then the marbles are replaced in the urn. This process is performed a total of 120 times, and the results obtained are shown in Table 12.17.

(*a*) Determine the expected frequencies.

(*b*) Determine at a significance level of 0.05 whether the results obtained are consistent with those expected.

Table 12.17

	0 Red 2 White	1 Red 1 White	2 Red 0 White
Number of drawings	6	53	61

12.32 Two hundred bolts were selected at random from the production of each of four machines. The numbers of defective bolts found were 2, 9, 10, and 3. Determine whether there is a significant difference between the machines, using a significance level of 0.05.

GOODNESS OF FIT

12.33 (*a*) Use the chi-square test to determine the goodness of fit of the data in Table 7.9 of Problem 7.75. (*b*) Is the fit "too good"? Use the 0.05 significance level.

12.34 Use the chi-square test to determine the goodness of fit of the data in (*a*) Table 3.8 of Problem 3.59 and (*b*) Table 3.10 of Problem 3.61. Use a significance level of 0.05, and in each case determine whether the fit is "too good."

12.35 Use the chi-square test to determine the goodness of fit of the data in (*a*) Table 7.9 of Problem 7.79 and (*b*) Table 7.10 of Problem 7.80. Is your result in part (*a*) consistent with that of Problem 12.33?

CONTINGENCY TABLES

12.36 Table 12.18 shows the result of an experiment to investigate the effect of vaccination of laboratory animals against a particular disease. Using the (*a*) 0.01 and (*b*) 0.05 significance levels, test the hypothesis that there is no difference between the vaccinated and unvaccinated groups (i.e., that vaccination and this disease are independent).

Table 12.18

	Got Disease	Did Not Get Disease
Vaccinated	9	42
Not vaccinated	17	28

Table 12.19

	Passed	Failed
Class *A*	72	17
Class *B*	64	23

12.37 Work Problem 12.36 using Yates' correction.

12.38 Table 12.19 shows the numbers of students in each of two classes, *A* and *B*, who passed and failed an examination given to both groups. Using the (*a*) 0.05 and (*b*) 0.01 significance levels, test the hypothesis that there is no difference between the two classes. Work the problem with and without Yates' correction.

12.39 Of a group of patients who complained that they did not sleep well, some were given sleeping pills while others were given sugar pills (although they all *thought* they were getting sleeping pills). They were later asked whether the pills helped them or not. The results of their responses are shown in Table 12.20. Assuming that all patients told the truth, test the hypothesis that there is no difference between sleeping pills and sugar pills at a significance level of 0.05.

Table 12.20

	Slept Well	Did Not Sleep Well
Took sleeping pills	44	10
Took sugar pills	81	35

12.40 On a particular proposal of national importance, Democrats and Republicans cast their votes as shown in Table 12.21. At significance levels of (*a*) 0.01 and (*b*) 0.05, test the hypothesis that there is no difference between the two parties insofar as this proposal is concerned.

Table 12.21

	In Favor	Opposed	Undecided
Democrats	85	78	37
Republicans	118	61	25

12.41 Table 12.22 shows the relation between the performances of students in mathematics and physics. Test the hypothesis that performance in physics is independent of performance in mathematics, using the (*a*) 0.05 and (*b*) 0.01 significance levels.

Table 12.22

		Mathematics		
		High grades	Medium grades	Low grades
Physics	High grades	56	71	12
	Medium grades	47	163	38
	Low grades	14	42	85

12.42 The results of a survey made to determine whether the age of a driver 21 years of age and older has any effect on the number of automobile accidents in which he is involved (including all minor accidents) are shown in Table 12.23. At significance levels of (*a*) 0.05 and (*b*) 0.01, test the hypothesis that the number of accidents is independent of the age of the driver. What possible sources of difficulty in sampling techniques, as well as other considerations, could affect your conclusions?

Table 12.23

		Age of Driver				
		21–30	31–40	41–50	51–60	61–70
Number of Accidents	0	748	821	786	720	672
	1	74	60	51	66	50
	2	31	25	22	16	15
	>2	9	10	6	5	7

12.43 (*a*) Prove that $\chi^2 = \sum (o_j^2/e_j) - N$ for all contingency tables, where N is the total frequency of all cells.

(*b*) Using the result in part (*a*), work Problem 12.41.

12.44 If N_i and N_j denote, respectively, the sum of the frequencies in the ith row and jth columns of a contingency table (the *marginal frequencies*), show that the expected frequency for the cell belonging to the ith row and jth column is N_iN_j/N, where N is the total frequency of all cells.

12.45 Prove formula (*9*) of this chapter. (*Hint:* Use Problems 12.43 and 12.44.)

12.46 Extend the result of formula (*9*) of this chapter to $2 \times k$ contingency tables, where $k > 3$.

12.47 Prove formula (*8*) of this chapter.

12.48 By analogy with the ideas developed for $h \times k$ contingency tables, discuss $h \times k \times l$ contingency tables, pointing out their possible applications.

COEFFICIENT OF CONTINGENCY

12.49 Table 12.24 shows the relationship between hair and eye color of a sample of 200 students.

(*a*) Find the coefficient of contingency without and with Yates' correction.

(*b*) Compare the result of part (*a*) with the maximum coefficient of contingency.

Table 12.24

		Hair Color	
		Blonde	Not blonde
Eye Color	Blue	49	25
	Not blue	30	96

12.50 Find the coefficient of contingency for the data of (*a*) Problem 12.36 and (*b*) Problem 12.38 without and with Yates' correction.

12.51 Find the coefficient of contingency for the data of Problem 12.41.

12.52 Prove that the maximum coefficient of contingency for a 3×3 table is $\sqrt{\frac{2}{3}} = 0.8165$ approximately.

12.53 Prove that the maximum coefficient of contingency for a $k \times k$ table is $\sqrt{(k-1)/k}$.

CORRELATION OF ATTRIBUTES

12.54 Find the correlation coefficient for the data in Table 12.24.

12.55 Find the correlation coefficient for the data in (*a*) Table 12.18 and (*b*) Table 12.19 without and with Yates' correction.

12.56 Find the correlation coefficient between the mathematics and physics grades in Table 12.22.

12.57 If C is the coefficient of contingency for a $k \times k$ table and r is the corresponding coefficient of correlation, prove that $r = C/\sqrt{(1-C^2)(k-1)}$.

ADDITIVE PROPERTY OF χ^2

12.58 To test a hypothesis H_0, an experiment is performed five times. The resulting values of χ^2, each corresponding to 4 degrees of freedom, are 8.3, 9.1, 8.9, 7.8, and 8.6, respectively. Show that while H_0 cannot be rejected at the 0.05 level on the basis of each experiment separately, it can be rejected at the 0.005 level on the basis of the combined experiments.

Chapter 13

Curve Fitting and the Method of Least Squares

RELATIONSHIP BETWEEN VARIABLES

Very often in practice a relationship is found to exist between two (or more) variables. For example, weights of adult males depend to some degree on their heights, the circumferences of circles depend on their radii, and the pressure of a given mass of gas depends on its temperature and volume.

It is frequently desirable to express this relationship in mathematical form by determining an equation that connects the variables.

CURVE FITTING

To determine an equation that connects variables, a first step is to collect data that show corresponding values of the variables under consideration. For example, suppose that X and Y denote, respectively, the height and weight of adult males; then a sample of N individuals would reveal the heights $X_1, X_2, \ldots, X_N$ and the corresponding weights $Y_1, Y_2, \ldots, Y_N$.

A next step is to plot the points $(X_1, Y_1), (X_2, Y_2), \ldots, (X_N, Y_N)$ on a rectangular coordinate system. The resulting set of points is sometimes called a *scatter diagram.*

From the scatter diagram it is often possible to visualize a smooth curve that approximates the data. Such a curve is called an *approximating curve.* In Fig. 13-1, for example, the data appear to be approximated well by a straight line, and so we say that a *linear relationship* exists between the variables. In Fig. 13-2, however, although a relationship exists between the variables, it is not a linear relationship, and so we call it a *nonlinear relationship.*

The general problem of finding equations of approximating curves that fit given sets of data is called *curve fitting.*

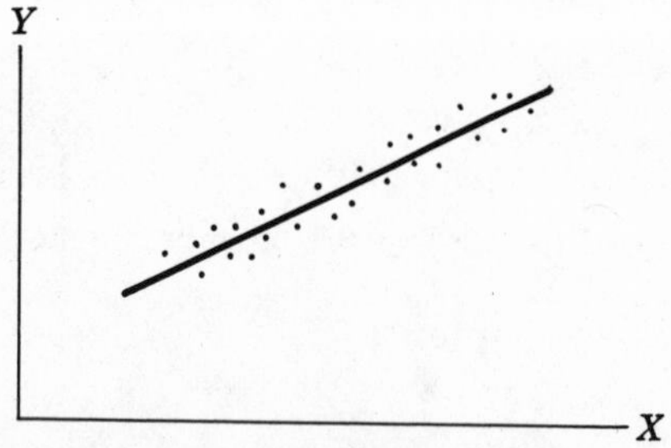

Fig. 13-1

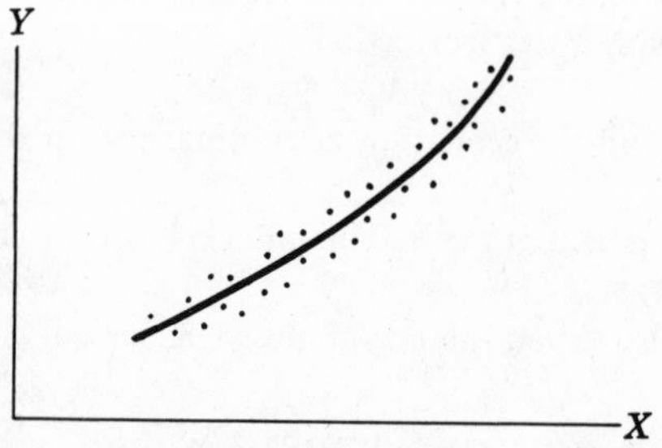

Fig. 13-2

EQUATIONS OF APPROXIMATING CURVES

Several common types of approximating curves and their equations are listed below for reference purposes. All letters other than X and Y represent constants. The variables X and Y are often referred to as *independent* and *dependent variables*, respectively, although these roles can be interchanged.

Straight line	$Y = a_0 + a_1 X$	*(1)*
Parabola, or quadratic curve	$Y = a_0 + a_1 X + a_2 X^2$	*(2)*
Cubic curve	$Y = a_0 + a_1 X + a_2 X^2 + a_3 X^3$	*(3)*
Quartic curve	$Y = a_0 + a_1 X + a_2 X^2 + a_3 X^3 + a_4 X^4$	*(4)*
nth-Degree curve	$Y = a_0 + a_1 X + a_2 X^2 + \cdots + a_n X^n$	*(5)*

The right sides of the above equations are called *polynomials* of the first, second, third, fourth, and nth degrees, respectively. The functions defined by the first four equations are sometimes called *linear, quadratic, cubic,* and *quartic* functions, respectively.

The following are some of the many other equations frequently used in practice:

Hyperbola	$Y = \dfrac{1}{a_0 + a_1 X}$ or $\dfrac{1}{Y} = a_0 + a_1 X$	(6)
Exponential curve	$Y = ab^X$ or $\log Y = \log a + (\log b)X = a_0 + a_1 X$	(7)
Geometric curve	$Y = aX^b$ or $\log Y = \log a + b(\log X)$	(8)
Modified exponential curve	$Y = ab^X + g$	(9)
Modified geometric curve	$Y = aX^b + g$	(10)
Gompertz curve	$Y = pq^{b^X}$ or $\log Y = \log p + b^X(\log q) = ab^X + g$	(11)
Modified Gompertz curve	$Y = pq^{b^X} + h$	(12)
Logistic curve	$Y = \dfrac{1}{ab^X + g}$ or $\dfrac{1}{Y} = ab^X + g$	(13)
	$Y = a_0 + a_1(\log X) + a_2(\log X)^2$	(14)

To decide which curve should be used, it is helpful to obtain scatter diagrams of transformed variables. For example, if a scatter diagram of $\log Y$ versus X shows a linear relationship, the equation has the form (7), while if $\log Y$ versus $\log X$ shows a linear relationship, the equation has the form (8). Special graph paper is often used in order to make it easy to decide which curve to use. Graph paper having one scale calibrated logarithmically is called *semilogarithmic* (or *semilog*) *graph paper,* and that having both scales calibrated logarithmically is called *log-log graph paper.*

FREEHAND METHOD OF CURVE FITTING

Individual judgment can often be used to draw an approximating curve to fit a set of data. This is called a *freehand method of curve fitting.* If the type of equation of this curve is known, it is possible to obtain the constants in the equation by choosing as many points on the curve as there are constants in the equation. For example, if the curve is a straight line, two points are necessary; if it is a parabola, three points are necessary. The method has the disadvantage that different observers will obtain different curves and equations.

THE STRAIGHT LINE

The simplest type of approximating curve is a straight line, whose equation can be written

$$Y = a_0 + a_1 X \tag{15}$$

Given any two points (X_1, Y_1) and (X_2, Y_2) on the line, the constants a_0 and a_1 can be determined. The resulting equation of the line can be written

$$Y - Y_1 = \left(\frac{Y_2 - Y_1}{X_2 - X_1}\right)(X - X_1) \quad \text{or} \quad Y - Y_1 = m(X - X_1) \tag{16}$$

where

$$m = \frac{Y_2 - Y_1}{X_2 - X_1}$$

is called the *slope* of the line and represents the change in Y divided by the corresponding change in X.

When the equation is written in the form (15), the constant a_1 is the slope m. The constant a_0, which is the value of Y when $X = 0$, is called the *Y intercept.*

THE METHOD OF LEAST SQUARES

To avoid individual judgment in constructing lines, parabolas, or other approximating curves to fit sets of data, it is necessary to agree on a definition of a "best-fitting line," "best-fitting parabola," etc.

By way of forming a definition, consider Fig. 13-3, in which the data points are given by $(X_1, Y_1), (X_2, Y_2), \ldots, (X_N, Y_N)$. For a given value of X, say X_1, there will be a difference between the value Y_1 and the corresponding value as determined from the curve C. As shown in the figure, we denote this difference by D_1, which is sometimes referred to as a *deviation*, *error*, or *residual* and may be positive, negative, or zero. Similarly, corresponding to the values $X_2, \ldots, X_N$ we obtain the deviations $D_2, \ldots, D_N$.

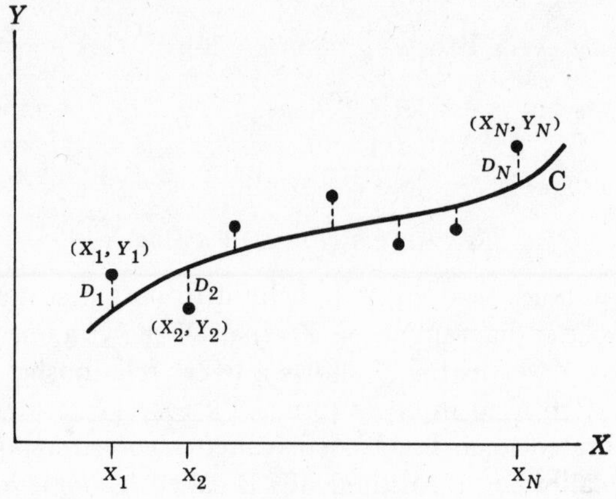

Fig. 13-3

A measure of the "goodness of fit" of the curve C to the given data is provided by the quantity $D_1^2 + D_2^2 + \cdots + D_N^2$. If this is small, the fit is good; if it is large, the fit is bad. We therefore make the following

> **Definition:** Of all curves approximating a given set of data points, the curve having the property that $D_1^2 + D_2^2 + \cdots + D_N^2$ is a minimum is called a *best-fitting curve.*

A curve having this property is said to fit the data in the *least-squares sense* and is called a *least-squares curve.* Thus a line having this property is called a *least-squares line*, a parabola with this property is called a *least-squares parabola*, etc.

It is customary to employ the above definition when X is the independent variable and Y is the dependent variable. If X is the dependent variable, the definition is modified by considering horizontal instead of vertical deviations, which amounts to an interchange of the X and Y axes. These two definitions generally lead to different least-squares curves. Unless otherwise specified, we shall consider Y the dependent variable and X the independent variable.

It is possible to define another least-squares curve by considering perpendicular distances from each of the data points to the curve instead of either vertical or horizontal distances. However, this is not used very often.

THE LEAST-SQUARES LINE

The least-squares line approximating the set of points $(X_1, Y_1), (X_2, Y_2), \ldots, (X_N, Y_N)$ has the equation

$$Y = a_0 + a_1 X \tag{17}$$

where the constants a_0 and a_1 are determined by solving simultaneously the equations

$$\begin{aligned} \sum Y &= a_0 N + a_1 \sum X \\ \sum XY &= a_0 \sum X + a_1 \sum X^2 \end{aligned} \tag{18}$$

which are called the *normal equations for the least-squares line* (*17*). The constants a_0 and a_1 of equations (*18*) can, if desired, be found from the formulas

$$a_0 = \frac{(\sum Y)(\sum X^2) - (\sum X)(\sum XY)}{N \sum X^2 - (\sum X)^2} \qquad a_1 = \frac{N \sum XY - (\sum X)(\sum Y)}{N \sum X^2 - (\sum X)^2} \tag{19}$$

The normal equations (*18*) are easily remembered by observing that the first equation can be obtained formally summing on both sides of (*17*) [i.e., $\sum Y = \sum (a_0 + a_1 X) = a_0 N + a_1 \sum X$], while the second equation is obtained formally by first multiplying both sides of (*17*) by X and then summing [i.e., $\sum XY = \sum X(a_0 + a_1 X) = a_0 \sum X + a_1 \sum X^2$]. Note that this is not a derivation of the normal equations, but simply a means for remembering them. Note also that in equations (*18*) and (*19*) we have used the short notation $\sum X, \sum XY$, etc., in place of $\sum_{j=1}^N X_j$, $\sum_{j=1}^N X_j Y_j$, etc.

The labor involved in finding a least-squares line can sometimes be shortened by transforming the data so that $x = X - \bar{X}$ and $y = Y - \bar{Y}$. The equation of the least-squares line can then be written (see Problem 13.15)

$$y = \left(\frac{\sum xy}{\sum x^2}\right) x \qquad \text{or} \qquad y = \left(\frac{\sum xY}{\sum x^2}\right) x \tag{20}$$

In particular, if X is such that $\sum X = 0$ (i.e., $\bar{X} = 0$), this becomes

$$Y = \bar{Y} + \left(\frac{\sum XY}{\sum X^2}\right) X \tag{21}$$

Equation (20) implies that $y = 0$ when $x = 0$; thus the least-squares line passes through the point $(\bar{X}, \bar{Y})$, called the *centroid*, or *center of gravity*, of the data.

If the variable X is taken to be the dependent instead of the independent variable, we write equation (*17*) as $X = b_0 + b_1 Y$. Then the above results hold if X and Y are interchanged and a_0 and a_1 are replaced by b_0 and b_1, respectively. The resulting least-squares line, however, is generally not the same as that obtained above [see Problems 13.11 and 13.15(*d*)].

NONLINEAR RELATIONSHIPS

Nonlinear relationships can sometimes be reduced to linear relationships by an appropriate transformation of the variables (see Problem 13.21).

THE LEAST-SQUARES PARABOLA

The least-squares parabola approximating the set of points $(X_1, Y_1), (X_2, Y_2), \ldots, (X_N, Y_N)$ has the equation

$$Y = a_0 + a_1 X + a_2 X^2 \tag{22}$$

where the constants a_0, a_1, and a_2 are determined by solving simultaneously the equations

$$\begin{aligned} \sum Y &= a_0 N + a_1 \sum X + a_2 \sum X^2 \\ \sum XY &= a_0 \sum X + a_1 \sum X^2 + a_2 \sum X^3 \\ \sum X^2 Y &= a_0 \sum X^2 + a_1 \sum X^3 + a_2 \sum X^4 \end{aligned} \tag{23}$$

called the *normal equations for the least-squares parabola* (*22*).

Equations (*23*) are easily remembered by observing that they can be obtained formally by multiplying equation (*22*) by 1, X, and X^2, respectively, and summing on both sides of the resulting equations. This technique can be extended to obtain normal equations for least-squares cubic curves, least-squares quartic curves, and in general any of the least-squares curves corresponding to equation (*5*).

As in the case of the least-squares line, simplifications of equations (*23*) occur if X is chosen so that $\sum X = 0$. Simplification also occurs by choosing the new variables $x = X - \bar{X}$ and $y = Y - \bar{Y}$.

REGRESSION

Often, on the basis of sample data, we wish to estimate the value of a variable Y corresponding to a given value of a variable X. This can be accomplished by estimating the value of Y from a least-squares curve that fits the sample data. The resulting curve is called a *regression curve of Y on X*, since Y is estimated from X.

If we wanted to estimate the value of X from a given value of Y, we would use a *regression curve of X on Y*, which amounts to interchanging the variables in the scatter diagram so that X is the dependent variable and Y is the independent variable. This is equivalent to replacing the vertical deviations in the definition of the least-squares curve on page 266 with horizontal deviations.

In general, the regression line or curve of Y on X is not the same as the regression line or curve of X on Y.

APPLICATIONS TO TIME SERIES

If the independent variable X is time, the data show the values of Y at various times. Data arranged according to time are called *time series*. The regression line or curve of Y on X in this case is often called a *trend line* or *trend curve* and is often used for purposes of *estimation*, *prediction*, or *forecasting*.

PROBLEMS INVOLVING MORE THAN TWO VARIABLES

Problems involving more than two variables can be treated in a manner analogous to that for two variables. For example, there may be a relationship between the three variables X, Y, and Z that can be described by the equation

$$Z = a_0 + a_1 X + a_2 Y \tag{24}$$

which is called a *linear equation in the variables X, Y, and Z*.

In a three-dimensional rectangular coordinate system this equation represents a plane, and the actual sample points $(X_1, Y_1, Z_1), (X_2, Y_2, Z_2), \ldots, (X_N, Y_N, Z_N)$ may "scatter" not too far from this plane, which we call an *approximating plane*.

By extension of the method of least squares, we can speak of a *least-squares plane* approximating the data. If we are estimating Z from given values of X and Y, this would be called a *regression plane of Z on X and Y*. The normal equations corresponding to the least-squares plane (*24*) are given by

$$\begin{aligned} \sum Z &= a_0 N + a_1 \sum X + a_2 \sum Y \\ \sum XZ &= a_0 \sum X + a_1 \sum X^2 + a_2 \sum XY \\ \sum YZ &= a_0 \sum Y + a_1 \sum XY + a_2 \sum Y^2 \end{aligned} \tag{25}$$

and can be remembered as being obtained from equation (*24*) by multiplying by 1, X, and Y successively and then summing.

More complicated equations than (*24*) can also be considered. These represent *regression surfaces*. If the number of variables exceeds three, geometric intuition is lost since we then require four-, five-, ... dimensional spaces.

Problems involving the estimation of a variable from two or more variables are called problems of *multiple regression* and will be considered in more detail in Chapter 15.

Solved Problems

STRAIGHT LINES

13.1 (*a*) Construct a straight line that approximates the data of Table 13.1.
(*b*) Find an equation for this line.

Table 13.1

X	2	3	5	7	9	10
Y	1	3	7	11	15	17

SOLUTION

(*a*) Plot the points (2, 1), (3, 3), (5, 7), (7, 11), (9, 15), and (10, 17) on a rectangular coordinate system, as shown in Fig. 13-4. It is clear from this figure that all the points lie on a straight line (shown dashed); thus a straight line fits the data *exactly*.

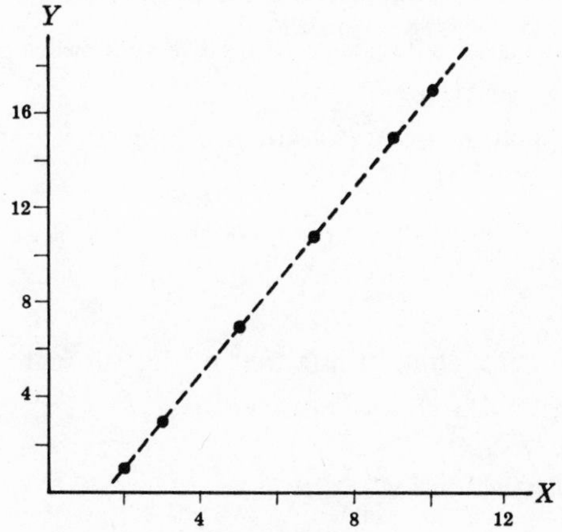

Fig. 13-4

(*b*) To determine the equation of the line given by

$$Y = a_0 + a_1 X \tag{26}$$

only two points are necessary. Choose the points (2, 1) and (3, 3), for example. For the point (2, 1), $X = 2$ and $Y = 1$; substituting these values into equation (*26*) yields

$$1 = a_0 + 2a_1 \tag{27}$$

Similarly, for the point (3, 3), $X = 3$ and $Y = 3$; substituting these values into equation (*26*) yields

$$3 = a_0 + 3a_1 \tag{28}$$

Solving equations (*27*) and (*28*) simultaneously, $a_0 = -3$ and $a_1 = 2$, and the required equation is

$$Y = -3 + 2X \qquad \text{or} \qquad Y = 2X - 3$$

As a check, we can show that the points (5, 7), (7, 11), (9, 15), and (10, 17) also lie on the line.

13.2 In Problem 13.1, find (*a*) Y when $X = 4$, (*b*) Y when $X = 15$, (*c*) Y when $X = 0$, (*d*) X when $Y = 7.5$, (*e*) X when $Y = 0$, and (*f*) the increase in Y corresponding to a unit increase in X.

SOLUTION

We assume that the same law of relationship, $Y = 2X - 3$, holds for values of X and Y other than those specified in Table 13.1.

(*a*) If $X = 4$, $Y = 2(4) - 3 = 8 - 3 = 5$. Since we are finding the value of Y corresponding to a value of X included *between* two given values of X, this process is often called *linear interpolation.*

(*b*) If $X = 15$, $Y = 2(15) - 3 = 30 - 3 = 27$. Since we are finding the value of Y corresponding to a value of X *outside* of, or *exterior* to, the given values of X, this process is often called *linear extrapolation.*

(*c*) If $X = 0$, $Y = 2(0) - 3 = 0 - 3 = -3$. The value of Y when $X = 0$ is called the *Y intercept.* It is the value of Y at the point where the line (extended if necessary) intersects the Y axis.

(*d*) If $Y = 7.5$, $7.5 = 2X - 3$; then $2X = 7.5 + 3 = 10.5$ and $X = 10.5/2 = 5.25$.

(*e*) If $Y = 0$, $0 = 2X - 3$; then $2X = 3$ and $X = 1.5$. The value of X when $Y = 0$ is called the *X intercept.* It is the value of X at the point where the line (extended if necessary) intersects the X axis.

(*f*) If X increases 1 unit from 2 to 3, Y increases from 1 to 3, a change of 2 units. If X increases from 2 to 10, or $(10 - 2) = 8$ units, then Y increases from 1 to 17, or $(17 - 1) = 16$ units; that is, a 16-unit increase in Y corresponds to an 8-unit increase in X, or Y increases 2 units for every unit increase in X.

In general, if ΔY denotes the change in Y due to a change in X of ΔX, then the change in Y per unit change in X is given by $\Delta Y/\Delta X = 2$. This is called the *slope* of the line and is always equal to a_1 in the equation $Y = a_0 + a_1X$. The constant a_0 is the *Y intercept* of the line [see part (*c*)].

The above questions can also be answered by direct reference to the graph, Fig. 13-4.

13.3 (*a*) Show that the equation of a straight line that passes through the points (X_1, Y_1) and (X_2, Y_2) is given by

$$Y - Y_1 = \frac{Y_2 - Y_1}{X_2 - X_1}(X - X_1)$$

(*b*) Find the equation of a straight line that passes through the points $(2, -3)$ and $(4, 5)$.

SOLUTION

(*a*) The equation of a straight line is

$$Y = a_0 + a_1X \tag{29}$$

Since (X_1, Y_1) lies on the line,

$$Y_1 = a_0 + a_1X_1 \tag{30}$$

Since (X_2, Y_2) lies on the line,

$$Y_2 = a_0 + a_1X_2 \tag{31}$$

Subtracting equation (*30*) from (*29*),

$$Y - Y_1 = a_1(X - X_1) \tag{32}$$

Subtracting equation (*30*) from (*31*),

$$Y_2 - Y_1 = a_1(X_2 - X_1) \qquad \text{or} \qquad a_1 = \frac{Y_2 - Y_1}{X_2 - X_1}$$

Substituting this value of a_1 into equation (*32*), we obtain

$$Y - Y_1 = \frac{Y_2 - Y_1}{X_2 - X_1}(X - X_1)$$

as required. The quantity

$$\frac{Y_2 - Y_1}{X_2 - X_1}$$

often abbreviated m, represents the change in Y divided by the corresponding change in X and is the *slope* of the line. The required equation can be written $Y - Y_1 = m(X - X_1)$.

(*b*) **First method** [using the result of part (*a*)]

Corresponding to the first point (2, −3), we have $X_1 = 2$ and $Y_1 = -3$; corresponding to the second point (4, 5), we have $X_2 = 4$ and $Y_2 = 5$. Thus the slope is

$$m = \frac{Y_2 - Y_1}{X_2 - X_1} = \frac{5-(-3)}{4-2} = \frac{8}{2} = 4$$

and the required equation is

$$Y - Y_1 = m(X - X_1) \qquad \text{or} \qquad Y-(-3) = 4(X-2)$$

which can be written $Y+3 = 4(X-2)$, or $Y = 4X - 11$.

Second method [using the method of Problem 13.1(*b*)]

The equation of a straight line is $Y = a_0 + a_1 X$. Since the point (2, −3) is on the line $-3 = a_0 + 2a_1$, and since the point (4, 5) is on the line, $5 = a_0 + 4a_1$; solving these two equations simultaneously, we obtain $a_1 = 4$ and $a_0 = -11$. Thus the required equation is

$$Y = -11 + 4X \qquad \text{or} \qquad Y = 4X - 11$$

13.4 Give a graphic interpretation of the derivation in Problem 13.3(*a*).

SOLUTION

Figure 13-5 shows the line passing through points P and Q, which have coordinates (X_1, Y_1) and (X_2, Y_2), respectively. The point R, with coordinates (X, Y), represents any other point on this line.

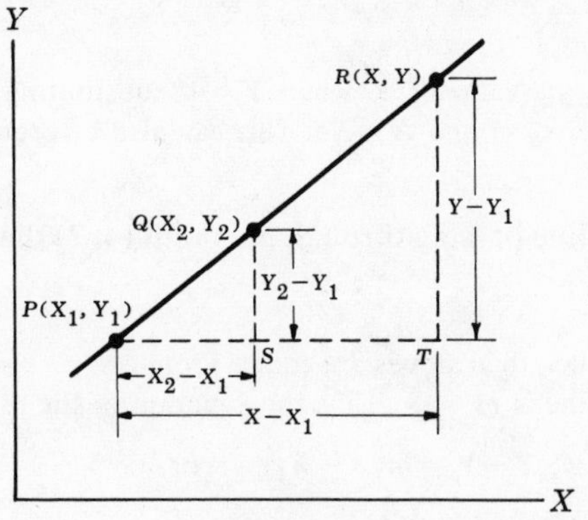

Fig. 13-5

From the similar triangles PRT and PQS

$$\frac{RT}{TP} = \frac{QS}{SP} \qquad \text{or} \qquad \frac{Y - Y_1}{X - X_1} = \frac{Y_2 - Y_1}{X_2 - X_1} \tag{33}$$

Then multiplying both sides by $X - X_1$,

$$Y - Y_1 = \frac{Y_2 - Y_1}{X_2 - X_1}(X - X_1)$$

which is the required equation of the line.

Note that each of the ratios in equation (*33*) is the slope m; this can be written $Y - Y_1 = m(X - X_1)$.

13.5 Find (*a*) the slope, (*b*) the equation, (*c*) the Y intercept, and (*d*) the X intercept of the line that passes through the points (1, 5) and (4, −1).

SOLUTION

(*a*) $(X_1 = 1, Y_1 = 5)$ and $(X_2 = 4, Y_2 = -1)$. Thus

$$m = \text{slope} = \frac{Y_2 - Y_1}{X_2 - X_1} = \frac{-1-5}{4-1} = \frac{-6}{3} = -2$$

The negative sign of the slope indicates that as X increases, Y decreases, as shown in Fig. 13-6.

(*b*) The equation of the line is

$$Y - Y_1 = m(X - X_1) \quad \text{or} \quad Y - 5 = -2(X - 1)$$

That is, $$Y - 5 = -2X + 2 \quad \text{or} \quad Y = 7 - 2X$$

This can also be obtained by the second method of Problem 13.3(*b*).

(*c*) The Y intercept, which is the value of Y when $X = 0$, is given by $Y = 7 - 2(0) = 7$. This can also be seen directly from Fig. 13.6.

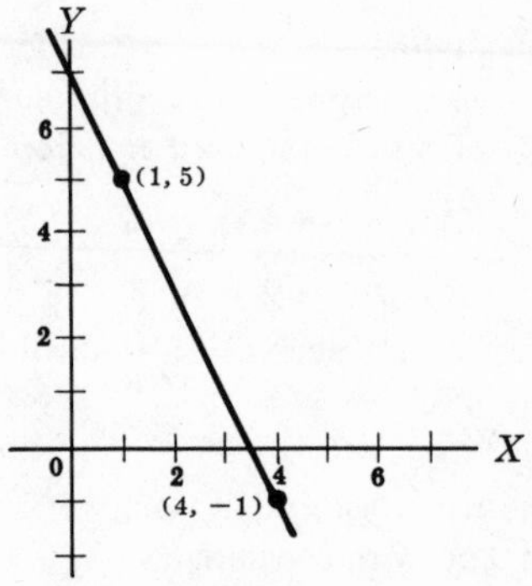

Fig. 13-6

(*d*) The X intercept is the value of X when $Y = 0$. Substituting $Y = 0$ in the equation $Y = 7 - 2X$, we have $0 = 7 - 2X$, or $2X = 7$ and $X = 3.5$. This can also be seen directly from Fig. 13-6.

13.6 Find the equation of a line passing through the point (4, 2) that is parallel to the line $2X + 3Y = 6$.

SOLUTION

If two lines are parallel, their slopes are equal. From $2X + 3Y = 6$ we have $3Y = 6 - 2X$, or $Y = 2 - \frac{2}{3}X$, so that the slope of the line is $m = -\frac{2}{3}$. Thus the equation of the required line is

$$Y - Y_1 = m(X - X_1) \quad \text{or} \quad Y - 2 = -\tfrac{2}{3}(X - 4)$$

which can also be written $2X + 3Y = 14$.

Another method

Any line parallel to $2X + 3Y = 6$ has the equation $2X + 3Y = c$. To find c, let $X = 4$ and $Y = 2$. Then $2(4) + 3(2) = c$, or $c = 14$, and the required equation is $2X + 3Y = 14$.

13.7 Find the equation of a line whose slope is −4 and whose Y intercept is 16.

SOLUTION

In the equation $Y = a_0 + a_1X$, $a_0 = 16$ is the Y intercept and $a_1 = -4$ is the slope. Thus the required equation is $Y = 16 - 4X$.

Mathcad **13.8** (*a*) Construct a straight line that approximates the data of Table 13.2.
(*b*) Find an equation for this line.

Table 13.2

X	1	3	4	6	8	9	11	14
Y	1	2	4	4	5	7	8	9

SOLUTION

(*a*) Plot the points (1, 1), (3, 2), (4, 4), (6, 4), (8, 5), (9, 7), (11, 8), and (14, 9) on a rectangular coordinate system, as shown in Fig. 13-7. A straight line approximating the data is drawn *freehand* in the figure. For a method eliminating the need for individual judgment, see Problem 13.11, which uses the method of least squares.

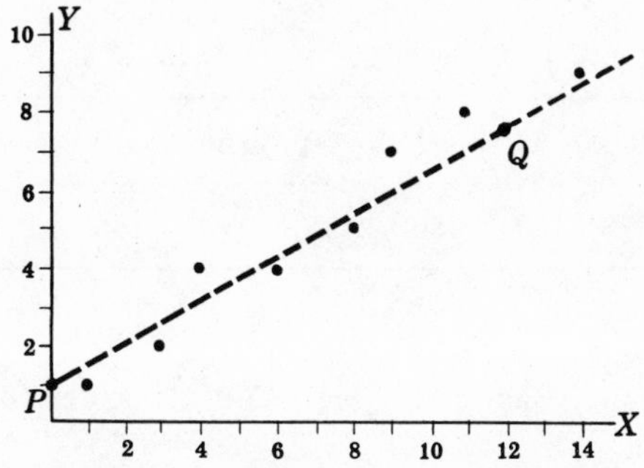

Fig. 13-7

(*b*) To obtain the equation of the line constructed in part (*a*), choose any two points on the line, such as P and Q; the coordinates of points P and Q, as read from the graph, are approximately (0, 1) and (12, 7.5). The equation of the line is $Y = a_0 + a_1 X$. Thus for point (0, 1) we have $1 = a_0 + a_1(0)$, and for point (12, 7.5) we have $7.5 = a_0 + 12a_1$; since the first of these equations gives us $a_0 = 1$, the second gives us $a_1 = 6.5/12 = 0.542$. Thus the required equation is $Y = 1 + 0.542X$.

Another method

$$Y - Y_1 = \frac{Y_2 - Y_1}{X_2 - X_1}(X - X_1) \quad \text{and} \quad Y - 1 = \frac{7.5 - 1}{12 - 0}(X - 0) = 0.542X$$

Thus $Y = 1 + 0.542X$.

13.9 (*a*) Compare the values of Y obtained from the approximating line with those given in Table 13.2.
(*b*) Estimate the value of Y when $X = 10$.

SOLUTION

(*a*) For $X = 1$, $Y = 1 + 0.542(1) = 1.542$, or 1.5. For $X = 3$, $Y = 1 + 0.542(3) = 2.626$, or 2.6. The values of Y corresponding to other values of X can be obtained similarly. The values of Y estimated from the equation $Y = 1 + 0.542X$ are denoted by Y_{est}. These estimated values, together with the actual data from Table 13.2, are shown in Table 13.3.

(*b*) The estimated value of Y when $X = 10$ is $Y = 1 + 0.542(10) = 6.42$, or 6.4.

Table 13.3

X	1	3	4	6	8	9	11	14
Y	1	2	4	4	5	7	8	9
Y_{est}	1.5	2.6	3.2	4.3	5.3	5.9	7.0	8.6

13.10 Table 13.4 shows the heights to the nearest inch (in) and the weights to the nearest pound (lb) of a sample of 12 male students drawn at random from the first-year students at State College.

(*a*) Obtain a scatter diagram of the data.

(*b*) Construct a line that approximates the data.

(*c*) Find the equation of the line constructed in part (*b*).

(*d*) Estimate the weight of a student whose height is known to be 63 in.

(*e*) Estimate the height of a student whose weight is known to be 168 lb.

Table 13.4

Height X (in)	70	63	72	60	66	70	74	65	62	67	65	68
Weight Y (lb)	155	150	180	135	156	168	178	160	132	145	139	152

SOLUTION

(*a*) The scatter diagram, shown in Fig. 13-8, is obtained by plotting the points (70, 155), (63, 150), ..., (68, 152).

(*b*) A straight line that approximates the data is shown dashed in Fig. 13-8. This is but one of the many possible lines that could have been constructed.

(*c*) Choose any two points on the line constructed in part (*b*), such as P and Q, for example. The coordinates of these points as read from the graph are approximately (60, 130) and (72, 170). Thus

$$Y - Y_1 = \frac{Y_2 - Y_1}{X_2 - X_1}(X - X_1) \qquad Y - 130 = \frac{170 - 130}{72 - 60}(X - 60) \qquad Y = \frac{10}{3}X - 70$$

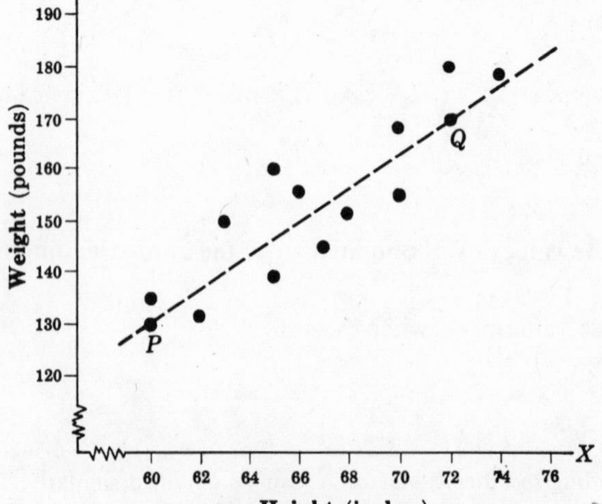

Fig. 13-8

(*d*) If $X = 63$, then $Y = \frac{10}{3}(63) - 70 = 140$ lb.

(*e*) If $Y = 168$, then $168 = \frac{10}{3}X - 70$, $\frac{10}{3}X = 238$, and $X = 71.4$, or 71 in.

THE LEAST-SQUARES LINE

13.11 Fit a least-squares line to the data of Problem 13.8 by using (*a*) X as the independent variable and (*b*) X as the dependent variable.

SOLUTION

(*a*) The equation of the line is $Y = a_0 + a_1 X$. The normal equations are

$$\sum Y = a_0 N + a_1 \sum X$$
$$\sum XY = a_0 \sum X + a_1 \sum X^2$$

The work involved in computing the sums can be arranged as in Table 13.5. Although the right-hand column is not needed for this part of the problem, it has been added to the table for use in part (*b*).

Table 13.5

X	Y	X^2	XY	Y^2
1	1	1	1	1
3	2	9	6	4
4	4	16	16	16
6	4	36	24	16
8	5	64	40	25
9	7	81	63	49
11	8	121	88	64
14	9	196	126	81
$\sum X = 56$	$\sum Y = 40$	$\sum X^2 = 524$	$\sum XY = 364$	$\sum Y^2 = 256$

Since there are eight pairs of values of X and Y, $N = 8$ and the normal equations become

$$8a_0 + 56a_1 = 40$$
$$56a_0 + 524a_1 = 364$$

Solving simultaneously, $a_0 = \frac{6}{11}$, or 0.545; $a_1 = \frac{7}{11}$, or 0.636; and the required least-squares line is $Y = \frac{6}{11} + \frac{7}{11}X$, or $Y = 0.545 + 0.636X$.

Another method

$$a_0 = \frac{(\sum Y)(\sum X^2) - (\sum X)(\sum XY)}{N \sum X^2 - (\sum X)^2} = \frac{(40)(524) - (56)(364)}{(8)(524) - (56)^2} = \frac{6}{11} \quad \text{or} \quad 0.545$$

$$a_1 = \frac{N \sum XY - (\sum X)(\sum Y)}{N \sum X^2 - (\sum X)^2} = \frac{(8)(364) - (56)(40)}{(8)(524) - (56)^2} = \frac{7}{11} \quad \text{or} \quad 0.636$$

Thus $Y = a_0 + a_1 X$, or $Y = 0.545 + 0.636X$, as before.

(*b*) If X is considered the dependent variable, and Y the independent variable, the equation of the least-squares line is $X = b_0 + b_1 Y$ and the normal equations are

$$\sum X = b_0 N + b_1 \sum Y$$
$$\sum XY = b_0 \sum Y + b_1 \sum Y^2$$

Then from Table 13.5 the normal equations become

$$8b_0 + 40b_1 = 56$$
$$40b_0 + 256b_1 = 364$$

from which $b_0 = -\frac{1}{2}$, or -0.50, and $b_1 = \frac{3}{2}$, or 1.50. These values can also be obtained from

$$b_0 = \frac{(\sum X)(\sum Y^2) - (\sum Y)(\sum XY)}{N \sum Y^2 - (\sum Y)^2} = \frac{(56)(256) - (40)(364)}{(8)(256) - (40)^2} = -0.50$$

$$b_1 = \frac{N \sum XY - (\sum X)(\sum Y)}{N \sum Y^2 - (\sum Y)^2} = \frac{(8)(364) - (56)(40)}{(8)(256) - (40)^2} = 1.50$$

Thus the required equation of the least-squares line is $X = b_0 + b_1 Y$, or $X = -0.50 + 1.50Y$.

Note that by solving this equation for Y we obtain $Y = \frac{1}{3} + \frac{2}{3}X$, or $Y = 0.333 + 0.667X$, which is not the same as the line obtained in part (*a*).

13.12 Graph the two lines obtained in Problem 13.11.

SOLUTION

The graphs of the two lines, $Y = 0.545 + 0.636X$ and $X = -0.500 + 1.50Y$, are shown in Fig. 13-9. Note that the two lines in this case are practically coincident, which is an indication that the data are very well described by a linear relationship.

The line obtained in part (*a*) of Problem 13.11 is often called the *regression line of Y on X* and is used for estimating Y for given values of X. The line obtained in part (*b*) is called the *regression line of X on Y* and is used for estimating X for given values of Y.

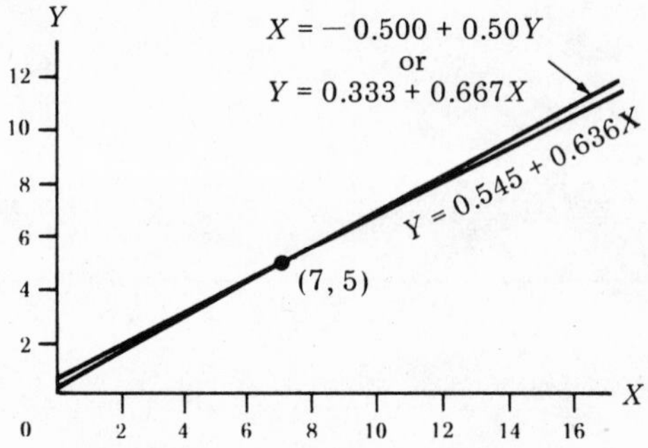

Fig. 13-9

13.13 (*a*) Show that the two least-squares lines obtained in Problem 13.11 intersect at point $(\bar{X}, \bar{Y})$.

(*b*) Estimate the value of Y when $X = 12$.

(*c*) Estimate the value of X when $Y = 3$.

SOLUTION

$$\bar{X} = \frac{\sum X}{N} = \frac{56}{8} = 7 \qquad \bar{Y} = \frac{\sum Y}{N} = \frac{40}{8} = 5$$

Thus point $(\bar{X}, \bar{Y})$, called the *centroid*, is (7, 5).

(*a*) Point (7, 5) lies on line $Y = 0.545 + 0.636X$; or, more exactly, $Y = \frac{6}{11} + \frac{7}{11}X$, since $5 = \frac{6}{11} + \frac{7}{11}(7)$. Point (7, 5) lies on line $X = -\frac{1}{2} + \frac{3}{2}Y$, since $7 = -\frac{1}{2} + \frac{3}{2}(5)$.

Another method

The equations of the two lines are $Y = \frac{6}{11} + \frac{7}{11}X$ and $X = -\frac{1}{2} + \frac{3}{2}Y$. Solving simultaneously, we find that $X = 7$ and $Y = 5$. Thus the lines intersect at point (7.5).

(*b*) Putting $X = 12$ into the regression line of Y (Problem 13.11), $Y = 0.545 + 0.636(12) = 8.2$.

(*c*) Putting $Y = 3$ into the regression line of X (Problem 13.11), $X = -0.50 + 1.50(3) = 4.0$.

13.14 Prove that a least-squares line always passes through the point $(\bar{X}, \bar{Y})$.

SOLUTION

Case 1 (X is the independent variable)

The equation of the least-squares line is

$$Y = a_0 + a_1 X \tag{34}$$

A normal equation for the least-squares line is

$$\sum Y = a_0 N + a_1 \sum X \tag{35}$$

Dividing both sides of equation (*35*) by N gives

$$\bar{Y} = a_0 + a_1 \bar{X} \tag{36}$$

Subtracting equation (*36*) from equation (*34*), the least-squares line can be written

$$Y - \bar{Y} = a_1(X - \bar{X}) \tag{37}$$

which shows that the line passes through the point $(\bar{X}, \bar{Y})$.

Case 2 (Y is the independent variable)

Proceeding as in Case 1, but interchanging X and Y and replacing the constants a_0 and a_1 with b_0 and b_1, respectively, we find that the least-squares line can be written

$$X - \bar{X} = b_1(Y - \bar{Y}) \tag{38}$$

which indicates that the line passes through the point $(\bar{X}, \bar{Y})$.

Note that lines (*37*) and (*38*) are not coincident, but intersect in $(\bar{X}, \bar{Y})$.

13.15 (*a*) Considering X to be the independent variable, show that the equation of the least-squares line can be written

$$y = \left(\frac{\sum xy}{\sum x^2}\right)x \qquad \text{or} \qquad y = \left(\frac{\sum xY}{\sum x^2}\right)x$$

where $x = X - \bar{X}$ and $y = Y - \bar{Y}$.

(*b*) If $\bar{X} = 0$, show that the least-squares line in part (*a*) can be written

$$Y = \bar{Y} + \left(\frac{\sum XY}{\sum X^2}\right)X$$

(*c*) Write the equation of the least-squares line corresponding to that in part (*a*) if Y is the independent variable.

(*d*) Verify that the lines in parts (*a*) and (*c*) are not necessarily the same.

SOLUTION

(*a*) Equation (*37*) can be written $y = a_1 x$, where $x = X - \bar{X}$ and $y = Y - \bar{Y}$. Also, from the simultaneous solution of the normal equations (*18*) we have

$$a_1 = \frac{N \sum XY - (\sum X)(\sum Y)}{N \sum X^2 - (\sum X)^2} = \frac{N \sum (x+\bar{X})(y+\bar{Y}) - [\sum (x+\bar{X})][\sum (y+\bar{Y})]}{N \sum (x+\bar{X})^2 - [\sum (x+\bar{X})]^2}$$

$$= \frac{N \sum (xy + x\bar{Y} + \bar{X}y + \bar{X}\bar{Y}) - (\sum x + N\bar{X})(\sum y + N\bar{Y})}{N \sum (x^2 + 2x\bar{X} + \bar{X}^2) - (\sum x + N\bar{X})^2}$$

$$= \frac{N \sum xy + N\bar{Y} \sum x + N\bar{X} \sum y + N^2 \bar{X}\bar{Y} - (\sum x + N\bar{X})(\sum y + N\bar{Y})}{N \sum x^2 + 2N\bar{X} \sum x + N^2 \bar{X}^2 - (\sum x + N\bar{X})^2}$$

But $\sum x = \sum (X - \bar{X}) = 0$ and $\sum y = \sum (Y - \bar{Y}) = 0$; hence the above simplifies to

$$a_1 = \frac{N \sum xy + N^2 \bar{X}\bar{Y} - N^2 \bar{X}\bar{Y}}{N \sum x^2 + N^2 \bar{X}^2 - N^2 \bar{X}^2} = \frac{\sum xy}{\sum x^2}$$

This can also be written

$$a_1 = \frac{\sum xy}{\sum x^2} = \frac{\sum x(Y - \bar{Y})}{\sum x^2} = \frac{\sum xY - \bar{Y} \sum x}{\sum x^2} = \frac{\sum xY}{\sum x^2}$$

Thus the least-squares line is $y = a_1 x$; that is,

$$y = \left(\frac{\sum xy}{\sum x^2}\right) x \qquad \text{or} \qquad y = \left(\frac{\sum xY}{\sum x^2}\right) x$$

(*b*) If $\bar{X} = 0$, $x = X - \bar{X} = X$. Then from

$$y = \left(\frac{\sum xY}{\sum x^2}\right)$$

we have

$$y = \left(\frac{\sum XY}{\sum X^2}\right) X \qquad \text{or} \qquad Y = \bar{Y} + \left(\frac{\sum XY}{\sum X^2}\right) X$$

Another method

The normal equations of the least-squares line $Y = a_0 + a_1 X$ are

$$\sum Y = a_0 N + a_1 \sum X \qquad \text{and} \qquad \sum XY = a_0 \sum X + a_1 \sum X^2$$

If $\bar{X} = (\sum X)/N = 0$, then $\sum X = 0$ and the normal equations become

$$\sum Y = a_0 N \qquad \text{and} \qquad \sum XY = a_1 \sum X^2$$

from which

$$a_0 = \frac{\sum Y}{N} = \bar{Y} \qquad \text{and} \qquad a_1 = \frac{\sum XY}{\sum X^2}$$

Thus the required equation of the least-squares line is

$$Y = a_0 + a_1 X \qquad \text{or} \qquad Y = \bar{Y} + \left(\frac{\sum XY}{\sum X^2}\right) X$$

(*c*) By interchanging X and Y or x and y, we can show as in part (*a*) that

$$x = \left(\frac{\sum xy}{\sum y^2}\right) y$$

(*d*) From part (*a*), the least-squares line is

$$y = \left(\frac{\sum xy}{\sum x^2}\right) x \tag{39}$$

From part (c), the least-squares line is

$$x = \left(\frac{\sum xy}{\sum y^2}\right) y$$

or

$$y = \left(\frac{\sum y^2}{\sum xy}\right) x \tag{40}$$

Since in general

$$\frac{\sum xy}{\sum x^2} \neq \frac{\sum y^2}{\sum xy}$$

the least-squares lines (39) and (40) are different in general. Note, however, that they intersect at $x=0$ and $y=0$ [i.e., at the point $(\bar{X}, \bar{Y})$].

13.16 If $X' = X + A$ and $Y' = Y + B$, where A and B are any constants, prove that

$$a_1 = \frac{N\sum XY - (\sum X)(\sum Y)}{N\sum X^2 - (\sum X)^2} = \frac{N\sum X'Y' - (\sum X')(\sum Y')}{N\sum X'^2 - (\sum X')^2} = a_1'$$

SOLUTION

$$x' = X' - \bar{X}' = (X + A) - (\bar{X} + A) = X - \bar{X} = x$$
$$y' = Y' - \bar{Y}' = (Y + B) - (\bar{Y} + B) = Y - \bar{Y} = y$$

Then

$$\frac{\sum xy}{\sum x^2} = \frac{\sum x'y'}{\sum x'^2}$$

and the result follows from Problem 13.15. A similar result holds for b_1.

This result is useful, since it enables us to simplify calculations in obtaining the regression line by subtracting suitable constants from the variables X and Y (see the second method of Problem 13.17).

Note: The result does not hold if $X' = c_1X + A$ and $Y' = c_2Y + B$ unless $c_1 = c_2$.

13.17 Fit a least-squares line to the data of Problem 13.10 by using (a) X as the independent variable and (b) X as the dependent variable.

SOLUTION

First method

(a) From Problem 13.15(a) the required line is

$$y = \left(\frac{\sum xy}{\sum x^2}\right) x$$

where $x = X - \bar{X}$ and $y = Y - \bar{Y}$. The work involved in computing the sums can be arranged as in Table 13.6. From the first two columns we find $\bar{X} = 802/12 = 66.8$ and $\bar{Y} = 1850/12 = 154.2$. The last column has been added for use in part (b).

The required least-squares line is

$$y = \left(\frac{\sum xy}{\sum x^2}\right) x = \frac{616.32}{191.68} x = 3.22x$$

or $Y - 154.2 = 3.22(X - 66.8)$, which can be written $Y = 3.22X - 60.9$. This equation is called the *regression line of Y on X* and is used for estimating Y from given values of X.

(b) If X is the dependent variable, the required line is

$$x = \left(\frac{\sum xy}{\sum y^2}\right) y = \frac{616.32}{2659.68} y = 0.232y$$

Table 13.6

Height X	Weight Y	$x = X - \bar{X}$	$y = Y - \bar{Y}$	xy	x^2	y^2
70	155	3.2	0.8	2.56	10.24	0.64
63	150	−3.8	−4.2	15.96	14.44	17.64
72	180	5.2	25.8	134.16	27.04	665.64
60	135	−6.8	−19.2	130.56	46.24	368.64
66	156	−0.8	1.8	−1.44	0.64	3.24
70	168	3.2	13.8	44.16	10.24	190.44
74	178	7.2	23.8	171.36	51.84	566.44
65	160	−1.8	5.8	−10.44	3.24	33.64
62	132	−4.8	−22.2	106.56	23.04	492.84
67	145	0.2	−9.2	−1.84	0.04	84.64
65	139	−1.8	−15.2	27.36	3.24	231.04
68	152	1.2	−2.2	−2.64	1.44	4.84
$\sum X = 802$ $\bar{X} = 66.8$	$\sum Y = 1850$ $\bar{Y} = 154.2$			$\sum xy = 616.32$	$\sum x^2 = 191.68$	$\sum y^2 = 2659.68$

which can be written $X - 66.8 = 0.232(Y - 154.2)$, or $X = 31.0 + 0.232Y$. This equation is called the *regression line of X on Y* and is used for estimating X from given values of Y.

Note that the method of Problem 13.11 can also be used if desired.

Second method

Using the result of Problem 13.16, we may subtract suitable constants from X and Y. We choose to subtract 65 from X and 150 from Y. Then the results can be arranged as in Table 13.7.

Table 13.7

X'	Y'	X'^2	$X'Y'$	Y'^2
5	5	25	25	25
−2	0	4	0	0
7	30	49	210	900
−5	−15	25	75	225
1	6	1	6	36
5	18	25	90	324
9	28	81	252	784
0	10	0	0	100
−3	−18	9	54	324
2	−5	4	−10	25
0	−11	0	0	121
3	2	9	6	4
$\sum X' = 22$	$\sum Y' = 50$	$\sum X'^2 = 232$	$\sum X'Y' = 708$	$\sum Y'^2 = 2868$

$$a_1 = \frac{N\sum X'Y' - (\sum X')(\sum Y')}{N\sum X'^2 - (\sum X')^2} = \frac{(12)(708) - (22)(50)}{(12)(232) - (22)^2} = 3.22$$

$$b_1 = \frac{N\sum X'Y' - (\sum Y')(\sum X')}{N\sum Y'^2 - (\sum Y')^2} = \frac{(12)(708) - (50)(22)}{(12)(2868) - (50)^2} = 0.232$$

Since $\bar{X} = 65 + 22/12 = 66.8$ and $\bar{Y} = 150 + 50/12 = 154.2$, the regression equations are $Y - 154.2 = 3.22(X - 66.8)$ and $X - 66.8 = 0.232(Y - 154.2)$; that is $Y = 3.22X - 60.9$ and $X = 0.232Y + 31.0$, in agreement with the first method.

13.18 (*a*) On the same set of axes, draw the graphs of the two lines in Problem 13.17.

(*b*) Estimate the weight of a student whose height is known to be 63 in.

(*c*) Estimate the height of a student whose weight is known to be 168 lb.

SOLUTION

(*a*) The two lines are shown in Fig. 13-10, together with the original data points. Note that they intersect at $(\bar{X}, \bar{Y})$, or (66.8, 154.2).

(*b*) To estimate Y from X, use the regression line of Y on X, given from Problem 13.17 by $Y = 3.22X - 60.9$. Then if $X = 63$, $Y = 3.22(63) - 60.9 = 142$ lb.

(*c*) To estimate X from Y, use the regression line of X on Y, given from Problem 13.17 by $X = 31.0 + 0.232Y$. Then if $Y = 168$, $X = 31.0 + 0.232(168) = 70.0$ in.

The results in parts (*b*) and (*c*) should be compared with those in Problem 13.10, parts (*d*) and (*c*).

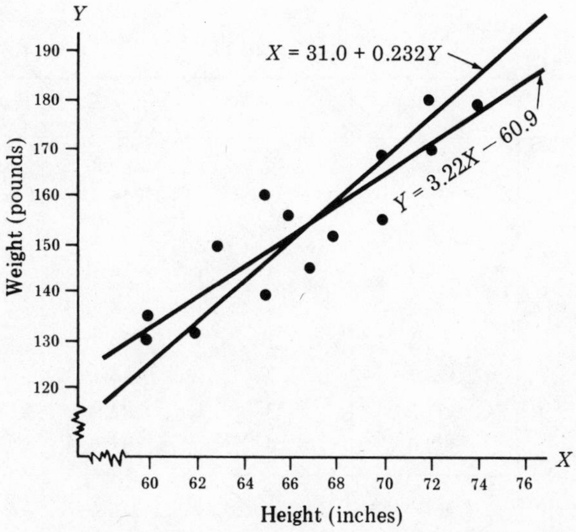

Fig. 13-10

APPLICATIONS TO TIME SERIES

13.19 The index of medical-care costs in the United States for the years 1976–1984, taking the index for 1967 as 100, is given in Table 13.8.

(*a*) Graph the data.

(*b*) Find the equation of a least-squares line fitting the data.

(*c*) Estimate the index for the year 1985 and compare it with the actual value, 396.1.

(*d*) Estimate the index for the year 1975 and compare it with the actual value, 168.6.

SOLUTION

(*a*) See Fig. 13-11.

(*b*) **First method**

Use the equation $y = (\sum xy / \sum x^2)x$, where $x = X - \bar{X}$ and $y = Y - \bar{Y}$. The work can be arranged as in Table 13.9. The required equation becomes $y = (1511.3/60)x$, or $y = 25.19x$, which can be written

$$Y - 274.5 = 25.19(X - 4) \qquad \text{or} \qquad Y = 173.7 + 25.19X$$

Table 13.8

Year	Index of U.S. Medical-Care Costs (1967 = 100)
1976	184.7
1977	202.4
1978	219.4
1979	239.7
1980	265.9
1981	294.5
1982	328.7
1983	357.3
1984	378.0

Source: U.S. Bureau of Labor Statistics.

Table 13.9

Year	X	Y	$x = X - \bar{X}$	$y = Y - \bar{Y}$	x^2	xy
1976	0	184.7	−4	−89.8	16	359.2
1977	1	202.4	−3	−72.1	9	216.3
1978	2	219.4	−2	−55.1	4	110.2
1979	3	239.7	−1	−34.8	1	34.8
1980	4	265.9	0	−8.6	0	0.0
1981	5	294.5	1	20.0	1	20.0
1982	6	328.7	2	54.2	4	108.4
1983	7	357.3	3	82.8	9	248.4
1984	8	378.0	4	103.5	16	414.0
	$\sum X = 36$ $\bar{X} = 4$	$\sum Y = 2470.6$ $\bar{Y} = 274.5$			$\sum x^2 = 60$	$\sum xy = 1511.3$

where the origin $X = 0$ is the year 1976 (usually taken to be the midyear, such as July 1, 1976) and the unit of X is 1 year. The graph of this line, sometimes called a *trend line*, is shown dashed in Fig. 13-11. The equation is often called the *trend equation*, and the values of Y computed for various values of X are called the *trend values.*

Second method

If we assign values of X to the years 1976–1984 so that $\sum X = 0$, the equation of the least-squares line can be written

$$Y = \bar{Y} + \left(\frac{\sum XY}{\sum X^2}\right) X$$

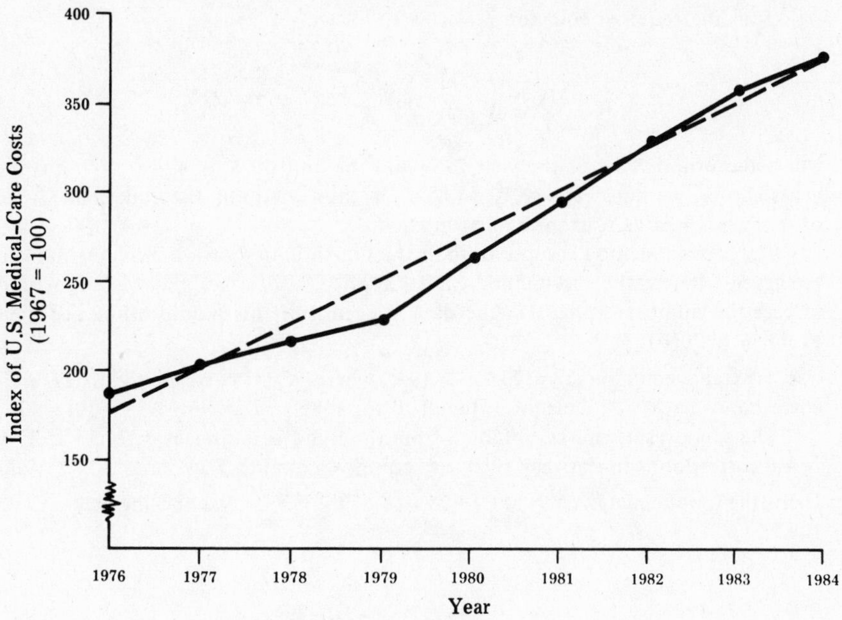

Fig. 13-11

Since there is an odd number of years in the data, we can assign $X = 0$ to the middle year, 1980; assign $X = 1, 2, 3$, and 4 to the successive years; and assign $X = -1, -2, -3$, and -4 to the years that precede this middle year. The result is shown in column 2 of Table 13.10 and is equivalent to using column 4 of the table for the first method.

The middle year, 1980, is called the *origin*; we shall also assume that the values of Y refer to midyear values (i.e., as of July 1). Thus $X = 0$ corresponds to July 1, 1980; $X = -1$ corresponds to July 1, 1979; etc. The computations involved can be organized as in Table 13.10.

Table 13.10

Year	X	Y	X^2	XY
1976	−4	184.7	16	−738.8
1977	−3	202.4	9	−607.2
1978	−2	219.4	4	−438.8
1979	−1	239.7	1	−239.7
1980	0	265.9	0	0.0
1981	1	294.5	1	294.5
1982	2	328.7	4	657.4
1983	3	357.3	9	1071.9
1984	4	378.0	16	1512.0
	$\bar{X} = 0$	$\sum Y = 2470.6$ $\bar{Y} = 274.5$	$\sum X^2 = 60$	$\sum XY = 1511.3$

Thus the required equation is

$$Y = 274.5 + \left(\frac{1511.3}{60}\right)X \qquad \text{or} \qquad Y = 274.5 + 25.19X$$

where the origin $X = 0$ is the year 1980 and the unit of X is 1 year. To shift the origin to 1976, 4 years earlier, we must replace X with $X - 4$, thus obtaining the equation $Y = 274.5 + 25.19(X - 4)$, or $Y = 173.7 + 25.19X$, as in the first method.

The second method is superior to the first method in terms of reducing the labor of computation. However, whereas the first method can be applied in all cases, the second method must be modified in case the number of years in the data is even. For this modification, see the second method of Problem 13.20(*b*).

(*c*) Use the trend equation $Y = 173.7 + 25.19X$, where $X = 0$ corresponds to 1976. Then the year 1985 corresponds to $X = 9$. Thus the value of Y for 1985 is $Y = 173.7 + 25.19(9) = 400.4$.

The same result can be obtained from the trend equation $Y = 274.5 + 25.19X$, where the origin $X = 0$ corresponds to the year 1980, by setting X equal to 5.

(*d*) Using the trend equation $Y = 173.7 + 25.19X$, with $X = -1$, we find the value $Y = 173.7 + 25.19(-1) = 148.5$.

13.20 The farm employment of the United States for the years 1935, 1940, 1945, . . . , 1980, given in millions of workers, is shown in Table 13.11.

(*a*) Graph the data.

(*b*) Find an equation for the least-squares line fitting the data.

(*c*) Predict the farm employment in the years 1990 and 2000, assuming that the trend continues.

Table 13.11

Year	1935	1940	1945	1950	1955	1960	1965	1970	1975	1980
U.S. farm employment (millions)	12.7	11.0	10.0	9.9	8.4	7.1	5.6	4.5	4.3	3.7

Source: U.S. Department of Agriculture.

SOLUTION

(*a*) See Fig. 13-12.

(*b*) **First method**

See Table 13.12. The required equation, $y = (\sum xy/\sum x^2)x$, becomes $y = (-84.80/82.5)x$ or $y = -1.03x$, which can be written

$$Y - 7.7 = -1.03(X - 4.5) \qquad \text{or} \qquad Y = 12.3 - 1.03X$$

where the origin $X = 0$ is the year 1935 and the unit of X is 5 years. The graph of this line, sometimes called the *trend line*, is shown dashed in Fig. 13-12.

Table 13.12

Year	X	Y	$x=X-\bar{X}$	$y=Y-\bar{Y}$	x^2	xy
1935	0	12.7	−4.5	5.0	20.25	−22.50
1940	1	11.0	−3.5	3.3	12.25	−11.55
1945	2	10.0	−2.5	2.3	6.25	−5.75
1950	3	9.9	−1.5	2.2	2.25	−3.30
1955	4	8.4	−0.5	0.7	0.25	−0.35
1960	5	7.1	0.5	−0.6	0.25	−0.30
1965	6	5.6	1.5	−2.1	2.25	−3.15
1970	7	4.5	2.5	−3.2	6.25	−8.00
1975	8	4.3	3.5	−3.4	12.25	−11.90
1980	9	3.7	4.5	−4.0	20.25	−18.00
	$\sum X=45$ $\bar{X}=4.5$	$\sum Y=77.2$ $\bar{Y}=7.7$			$\sum x^2=82.5$	$\sum xy=-84.80$

Second method

In this method we wish to assign values of X to the years so that $\sum X=0$. Since an even number of years is present, there is no middle year and the second method of Problem 13.19(b) cannot be used. However, we can associate the numbers −0.5 and 0.5 to the middle years, 1955 and 1960, so that 1965, 1970, 1975, and 1980 are represented by 1.5, 2.5, 3.5, and 4.5 and so that 1950, 1945, 1940, and 1935 are represented by −1.5, −2.5, −3.5, and −4.5. This essentially amounts to column 4 in Table 13.12.

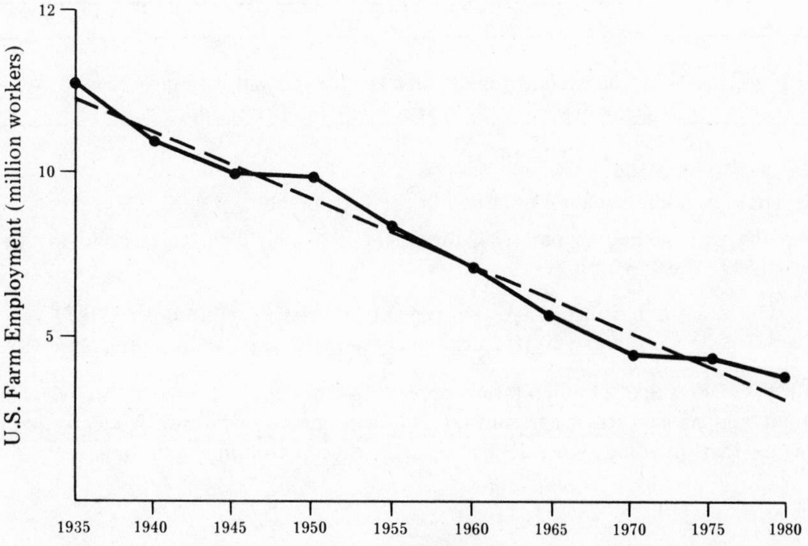

Fig. 13-12

Also, in order to avoid fractions, we double these values, obtaining column 2 in Table 13.13. Note that with these values of X, the origin $X = 0$ is midway between July 1, 1955, and July 1, 1960, which is Jan. 1, 1958, or Dec. 31, 1957. The unit of X is $\frac{1}{2}$(5 years) = $2\frac{1}{2}$ years. Since $\bar{X} = 0$, the required equation has the form $Y = \bar{Y} + (\sum X\bar{Y}/\sum X^2)X$, which gives (see Table 13.13)

$$Y = 7.7 + \left(\frac{-169.6}{330}\right)X \qquad \text{or} \qquad Y = 7.7 - 0.514X$$

where the origin $X = 0$ corresponds to Jan. 1, 1958, and X is measured in $2\frac{1}{2}$-year units.

If we wish to measure X in 5-year intervals instead of $2\frac{1}{2}$-year intervals, we must replace X with $2X$, so that the equation is

$$Y = 7.7 - 1.028X \qquad \text{or} \qquad Y = 7.7 - 1.03X$$

where the origin is Jan. 1, 1958, and X is measured in 5-year units.

Table 13.13

Year	X	Y	X^2	XY
1935	−9	12.7	81	−114.3
1940	−7	11.0	49	−77.0
1945	−5	10.0	25	−50.0
1950	−3	9.9	9	−29.7
1955	−1	8.4	1	−8.4
1960	1	7.1	1	7.1
1965	3	5.6	9	16.8
1970	5	4.5	25	22.5
1975	7	4.3	49	30.1
1980	9	3.7	81	33.3
	$\sum X = 0$ $\bar{X} = 0$	$\sum Y = 77.2$ $\bar{Y} = 7.7$	$\sum X^2 = 330$	$\sum XY = -169.6$

If we now want the origin to be at July 1, 1935, we must replace X with $X - 4.5$ (since it is 4.5 five-year intervals from July 1, 1935, to Jan. 1, 1958). The result is

$$Y = 7.7 - 1.03(X - 4.5) \qquad \text{or} \qquad Y = 12.3 - 1.03X$$

This agrees with the equation obtained in the first method.

(*c*) Using the first method in part (*b*), the years 1990 and 2000 correspond to $X = 11$ and $X = 13$, respectively. Then

$$Y = 12.3 - 1.03X = 12.3 - 1.03(11) = 0.97 \text{ million in 1990}$$
$$Y = 12.3 - 1.03X = 12.3 - 1.03(13) = -1.09 \text{ million in 2000}$$

While the first result of 1 million farm workers in 1990 is possible, especially in view of high-technology farming and of imports of agricultural products, the second result is clearly impossible. We must conclude that the trend shown in Table 13.13 will not continue very long.

NONLINEAR EQUATIONS REDUCIBLE TO LINEAR FORM

Mathcad **13.21** Table 13.14 gives experimental values of the pressure P of a given mass of gas corresponding to various values of the volume V. According to thermodynamic principles, a relationship having

Table 13.14

Volume V in cubic inches (in^3)	54.3	61.8	72.4	88.7	118.6	194.0
Pressure P in pounds per square inch (lb/in^2)	61.2	49.5	37.6	28.4	19.2	10.1

the form $PV^{\gamma} = C$, where γ and C are constants, should exist between the variables.

(*a*) Find the values of γ and C.

(*b*) Write the equation connecting P and V.

(*c*) Estimate P when $V = 100.0$ in^3.

SOLUTION

Since $PV^{\gamma} = C$, we have

$$\log P + \gamma \log V = \log C \qquad \text{or} \qquad \log P = \log C - \gamma \log V$$

Calling $\log V = X$ and $\log P = Y$, the last equation can be written

$$Y = a_0 + a_1 X \tag{41}$$

where $a_0 = \log C$ and $a_1 = -\gamma$.

Table 13.15 gives $X = \log V$ and $Y = \log P$, corresponding to the values of V and P in Table 13.14, and also indicates the calculations involved in computing the least-squares line (*41*). The normal equations corresponding to the least-squares line (*41*) are

$$\sum Y = a_0 N + a_1 \sum X \qquad \text{and} \qquad \sum XY = a_0 \sum X + a_1 \sum X^2$$

Table 13.15

$X = \log V$	$Y = \log P$	X^2	XY
1.7348	1.7868	3.0095	3.0997
1.7910	1.6946	3.2077	3.0350
1.8597	1.5752	3.4585	2.9294
1.9479	1.4533	3.7943	2.8309
2.0741	1.2833	4.3019	2.6617
2.2878	1.0043	5.2340	2.2976
$\sum X = 11.6953$	$\sum Y = 8.7975$	$\sum X^2 = 23.0059$	$\sum XY = 16.8543$

from which

$$a_0 = \frac{(\sum Y)(\sum X^2) - (\sum X)(\sum XY)}{N \sum X^2 - (\sum X)^2} = 4.20 \qquad a_1 = \frac{N \sum XY - (\sum X)(\sum Y)}{N \sum X^2 - (\sum X)^2} = -1.40$$

Thus $Y = 4.20 - 1.40\,X$.

(*a*) Since $a_0 = 4.20 = \log C$ and $a_1 = -1.40 = -\gamma$, $C = 1.60 \times 10^4$ and $\gamma = 1.40$.

(*b*) The required equation in terms of P and V can be written $PV^{1.40} = 16{,}000$.

(*c*) When $V = 100$, $X = \log V = 2$ and $Y = \log P = 4.20 - 1.40(2) = 1.40$. Then $P = \text{antilog } 1.40 = 25.1$ lb/in^2.

13.22 Solve Problem 13.21 by plotting by plotting the data on log-log graph paper.

SOLUTION

We first obtain a point for each pair of values of the pressure P and volume V in Table 13.14 and plot these points on log-log graph paper, as shown in Fig. 13-13. We then draw a line that approximates these points (the line in Fig. 13-13 is drawn freehand). The resulting graph shows that there is a linear relationship between log P and log V that can be represented by the equation

$$\log P = a_0 + a_1 \log V \qquad \text{or} \qquad Y = a_0 + a_1 X$$

The slope a_1, which is negative in this case, is given numerically by the ratio of the lengths of AB to AC (using an appropriate unit of length). Measurement in this case yields $a_1 = -1.4$.

To obtain a_0, one point on the line is needed. For example, when $V = 100$, $P = 25$ from the graph; therefore, $a_0 = \log P - a_1 \log V = \log 25 + 1.4 \log 100 = 1.4 + (1.4)(2) = 4.2$, and we thus have $\log P + 1.4 \log V = 4.2$, $\log PV^{1.4} = 4.2$, and $PV^{1.4} = 16{,}000$.

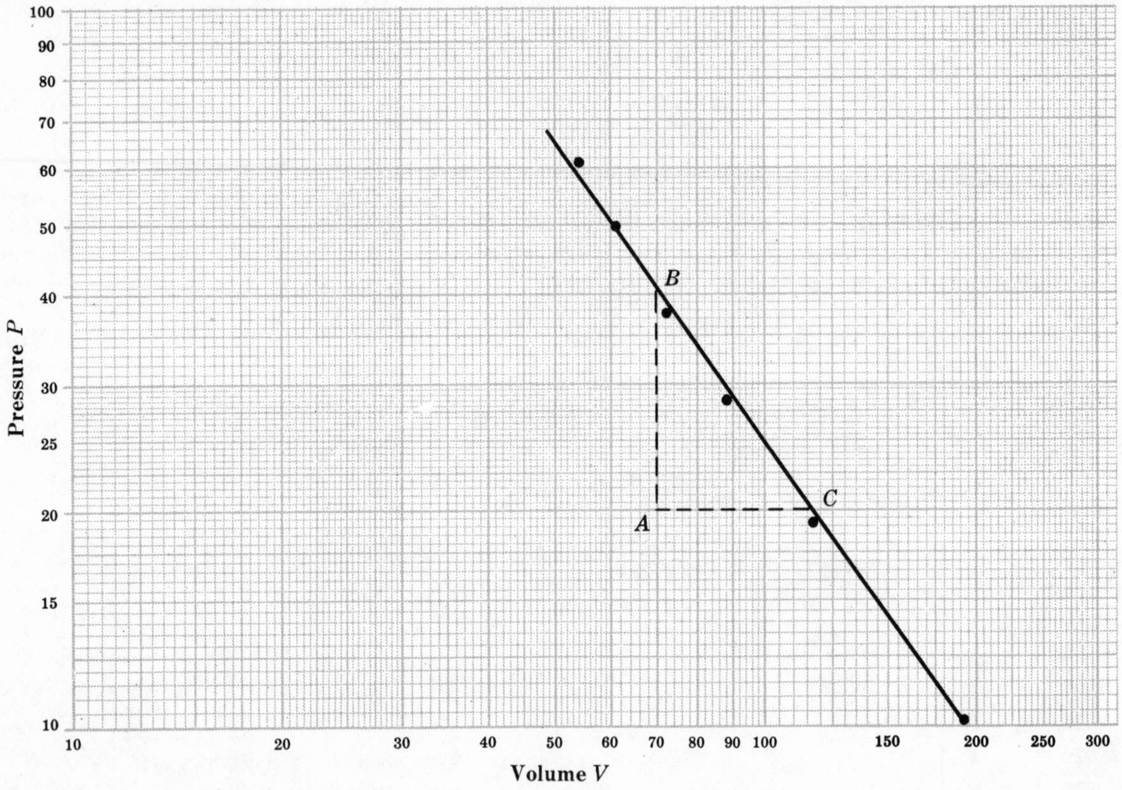

Fig. 13-13

THE LEAST-SQUARES PARABOLA

13.23 Table 13.16 shows the population of the United States during the years 1880–1980 in 10-year intervals.

(*a*) Find the equation of a least-squares parabola fitting the data.

(*b*) Compute the trend values for the years given in Table 13.16, and compare these values with the actual values.

(*c*) Estimate the population in 1990 and 2000.

(*d*) Estimate the population in 1870 and 1860, and compare these estimates with the true values (see page 16).

Table 13.16

Year	1880	1890	1900	1910	1920	1930	1940	1950	1960	1970	1980
U.S. population (millions)	50.2	62.9	76.0	92.0	105.7	122.8	131.7	151.1	179.3	203.3	226.5

Source: U.S. Bureau of the Census.

SOLUTION

(*a*) Let the variables X and Y denote, respectively, the year and the population during that year. The equation of a least-squares parabola fitting the data is

$$Y = a_0 + a_1 X + a_2 X^2 \tag{42}$$

where a_0, a_1, and a_2 are found from the normal equation

$$\begin{aligned} \sum Y &= a_0 N + a_1 \sum X + a_2 \sum X^2 \\ \sum XY &= a_0 \sum X + a_1 \sum X^2 + a_2 \sum X^3 \\ \sum X^2 Y &= a_0 \sum X^2 + a_1 \sum X^3 + a_2 \sum X^4 \end{aligned} \tag{43}$$

It is convenient to choose X so that the middle year, 1930, corresponds to $X = 0$; so that the years 1940, 1950, 1960, 1970, and 1980 correspond to $X = 1, 2, 3, 4$, and 5; and so that the years 1880, 1890, 1910, and 1920 correspond to $X = -1, -2, -3, -4$, and -5. With this choice, $\sum X$ and $\sum X^3$ are zero and equations (*43*) are simplified.

The work involved in computation can be arranged as in Table 13.17. From this table the normal equations become

$$\begin{aligned} 11a_0 + 110a_2 &= 1401.5 \\ 110a_1 &= 1897.2 \\ 110a_0 + 1958a_2 &= 14{,}684.2 \end{aligned} \tag{44}$$

Table 13.17

Year	X	Y	X^2	X^3	X^4	XY	X^2Y
1880	−5	50.2	25	−125	625	−251.0	1255.0
1890	−4	62.9	16	−64	256	−251.6	1006.4
1900	−3	76.0	9	−27	81	−228.0	684.0
1910	−2	92.0	4	−8	16	−184.0	368.0
1920	−1	105.7	1	−1	1	−105.7	105.7
1930	0	122.8	0	0	0	0.0	0.0
1940	1	131.7	1	1	1	131.7	131.7
1950	2	151.1	4	8	16	302.2	604.4
1960	3	179.3	9	27	81	537.9	1613.7
1970	4	203.3	16	64	256	813.2	3252.8
1980	5	226.5	25	125	625	1132.5	5662.5
	$\sum X = 0$	$\sum Y = 1401.5$	$\sum X^2 = 110$	$\sum X^3 = 0$	$\sum x^4 = 1958$	$\sum XY = 1897.2$	$\sum X^2Y = 14{,}684.2$

From the second equation in (*44*), $a_1 = 17.25$; from the first equation, $a_0 = 119.61$; and from the third equation, $a_2 = 0.7800$. Thus the required equation is

$$Y = 119.61 + 17.25X + 0.7800X^2 \tag{45}$$

where the origin $X = 0$ is July 1, 1930, and the unit of X is 10 years.

(*b*) The trend values are obtained by placing $X = -5, -4, -3, -2, -1, 0, 1, 2, 3, 4$, and 5 in equation (*45*). These trend values, together with the actual values, are shown in Table 13.18. It is seen that the agreement is good.

Table 13.18

Year	$X=-5$ 1880	$X=-4$ 1890	$X=-3$ 1900	$X=-2$ 1910	$X=-1$ 1920	$X=0$ 1930	$X=1$ 1940	$X=2$ 1950	$X=3$ 1960	$X=4$ 1970	$X=5$ 1980
Trend value	52.9	63.1	74.9	88.2	103.1	119.6	137.6	157.2	178.4	201.1	225.4
Actual value	50.2	62.9	76.0	92.0	105.7	122.8	131.7	151.1	179.3	203.3	226.5

(*c*) The year 1990 corresponds to $X = 6$, for which $Y = 119.61 + 17.25(6) + 0.7800(6)^2 = 251.2$, and the year 2000 corresponds to $X = 7$, for which $Y = 119.61 + 17.25(7) + 0.7800(7)^2 = 278.6$. Thus, if present trends continue, we may expect the U.S. population in 1990 and 2000 to be 251.2 million and 278.6 million, respectively.

(*d*) The year 1870 corresponds to $X = -6$, for which $Y = 119.61 + 17.25(-6) + 0.7800(-6)^2 = 44.2$. Since the true value is 39.8, the error is approximately 10% and indicates the risk in extrapolation.

Supplementary Problems

STRAIGHT LINES

13.24 If $3X + 2Y = 18$, find (*a*) X when $Y = 3$, (*b*) Y when $X = 2$, (*c*) X when $Y = -5$, (*d*) Y when $X = -1$, (*e*) the X intercept, and (*f*) the Y intercept.

13.25 Construct a graph of the equations (*a*) $Y = 3X - 5$ and (*b*) $X + 2Y = 4$ on the same set of axes. In what point do the graphs intersect?

13.26 (*a*) Find an equation for the straight line passing through the points $(3, -2)$ and $(-1, 6)$.

(*b*) Determine the X and Y intercepts of the line in part (*a*).

(*c*) Find the value of Y corresponding to $X = 3$ and to $X = 5$.

(*d*) Verify your answers to parts (*a*), (*b*), and (*c*) directly from a graph.

13.27 Find an equation for the straight line whose slope is $\frac{2}{3}$ and whose Y intercept is -3.

13.28 (*a*) Find the slope and Y intercept of the line whose equation is $3X - 5Y = 20$.

(*b*) What is the equation of a line which is parallel to the line in part (*a*) and which passes through the point $(2, -1)$?

13.29 Find (*a*) the slope, (*b*) the Y intercept, and (*c*) the equation of the line passing through the points $(5, 4)$ and $(2, 8)$.

13.30 Find the equation of a straight line whose X and Y intercepts are 3 and -5, respectively.

13.31 A temperature of 100 degrees Celsius (°C) corresponds to 212 degrees Fahrenheit (°F), while a temperature of 0 °C corresponds to 32 °F. Assuming that a linear relationship exists between Celsius and Fahrenheit temperatures, find (*a*) the equation connecting Celsius and Fahrenheit temperatures, (*b*) the Fahrenheit temperature corresponding to 80 °C, and (*c*) the Celsius temperature corresponding to 68 °F.

THE LEAST-SQUARES LINE

13.32 Fit a least-squares line to the data in Table 13.19, using (*a*) X as the independent variable and (*b*) X as the dependent variable. Graph the data and the least-squares lines, using the same set of coordinate axes.

Table 13.19

X	3	5	6	8	9	11
Y	2	3	4	6	5	8

13.33 For the data of Problem 13.32, find (*a*) the values of Y when $X = 5$ and $X = 12$ and (*b*) the value of X when $Y = 7$.

13.34 (*a*) Use the freehand method to obtain an equation for a line fitting the data of Problem 13.32.
(*b*) Using the result of part (*a*), answer Problem 13.33.

13.35 Table 13.20 shows the final grades in algebra and physics obtained by 10 students selected at random from a large group of students.

Table 13.20

Algebra (X)	75	80	93	65	87	71	98	68	84	77
Physics (Y)	82	78	86	72	91	80	95	72	89	74

(*a*) Graph the data.
(*b*) Find a least-squares line fitting the data, using X as the independent variable.
(*c*) Find a least-squares line fitting the data, using Y as the independent variable.
(*d*) If a student receives a grade of 75 in algebra, what is her expected grade in physics?
(*e*) If a student receives a grade of 95 in physics, what is her expected grade in algebra?

13.36 Table 13.21 shows the birth rate per 1000 population in the United States during the years 1920–1980 in 10-year intervals.

(*a*) Graph the data.
(*b*) Find a least-squares line fitting the data.
(*c*) Compute the trend values, and compare these with the actual values.
(*d*) Predict the birth rate in 1990 and 2000, and discuss possible sources of error in this prediction.

Table 13.21

Year	1920	1930	1940	1950	1960	1970	1980
Birth rate per 1000 population	27.7	21.3	19.4	24.1	23.7	18.4	15.9

Source: National Center for Health Statistics.

13.37 Table 13.22 shows the percentage of the U.S. population aged 65 and older for the years 1890–1980.

(*a*) Graph the data.

(*b*) Find a least-squares line fitting the data.

(*c*) Compute the trend values, and compare these with the actual values.

(*d*) Predict the percentage of the population aged 65 and older in 1990 and 2000, and discuss possible sources of error in this prediction.

(*e*) When would you expect the percentage to reach 25%, 35%, and 50%, and what assumptions must you make in your answer?

Table 13.22

Year	1890	1900	1910	1920	1930	1940	1950	1960	1970	1980
Percentage	3.84	4.05	4.29	4.67	5.40	6.85	8.12	9.30	9.89	11.35

Source: U.S. Bureau of the Census.

LEAST-SQUARES CURVES

13.38 Fit a least-squares parabola, $Y = a_0 + a_1X + a_2X^2$, to the data in Table 13.23.

Table 13.23

X	0	1	2	3	4	5	6
Y	2.4	2.1	3.2	5.6	9.3	14.6	21.9

Mathcad **13.39** The total time required to bring an automobile to a stop after one perceives danger is the reaction time (the time between recognizing danger and applying the brakes) plus the braking time (the time for stopping after applying the brakes). Table 13.24 gives the stopping distance D (in feet) of an automobile traveling at speeds V (in miles per hour, or mi/h) from the instant that danger is perceived.

(*a*) Graph D against V.

(*b*) Fit a least-squares parabola of the form $D = a_0 + a_1V + a_2V^2$ to the data.

(*c*) Estimate D when $V = 45$ mi/h and 80 mi/h.

Table 13.24

Speed V (mi/h)	20	30	40	50	60	70
Stopping distance D (ft)	54	90	138	206	292	396

13.40 Table 13.25 shows the male and female populations of the United States during the years 1920–1980.

(*a*) Graph the differences in these populations.

(*b*) Using an appropriate equation, find a least-squares curve that fits the data.

(c) Estimate the differences for the years 1990 and 2000.

(d) Determine the year in which there will be a 2:1 ratio of females to males. In determining this, what assumptions must you make?

Table 13.25

Year	1920	1930	1940	1950	1960	1970	1980
Male population	53.90	62.14	66.06	75.19	88.33	98.93	110.05
Female population	51.81	60.64	65.61	76.14	90.99	104.31	116.49

Source: U.S. Bureau of the Census.

13.41 Work Problem 13.40 by using the ratio of male and female populations instead of the difference in populations.

13.42 Work Problem 13.37 by using a least-squares parabola, and compare the results.

13.43 The number Y of bacteria per unit volume present in a culture after X hours is given in Table 13.26.

(a) Graph the data on semilog graph paper, using the logarithmic scale for Y and the arithmetic scale for X.

(b) Fit a least-squares curve of the form $Y = ab^x$ to the data and explain why this particular equation should yield good results.

(c) Compare the values of Y obtained form this equation with the actual values.

(d) Estimate the value of Y when $X = 7$.

Table 13.26

Number of hours (X)	0	1	2	3	4	5	6
Number of bacteria per unit volume (Y)	32	47	65	92	132	190	275

13.44 In Problem 13.43, show how a graph on semilog graph paper can be used to obtain the required equation without employing the method of least squares.

Chapter 14

Correlation Theory

CORRELATION AND REGRESSION

In the last chapter we considered the problem of *regression*, or *estimation*, of one variable (the dependent variable) from one or more related variables (the independent variables). In this chapter we consider the closely related problem of *correlation*, or the degree of relationship between variables, which seeks to determine *how well* a linear or other equation describes or explains the relationship between variables.

If all values of the variables satisfy an equation exactly, we say that the variables are *perfectly correlated* or that there is *perfect correlation* between them. Thus the circumferences C and radii r of all circles are perfectly correlated since $C = 2\pi r$. If two dice are tossed simultaneously 100 times, there is no relationship between corresponding points on each die (unless the dice are loaded); that is, they are *uncorrelated.* Such variables as the height and weight of individuals would show *some* correlation.

When only two variables are involved, we speak of *simple correlation* and *simple regression.* When more than two variables are involved, we speak of *multiple correlation* and *multiple regression.* This chapter considers only simple correlation. Multiple correlation and regression are considered in Chapter 15.

LINEAR CORRELATION

If X and Y denote the two variables under consideration, a *scatter diagram* shows the location of points (X, Y) on a rectangular coordinate system. If all points in this scatter diagram seem to lie near a line, as in Figs. 14-1(a) and 14-1(b), the correlation is called *linear.* In such cases, as we have seen in Chapter 13, a linear equation is appropriate for purposes of regression (or estimation).

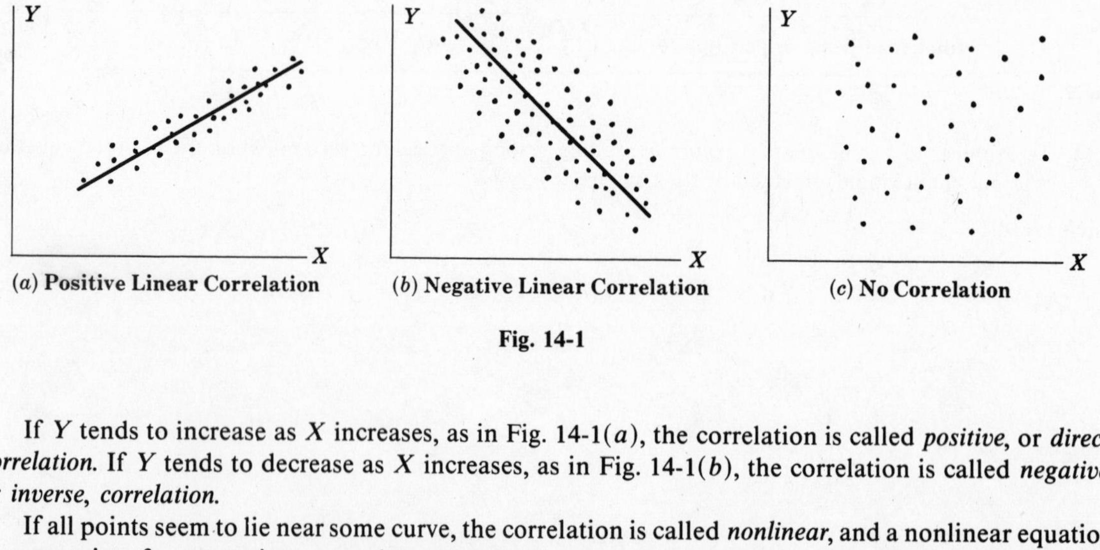

Fig. 14-1

If Y tends to increase as X increases, as in Fig. 14-1(a), the correlation is called *positive*, or *direct, correlation.* If Y tends to decrease as X increases, as in Fig. 14-1(b), the correlation is called *negative*, or *inverse, correlation.*

If all points seem to lie near some curve, the correlation is called *nonlinear*, and a nonlinear equation is appropriate for regression, as we have seen in Chapter 13. It is clear that nonlinear correlation can be sometimes positive and sometimes negative.

If there is no relationship indicated between the variables, as in Fig. 14-1(c), we say that there is *no correlation* between them (i.e., they are *uncorrelated*).

MEASURES OF CORRELATION

We can determine in a *qualitative* manner how well a given line or curve describes the relationship between variables by direct observation of the scatter diagram itself. For example, it is seen that a straight line is far more helpful in describing the relation between X and Y for the data of Fig. 14-1(a) than for the data of Fig. 14-1(b) because of the fact that there is less scattering about the line of Fig. 14-1(a).

If we are to deal with the problem of scattering of sample data about lines or curves in a *quantitative* manner, it will be necessary for us to devise *measures of correlation.*

THE LEAST-SQUARES REGRESSION LINES

We first consider the problem of how well a straight line explains the relationship between two variables. To do this, we shall need the equations for the least-squares regression lines obtained in Chapter 13. As we have seen, the least-squares regression line of Y on X is

$$Y = a_0 + a_1 X \tag{1}$$

where a_0 and a_1 are obtained from the normal equations

$$\begin{aligned} \sum Y &= a_0 N + a_1 \sum X \\ \sum XY &= a_0 \sum X + a_1 \sum X^2 \end{aligned} \tag{2}$$

which yield

$$\begin{aligned} a_0 &= \frac{(\sum Y)(\sum X^2) - (\sum X)(\sum XY)}{N \sum X^2 - (\sum X)^2} \\ a_1 &= \frac{N \sum XY - (\sum X)(\sum Y)}{N \sum X^2 - (\sum X)^2} \end{aligned} \tag{3}$$

Similarly, the regression line of X on Y is given by

$$X = b_0 + b_1 Y \tag{4}$$

where b_0 and b_1 are obtained from the normal equations

$$\begin{aligned} \sum X &= b_0 N + b_1 \sum Y \\ \sum XY &= b_0 \sum X + b_1 \sum Y^2 \end{aligned} \tag{5}$$

which yield

$$\begin{aligned} b_0 &= \frac{(\sum X)(\sum Y^2) - (\sum Y)(\sum XY)}{N \sum Y^2 - (\sum Y)^2} \\ b_1 &= \frac{N \sum XY - (\sum X)(\sum Y)}{N \sum Y^2 - (\sum Y)^2} \end{aligned} \tag{6}$$

Equations (1) and (4) can also be written, respectively, as

$$y = \left(\frac{\sum xy}{\sum x^2}\right) x \quad \text{and} \quad x = \left(\frac{\sum xy}{\sum y^2}\right) y \tag{7}$$

where $x = X - \bar{X}$ and $y = Y - \bar{Y}$.

The regression equations are identical if and only if all points of the scatter diagram lie on a line. In such case there is *perfect linear correlation* between X and Y.

STANDARD ERROR OF ESTIMATE

If we let Y_{est} represent the value of Y for given values of X as estimated from equation (*1*), a measure of the scatter about the regression line of Y on X is supplied by the quantity

$$s_{Y.X} = \sqrt{\frac{\sum (Y - Y_{\text{est}})^2}{N}} \tag{8}$$

which is called the *standard error of estimate of* Y *on* X.

If the regression line (*4*) is used, an analogous standard error of estimate of X on Y is defined by

$$s_{X.Y} = \sqrt{\frac{\sum (X - X_{\text{est}})^2}{N}} \tag{9}$$

In general, $s_{Y.X} \neq s_{X.Y}$.

Equation (*8*) can be written

$$s^2_{Y.X} = \frac{\sum Y^2 - a_0 \sum Y - a_1 \sum XY}{N} \tag{10}$$

which may be more suitable for computation (see Problem 14.3). A similar expression exists for equation (*9*).

The standard error of estimate has properties analogous to those of the standard deviation. For example, if we construct lines parallel to the regression line of Y on X at respective vertical distances $s_{Y.X}$, $2s_{Y.X}$, and $3s_{Y.X}$ from it, we should find, if N is large enough, that there would be included between these lines about 68%, 95%, and 99.7% of the sample points.

Just as a modified standard deviation given by

$$\hat{s} = \sqrt{\frac{N}{N-1}}\, s$$

was found useful for small samples, so a modified standard error of estimate given by

$$\hat{s}_{Y.X} = \sqrt{\frac{N}{N-2}}\, s_{Y.X}$$

is useful. For this reason, some statisticians prefer to define equation (*8*) or (*9*) with $N-2$ replacing N in the denominator.

EXPLAINED AND UNEXPLAINED VARIATION

The *total variation* of Y is defined as $\sum (Y - \bar{Y})^2$: that is, the sum of the squares of the deviations of the values of Y from the mean $\bar{Y}$. As shown in Problem 14.7, this can be written

$$\sum (Y - \bar{Y})^2 = \sum (Y - Y_{\text{est}})^2 + \sum (Y_{\text{est}} - \bar{Y})^2 \tag{11}$$

The first term on the right of equation (*11*) is called the *unexplained variation*, while the second term is called the *explained variation*—so called because the deviations $Y_{\text{est}} - \bar{Y}$ have a definite pattern, while the deviations $Y - Y_{\text{est}}$ behave in a random or unpredictable manner. Similar results hold for the variable X.

COEFFICIENT OF CORRELATION

The ratio of the explained variation to the total variation is called the *coefficient of determination*. If there is zero explained variation (i.e., the total variation is all unexplained), this ratio is 0. If there is zero unexplained variation (i.e., the total variation is all explained), the ratio is 1. In other cases the ratio lies between 0 and 1. Since the ratio is always nonnegative, we denote it by r^2. The quantity r, called the *coefficient of correlation* (or briefly *correlation coefficient*), is given by

$$r = \pm\sqrt{\frac{\text{explained variation}}{\text{total variation}}} = \pm\sqrt{\frac{\sum (Y_{\text{est}} - \bar{Y})^2}{\sum (Y - \bar{Y})^2}} \tag{12}$$

and varies between −1 and +1. The + and − signs are used for positive linear correlation and negative linear correlation, respectively. Note that r is a dimensionless quantity; that is, it does not depend on the units employed.

By using equations (*8*) and (*11*) and the fact that the standard deviation of Y is

$$s_Y = \sqrt{\frac{\sum (Y - \bar{Y})^2}{N}} \tag{13}$$

we find that equation (*12*) can be written, disregarding the sign, as

$$r = \sqrt{1 - \frac{s_{Y.X}^2}{s_Y^2}} \qquad \text{or} \qquad s_{Y.X} = s_Y\sqrt{1 - r^2} \tag{14}$$

Similar equations exist when X and Y are interchanged.

For the case of linear correlation, the quantity r is the same regardless of whether X or Y is considered the independent variable. Thus r is a very good measure of the linear correlation between two variables.

REMARKS CONCERNING THE CORRELATION COEFFICIENT

The definitions of the correlation coefficient in equations (*12*) and (*14*) are quite general and can be used for nonlinear relationships as well as for linear ones, the only differences being that Y_{est} is computed from a nonlinear regression equation in place of a linear equation and that the + and − signs are omitted. In such case equation (*8*), defining the standard error of estimate, is perfectly general. Equation (*10*), however, which applies to linear regression only, must be modified. If, for example, the estimating equation is

$$Y = a_0 + a_1 X + a_2 X^2 + \cdots + a_{n-1} X^{n-1} \tag{15}$$

then equation (*10*) is replaced by

$$s_{Y.X}^2 = \frac{\sum Y^2 - a_0 \sum Y - a_1 \sum XY - \cdots - a_{n-1} \sum X^{n-1} Y}{N} \tag{16}$$

In such case the *modified standard error of estimate* (discussed earlier in this chapter) is

$$\hat{s}_{Y.X} = \sqrt{\frac{N}{N-n}}\, s_{Y.X}$$

where the quantity $N - n$ is called the number of *degrees of freedom.*

It must be emphasized that in every case the computed value of r measures the degree of the relationship relative to the type of equation that is actually assumed. Thus if a linear equation is assumed and equation (*12*) or (*14*) yields a value of r near zero, it means that there is almost no *linear correlation* between the variables. However, it does not mean that there is no correlation at all, since there may actually be a high *nonlinear correlation* between the variables. In other words, the correlation coefficient measures the goodness of fit between (1) the equation actually assumed and (2) the data. Unless otherwise specified, the term *correlation coefficient* is used to mean *linear correlation coefficient.*

It should also be pointed out that a high correlation coefficient (i.e., near 1 or −1) does not necessarily indicate a direct dependence of the variables. Thus there may be a high correlation between the number of books published each year and the number of thunderstorms each year. Such examples are sometimes referred to as *nonsense,* or *spurious, correlations.*

PRODUCT-MOMENT FORMULA FOR THE LINEAR CORRELATION COEFFICIENT

If a linear relationship between two variables is assumed, equation (*12*) becomes

$$r = \frac{\sum xy}{\sqrt{(\sum x^2)(\sum y^2)}} \tag{17}$$

where $x = X - \bar{X}$ and $y = Y - \bar{Y}$ (see Problem 14.10). This formula, which automatically gives the proper sign of r, is called the *product-moment formula* and clearly shows the symmetry between X and Y.

If we write

$$s_{XY} = \frac{\sum xy}{N} \qquad s_X = \sqrt{\frac{\sum x^2}{N}} \qquad s_Y = \sqrt{\frac{\sum y^2}{N}} \tag{18}$$

then s_X and s_Y will be recognized as the standard deviations of the variables X and Y, respectively, while s_X^2 and s_Y^2 are their variances. The new quantity s_{XY} is called the *covariance* of X and Y. In terms of the symbols of formulas (*18*), formula (*17*) can be written

$$r = \frac{s_{XY}}{s_X s_Y} \tag{19}$$

Note that r is not only independent of the choice of units of X and Y, but is also independent of the choice of origin.

SHORT COMPUTATIONAL FORMULAS

Formula (*17*) can be written in the equivalent form

$$r = \frac{N\sum XY - (\sum X)(\sum Y)}{\sqrt{[N\sum X^2 - (\sum X)^2][N\sum Y^2 - (\sum Y)^2]}} \tag{20}$$

which is often used in computing r (see Problems 14.15 and 14.16).

For data grouped as in a *bivariate frequency table*, or *bivariate frequency distribution* (see Problem 14.17), it is convenient to use a *coding method* as in previous chapters. In such case, formula (*20*) can be written

$$r = \frac{N\sum fu_Xu_Y - (\sum f_Xu_X)(\sum f_Yu_Y)}{\sqrt{[N\sum f_Xu_X^2 - (\sum f_Xu_X)^2][N\sum f_Yu_Y^2 - (\sum f_Yu_Y)^2]}} \tag{21}$$

(see Problem 14.18). For convenience in calculations using this formula, a *correlation table* is used (see Problem 14.19).

For grouped data, formulas (*18*) can be written

$$s_{XY} = c_Xc_Y\left[\frac{\sum fu_Xu_Y}{N} - \left(\frac{\sum f_Xu_X}{N}\right)\left(\frac{\sum f_Yu_Y}{N}\right)\right] \tag{22}$$

$$s_X = c_X\sqrt{\frac{\sum f_Xu_X^2}{N} - \left(\frac{\sum f_Xu_X}{N}\right)^2} \tag{23}$$

$$s_Y = c_Y\sqrt{\frac{\sum f_Yu_Y^2}{N} - \left(\frac{\sum f_Yu_Y}{N}\right)^2} \tag{24}$$

where c_X and c_Y are the class-interval widths (assumed constant) corresponding to the variables X and Y, respectively. Note that (*23*) and (*24*) are equivalent to formula (*11*) of Chapter 4.

Formula (*19*) is seen to be equivalent to (*21*) if results (*22*) to (*24*) are used.

REGRESSION LINES AND THE LINEAR CORRELATION COEFFICIENT

The equation of the least-squares line $Y = a_0 + a_1 X$, the regression line of Y on X, can be written

$$Y - \bar{Y} = \frac{rs_Y}{s_X}(X - \bar{X}) \qquad \text{or} \qquad y = \frac{rs_Y}{s_X}x \tag{25}$$

Similarly, the regression line of X on Y, $X = b_0 + b_1 Y$, can be written

$$X - \bar{X} = \frac{rs_X}{s_Y}(Y - \bar{Y}) \qquad \text{or} \qquad x = \frac{rs_X}{s_Y}y \tag{26}$$

The slopes of the lines in equations (*25*) and (*26*) are equal if and only if $r = \pm 1$. In such case the two lines are identical and there is perfect linear correlation between the variables X and Y. If $r = 0$, the lines are at right angles and there is no linear correlation between X and Y. Thus the linear correlation coefficient measures the departure of the two regression lines.

Note that if equations (*25*) and (*26*) are written $Y = a_0 + a_1 X$ and $X = b_0 + b_1 Y$, respectively, then $a_1 b_1 = r^2$ (see Problem 14.22).

CORRELATION OF TIME SERIES

If each of the variables X and Y depends on time, it is possible that a relationship may exist between X and Y even though such relationship is not necessarily one of direct dependence and may produce "nonsense correlation." The correlation coefficient is obtained simply by considering the pairs of values (X, Y) corresponding to the various times and proceeding as usual, making use of the above formulas (see Problem 14.28).

It is possible to attempt to correlate values of a variable X at certain times with corresponding values of X at earlier times. Such correlation is often called *autocorrelation.*

CORRELATION OF ATTRIBUTES

The methods described in this chapter do not enable us to consider the correlation of variables that are nonnumerical by nature, such as the *attributes* of individuals (e.g., hair color, eye color, etc.). For a discussion of the correlation of attributes, see Chapter 12.

SAMPLING THEORY OF CORRELATION

The N pairs of values (X, Y) of two variables can be thought of as samples from a population of all such pairs that are possible. Since two variables are involved, this is called a *bivariate population,* which we assume to be a *bivariate normal distribution.*

We can think of a theoretical population coefficient of correlation, denoted by ρ, which is estimated by the sample correlation coefficient r. Tests of significance or hypotheses concerning various values of ρ require knowledge of the sampling distribution of r. For $\rho = 0$ this distribution is symmetrical, and a statistic involving Student's distribution can be used. For $\rho \neq 0$, the distribution is skewed; in such case a transformation developed by Fisher produces a statistic that is approximately normally distributed. The following tests summarize the procedures involved:

1. **Test of Hypothesis** $\rho = 0$. Here we use the fact that the statistic

$$t = \frac{r\sqrt{N-2}}{\sqrt{1-r^2}} \tag{27}$$

has Student's distribution with $\nu = N - 2$ degrees of freedom (see Problems 14.31 and 14.32).

2. **Test of Hypothesis** $\rho = \rho_0 \neq 0$. Here we use the fact that the statistic

$$Z = \tfrac{1}{2}\log_e\left(\frac{1+r}{1-r}\right) = 1.1513\log_{10}\left(\frac{1+r}{1-r}\right) \tag{28}$$

where $e = 2.71828\ldots$, is approximately normally distributed with mean and standard deviation given by

$$\mu_Z = \tfrac{1}{2}\log_e\left(\frac{1+\rho_0}{1-\rho_0}\right) = 1.1513\log_{10}\left(\frac{1+\rho_0}{1-\rho_0}\right) \qquad \sigma_Z = \frac{1}{\sqrt{N-3}} \tag{29}$$

Equations (*28*) and (*29*) can also be used to find confidence limits for correlation coefficients (see Problems 14.33 and 14.34). Equation (*28*) is called *Fisher's Z transformation.*

3. **Significance of a Difference between Correlation Coefficients.** To determine whether two correlation coefficients, r_1 and r_2, drawn from samples of sizes N_1 and N_2, respectively, differ significantly from each other, we compute Z_1 and Z_2 corresponding to r_1 and r_2 by using equation (*28*). We then use the fact that the test statistic

$$z = \frac{Z_1 - Z_2 - \mu_{Z1-Z2}}{\sigma_{Z1-Z2}} \tag{30}$$

where

$$\mu_{Z1-Z2} = \mu_{Z1} - \mu_{Z2}$$

and

$$\sigma_{Z1-Z2} = \sqrt{\sigma_{Z1}^2 + \sigma_{Z2}^2} = \sqrt{\frac{1}{N_1-3} + \frac{1}{N_2-3}}$$

is normally distributed (see Problem 14.35).

SAMPLING THEORY OF REGRESSION

The regression equation $Y = a_0 + a_1X$ is obtained on the basis of sample data. We are often interested in the corresponding regression equation for the population from which the sample was drawn. The following are three tests concerning such a population:

1. **Test of Hypothesis** $a_1 = A_1$. To test the hypothesis that the regression coefficient a_1 is equal to some specified value A_1, we use the fact that the statistic

$$t = \frac{a_1 - A_1}{s_{Y.X}/s_X}\sqrt{N-2} \tag{31}$$

has Student's distribution with $N-2$ degrees of freedom. This can also be used to find confidence intervals for population regression coefficients from sample values (see Problems 14.36 and 14.37).

2. **Test of Hypothesis for Predicted Values.** Let Y_0 denote the predicted value of Y corresponding to $X = X_0$ as estimated from the sample regression equation (i.e., $Y_0 = a_0 + a_1X_0$). Let Y_p denote the predicted value of Y corresponding to $X - X_0$ for the population. Then the statistic

$$t = \frac{Y_0 - Y_p}{s_{Y.X}\sqrt{N+1+(X_0-\bar{X})^2/s_X^2}}\sqrt{N-2} = \frac{Y_0 - Y_p}{\hat{s}_{Y.X}\sqrt{1+1/N+(X_0-\bar{X})^2/(Ns_X^2)}} \tag{32}$$

has Student's distribution with $N-2$ degrees of freedom. From this, confidence limits for predicted population values can be found (see Problem 14.38).

3. **Test of Hypothesis for Predicted Mean Values.** Let Y_0 denote the predicted value of Y corresponding to $X = X_0$ as estimated from the sample regression equation (i.e., $Y_0 = a_0 + a_1 X_0$). Let $\bar{Y}_p$ denote the predicted *mean value* of Y corresponding to $X = X_0$ for the population. Then the statistic

$$t = \frac{Y_0 - \bar{Y}_p}{s_{Y.X}\sqrt{1 + (X_0 - \bar{X})^2/s_X^2}}\sqrt{N-2} = \frac{Y_0 - \bar{Y}_p}{\hat{s}_{Y.X}\sqrt{1/N + (X_0 - \bar{X})^2/(Ns_X^2)}} \tag{33}$$

has Student's distribution with $N-2$ degrees of freedom. From this, confidence limits for predicted mean population values can be found (see Problem 14.39).

Solved Problems

SCATTER DIAGRAMS AND REGRESSION LINES

14.1 Table 14.1 shows in inches (in) the respective heights X and Y of a sample of 12 fathers and their oldest sons.

(*a*) Construct a scatter diagram.

(*b*) Find the least-squares regression line of Y on X.

(*c*) Find the least-squares regression line of X on Y.

Table 14.1

Height X of father (in)	65	63	67	64	68	62	70	66	68	67	69	71
Height Y of son (in)	68	66	68	65	69	66	68	65	71	67	68	70

SOLUTION

(*a*) The scatter diagram is obtained by plotting the points (X, Y) on a rectangular coordinate system, as shown in Fig. 14-2.

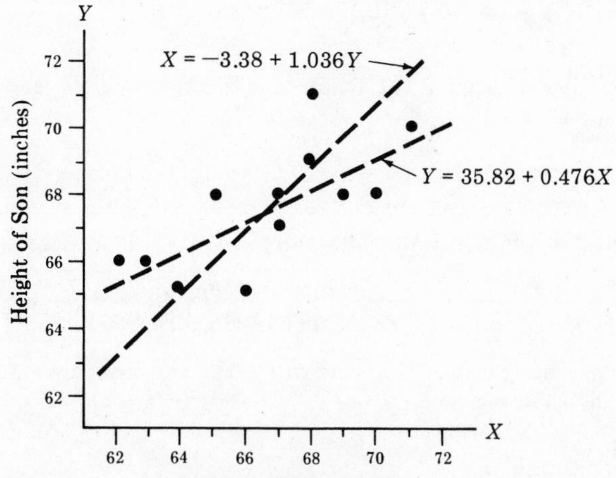

Fig. 14-2

(b) The regression line of Y on X is given by $Y = a_0 + a_1 X$, where a_0 and a_1 are obtained by solving the normal equations

$$\begin{aligned} \sum Y &= a_0 N + a_1 \sum X \\ \sum XY &= a_0 \sum X + a_1 \sum X^2 \end{aligned}$$

The sums are shown in Table 14.2, from which the normal equations become

$$\begin{aligned} 12a_0 + 800a_1 &= 811 \\ 800a_0 + 53{,}418a_1 &= 54{,}107 \end{aligned}$$

from which we find that $a_0 = 35.82$ and $a_1 = 0.476$, and thus $Y = 35.82 + 0.476X$. The graph of this equation is shown in Fig. 14-2.

Table 14.2

X	Y	X^2	XY	Y^2
65	68	4225	4420	4624
63	66	3969	4158	4356
67	68	4489	4556	4624
64	65	4096	4160	4225
68	69	4624	4692	4761
62	66	3844	4092	4356
70	68	4900	4760	4624
66	65	4356	4290	4225
68	71	4624	4828	5041
67	67	4489	4489	4489
69	68	4761	4692	4624
71	70	5041	4970	4900
$\sum X = 800$	$\sum Y = 811$	$\sum X^2 = 53{,}418$	$\sum XY = 54{,}107$	$\sum Y^2 = 54{,}849$

Another method

$$a_0 = \frac{(\sum Y)(\sum X^2) - (\sum X)(\sum XY)}{N \sum X^2 - (\sum X)^2} = 35.82 \qquad a_1 = \frac{N \sum XY - (\sum X)(\sum Y)}{N \sum X^2 - (\sum X)^2} = 0.476$$

(c) The regression line of X on Y is given by $X = b_0 + b_1 Y$, where b_0 and b_1 are obtained by solving the normal equations

$$\begin{aligned} \sum X &= b_0 N + b_1 \sum Y \\ \sum XY &= b_0 \sum Y + b_1 \sum Y^2 \end{aligned}$$

Using the sums in Table 14.2, these become

$$\begin{aligned} 12b_0 + 811b_1 &= 800 \\ 811b_0 + 54{,}849b_1 &= 54{,}107 \end{aligned}$$

from which we find that $b_0 = -3.38$ and $b_1 = 1.036$, and thus $X = -3.38 + 1.036Y$. The graph of this equation is shown in Fig. 14-2.

Another method

$$b_0 = \frac{(\sum X)(\sum Y^2) - (\sum Y)(\sum XY)}{N \sum Y^2 - (\sum Y)^2} = -3.38 \qquad b_1 = \frac{N \sum XY - (\sum Y)(\sum X)}{N \sum Y^2 - (\sum Y)^2} = 1.036$$

14.2 Work Problems 14.1(*b*) and 14.1(*c*) by using the regression lines

$$y = \left(\frac{\sum xy}{\sum x^2}\right)x \qquad \text{and} \qquad x = \left(\frac{\sum xy}{\sum y^2}\right)y$$

where $x = X - \bar{X}$ and $y = Y - \bar{Y}$.

SOLUTION

First method

The work may be arranged as in Table 14.3. The regression line of Y on X is

$$y = \left(\frac{\sum xy}{\sum x^2}\right)x = \left(\frac{40.34}{84.68}\right)x = 0.476x \qquad \text{or} \qquad Y - 67.6 = 0.476(X - 66.7)$$

Table 14.3

X	Y	$x = X - \bar{X}$	$y = Y - \bar{Y}$	x^2	xy	y^2
65	68	−1.7	0.4	2.89	−0.68	0.16
63	66	−3.7	−1.6	13.69	5.92	2.56
67	68	0.3	0.4	0.09	0.12	0.16
64	65	−2.7	−2.6	7.29	7.02	6.76
68	69	1.3	1.4	1.69	1.82	1.96
62	66	−4.7	−1.6	22.09	7.52	2.56
70	68	3.3	0.4	10.89	1.32	0.16
66	65	−0.7	−2.6	0.49	1.82	6.76
68	71	1.3	3.4	1.69	4.42	11.56
67	67	0.3	−0.6	0.09	−0.18	0.36
69	68	2.3	0.4	5.29	0.92	0.16
71	70	4.3	2.4	18.49	10.32	5.76
$\sum X = 800$ $\bar{X} = 800/12$ $= 66.7$	$\sum Y = 811$ $\bar{Y} = 811/12$ $= 67.6$			$\sum x^2 = 84.68$	$\sum xy = 40.34$	$\sum y^2 = 38.92$

The regression line of X on Y is

$$x = \left(\frac{\sum xy}{\sum y^2}\right)y = \left(\frac{40.34}{38.92}\right)y = 1.036y \qquad \text{or} \qquad X - 66.7 = 1.036(Y - 67.6)$$

These agree with the results of Problem 14.1.

Second method

Subtract a suitable constant, say 60, from each of the values of X and Y. The results may be arranged as in Table 14.4. Proceed using the second method of Problem 13.17. We thus have

$$a_1 = \frac{N\sum X'Y' - (\sum X')(\sum Y')}{N\sum X'^2 - (\sum X')^2} = 0.476 \qquad b_1 = \frac{N\sum X'Y' - (\sum Y')(\sum X')}{N\sum Y'^2 - (\sum Y')^2} = 1.036$$

Since $\bar{X} = 60 + 80/12 = 66.7$ and $\bar{Y} = 60 + 91/12 = 67.6$, the required regression equations are as before.

Note that if a_0 and b_0 were computed by this method, we would *not* get the same results as before, since a_0 and b_0 depend on the choice of origin. Thus this method is used *only* to obtain a_1 and b_1, which are independent of the choice of origin.

Table 14.4

X'	Y'	X'^2	$X'Y'$	Y'^2
5	8	25	40	64
3	6	9	18	36
7	8	49	56	64
4	5	16	20	25
8	9	64	72	81
2	6	4	12	36
10	8	100	80	64
6	5	36	30	25
8	11	64	88	121
7	7	49	49	49
9	8	81	72	64
11	10	121	110	100
$\sum X'=80$	$\sum Y'=91$	$\sum X'^2=618$	$\sum X'Y'=647$	$\sum Y'^2=729$

STANDARD ERROR OF ESTIMATE

14.3 If the regression line of Y on X is given by $Y=a_0+a_1X$, prove that the standard error of estimate $s_{Y.X}$ is given by

$$s_{Y.X}^2=\frac{\sum Y^2-a_0\sum Y-a_1\sum XY}{N}$$

SOLUTION

The values of Y as estimated from the regression line are given by $Y_{\text{est}}=a_0+a_1X$. Thus

$$s_{Y.X}^2=\frac{\sum(Y-Y_{\text{est}})^2}{N}=\frac{\sum(Y-a_0-a_1X)^2}{N}$$

$$=\frac{\sum Y(Y-a_0-a_1X)-a_0\sum(Y-a_0-a_1X)-a_1\sum X(Y-a_0-a_1X)}{N}$$

But $$\sum(Y-a_0-a_1X)=\sum Y-a_0N-a_1\sum X=0$$

and $$\sum X(Y-a_0-a_1X)=\sum XY-a_0\sum X-a_1\sum X^2=0$$

since from the normal equations

$$\sum Y=a_0N+a_1\sum X$$
$$\sum XY=a_0\sum X+a_1\sum X^2$$

Thus $$s_{Y.X}^2=\frac{\sum Y(Y-a_0-a_1X)}{N}=\frac{\sum Y^2-a_0\sum Y-a_1\sum XY}{N}$$

This result can be extended to nonlinear regression equations.

14.4 If $x=X-\bar{X}$ and $y=Y-\bar{Y}$, show that the result of Problem 14.3 can be written

$$s_{Y.X}^2=\frac{\sum y^2-a_1\sum xy}{N}$$

SOLUTION

From Problem 14.3, with $X = x + \bar{X}$ and $Y = y + \bar{Y}$, we have

$$\begin{aligned}
Ns^2_{Y.X} &= \sum Y^2 - a_0 \sum Y - a_1 \sum XY = \sum (y+\bar{Y})^2 - a_0 \sum (y+\bar{Y}) - a_1 \sum (x+\bar{X})(y+\bar{Y}) \\
&= \sum (y^2 + 2y\bar{Y} + \bar{Y}^2) - a_0(\sum y + N\bar{Y}) - a_1 \sum (xy + \bar{X}y + x\bar{Y} + \bar{X}\bar{Y}) \\
&= \sum y^2 + 2\bar{Y} \sum y + N\bar{Y}^2 - a_0 N\bar{Y} - a_1 \sum xy - a_1 \bar{X} \sum y - a_1 \bar{Y} \sum x - a_1 N\bar{X}\bar{Y} \\
&= \sum y^2 + N\bar{Y}^2 - a_0 N\bar{Y} - a_1 \sum xy - a_1 N\bar{X}\bar{Y} \\
&= \sum y^2 - a_1 \sum xy + N\bar{Y}(\bar{Y} - a_0 - a_1\bar{X}) \\
&= \sum y^2 - a_1 \sum xy
\end{aligned}$$

where we have used the results $\sum x = 0$, $\sum y = 0$, and $\bar{Y} = a_0 + a_1\bar{X}$ (which follows on dividing both sides of the normal equation $\sum Y = a_0 N + a_1 \sum X$ by N).

14.5 Compute the standard error of estimate, $s_{Y.X}$, for the data of Problem 14.1 by using (*a*) the definition and (*b*) the result of Problem 14.4.

SOLUTION

(*a*) From Problem 14.1(*b*) the regression line of Y on X is $Y = 35.82 + 0.476X$. Table 14.5 lists the actual values of Y (from Table 14.1) and the estimated values of Y, denoted by Y_{est}, as obtained from the regression line; for example, corresponding to $X = 65$ we have $Y_{est} = 35.82 + 0.476(65) = 66.76$. Also listed are the values $Y - Y_{est}$, which are needed in computing $s_{Y.X}$:

$$s^2_{Y.X} = \frac{\sum (Y - Y_{est})}{N} = \frac{(1.24)^2 + (0.19)^2 + \cdots + (0.38)^2}{12} = 1.642$$

and $s_{Y.X} = \sqrt{1.642} = 1.28$ in.

Table 14.5

X	65	63	67	64	68	62	70	66	68	67	69	71
Y	68	66	68	65	69	66	68	65	71	67	68	70
Y_{est}	66.76	65.81	67.71	66.28	68.19	65.33	69.14	67.24	68.19	67.71	68.66	69.62
$Y - Y_{est}$	1.24	0.19	0.29	−1.28	0.81	0.67	−1.14	−2.24	2.81	−0.71	−0.66	0.38

(*b*) From Problems 14.1, 14.2, and 14.4

$$s^2_{Y.X} = \frac{\sum y^2 - a_1 \sum xy}{N} = \frac{38.92 - 0.476(40.34)}{12} = 1.643$$

and $s_{Y.X} = \sqrt{1.643} = 1.28$ in.

14.6 (*a*) Construct two lines which are parallel to the regression line of Problem 14.1 and which have a vertical distance $s_{Y.X}$ from it.

(*b*) Determine the percentage of data points falling between these two lines.

SOLUTION

(*a*) The regression line $Y = 35.82 + 0.476X$, as obtained in Problem 14.1, is shown as a heavy line in Fig. 14-3. The two parallel lines, each having vertical distance $s_{Y.X} = 1.28$ from it (see Problem 14.5), are shown dashed in Fig. 14-3.

(*b*) It is seen in Fig. 14-3 that while seven of the 12 data points fall between the lines, three appear to lie on the lines. Further examination (using the bottom row in Table 14.5, for example) reveals that two of these three points lie between the lines. Thus the required percentage is $9/12 = 75\%$.

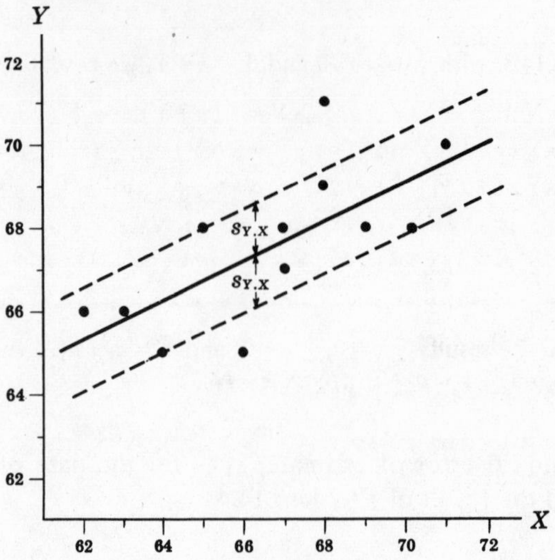

Fig. 14-3

Another method

From the bottom row in Table 14.5, $Y - Y_{\text{est}}$ lies between -1.28 and 1.28 (i.e., $\pm s_{Y.X}$) for nine points (X, Y). Thus the required percentage is $9/12 = 75\%$.

If the points are normally distributed about the regression line, theory predicts that about 68% of the points lie between the lines. This would have been more nearly the case if the sample size were large.

Note: A better estimate of the standard error of estimate of the population from which the sample heights were taken is given by $\hat{s}_{Y.X} = \sqrt{N/(N-2)}\, s_{Y.X} = \sqrt{12/10}(1.28) = 1.40$ in.

EXPLAINED AND UNEXPLAINED VARIATION

14.7 Prove that $\sum (Y - \bar{Y})^2 = \sum (Y - Y_{\text{est}})^2 + \sum (Y_{\text{est}} - \bar{Y})^2$.

SOLUTION

Squaring both sides of $Y - \bar{Y} = (Y - Y_{\text{est}}) + (Y_{\text{est}} - \bar{Y})$ and then summing, we have

$$\sum (Y - \bar{Y})^2 = \sum (Y - Y_{\text{est}})^2 + \sum (Y_{\text{est}} - \bar{Y})^2 + 2 \sum (Y - Y_{\text{est}})(Y_{\text{est}} - \bar{Y})$$

The required result follows at once if we can show that the last sum is zero; in the case of linear regression, this is so since

$$\begin{aligned} \sum (Y - Y_{\text{est}})(Y_{\text{est}} - \bar{Y}) &= \sum (Y - a_0 - a_1 X)(a_0 + a_1 X - \bar{Y}) \\ &= a_0 \sum (Y - a_0 - a_1 X) + a_1 \sum X(Y - a_0 - a_1 X) - \bar{Y} \sum (Y - a_0 - a_1 X) = 0 \end{aligned}$$

because of the normal equations $\sum (Y - a_0 - a_1 X) = 0$ and $\sum X(Y - a_0 - a_1 X) = 0$.

The result can similarly be shown valid for nonlinear regression by using a least-squares curve given by $Y_{\text{est}} = a_0 + a_1 X + a_2 X^2 + \cdots + a_n X^n$.

Mathcad **14.8** Compute (*a*) the total variation, (*b*) the unexplained variation, and (*c*) the explained variation for the data of Problem 14.1.

SOLUTION

(*a*) The total variation (from Problem 14.2) is $\sum (Y - \bar{Y})^2 = \sum y^2 = 38.92$.

(*b*) The unexplained variation (from Problem 14.5) is $\sum (Y - Y_{\text{est}})^2 = N s_{Y.X}^2 = 19.70$.

(*c*) The explained variation (using Problem 14.7) is $\sum (Y_{\text{est}} - \bar{Y})^2 = 38.92 - 19.70 = 19.22$.

Another method

Since $\bar{Y} = 811/12 = 67.58$, we can construct Table 14.6 by using the Y_{est} values from Table 14.5; then $\sum (Y_{est} - \bar{Y})^2 = (-0.82)^2 + (-1.77)^2 + \cdots + (2.04)^2 = 19.21$. The results of parts (*a*) and (*b*) can also be obtained directly.

Table 14.6

$Y_{est} - \bar{Y}$ or $Y_{est} - 67.58$	−0.82	−1.77	0.13	−1.30	0.61	−2.25	1.56	−0.34	0.61	0.13	1.08	2.04

COEFFICIENT OF CORRELATION

14.9 Find (*a*) the coefficient of determination and (*b*) the coefficient of correlation for the data of Problem 14.1. Use the results of Problem 14.8.

SOLUTION

(*a*) Coefficient of determination $= r^2 = \dfrac{\text{explained variation}}{\text{total variation}} = \dfrac{19.22}{38.92} = 0.4938$

(*b*) Coefficient of correlation $= r = \pm\sqrt{0.4938} = \pm 0.7027$

Since the variable Y_{est} increases as X increases, the correlation is positive and we therefore write $r = 0.7027$, or 0.70 to two significant figures.

14.10 Prove that for linear regression the coefficient of correlation between the variables X and Y can be written

$$r = \frac{\sum xy}{\sqrt{(\sum x^2)(\sum y^2)}}$$

where $x = X - \bar{X}$ and $y = Y - \bar{Y}$.

SOLUTION

The least-squares regression line of Y on X can be written $Y_{est} = a_0 + a_1 X$ or $y_{est} = a_1 x$, where [see Problem 13.15(*a*)]

$$a_1 = \frac{\sum xy}{\sum x^2} \qquad \text{and} \qquad y_{est} = Y_{est} - \bar{Y}$$

Then

$$r^2 = \frac{\text{explained variation}}{\text{total variation}} = \frac{\sum (Y_{est} - \bar{Y})^2}{\sum (Y - \bar{Y})^2} = \frac{\sum y_{est}^2}{\sum y^2}$$

$$= \frac{\sum a_1^2 x^2}{\sum y^2} = \frac{a_1^2 \sum x^2}{\sum y^2} = \left(\frac{\sum xy}{\sum x^2}\right)^2 \frac{\sum x^2}{\sum y^2} = \frac{(\sum xy)^2}{(\sum x^2)(\sum y^2)}$$

and

$$r = \pm \frac{\sum xy}{\sqrt{(\sum x^2)(\sum y^2)}}$$

However, since the quantity

$$\frac{\sum xy}{\sqrt{(\sum x^2)(\sum y^2)}}$$

is positive when y_{est} increases as x increases (i.e., positive linear correlation) and negative when y_{est} decreases as x increases (i.e., negative linear correlation), it *automatically* has the correct sign associated with it. Hence we define the coefficient of linear correlation to be

$$r = \frac{\sum xy}{\sqrt{(\sum x^2)(\sum y^2)}}$$

This is often called the ***product-moment formula*** for the linear correlation coefficient.

PRODUCT-MOMENT FORMULA FOR THE LINEAR CORRELATION COEFFICIENT

14.11 Find the coefficient of linear correlation between the variables X and Y presented in Table 14.7.

Table 14.7

X	1	3	4	6	8	9	11	14
Y	1	2	4	4	5	7	8	9

SOLUTION

The work involved in the computation can be organized as in Table 14.8.

$$r = \frac{\sum xy}{\sqrt{(\sum x^2)(\sum y^2)}} = \frac{84}{\sqrt{(132)(56)}} = 0.977$$

This shows that there is a very high linear correlation between the variables, as we have already observed in Problems 13.8 and 13.12.

Table 14.8

X	Y	$x = X - \bar{X}$	$y = Y - \bar{Y}$	x^2	xy	y^2
1	1	−6	−4	36	24	16
3	2	−4	−3	16	12	9
4	4	−3	−1	9	3	1
6	4	−1	−1	1	1	1
8	5	1	0	1	0	0
9	7	2	2	4	4	4
11	8	4	3	16	12	9
14	9	7	4	49	28	16
$\sum X = 56$ $\bar{X} = 56/8 = 7$	$\sum Y = 40$ $\bar{Y} = 40/8 = 5$			$\sum x^2 = 132$	$\sum xy = 84$	$\sum y^2 = 56$

14.12 For the data of Problem 14.11, find (a) the standard deviation of X, (b) the standard deviation of Y, (c) the variance of X, (d) the variance of Y, and (e) the covariance of X and Y.

SOLUTION

(a) Standard deviation of $X = s_X = \sqrt{\frac{\sum (X - \bar{X})^2}{N}} = \sqrt{\frac{\sum x^2}{N}} = \sqrt{\frac{132}{8}} = 4.06$

(b) Standard deviation of $Y = s_Y = \sqrt{\frac{\sum (Y - \bar{Y})^2}{N}} = \sqrt{\frac{\sum y^2}{N}} = \sqrt{\frac{56}{8}} = 2.65$

(c) Variance of $X = s_X^2 = 16.50$

(d) Variance of $Y = s_Y^2 = 7.00$

(e) Covariance of X and $Y = s_{XY} = \frac{\sum xy}{N} = \frac{84}{8} = 10.50$

14.13 For the data of Problem 14.11, verify the formula

$$r = \frac{s_{XY}}{s_X s_Y}$$

SOLUTION

From Problem 14.12

$$r = \frac{s_{XY}}{s_X s_Y} = \frac{10.50}{(4.06)(2.65)} = 0.976$$

which, except for rounding errors, agrees with the result of Problem 14.11.

14.14 By using the product-moment formula, obtain the linear correlation coefficient for the data of Problem 14.1.

SOLUTION

The work involved in the computation can be organized as in Table 14.3 of Problem 14.2. Then

$$r = \frac{\sum xy}{\sqrt{(\sum x^2)(\sum y^2)}} = \frac{40.34}{\sqrt{(84.68)(38.92)}} = 0.7027$$

agreeing with the longer method of Problem 14.9.

14.15 Show that the linear correlation coefficient is given by

$$r = \frac{N \sum XY - (\sum X)(\sum Y)}{\sqrt{[N \sum X^2 - (\sum X)^2][N \sum Y^2 - (\sum Y)^2]}}$$

SOLUTION

Writing $x = X - \bar{X}$ and $y = Y - \bar{Y}$ in the result of Problem 14.10, we have

$$r = \frac{\sum xy}{\sqrt{(\sum x^2)(\sum y^2)}} = \frac{\sum (X - \bar{X})(Y - \bar{Y})}{\sqrt{[\sum (X - \bar{X})^2][\sum (Y - \bar{Y})^2]}} \tag{34}$$

But

$$\begin{aligned} \sum (X - \bar{X})(Y - \bar{Y}) &= \sum (XY - \bar{X}Y - X\bar{Y} + \bar{X}\bar{Y}) = \sum XY - \bar{X} \sum Y - \bar{Y} \sum X + N\bar{X}\bar{Y} \\ &= \sum XY - N\bar{X}\bar{Y} - N\bar{Y}\bar{X} + N\bar{X}\bar{Y} = \sum XY - N\bar{X}\bar{Y} \\ &= \sum XY - \frac{(\sum X)(\sum Y)}{N} \end{aligned}$$

since $\bar{X} = (\sum X)/N$ and $\bar{Y} = (\sum Y)/N$. Similarly,

$$\begin{aligned} \sum (X - \bar{X})^2 &= \sum (X^2 - 2X\bar{X} + \bar{X}^2) = \sum X^2 - 2\bar{X} \sum X + N\bar{X}^2 \\ &= \sum X^2 - \frac{2(\sum X)^2}{N} + \frac{(\sum X)^2}{N} = \sum X^2 - \frac{(\sum X)^2}{N} \end{aligned}$$

and

$$\sum (Y - \bar{Y})^2 = \sum Y^2 - \frac{(\sum Y)^2}{N}$$

Thus equation (34) becomes

$$r = \frac{\sum XY - (\sum X)(\sum Y)/N}{\sqrt{[\sum X^2 - (\sum X)^2/N][\sum Y^2 - (\sum Y)^2/N]}} = \frac{N \sum XY - (\sum X)(\sum Y)}{\sqrt{[N \sum X^2 - (\sum X)^2][N \sum Y^2 - (\sum Y)^2]}}$$

14.16 Use the formula of Problem 14.15 to obtain the linear correlation coefficient for the data of Problem 14.1.

SOLUTION

From Table 14.2 of Problem 14.1 we have

$$r=\frac{N\sum XY-(\sum X)(\sum Y)}{\sqrt{[N\sum X^2-(\sum X)^2][N\sum Y^2-(\sum Y)^2]}}$$

$$=\frac{(12)(54{,}107)-(800)(811)}{\sqrt{[(12)(53{,}418)-(800)^2][(12)(54{,}849)-(811)^2]}}=0.7027$$

as in Problems 14.9 and 14.14.

Another method

The value of r is independent of the choice of origin of X and Y. We can thus use the results of the second method of Problem 14.2 to obtain

$$r=\frac{N\sum X'Y'-(\sum X')(\sum Y')}{\sqrt{[N\sum X'^2-(\sum X')^2][N\sum Y'^2-(\sum Y')^2]}}=\frac{(12)(647)-(80)(91)}{\sqrt{[(12)(618)-(80)^2][(12)(729)-(91)^2]}}=0.7027$$

CORRELATION COEFFICIENT FOR GROUPED DATA

14.17 Table 14.9 shows the frequency distributions of the final grades of 100 students in mathematics and physics. Referring to this table, determine:

(*a*) The number of students who received grades of 70–79 in mathematics and 80–89 in physics.

(*b*) The percentage of students with mathematics grades below 70.

(*c*) The number of students who received a grade of 70 or more in physics and of less than 80 in mathematics.

(*d*) The percentage of students who passed at least one of the subjects; assume that the minimum passing grade is 60.

Table 14.9

		Mathematics Grades						
		40–49	50–59	60–69	70–79	80–89	90–99	Total
Physics Grades	90–99				2	4	4	10
	80–89			1	4	6	5	16
	70–79			5	10	8	1	24
	60–69	1	4	9	5	2		21
	50–59	3	6	6	2			17
	40–49	3	5	4				12
	Total	7	15	25	23	20	10	100

SOLUTION

(*a*) In Table 14.9, proceed down the column headed 70–79 (mathematics grade) to the row marked 80–89 (physics grade), where the entry is 4, which is the required number of students.

(*b*) The total number of students with mathematics grades below 70 is the number with grades 40–49 + the number with grades 50–59 + the number with grades 60–69 = 7 + 15 + 25 = 47. Thus the required percentage of students is 47/100 = 47%.

(*c*) The required number of students is the total of the entries in Table 14.10 (which represents part of Table 14.9). Thus the required number of students is 1 + 5 + 2 + 4 + 10 = 22.

(*d*) Table 14.11 (taken from Table 14.9) shows that the number of students with grades below 60 in both mathematics and physics is 3 + 3 + 6 + 5 = 17. Thus the number of students with grades 60 or over in either physics or mathematics or in both is 100 − 17 = 83, and the required percentage is 83/100 = 83%.

Table 14.10

		Mathematics Grades	
		60–69	70–79
Physics Grades	90–99		2
	80–89	1	4
	70–79	5	10

Table 14.11

		Mathematics Grades	
		40–49	50–59
Physics Grades	50–59	3	6
	40–49	3	5

Table 14.9 is sometimes called a *bivariate frequency table*, or *bivariate frequency distribution*. Each square in the table is called a *cell* and corresponds to a pair of classes or class intervals. The number indicated in the cell is called the *cell frequency*. For example, in part (*a*) the number 4 is the frequency of the cell corresponding to the pair of class intervals 70–79 in mathematics and 80–89 in physics.

The totals indicated in the last row and last column are called *marginal totals*, or *marginal frequencies*. They correspond, respectively, to the class frequencies of the separate frequency distributions of the mathematics and physics grades.

14.18 Show how to modify the formula of Problem 14.15 for the case of data grouped as in the bivariate frequency table (Table 14.9).

SOLUTION

For grouped data, we can consider the various values of the variables X and Y as coinciding with the class marks, while f_X and f_Y are the corresponding class frequencies, or marginal frequencies, shown in the last row and column of the bivariate frequency table. If we let f represent the various cell frequencies corresponding to the pairs of class marks (X, Y), then we can replace the formula of Problem 14.15 with

$$r = \frac{N\sum fXY - (\sum f_X X)(\sum f_Y Y)}{\sqrt{[N\sum f_X X^2 - (\sum f_X X)^2][N\sum f_Y Y^2 - (\sum f_Y Y)^2]}} \tag{35}$$

If we let $X = A + c_X u_X$ and $Y = B + c_Y u_Y$, where c_X and c_Y are the class-interval widths (assumed constant) and A and B are arbitrary class marks corresponding to the variables, formula (*35*) becomes formula (*21*) of this chapter:

$$r = \frac{N\sum f u_X u_Y - (\sum f_X u_X)(\sum f_Y u_Y)}{\sqrt{[N\sum f_X u_X^2 - (\sum f_X u_X)^2][N\sum f_Y u_Y^2 - (\sum f_Y u_Y)^2]}} \tag{21}$$

This is the *coding method* used in previous chapters as a short method for computing means, standard deviations, and higher moments.

14.19 Find the coefficient of linear correlation of the mathematics and physics grades of Problem 14.17.

SOLUTION

We use formula (*21*). The work can be arranged as in Table 14.12, which is called a *correlation table.* The sums $\sum f_X$, $\sum f_X u_X$, $\sum f_X u_X^2$, $\sum f_Y$, $\sum f_Y u_Y$, and $\sum f_Y u_Y^2$ are obtained by using the coding method, as in earlier chapters.

The number in the corner of each cell in Table 14.12 represents the product $f u_X u_Y$, where f is the cell frequency. The sum of these corner numbers in each row is indicated in the corresponding row of the last column. The sum of these corner numbers in each column is indicated in the corresponding column of the last row. The final totals of the last row and last column are equal and represent $\sum f u_X u_Y$.

From Table 14.12 we have

$$r = \frac{N \sum f u_X u_Y - (\sum f_X u_X)(\sum f_Y u_Y)}{\sqrt{[N \sum f_X u_X^2 - (\sum f_X u_X)^2][N \sum f_Y u_Y^2 - (\sum f_Y u_Y)^2]}}$$

$$= \frac{(100)(125) - (64)(-55)}{\sqrt{[(100)(236) - (64)^2][(100)(253) - (-55)^2]}} = \frac{16{,}020}{\sqrt{(19{,}504)(22{,}275)}} = 0.7686$$

14.20 Use Table 14.12 to compute (*a*) s_X, (*b*) s_Y, and (*c*) s_{XY} and thus to verify the formula $r = s_{XY}/(s_X s_Y)$.

Table 14.12

		Mathematics Grades X									
	X	44.5	54.5	64.5	74.5	84.5	94.5				
Y	u_X / u_Y	−2	−1	0	1	2	3	f_Y	$f_Y u_Y$	$f_Y u_Y^2$	Sum of corner numbers in each row
Physics Grades Y: 94.5	2				2 [4]	4 [16]	4 [24]	10	20	40	44
84.5	1			1 [0]	4 [4]	6 [12]	5 [15]	16	16	16	31
74.5	0			5 [0]	10 [0]	8 [0]	1 [0]	24	0	0	0
64.5	−1	1 [2]	4 [4]	9 [0]	5 [−5]	2 [−4]		21	−21	21	−3
54.5	−2	3 [12]	6 [12]	6 [0]	2 [−4]			17	−34	68	20
44.5	−3	3 [18]	5 [15]	4 [0]				12	−36	108	33
	f_X	7	15	25	23	20	10	$\sum f_X = \sum f_Y = N = 100$	$\sum f_Y u_Y = -55$	$\sum f_Y u_Y^2 = 253$	$\sum f u_X u_Y = 125$
	$f_X u_X$	−14	−15	0	23	40	30	$\sum f_X u_X = 64$			
	$f_X u_X^2$	28	15	0	23	80	90	$\sum f_X u_X^2 = 236$			
	Sum of corner numbers in each column	32	31	0	−1	24	39	$\sum f u_X u_Y = 125$			

Check

SOLUTION

(a) $$s_X = c_X\sqrt{\frac{\sum f_X u_X^2}{N} - \left(\frac{\sum f_X u_X}{N}\right)^2} = 10\sqrt{\frac{236}{100} - \left(\frac{64}{100}\right)^2} = 13.966$$

(b) $$s_Y = c_Y\sqrt{\frac{\sum f_Y u_Y^2}{N} - \left(\frac{\sum f_Y u_Y}{N}\right)^2} = 10\sqrt{\frac{253}{100} - \left(\frac{-55}{100}\right)^2} = 14.925$$

(c) $$s_{XY} = c_X c_Y\left[\frac{\sum f u_X u_Y}{N} - \left(\frac{\sum f_X u_X}{N}\right)\left(\frac{\sum f_Y u_Y}{N}\right)\right] = (10)(10)\left[\frac{125}{100} - \left(\frac{64}{100}\right)\left(\frac{-55}{100}\right)\right] = 160.20$$

Thus the standard deviations of the mathematics and physics grades are 14.0 and 14.9, respectively, while their covariance is 160.2. The correlation coefficient r is therefore

$$r = \frac{s_{XY}}{s_X s_Y} = \frac{160.20}{(13.966)(14.925)} = 0.7686$$

agreeing with Problem 14.19.

REGRESSION LINES AND THE CORRELATION COEFFICIENT

14.21 Prove that the regression lines of Y on X and of X on Y have equations given, respectively, by (a) $Y - \bar{Y} = (rs_Y/s_X)(X - \bar{X})$ and (b) $X - \bar{X} = (rs_X/s_Y)(Y - \bar{Y})$.

SOLUTION

(a) From Problem 13.15(a), the regression line of Y on X has the equation

$$y = \left(\frac{\sum xy}{\sum x^2}\right)x \qquad \text{or} \qquad Y - \bar{Y} = \left(\frac{\sum xy}{\sum x^2}\right)(X - \bar{X})$$

Then, since $$r = \frac{\sum xy}{\sqrt{(\sum x^2)(\sum y^2)}} \qquad \text{(see Problem 14.10)}$$

we have $$\frac{\sum xy}{\sum x^2} = \frac{r\sqrt{(\sum x^2)(\sum y^2)}}{\sum x^2} = \frac{r\sqrt{\sum y^2}}{\sqrt{\sum x^2}} = \frac{rs_Y}{s_X}$$

and the required result follows.

(b) This follows by interchanging X and Y in part (a).

14.22 If the regression lines of Y on X and of X on Y are given, respectively, by $Y = a_0 + a_1 X$ and $X = b_0 + b_1 Y$, prove that $a_1 b_1 = r^2$.

SOLUTION

From Problem 14.21, parts (a) and (b),

$$a_1 = \frac{rs_Y}{s_X} \qquad \text{and} \qquad b_1 = \frac{rs_X}{s_Y}$$

Thus $$a_1 b_1 = \left(\frac{rs_Y}{s_X}\right)\left(\frac{rs_X}{s_Y}\right) = r^2$$

This result can be taken as the starting point for a definition of the linear correlation coefficient.

14.23 Use the result of Problem 14.22 to find the linear correlation coefficient for the data of Problem 14.1.

SOLUTION

From Problem 14.1 [parts (b) and (c), respectively] $a_1 = 484/1016 = 0.476$ and $b_1 = 484/467 = 1.036$. Thus $r^2 = a_1 b_1 = (484/1016)(484/467)$ and $r = 0.7027$, agreeing with Problems 14.9, 14.14, and 14.16.

14.24 For the data of Problem 14.19, write the equations of the regression lines of (*a*) Y on X and (*b*) X on Y.

SOLUTION

From the correlation table (Table 14.12) of Problem 14.19 we have

$$\bar{X} = A + c_X \frac{\sum f_X u_X}{N} = 64.5 + \frac{(10)(64)}{100} = 70.9$$

$$\bar{Y} = B + c_Y \frac{\sum f_Y u_Y}{N} = 74.5 + \frac{(10)(-55)}{100} = 69.0$$

From the results of Problem 14.20, $s_X = 13.966$, $s_Y = 14.925$, and $r = 0.7686$. We now use Problem 14.21, parts (*a*) and (*b*), to obtain the equations of the regression lines.

(*a*) $$Y - \bar{Y} = \frac{rs_Y}{s_X}(X - \bar{X}) \qquad Y - 69.0 = \frac{(0.7686)(14.925)}{13.966}(X - 70.9) = 0.821(X - 70.9)$$

(*b*) $$X - \bar{X} = \frac{rs_X}{s_Y}(Y - \bar{Y}) \qquad X - 70.9 = \frac{(0.7686)(13.966)}{14.925}(Y - 69.0) = 0.719(Y - 69.0)$$

14.25 For the data of Problem 14.19, compute the standard errors of estimate (*a*) $s_{Y.X}$ and (*b*) $s_{X.Y}$. Use the results of Problem 14.20.

SOLUTION

(*a*) $s_{Y.X} = s_Y\sqrt{1 - r^2} = 14.925\sqrt{1 - (0.7686)^2} = 9.548$

(*b*) $s_{X.Y} = s_X\sqrt{1 - r^2} = 13.966\sqrt{1 - (0.7686)^2} = 8.934$

14.26 Table 14.13 shows the U.S. consumer price indexes for food and medical-care costs during the years 1975–1983 compared with prices in the base year, 1967 (taken as 100). Compute the correlation coefficient between the two indexes.

Table 14.13

Year	1975	1976	1977	1978	1979	1980	1981	1982	1983
Food	175	181	192	211	235	255	275	286	292
Medical care	169	185	202	219	240	266	295	329	357

Source: Survey of Current Business.

SOLUTION

(*a*) Denoting the index numbers for food and medical care as X and Y, respectively, the calculation of the correlation coefficient can be organized as in Table 14.14. (Note that the year is used only to specify the corresponding values of X and Y.) Then by the product-moment formula,

$$r = \frac{\sum xy}{\sqrt{(\sum x^2)(\sum y^2)}} = \frac{23,442}{\sqrt{(16,774)(34,107)}} = 0.98$$

Thus there is a very good linear correlation between the food and medical-care costs. It should be noted, however, that this does not mean that the costs have gone up the *same* throughout the years; thus, for example, for 1975 to 1983 the food costs increased by 67% while the medical care costs increased by 111%.

Table 14.14

X	Y	$x=X-\bar{X}$	$y=Y-\bar{Y}$	x^2	xy	y^2
175	169	−59	−82	3,481	4,838	6,724
181	185	−53	−66	2,809	3,498	4,356
192	202	−42	−49	1,764	2,058	2,401
211	219	−23	−32	529	736	1,024
235	240	1	−11	1	−11	121
255	266	21	15	441	315	225
275	295	41	44	1,681	1,804	1,936
286	329	52	78	2,704	4,056	6,084
292	357	58	106	3,364	6,148	11,236
$\sum X=2{,}102$ $\bar{X}=234$	$\sum Y=2{,}262$ $\bar{Y}=251$			$\sum x^2=16{,}774$	$\sum xy=23{,}442$	$\sum y^2=34{,}107$

NONLINEAR CORRELATION

14.27 Fit a least-squares parabola of the form $Y=a_0+a_1X+a_2X^2$ to the set of data in Table 14.15.

Table 14.15

X	1.2	1.8	3.1	4.9	5.7	7.1	8.6	9.8
Y	4.5	5.9	7.0	7.8	7.2	6.8	4.5	2.7

SOLUTION

The normal equations (*23*) of Chapter 13 are

$$\begin{aligned} \sum Y &= a_0N + a_1\sum X + a_2\sum X^2 \\ \sum XY &= a_0\sum X + a_1\sum X^2 + a_2\sum X^3 \\ \sum X^2Y &= a_0\sum X^2 + a_1\sum X^3 + a_2\sum X^4 \end{aligned} \tag{36}$$

The work involved in computing the sums can be arranged as in Table 14.16. Then, since $N=8$, the normal equations (*36*) become

$$\begin{aligned} 8a_0 + 42.2a_1 + 291.20a_2 &= 46.4 \\ 42.2a_0 + 291.20a_1 + 2275.35a_2 &= 230.42 \\ 291.20a_0 + 2275.35a_1 + 18971.92a_2 &= 1449.00 \end{aligned} \tag{37}$$

Solving, $a_0=2.588$, $a_1=2.065$, and $a_2=-0.2110$; hence the required least-squares parabola has the equation

$$Y=2.588+2.065X-0.2110X^2$$

14.28 Use the least-squares parabola of Problem 14.27 to estimate the values of Y from the given values of X.

SOLUTION

For $X=1.2$, $Y_{est}=2.588+2.065(1.2)-0.2110(1.2)^2=4.762$. Other estimated values are obtained similarly. The results are shown in Table 14.17 together with the actual values of Y.

Table 14.16

X	Y	X^2	X^3	X^4	XY	X^2Y
1.2	4.5	1.44	1.73	2.08	5.40	6.48
1.8	5.9	3.24	5.83	10.49	10.62	19.12
3.1	7.0	9.61	29.79	92.35	21.70	67.27
4.9	7.8	24.01	117.65	576.48	38.22	187.28
5.7	7.2	32.49	185.19	1055.58	41.04	233.93
7.1	6.8	50.41	357.91	2541.16	48.28	342.79
8.6	4.5	73.96	636.06	5470.12	38.70	332.82
9.8	2.7	96.04	941.19	9223.66	26.46	259.31
$\sum X = 42.2$	$\sum Y = 46.4$	$\sum X^2 = 291.20$	$\sum X^3 = 2275.35$	$\sum X^4 = 18{,}971.92$	$\sum XY = 230.42$	$\sum X^2Y = 1449.00$

Table 14.17

Y_{est}	4.762	5.621	6.962	7.640	7.503	6.613	4.741	2.561
Y	4.5	5.9	7.0	7.8	7.2	6.8	4.5	2.7

Mathcad **14.29** (*a*) Find the linear correlation coefficient between the variables X and Y of Problem 14.27.

(*b*) Find the nonlinear correlation coefficient between these variables, assuming the parabolic relationship obtained in Problem 14.27.

(*c*) Explain the difference between the correlation coefficients obtained in parts (*a*) and (*b*).

(*d*) What percentage of the total variation remains unexplained by assuming a parabolic relationship between X and Y?

SOLUTION

(*a*) Using the calculations already obtained in Table 14.16 and the added fact that $\sum Y^2 = 290.52$, we find that

$$r = \frac{N\sum XY - (\sum X)(\sum Y)}{\sqrt{[N\sum X^2 - (\sum X)^2][N\sum Y^2 - (\sum Y)^2]}} = \frac{(8)(230.42) - (42.2)(46.4)}{\sqrt{[(8)(291.20) - (42.2)^2][(8)(290.52) - (46.4)^2]}} = -0.3743$$

(*b*) From Table 14.16, $\bar{Y} = (\sum Y)/N = 46.4/8 = 5.80$; thus the total variation is $\sum (Y - \bar{Y})^2 = 21.40$. From Table 14.17, the explained variation is $\sum (Y_{est} - \bar{Y})^2 = 21.02$. Thus

$$r^2 = \frac{\text{explained variation}}{\text{total variation}} = \frac{21.02}{21.40} = 0.9822 \qquad \text{and} \qquad r = 0.9911 \qquad \text{or} \qquad 0.99$$

(*c*) The fact that part (*a*) shows a linear correlation coefficient of only -0.3743 indicates that there is practically no *linear relationship* between X and Y. However, there is a very good *nonlinear relationship* supplied by the parabola of Problem 14.27, as indicated by the fact that the correlation coefficient in part (*b*) is 0.99.

(*d*)
$$\frac{\text{Unexplained variation}}{\text{Total variation}} = 1 - r^2 = 1 - 0.9822 = 0.0178$$

Thus 1.78% of the total variation remains unexplained. This could be due to random fluctuations or to an additional variable that has not been considered.

14.30 Find (a) s_Y and (b) $s_{Y.X}$ for the data of Problem 14.27.

SOLUTION

(a) From Problem 14.29(a), $\sum (Y-\bar{Y})^2 = 21.40$. Thus the standard deviation of Y is

$$s_Y = \sqrt{\frac{\sum (Y-\bar{Y})^2}{N}} = \sqrt{\frac{21.40}{8}} = 1.636 \quad \text{or} \quad 1.64$$

(b) **First method**

Using part (a) and Problem 14.29(b), the standard error of estimate of Y on X is

$$s_{Y.X} = s_Y\sqrt{1-r^2} = 1.636\sqrt{1-(0.9911)^2} = 0.218 \quad \text{or} \quad 0.22$$

Second method

Using Problem 14.29,

$$s_{Y.X} = \sqrt{\frac{\sum (Y-Y_{\text{est}})^2}{N}} = \sqrt{\frac{\text{unexplained variation}}{N}} = \sqrt{\frac{21.40-21.02}{8}} = 0.218 \quad \text{or} \quad 0.22$$

Third method

Using Problem 14.27 and the additional calculation $\sum Y^2 = 290.52$, we have

$$s_{Y.X} = \sqrt{\frac{\sum Y^2 - a_0 \sum Y - a_1 \sum XY - a_2 \sum X^2 Y}{N}} = 0.218 \quad \text{or} \quad 0.22$$

SAMPLING THEORY OF CORRELATION

14.31 A correlation coefficient based on a sample of size 18 was computed to be 0.32. Can we conclude at significance levels of (a) 0.05 and (b) 0.01 that the corresponding population correlation coefficient differs from zero?

SOLUTION

We wish to decide between the hypotheses $H_0: \rho = 0$ and $H_1: \rho > 0$.

$$t = \frac{r\sqrt{N-2}}{\sqrt{1-r^2}} = \frac{0.32\sqrt{18-2}}{\sqrt{1-(0.32)^2}} = 1.35$$

(a) Using a one-tailed test of Student's distribution at the 0.05 level, we would reject H_0 if $t > t_{.95} = 1.75$ for $(18-2) = 16$ degrees of freedom. Thus we cannot reject H_0 at the 0.05 level.

(b) Since we cannot reject H_0 at the 0.05 level, we certainly cannot reject it at the 0.01 level.

14.32 What is the minimum sample size necessary in order that we may conclude that a correlation coefficient of 0.32 differs significantly from zero at the 0.05 level?

SOLUTION

Using a one-tailed test of Student's distribution at the 0.05 level, the minimum value of N must be such that

$$\frac{0.32\sqrt{N-2}}{\sqrt{1-(0.32)^2}} = t_{.95}$$

for $N-2$ degrees of freedom. For an infinite number of degrees of freedom, $t_{.95} = 1.64$ and hence $N = 25.6$.

For $N = 26$:	$\nu = 24$	$t_{.95} = 1.71$	$t = 0.32\sqrt{24}/\sqrt{1-(0.32)^2} = 1.65$
For $N = 27$:	$\nu = 25$	$t_{.95} = 1.71$	$t = 0.32\sqrt{25}/\sqrt{1-(0.32)^2} = 1.69$
For $N = 28$:	$\nu = 26$	$t_{.95} = 1.71$	$t = 0.32\sqrt{26}/\sqrt{1-(0.32)^2} = 1.72$

Thus the minimum sample size is $N = 28$.

Mathcad

14.33 A correlation coefficient on a sample of size 24 was computed to be $r = 0.75$. At the 0.05 significance level, can we reject the hypothesis that the population correlation coefficient is as small as (*a*) $\rho = 0.60$ and (*b*) $\rho = 0.50$?

SOLUTION

(*a*)
$$Z = 1.1513 \log\left(\frac{1+0.75}{1-0.75}\right) = 0.9730 \qquad \mu_Z = 1.1513 \log\left(\frac{1+0.60}{1-0.60}\right) = 0.6932$$

and
$$\sigma_Z = \frac{1}{\sqrt{N-3}} = \frac{1}{\sqrt{21}} = 0.2182$$

Thus
$$z = \frac{Z - \mu_Z}{\sigma_Z} = \frac{0.9730 - 0.6932}{0.2182} = 1.28$$

Using a one-tailed test of the normal distribution at the 0.05 level, we would reject the hypothesis only if z were greater than 1.64. Thus we cannot reject the hypothesis that the population correlation coefficient is as small as 0.60.

(*b*) If $\rho = 0.50$, then $\mu_Z = 1.1513 \log 3 = 0.5493$ and $z = (0.9730 - 0.5493)/0.2182 = 1.94$. Thus we can reject the hypothesis that the population correlation coefficient is as small as $\rho = 0.50$ at the 0.05 level.

14.34 The correlation coefficient between the final grades in physics and mathematics for a group of 21 students was computed to be 0.80. Find the 95% confidence limits for this coefficient.

SOLUTION

Since $r = 0.80$ and $N = 21$, the 95% confidence limits for μ_Z are given by

$$Z \pm 1.96\sigma_Z = 1.1513 \log\left(\frac{1+r}{1-r}\right) \pm 1.96\left(\frac{1}{\sqrt{N-3}}\right) = 1.0986 \pm 0.4620$$

Thus μ_Z has the 95% confidence interval 0.5366 to 1.5606. Now if

$$\mu_Z = 1.1513 \log\left(\frac{1+\rho}{1-\rho}\right) = 0.5366 \qquad \text{then} \qquad \rho = 0.4904$$

and if
$$\mu_Z = 1.1513 \log\left(\frac{1+\rho}{1-\rho}\right) = 1.5606 \qquad \text{then} \qquad \rho = 0.9155$$

Thus the 95% confidence limits for ρ are 0.49 and 0.92.

14.35 Two correlation coefficients obtained from samples of size $N_1 = 28$ and $N_3 = 35$ were computed to be $r_1 = 0.50$ and $r_2 = 0.30$, respectively. Is there a significant difference between the two coefficients at the 0.05 level?

SOLUTION

$$Z_1 = 1.1513 \log\left(\frac{1+r_1}{1-r_1}\right) = 0.5493 \qquad Z_2 = 1.1513 \log\left(\frac{1+r_2}{1-r_2}\right) = 0.3095$$

and
$$\sigma_{Z1-Z2} = \sqrt{\frac{1}{N_1-3} + \frac{1}{N_2-3}} = 0.2669$$

We wish to decide between the hypotheses H_0: $\mu_{Z1} = \mu_{Z2}$ and H_1: $\mu_{Z1} \neq \mu_{Z2}$. Under hypothesis H_0,

$$z = \frac{Z_1 - Z_2 - (\mu_{Z1} - \mu_{Z2})}{\sigma_{Z1-Z2}} = \frac{0.5493 - 0.3095 - 0}{0.2669} = 0.8985$$

Using a two-tailed test of the normal distribution, we would reject H_0 only if $z > 1.96$ or $z < -1.96$. Thus we cannot reject H_0, and we conclude that the results are not significantly different at the 0.05 level.

SAMPLING THEORY OF REGRESSION

14.36 In Problem 14.1 we found the regression equation of Y on X to be $Y = 35.82 + 0.476X$. Test the hypothesis at the 0.05 significance level that the regression coefficient of the population regression equation is as low as 0.180.

SOLUTION

$$t = \frac{a_1 - A_1}{s_{Y.X}/s_X}\sqrt{N-2} = \frac{0.476 - 0.180}{1.28/2.66}\sqrt{12-2} = 1.95$$

since $s_{Y.X} = 1.28$ (computed in Problem 14.5) and $s_X = \sqrt{(\sum x^2)/N} = \sqrt{84.68/12} = 2.66$ (from Problem 14.2). Using a one-tailed test of Student's distribution at the 0.05 level, we would reject the hypothesis that the regression coefficient is as low as 0.180 if $t > t_{.95} = 1.81$ for $(12-2) = 10$ degrees of freedom. Thus we cannot reject the hypothesis.

14.37 Find the 95% confidence limits for the regression coefficient of Problem 14.36.

SOLUTION

$$A_1 = a_1 - \frac{t}{\sqrt{N-2}}\left(\frac{s_{Y.X}}{s_X}\right)$$

Thus the 95% confidence limits for A_1 (obtained by setting $t = \pm t_{.975} = \pm 2.23$ for $12 - 2 = 10$ degrees of freedom) are given by

$$a_1 \pm \frac{2.23}{\sqrt{12-2}}\left(\frac{s_{Y.X}}{s_X}\right) = 0.476 \pm \frac{2.23}{\sqrt{10}}\left(\frac{1.28}{2.66}\right) = 0.476 \pm 0.340$$

That is, we are 95% confident that A_1 lies between 0.136 and 0.816.

14.38 In Problem 14.1, find the 95% confidence limits for the heights of sons whose fathers' heights are (*a*) 65.0 and (*b*) 70.0 in.

SOLUTION

Since $t_{.975} = 2.23$ for $(12-2) = 10$ degrees of freedom, the 95% confidence limits for Y_p (see page 300) are given by

$$Y_0 \pm \frac{2.23}{\sqrt{N-2}} s_{Y.X}\sqrt{N+1+\frac{(X_0-\bar{X})^2}{s_X^2}}$$

where $Y_0 = 35.82 + 0.476X_0$ (Problem 14.1), $s_{Y.X} = 1.28$, $s_X = 2.66$ (Problem 14.36), and $N = 12$.

(*a*) If $X_0 = 65.0$, then $Y_0 = 66.76$ in. Also, $(X_0 - \bar{X})^2 = (65.0 - 800/12)^2 = 2.78$. Thus the 95% confidence limits are

$$66.76 \pm \frac{2.23}{\sqrt{10}}(1.28)\sqrt{12+1+\frac{2.78}{(2.66)^2}} = 66.76 \pm 3.31 \text{ in}$$

That is, we can be about 95% confident that the sons' heights are between 63.4 and 70.1 in.

(*b*) If $X_0 = 70.0$, then $Y_0 = 69.14$ in. Also, $(X_0 - \bar{X})^2 = (70.0 - 800/12)^2 = 11.11$. Thus the 95% confidence limits are computed to be 69.14 ± 3.45 in; that is, we can be about 95% confident that the sons' heights are between 65.7 and 72.6 in.

Note that for large values of N, the 95% confidence limits are given approximately by $Y_0 \pm 1.96 s_{Y.X}$ or $Y_0 \pm 2 s_{Y.X}$, provided $(X_0 - \bar{X})$ is not too large. This agrees with the approximate results mentioned on page 195. The methods of this problem hold regardless of the size of N or $(X_0 - \bar{X})$; that is, the sampling methods are exact.

14.39 In Problem 14.1, find the 95% confidence limits for the mean heights of sons whose fathers' heights are (*a*) 65.0 in and (*b*) 70.0 in.

SOLUTION

Since $t_{.975} = 2.23$ for 10 degrees of freedom, the 95% confidence limits for $\bar{Y}_p$ (see page 301) are given by

$$Y_0 \pm \frac{2.23}{\sqrt{10}} s_{Y.X} \sqrt{1 + \frac{(X_0 - \bar{X})^2}{s_X^2}}$$

where $Y_0 = 35.82 + 0.476X_0$ (Problem 14.1), $s_{Y.X} = 1.28$, and $s_X = 2.66$ (Problem 14.36).

(*a*) If $X_0 = 65.0$, we find the 95% confidence limits to be 66.76 ± 1.07 in [compare the result in Problem 14.38(*a*)]. That is, we can be about 95% confident that the *mean height* of all sons whose fathers' heights are 65.0 in will lie between 65.7 and 67.8 in.

(*b*) If $X_0 = 70.0$, we find the 95% confidence limits to be 69.14 ± 1.45 in (compare the result in Problem 14.38(*b*)]. That is, we can be about 95% confident that the mean height of all sons whose fathers' heights are 70.0 in will lie between 67.7 and 70.6 in.

Supplementary Problems

LINEAR REGRESSION AND CORRELATION

14.40 Table 14.18 shows the first two grades (denoted by *X* and *Y*, respectively) of 10 students on two short quizzes in biology.

(*a*) Construct a scatter diagram.

(*b*) Find the least-squares regression line of *Y* on *X*.

(*c*) Find the least-squares regression line of *X* on *Y*.

(*d*) Graph the two regression lines of parts (*b*) and (*c*) on the scatter diagram of part (*a*).

Table 14.18

Grade on first quiz (*X*)	6	5	8	8	7	6	10	4	9	7
Grade on second quiz (*Y*)	8	7	7	10	5	8	10	6	8	6

14.41 Find (*a*) $s_{Y.X}$ and (*b*) $s_{X.Y}$ for the data in Table 14.18.

14.42 Compute (*a*) the total variation in *Y*, (*b*) the unexplained variation in *Y*, and (*c*) the explained variation in *Y* for the data of Problem 14.40.

14.43 Use the results of Problem 14.42 to find the correlation coefficient between the two sets of quiz grades of Problem 14.40.

14.44 (*a*) Find the correlation coefficient between the two sets of quiz grades in Problem 14.40 by using the product-moment formula, and compare this finding with the result of Problem 14.45.

(*b*) Obtain the correlation coefficient directly from the slopes of the regression lines of Problem 14.42, parts (*b*) and (*c*).

14.45 Find the covariance for the data of Problem 14.40(*a*) directly and (*b*) by using the formula $s_{XY} = rs_Xs_Y$ and the result of Problem 14.43 or Problem 14.44.

14.46 Table 14.19 shows the ages X and the systolic blood pressures Y of 12 women.

(a) Find the correlation coefficient between X and Y.

(b) Determine the least-squares regression equation of Y on X.

(c) Estimate the blood pressure of a woman whose age is 45 years.

Table 14.19

Age (X)	56	42	72	36	63	47	55	49	38	42	68	60
Blood pressure (Y)	147	125	160	118	149	128	150	145	115	140	152	155

14.47 Find the correlation coefficients for the data of (a) Problem 13.32 and (b) Problem 13.35.

14.48 The correlation coefficient between two variables X and Y is $r = 0.60$. If $s_X = 1.50$, $s_Y = 2.00$, $\bar{X} = 10$, and $\bar{Y} = 20$, find the equations of the regression lines of (a) Y on X and (b) X on Y.

14.49 Compute (a) $s_{Y.X}$ and (b) $s_{X.Y}$ for the data of Problem 14.48.

14.50 If $s_{Y.X} = 3$ and $s_Y = 5$, find r.

14.51 If the correlation coefficient between X and Y is 0.50, what percentage of the total variation remains unexplained by the regression equation?

14.52 (a) Prove that the equation of the regression line of Y on X can be written

$$Y - \bar{Y} = \frac{s_{XY}}{s_X^2}(X - \bar{X})$$

(b) Write the analogous equation for the regression line of X on Y.

14.53 (a) Compute the correlation coefficient between the corresponding values of X and Y given in Table 14.20.

(b) Multiply each X value in the table by 2 and add 6. Multiply each Y value in the table by 3 and subtract 15. Find the correlation coefficient between the two new sets of values, explaining why you do or do not obtain the same result as in part (a).

Table 14.20

X	2	4	5	6	8	11
Y	18	12	10	8	7	5

14.54 (a) Find the regression equations of Y on X for the data considered in Problem 14.53, parts (a) and (b).

(b) Discuss the relationship between these regression equations.

14.55 (a) Prove that the correlation coefficient between X and Y can be written

$$r = \frac{\overline{XY} - \bar{X}\bar{Y}}{\sqrt{[\overline{X^2} - \bar{X}^2][\overline{Y^2} - \bar{Y}^2]}}$$

(b) Using this method, work Problem 14.1.

14.56 Prove that a correlation coefficient is independent of the choice of origin of the variables or the units in which they are expressed. (*Hint:* Assume that $X' = c_1 X + A$ and $Y' = c_2 Y + B$, where c_1, c_2, A, and B are any constants, and prove that the correlation coefficient between X' and Y' is the same as that between X and Y.)

14.57 (*a*) Prove that, for linear regression,

$$\frac{s_{Y.X}^2}{s_Y^2} = \frac{s_{X.Y}^2}{s_X^2}$$

(*b*) Does the result hold for nonlinear regression?

CORRELATION COEFFICIENT FOR GROUPED DATA

14.58 Find the correlation coefficient between the heights and weights of the 300 U.S. adult males given in Table 14.21, a frequency table.

Table 14.21

		Heights X (in)				
		59–62	63–66	67–70	71–74	75–78
Weights Y (lb)	90–109	2	1			
	110–129	7	8	4	2	
	130–149	5	15	22	7	1
	150–169	2	12	63	19	5
	170–189		7	28	32	12
	190–209		2	10	20	7
	210–229			1	4	2

14.59 (*a*) Find the least-squares regression equation of Y on X for the data of Problem 14.58.
(*b*) Estimate the weights of two men whose heights are 64 and 72 in, respectively.

14.60 Find (*a*) $s_{Y.X}$ and (*b*) $s_{X.Y}$ for the data of Problem 14.58.

14.61 Establish formula (*21*) of this chapter for the correlation coefficient of grouped data.

CORRELATION OF TIME SERIES

14.62 Table 14.22 shows the retail prices of zinc in the United States and the corresponding consumer retail price index for the years 1978–1985. Find the correlation coefficient.

14.63 Table 14.23 shows the average temperature and precipitation in a city for the month of July during the years 1975–1984. Find the correlation coefficient.

SAMPLING THEORY OF CORRELATION

14.64 A correlation coefficient based on a sample of size 27 was computed to be 0.40. Can we conclude at significance levels of (*a*) 0.05 and (*b*) 0.01, that the corresponding population correlation coefficient differs from zero?

Table 14.22

Year	1978	1979	1980	1981	1982	1983	1984	1985
Price of zinc (cents per pound)	31.0	37.3	37.4	44.6	38.5	41.4	48.6	40.3
Consumer price index (1967 = 100)	195.4	217.4	246.8	272.4	289.1	298.4	311.1	322.2

Source: U.S. Bureau of Labor Statistics and Bureau of Mines.

Table 14.23

Year	1975	1976	1977	1978	1979	1980	1981	1982	1983	1984
Temperature (°F)	78.1	71.8	75.6	72.7	75.3	73.6	75.1	75.3	73.8	70.4
Precipitation (in)	6.23	3.64	3.42	2.84	1.83	2.82	4.04	2.56	1.18	4.19

14.65 A correlation coefficient based on a sample of size 35 was computed to be 0.50. At the 0.05 significance level, can we reject the hypothesis that the population correlation coefficient is (*a*) as small as $\rho = 0.30$ and (*b*) as large as $\rho = 0.70$?

14.66 Find the (*a*) 95% and (*b*) 99% confidence limits for a correlation coefficient that is computed to be 0.60 from a sample of size 28.

14.67 Work Problem 14.66 if the sample size is 52.

14.68 Find the 95% confidence limits for the correlation coefficients computed in (*a*) Problem 14.46 and (*b*) Problem 14.58.

14.69 Two correlation coefficients obtained from samples of size 23 and 28 were computed to be 0.80 and 0.95, respectively. Can we conclude at levels of (*a*) 0.05 and (*b*) 0.01 that there is a significant difference between the two coefficients?

SAMPLING THEORY OF REGRESSION

14.70 On the basis of a sample of size 27, a regression equation of Y on X was found to be $Y = 25.0 + 2.00X$. If $s_{Y.X} = 1.50$, $s_X = 3.00$, and $\bar{X} = 7.50$, find the (*a*) 95% and (*b*) 99% confidence limits for the regression coefficient.

14.71 In Problem 14.70, test the hypothesis that the population regression coefficient at the 0.01 significance level is (*a*) as low as 1.70 and (*b*) as high as 2.20.

14.72 In Problem 14.70, find the (*a*) 95% and (*b*) 99% confidence limits for Y when $X = 6.00$.

14.73 In Problem 14.70, find the (*a*) 95% and (*b*) 99% confidence limits for the mean of all values of Y corresponding to $X = 6.00$.

14.74 Referring to Problem 14.46, find the 95% confidence limits for (*a*) the regression coefficient of Y on X, (*b*) the blood pressures of all women who are 45 years old, and (*c*) the mean of the blood pressures of all women who are 45 years old.

Chapter 15

Multiple and Partial Correlation

MULTIPLE CORRELATION

The degree of relationship existing between three or more variables is called *multiple correlation.* The fundamental principles involved in problems of multiple correlation are analogous to those of simple correlation, as treated in Chapter 14.

SUBSCRIPT NOTATION

To allow for generalizations to large numbers of variables, it is convenient to adopt a notation involving subscripts.

We shall let $X_1, X_2, X_3, \ldots$ denote the variables under consideration. Then we can let $X_{11}, X_{12}, X_{13}, \ldots$ denote the values assumed by the variable X_1, and $X_{21}, X_{22}, X_{23}, \ldots$ denote the values assumed by the variable X_2, and so on. With this notation, a sum such as $X_{21}+X_{22}+X_{23}+\cdots+X_{2N}$ could be written $\sum_{j=1}^{N} X_{2j}$, $\sum_j X_{2j}$, or simply $\sum X_2$. When no ambiguity can result, we use the last notation. In such case the mean of X_2 is written $\bar{X}_2 = \sum X_2/N$.

REGRESSION EQUATIONS AND REGRESSION PLANES

A *regression equation* is an equation for estimating a dependent variable, say X_1, from the independent variables $X_2, X_3, \ldots$ and is called a *regression equation of* X_1 *on* $X_2, X_3, \ldots$. In functional notation this is sometimes written briefly as $X_1 = F(X_2, X_3, \ldots)$ (read "X_1 is a function of X_2, X_3, and so on").

For the case of three variables, the simplest regression equation of X_1 on X_2 and X_3 has the form

$$X_1 = b_{1.23} + b_{12.3}X_2 + b_{13.2}X_3 \tag{1}$$

where $b_{1.23}$, $b_{12.3}$, and $b_{13.2}$ are constants. If we keep X_3 constant in equation (*1*), the graph of X_1 versus X_2 is a straight line with slope $b_{12.3}$. If we keep X_2 constant, the graph of X_1 versus X_3 is a straight line with slope $b_{13.2}$. It is clear that the subscripts after the dot indicate the variables held constant in each case.

Due to the fact that X_1 varies partially because of variation in X_2 and partially because of variation in X_3, we call $b_{12.3}$ and $b_{13.2}$ the *partial regression coefficients* of X_1 on X_2 keeping X_3 constant and of X_1 on X_3 keeping X_2 constant, respectively.

Equation (*1*) is called a *linear regression equation* of X_1 on X_2 and X_3. In a three-dimensional rectangular coordinate system it represents a plane called a *regression plane* and is a generalization of the regression line for two variables, as considered in Chapter 13.

NORMAL EQUATIONS FOR THE LEAST-SQUARES REGRESSION PLANE

Just as there exist least-squares regression lines approximating a set of N data points (X, Y) in a two-dimensional scatter diagram, so also there exist *least-squares regression planes* fitting a set of N data points (X_1, X_2, X_3) in a three-dimensional scatter diagram.

The least-squares regression plane of X_1 on X_2 and X_3 has the equation (*1*) where $b_{1.23}$, $b_{12.3}$, and $b_{13.2}$ are determined by solving simultaneously the *normal equations*

$$\begin{aligned} \sum X_1 &= b_{1.23}N + b_{12.3}\sum X_2 + b_{13.2}\sum X_3 \\ \sum X_1X_2 &= b_{1.23}\sum X_2 + b_{12.3}\sum X_2^2 + b_{13.2}\sum X_2X_3 \\ \sum X_1X_3 &= b_{1.23}\sum X_3 + b_{12.3}\sum X_2X_3 + b_{13.2}\sum X_3^2 \end{aligned} \tag{2}$$

These can be obtained formally by multiplying both sides of equation (*1*) by 1, X_2, and X_3 successively and summing on both sides.

Unless otherwise specified, whenever we refer to a regression equation it will be assumed that the least-squares regression equation is meant.

If $x_1 = X_1 - \bar{X}_1$, $x_2 = X_2 - \bar{X}_2$, and $x_3 = X_3 - \bar{X}_3$, the regression equation of X_1 on X_2 and X_3 can be written more simply as

$$x_1 = b_{12.3}x_2 + b_{13.2}x_3 \tag{3}$$

where $b_{12.3}$ and $b_{13.2}$ are obtained by solving simultaneously the equations

$$\begin{aligned} \sum x_1x_2 &= b_{12.3}\sum x_2^2 + b_{13.2}\sum x_2x_3 \\ \sum x_1x_3 &= b_{12.3}\sum x_2x_3 + b_{13.2}\sum x_3^2 \end{aligned} \tag{4}$$

These equations which are equivalent to the normal equations (*2*) can be obtained formally by multiplying both sides of equation (*3*) by x_2 and x_3 successively and summing on both sides (see Problem 15.8).

REGRESSION PLANES AND CORRELATION COEFFICIENTS

If the linear correlation coefficients between variables X_1 and X_2, X_1 and X_3, and X_2 and X_3, as computed in Chapter 14, are denoted respectively by r_{12}, r_{13}, and r_{23} (sometimes called *zero-order correlation coefficients*), then the least-squares regression plane has the equation

$$\frac{x_1}{s_1} = \left(\frac{r_{12} - r_{13}r_{23}}{1 - r_{23}^2}\right)\frac{x_2}{s_2} + \left(\frac{r_{13} - r_{12}r_{23}}{1 - r_{23}^2}\right)\frac{x_3}{s_3} \tag{5}$$

where $x_1 = X - \bar{X}_1$, $x_2 = X_2 - \bar{X}_2$, and $x_3 = X_3 - \bar{X}_3$ and where s_1, s_2, and s_3 are the standard deviations of X_1, X_2, and X_3, respectively (see Problem 15.9).

Note that if the variable X_3 is nonexistent and if $X_1 = Y$ and $X_2 = X$, then equation (*5*) reduces to equation (*25*) of Chapter 14.

STANDARD ERROR OF ESTIMATE

By an obvious generalization of equation (*8*) of Chapter 14, we can define the *standard error of estimate* of X_1 on X_2 and X_3 by

$$s_{1.23} = \sqrt{\frac{\sum (X_1 - X_{1,\text{est}})^2}{N}} \tag{6}$$

where $X_{1,\text{est}}$ indicates the estimated values of X_1 as calculated from the regression equations (*1*) or (*5*).

In terms of the correlation coefficients r_{12}, r_{13}, and r_{23}, the standard error of estimate can also be computed from the result

$$s_{1.23} = s_1\sqrt{\frac{1 - r_{12}^2 - r_{13}^2 - r_{23}^2 + 2r_{12}r_{13}r_{23}}{1 - r_{23}^2}} \tag{7}$$

The sampling interpretation of the standard error of estimate for two variables as given on page 296 for the case when N is large can be extended to three dimensions by replacing the lines parallel to the regression line with planes parallel to the regression plane. A better estimate of the population standard error of estimate is given by $\hat{s}_{1.23} = \sqrt{N/(N-3)}\, s_{1.23}$.

COEFFICIENT OF MULTIPLE CORRELATION

The coefficient of multiple correlation is defined by an extension of equation (*12*) or (*14*) of Chapter 14. In the case of two independent variables, for example, the *coefficient of multiple correlation* is given by

$$R_{1.23} = \sqrt{1 - \frac{s_{1.23}^2}{s_1^2}} \tag{8}$$

where s_1 is the standard deviation of the variable X_1 and $s_{1.23}$ is given by equation (*6*) or (*7*). The quantity $R_{1.23}^2$ is called the *coefficient of multiple determination.*

When a linear regression equation is used, the coefficient of multiple correlation is called the *coefficient of linear multiple correlation.* Unless otherwise specified, whenever we refer to multiple correlation, we shall imply linear multiple correlation.

In terms of r_{12}, r_{13}, and r_{23}, equation (*8*) can also be written

$$R_{1.23} = \sqrt{\frac{r_{12}^2 + r_{13}^2 - 2r_{12}r_{13}r_{23}}{1 - r_{23}^2}} \tag{9}$$

A coefficient of multiple correlation, such as $R_{1.23}$, lies between 0 and 1. The closer it is to 1, the better is the linear relationship between the variables. The closer it is to 0, the worse is the linear relationship. If the coefficient of multiple correlation is 1, the correlation is called *perfect.* Although a correlation coefficient of 0 indicates no linear relationship between the variables, it is possible that a *nonlinear relationship* may exist.

CHANGE OF DEPENDENT VARIABLE

The above results hold when X_1 is considered the dependent variable. However, if we want to consider X_3 (for example) to be the dependent variable instead of X_1, we would only have to replace the subscripts 1 with 3, and 3 with 1, in the formulas already obtained. For example, the regression equation of X_3 on X_1 and X_2 would be

$$\frac{x_3}{s_3} = \left(\frac{r_{23} - r_{13}r_{12}}{1 - r_{12}^2}\right)\frac{x_2}{s_2} + \left(\frac{r_{13} - r_{23}r_{12}}{1 - r_{12}^2}\right)\frac{x_1}{s_1} \tag{10}$$

as obtained from equation (*5*), using the results $r_{32} = r_{23}$, $r_{31} = r_{13}$, and $r_{21} = r_{12}$.

GENERALIZATIONS TO MORE THAN THREE VARIABLES

These are obtained by analogy with the above results. For example, the linear regression equations of X_1 on X_2, X_3, and X_4 can be written

$$X_1 = b_{1.234} + b_{12.34}X_2 + b_{13.24}X_3 + b_{14.23}X_4 \tag{11}$$

and represents a *hyperplane in four-dimensional space.* By formally multiplying both sides of equation (*11*) by 1, X_2, X_3, and X_4 successively and then summing on both sides, we obtain the normal equations for determining $b_{1.234}$, $b_{12.34}$, $b_{13.24}$, and $b_{14.23}$; substituting these in equation (*11*) then gives us the *least-squares regression equation of X_1 on X_2, X_3, and X_4*. This least-squares regression equation can be written in a form similar to that of equation (*5*). (See Problem 15.41.)

PARTIAL CORRELATION

It is often important to measure the correlation between a dependent variable and one particular independent variable when all other variables involved are kept constant; that is, when the effects of all other variables are removed (often indicated by the phrase "other things being equal"). This can be obtained by defining a *coefficient of partial correlation*, as in equation (*12*) of Chapter 14, except that we must consider the explained and unexplained variations that arise both with and without the particular independent variable.

If we denote by $r_{12.3}$ the coefficient of partial correlation between X_1 and X_2 keeping X_3 constant, we find that

$$r_{12.3} = \frac{r_{12} - r_{13}r_{23}}{\sqrt{(1 - r_{13}^2)(1 - r_{23}^2)}} \tag{12}$$

Similarly, if $r_{12.34}$ is the coefficient of partial correlation between X_1 and X_2 keeping X_3 and X_4 constant, then

$$r_{12.34} = \frac{r_{12.4} - r_{13.4}r_{23.4}}{\sqrt{(1 - r_{13.4}^2)(1 - r_{23.4}^2)}} = \frac{r_{12.3} - r_{14.3}r_{24.3}}{\sqrt{(1 - r_{14.3}^2)(1 - r_{24.3}^2)}} \tag{13}$$

These results are useful since by means of them any partial correlation coefficient can ultimately be made to depend on the correlation coefficients r_{12}, r_{23}, etc. (i.e., the *zero-order correlation coefficients*).

In the case of two variables, X and Y, if the two regression lines have equations $Y = a_0 + a_1X$ and $X = b_0 + b_1Y$, we have seen that $r^2 = a_1b_1$ (see Problem 14.22). This result can be generalized. For example, if

$$X_1 = b_{1.234} + b_{12.34}X_2 + b_{13.24}X_3 + b_{14.23}X_4 \tag{14}$$

and

$$X_4 = b_{4.123} + b_{41.23}X_1 + b_{42.13}X_2 + b_{43.12}X_3 \tag{15}$$

are linear regression equations of X_1 on X_2, X_3, and X_4 and of X_4 on X_1, X_2, and X_3, respectively, then

$$r_{14.23}^2 = b_{14.23}b_{41.23} \tag{16}$$

(see Problem 15.18). This can be taken as the starting point for a definition of linear partial correlation coefficients.

RELATIONSHIPS BETWEEN MULTIPLE AND PARTIAL CORRELATION COEFFICIENTS

Interesting results connecting the multiple correlation coefficients can be found. For example, we find that

$$1 - R_{1.23}^2 = (1 - r_{12}^2)(1 - r_{13.2}^2) \tag{17}$$

$$1 - R_{1.234}^2 = (1 - r_{12}^2)(1 - r_{13.2}^2)(1 - r_{14.23}^2) \tag{18}$$

Generalizations of these results are easily made.

NONLINEAR MULTIPLE REGRESSION

The above results for linear multiple regression can be extended to nonlinear multiple regression. Coefficients of multiple and partial correlation can then be defined by methods similar to those given above.

Solved Problems

REGRESSION EQUATIONS INVOLVING THREE VARIABLES

15.1 Using an appropriate subscript notation, write the regression equations of (a), X_2 on X_1 and X_3; (b) X_3 on X_1, X_2, and X_4; and (c) X_5 on X_1, X_2, X_3, and X_4.

SOLUTION

(a) $X_2 = b_{2.13} + b_{21.3}X_1 + b_{23.1}X_3$

(b) $X_3 = b_{3.124} + b_{31.24}X_1 + b_{32.14}X_2 + b_{34.12}X_4$

(c) $X_5 = b_{5.1234} + b_{51.234}X_1 + b_{52.134}X_2 + b_{53.124}X_3 + b_{54.123}X_4$

15.2 Write the normal equations corresponding to the regression equations (a) $X_3 = b_{3.12} + b_{31.2}X_1 + b_{32.1}X_2$ and (b) $X_1 = b_{1.234} + b_{12.34}X_2 + b_{13.24}X_3 + b_{14.23}X_4$.

SOLUTION

(a) Multiply the equation successively by 1, X_1, and X_2, and sum on both sides. The normal equations are

$$\begin{aligned}
\sum X_3 &= b_{3.12}N + b_{31.2}\sum X_1 + b_{32.1}\sum X_2 \\
\sum X_1X_3 &= b_{3.12}\sum X_1 + b_{31.2}\sum X_1^2 + b_{32.1}\sum X_1X_2 \\
\sum X_2X_3 &= b_{3.12}\sum X_2 + b_{31.2}\sum X_1X_2 + b_{32.1}\sum X_2^2
\end{aligned}$$

(b) Multiply the equation successively by 1, X_2, X_3, and X_4, and sum on both sides. The normal equations are

$$\begin{aligned}
\sum X_1 &= b_{1.234}N + b_{12.34}\sum X_2 + b_{13.24}\sum X_3 + b_{14.23}\sum X_4 \\
\sum X_1X_2 &= b_{1.234}\sum X_2 + b_{12.34}\sum X_2^2 + b_{13.24}\sum X_2X_3 + b_{14.23}\sum X_2X_4 \\
\sum X_1X_3 &= b_{1.234}\sum X_3 + b_{12.34}\sum X_2X_3 + b_{13.24}\sum X_3^2 + b_{14.23}\sum X_3X_4 \\
\sum X_1X_4 &= b_{1.234}\sum X_4 + b_{12.34}\sum X_2X_4 + b_{13.24}\sum X_3X_4 + b_{14.23}\sum X_4^2
\end{aligned}$$

Note that these are not derivations of the normal equations, but only formal means for remembering them.

The number of normal equations is equal to the number of unknown constants.

Mathcad **15.3** Table 15.1 shows the weights X_1 to the nearest pound (lb), the heights X_2 to the nearest inch (in), and the ages X_3 to the nearest year of 12 boys.

(a) Find the least-squares regression equation of X_1 on X_2 and X_3.

(b) Determine the estimated values of X_1 from the given values of X_2 and X_3.

(c) Estimate the weight of a boy who is 9 years old and 54 in tall.

Table 15.1

Weight (X_1)	64	71	53	67	55	58	77	57	56	51	76	68
Height (X_2)	57	59	49	62	51	50	55	48	52	42	61	57
Age (X_3)	8	10	6	11	8	7	10	9	10	6	12	9

SOLUTION

(a) The linear regression equation of X_1 on X_2 and X_3 can be written

$$X_1 = b_{1.23} + b_{12.3}X_2 + b_{13.2}X_3$$

The normal equations of the least-squares regression equation are

$$
\begin{aligned}
\sum X_1 &= b_{1.23}N + b_{12.3}\sum X_2 + b_{13.2}\sum X_3 \\
\sum X_1X_2 &= b_{1.23}\sum X_2 + b_{12.3}\sum X_2^2 + b_{13.2}\sum X_2X_3 \\
\sum X_1X_3 &= b_{1.23}\sum X_3 + b_{12.3}\sum X_2X_3 + b_{13.2}\sum X_3^2
\end{aligned} \qquad (19)
$$

The work involved in computing the sums can be arranged as in Table 15.2. (Although the column headed X_1^2 is not needed at present, it has been added for future reference.)

Table 15.2

X_1	X_2	X_3	X_1^2	X_2^2	X_3^2	X_1X_2	X_1X_3	X_2X_3
64	57	8	4096	3249	64	3648	512	456
71	59	10	5041	3481	100	4189	710	590
53	49	6	2809	2401	36	2597	318	294
67	62	11	4489	3844	121	4154	737	682
55	51	8	3025	2601	64	2805	440	408
58	50	7	3364	2500	49	2900	406	350
77	55	10	5929	3025	100	4235	770	550
57	48	9	3249	2304	81	2736	513	432
56	52	10	3136	2704	100	2912	560	520
51	42	6	2601	1764	36	2142	306	252
76	61	12	5776	3721	144	4636	912	732
68	57	9	4624	3249	81	3876	612	513
$\sum X_1 = 753$	$\sum X_2 = 643$	$\sum X_3 = 106$	$\sum X_1^2 = 48{,}139$	$\sum X_2^2 = 34{,}843$	$\sum X_3^2 = 976$	$\sum X_1X_2 = 40{,}830$	$\sum X_1X_3 = 6796$	$\sum X_2X_3 = 5779$

Using Table 15.2, the normal equations (*19*) become

$$
\begin{aligned}
12b_{1.23} + 643b_{12.3} + 106b_{13.2} &= 753 \\
643b_{1.23} + 34{,}843b_{12.3} + 5{,}779b_{13.2} &= 40{,}830 \\
106b_{1.23} + 5{,}779b_{12.3} + 976b_{13.2} &= 6{,}796
\end{aligned} \qquad (20)
$$

Solving, $b_{1.23} = 3.6512$, $b_{12.3} = 0.8546$, and $b_{13.2} = 1.5063$, and the required regression equation is

$$X_1 = 3.6512 + 0.8546X_2 + 1.5063X_3 \quad \text{or} \quad X_1 = 3.65 + 0.855X_2 + 1.506X_3 \qquad (21)$$

For another method, which avoids solving simultaneous equations, see Problem 15.6.

(*b*) Using the regression equation (*21*), we obtain the estimated values of X_1, denoted by $X_{1,\text{est}}$, by substituting the corresponding values of X_2 and X_3. For example, substituting $X_2 = 57$ and $X_3 = 8$ in (*21*), we find $X_{1,\text{est}} = 64.414$.

The other estimated values of X_1 are obtained similarly. They are given in Table 15.3 together with the sample values of X_1.

(*c*) Putting $X_2 = 54$ and $X_3 = 9$ in equation (*21*), the estimated weight is $X_{1,\text{est}} = 63.356$, or about 63 lb.

Table 15.3

$X_{1,\text{est}}$	64.414	69.136	54.564	73.206	59.286	56.925	65.717	58.229	63.153	48.582	73.857	65.920
X_1	64	71	53	67	55	58	77	57	56	51	76	68

15.4 Calculate the standard deviations (*a*) s_1, (*b*) s_2, and (*c*) s_3 for the data of Problem 15.3.

SOLUTION

(*a*) The quantity s_1 is the standard deviation of the variable X_1. Then, using Table 15.2 of Problem 15.3(*a*) and the methods of Chapter 4, we find

$$s_1 = \sqrt{\frac{\sum X_1^2}{N} - \left(\frac{\sum X_1}{N}\right)^2} = \sqrt{\frac{48{,}139}{12} - \left(\frac{753}{12}\right)^2} = 8.6035 \quad \text{or} \quad 8.6 \text{ lb}$$

(*b*)
$$s_2 = \sqrt{\frac{\sum X_2^2}{N} - \left(\frac{\sum X_2}{N}\right)^2} = \sqrt{\frac{34{,}843}{12} - \left(\frac{643}{12}\right)^2} = 5.6930 \quad \text{or} \quad 5.7 \text{ in}$$

(*c*)
$$s_3 = \sqrt{\frac{\sum X_3^2}{N} - \left(\frac{\sum X_3}{N}\right)^2} = \sqrt{\frac{976}{12} - \left(\frac{106}{12}\right)^2} = 1.8181 \quad \text{or} \quad 1.8 \text{ years}$$

15.5 Compute (*a*) r_{12}, (*b*) r_{13}, and (*c*) r_{23} for the data of Problem 15.3.

SOLUTION

(*a*) The quantity r_{12} is the linear correlation coefficient between the variables X_1 and X_2, ignoring the variable X_3. Then, using the methods of Chapter 14, we have

$$r_{12} = \frac{N\sum X_1X_2 - (\sum X_1)(\sum X_2)}{\sqrt{[N\sum X_1^2 - (\sum X_1)^2][N\sum X_2^2 - (\sum X_2)^2]}}$$

$$= \frac{(12)(40{,}830) - (753)(643)}{\sqrt{[(12)(48{,}139) - (753)^2][(12)(34{,}843) - (643)^2]}} = 0.8196 \quad \text{or} \quad 0.82$$

(*b*) and (*c*) Using corresponding formulas, we obtain $r_{12} = 0.7698$, or 0.77, and $r_{23} = 0.7984$, or 0.80.

15.6 Work Problem 15.3(*a*) by using equation (*5*) of this chapter and the results of Problems 15.4 and 15.5.

SOLUTION

The regression equation of X_1 on X_2 and X_3 is, on multiplying both sides of equation (*5*) by s_1,

$$x_1 = \left(\frac{r_{12} - r_{13}r_{23}}{1 - r_{23}^2}\right)\left(\frac{s_1}{s_2}\right)x_2 + \left(\frac{r_{13} - r_{12}r_{23}}{1 - r_{23}^2}\right)\left(\frac{s_1}{s_3}\right)x_3 \qquad (22)$$

where $x_1 = X_1 - \bar{X}_1$, $x_2 = X_2 - \bar{X}_2$, and $x_3 = X_3 - \bar{X}_3$. Using the results of Problems 15.4 and 15.5, equation (*22*) becomes

$$x_1 = 0.8546x_2 + 1.5063x_3$$

Since
$$\bar{X}_1 = \frac{\sum X_1}{N} = \frac{753}{12} = 62.750 \qquad \bar{X}_2 = \frac{\sum X_2}{N} = 53.583 \quad \text{and} \quad \bar{X}_3 = 8.833$$

(from Table 15.2 of Problem 15.3), the required equation can be written

$$X_1 - 62.750 = 0.8546(X_2 - 53.583) + 1.506(X_3 - 8.833)$$

agreeing with the result of Problem 15.3(*a*).

15.7 For the data of Problem 15.3, determine (*a*) the average increase in weight per inch of increase in height for boys of the same age and (*b*) the average increase in weight per year for boys having the same height.

SOLUTION

From the regression equation obtained in Problem 15.3(*a*) or 15.6 we see that the answer to (*a*) is 0.8546, or about 0.9 lb, and that the answer to (*b*) is 1.5063, or about 1.5 lb.

15.8 Show that equations (*3*) and (*4*) of this chapter follow from equations (*1*) and (*2*).

SOLUTION

From the first of equations (*2*), on dividing both sides by N, we have

$$\bar{X}_1 = b_{1.23} + b_{12.3}\bar{X}_2 + b_{13.2}\bar{X}_3 \tag{23}$$

Subtracting equation (*23*) from equation (*1*) gives

$$X_1 - \bar{X}_1 = b_{12.3}(X_2 - \bar{X}_2) + b_{13.2}(X_3 - \bar{X}_3)$$

or

$$x_1 = b_{12.3}x_2 + b_{13.2}x_3 \tag{24}$$

which is equation (*3*).

Let $X_1 = x_1 + \bar{X}_1$, $X_2 = x_2 + \bar{X}_2$, and $X_3 = x_3 + \bar{X}_3$ in the second and third of equations (*2*). Then after some algebraic simplifications, using the results $\sum x_1 = \sum x_2 = \sum x_3 = 0$, they become

$$\sum x_1x_2 = b_{12.3}\sum x_2^2 + b_{13.2}\sum x_2x_3 + N\bar{X}_2[b_{1.23} + b_{12.3}\bar{X}_2 + b_{13.2}\bar{X}_3 - \bar{X}_1] \tag{25}$$

$$\sum x_1x_3 = b_{12.3}\sum x_2x_3 + b_{13.2}\sum x_3^2 + N\bar{X}_3[b_{1.23} + b_{12.3}\bar{X}_2 + b_{13.2}\bar{X}_3 - \bar{X}_1] \tag{26}$$

which reduce to equations (*4*) since the quantities in brackets on the right-hand sides of equations (*25*) and (*26*) are zero because of equation (*1*).

Another method

See Problem 15.30.

15.9 Establish equation (*5*), repeated here:

$$\frac{x_1}{s_1} = \left(\frac{r_{12} - r_{13}r_{23}}{1 - r_{23}^2}\right)\frac{x_2}{s_2} + \left(\frac{r_{13} - r_{12}r_{23}}{1 - r_{23}^2}\right)\frac{x_3}{s_3} \tag{5}$$

SOLUTION

From equations (*25*) and (*26*)

$$\begin{aligned} b_{12.3}\sum x_2^2 + b_{13.2}\sum x_2x_3 &= \sum x_1x_2 \\ b_{12.3}\sum x_2x_3 + b_{13.2}\sum x_3^2 &= \sum x_1x_3 \end{aligned} \tag{27}$$

Since

$$s_2^2 = \frac{\sum x_2^2}{N} \quad \text{and} \quad s_3^2 = \frac{\sum x_3^2}{N}$$

$\sum x_2^2 = Ns_2^2$ and $\sum x_3^2 = Ns_3^2$. Since

$$r_{23} = \frac{\sum x_2x_3}{\sqrt{(\sum x_2^2)(\sum x_3^2)}} = \frac{\sum x_2x_3}{Ns_2s_3}$$

$\sum x_2x_3 = Ns_2s_3r_{23}$. Similarly, $\sum x_1x_2 = Ns_1s_2r_{12}$ and $\sum x_1x_3 = Ns_1s_3r_{13}$.

Substituting in (*27*) and simplifying, we find

$$\begin{aligned} b_{12.3}s_2 + b_{13.2}s_3r_{23} &= s_1r_{12} \\ b_{12.3}s_2r_{23} + b_{13.2}s_3 &= s_1r_{13} \end{aligned} \tag{28}$$

Solving equations (*28*) simultaneously, we have

$$b_{12.3} = \left(\frac{r_{12} - r_{13}r_{23}}{1 - r_{23}^2}\right)\left(\frac{s_1}{s_2}\right) \quad \text{and} \quad b_{13.2} = \left(\frac{r_{13} - r_{12}r_{23}}{1 - r_{23}^2}\right)\left(\frac{s_1}{s_3}\right)$$

Substituting these in the equation $x_1 = b_{12.3}x_2 + b_{13.2}x_3$ [equation (*24*)] and dividing by s_1 yields the required result.

STANDARD ERROR OF ESTIMATE

Mathcad

15.10 Compute the standard error of estimate of X_1 on X_2 and X_3 for the data of Problem 15.3.

SOLUTION

From Table 15.3 of Problem 15.3(*b*) we have

$$s_{1.23} = \sqrt{\frac{\sum (X_1 - X_{1,\text{est}})^2}{N}}$$

$$= \sqrt{\frac{(64-64.414)^2 + (71-69.136)^2 + \cdots + (68-65.920)^2}{12}} = 4.6447 \quad \text{or} \quad 4.6 \text{ lb}$$

The population standard error of estimate is estimated by $\hat{s}_{1.23} = \sqrt{N/(N-3)}s_{1.23} = 5.3$ lb in this case.

15.11 To obtain the result of Problem 15.10, use

$$s_{1.23} = s_1 \sqrt{\frac{1 - r_{12}^2 - r_{13}^2 - r_{23}^2 + 2r_{12}r_{13}r_{23}}{1 - r_{23}^2}}$$

SOLUTION

From Problems 15.4(*a*) and 15.5 we have

$$s_{1.23} = 8.6035\sqrt{\frac{1-(0.8196)^2-(0.7698)^2-(0.7984)^2+2(0.8196)(0.7698)(0.7984)}{1-(0.7984)^2}} = 4.6 \text{ lb}$$

Note that by the method of this problem the standard error of estimate can be found without using the regression equation.

COEFFICIENT OF MULTIPLE CORRELATION

Mathcad

15.12 Compute the coefficient of linear multiple correlation of X_1 on X_2 and X_3 for the data of Problem 15.3.

SOLUTION

First method

From the results of Problems 15.4(*a*) and 15.10 we have

$$R_{1.23} = \sqrt{1 - \frac{s_{1.23}^2}{s_1^2}} = \sqrt{1 - \frac{(4.6447)^2}{(8.6035)^2}} = 0.8418$$

Second method

From the results of Problem 15.5 we have

$$R_{1.23} = \sqrt{\frac{r_{12}^2 + r_{13}^2 - 2r_{12}r_{13}r_{23}}{1 - r_{23}^2}} = \sqrt{\frac{(0.8196)^2 + (0.7698)^2 - 2(0.8196)(0.7698)(0.7984)}{1-(0.7984)^2}} = 0.8418$$

Note that the coefficient of multiple correlation, $R_{1.23}$, is larger than either of the coefficients r_{12} or r_{13} (see Problem 15.5). This is always true and is in fact to be expected, since by taking into account additional relevant independent variables we should arrive at a better relationship between the variables.

15.13 Compute the coefficient of multiple determination of X_1 on X_2 and X_3 for the data of Problem 15.3.

SOLUTION

The coefficient of multiple determination of X_1 on X_2 and X_3 is

$$R^2_{1.23} = (0.8418)^2 = 0.7086$$

using Problem 15.12. Thus about 71% of the total variation in X_1 is explained by using the regression equation.

15.14 For the data of Problem 15.3, calculate (*a*) $R_{2.13}$ and (*b*) $R_{3.12}$ and compare their values with the value of $R_{1.23}$.

SOLUTION

(*a*) $$R_{2.13} = \sqrt{\frac{r^2_{12} + r^2_{23} - 2r_{12}r_{13}r_{23}}{1 - r^2_{13}}} = \sqrt{\frac{(0.8196)^2 + (0.7984)^2 - 2(0.8196)(0.7698)(0.7984)}{1 - (0.7698)^2}} = 0.8606$$

(*b*) $$R_{3.12} = \sqrt{\frac{r^2_{13} + r^2_{23} - 2r_{12}r_{13}r_{23}}{1 - r^2_{12}}} = \sqrt{\frac{(0.7698)^2 + (0.7984)^2 - 2(0.8196)(0.7698)(0.7984)}{1 - (0.8196)^2}} = 0.8234$$

This problem illustrates the fact that, in general, $R_{2.13}$, $R_{3.12}$, and $R_{1.23}$ are not necessarily equal, as seen by comparison with Problem 15.12.

15.15 If $R_{1.23} = 1$, prove that (*a*) $R_{2.13} = 1$ and (*b*) $R_{3.12} = 1$.

SOLUTION

$$R_{1.23} = \sqrt{\frac{r^2_{12} + r^2_{13} - 2r_{12}r_{13}r_{23}}{1 - r^2_{23}}} \qquad (29)$$

and

$$R_{2.13} = \sqrt{\frac{r^2_{12} + r^2_{23} - 2r_{12}r_{13}r_{23}}{1 - r^2_{13}}} \qquad (30)$$

(*a*) In equation (*29*), setting $R_{1.23} = 1$ and squaring both sides, $r^2_{12} + r^2_{13} - 2r_{12}r_{13}r_{23} = 1 - r^2_{23}$. Then

$$r^2_{12} + r^2_{23} - 2r_{12}r_{13}r_{23} = 1 - r^2_{13} \qquad \text{or} \qquad \frac{r^2_{12} + r^2_{23} - 2r_1 r_{13}r_{23}}{1 - r^2_{13}} = 1$$

That is, $R^2_{2.13} = 1$ or $R_{2.13} = 1$, since the coefficient of multiple correlation is considered nonnegative.

(*b*) $R_{3.12} = 1$ follows from part (*a*) by interchanging subscripts 2 and 3 in the result $R_{2.13} = 1$.

15.16 If $R_{1.23} = 0$, does it necessarily follow that $R_{2.13} = 0$?

SOLUTION

From equation (*29*), $R_{1.23} = 0$ if and only if

$$r^2_{12} + r^2_{13} - 2r_{12}r_{13}r_{23} = 0 \qquad \text{or} \qquad 2r_{12}r_{13}r_{23} = r^2_{12} + r^2_{13}$$

Then from equation (*30*) we have

$$R_{2.13} = \sqrt{\frac{r^2_{12} + r^2_{23} - (r^2_{12} + r^2_{13})}{1 - r^2_{13}}} = \sqrt{\frac{r^2_{23} - r^2_{13}}{1 - r^2_{13}}}$$

which is not necessarily zero.

PARTIAL CORRELATION

15.17 For the data of Problem 15.3, compute the coefficients of linear partial correlation (*a*) $r_{12.3}$, (*b*) $r_{13.2}$, and (*c*) $r_{23.1}$.

SOLUTION

$$r_{12.3}=\frac{r_{12}-r_{13}r_{23}}{\sqrt{(1-r_{13}^2)(1-r_{23}^2)}} \qquad r_{13.2}=\frac{r_{13}-r_{12}r_{23}}{\sqrt{(1-r_{12}^2)(1-r_{23}^2)}} \qquad r_{23.1}=\frac{r_{23}-r_{12}r_{13}}{\sqrt{(1-r_{12}^2)(1-r_{13}^2)}}$$

Using the results of Problem 15.5, we find that $r_{12.3}=0.5334$, $r_{13.2}=0.3346$, and $r_{23.1}=0.4580$. It follows that for boys of the same age, the correlation coefficient between weight and height is 0.53; for boys of the same height, the correlation coefficient between weight and age is only 0.33. Since these results are based on a small sample of only 12 boys, they are of course not as reliable as those which would be obtained from a larger sample.

15.18 If $X_1=b_{1.23}+b_{12.3}X_2+b_{13.2}X_3$ and $X_3=b_{3.12}+b_{32.1}X_2+b_{31.2}X_1$ are the regression equations of X_1 on X_2 and X_3 and of X_3 on X_2 and X_1, respectively, prove that $r_{13.2}^2=b_{13.2}b_{31.2}$.

SOLUTION

The regression equation of X_1 on X_2 and X_3 can be written [see equation (*5*) of this chapter]

$$X_1=\bar{X}_1=\left(\frac{r_{12}-r_{13}r_{23}}{1-r_{23}^2}\right)\left(\frac{s_1}{s_2}\right)(X_2-\bar{X}_2)+\left(\frac{r_{13}-r_{12}r_{23}}{1-r_{23}^2}\right)\left(\frac{s_1}{s_3}\right)(X_3-\bar{X}_3) \qquad (31)$$

The regression equation of X_3 on X_2 and X_1 can be written [see equation (*10*)]

$$X_3-\bar{X}_3=\left(\frac{r_{23}-r_{13}r_{12}}{1-r_{12}^2}\right)\left(\frac{s_3}{s_2}\right)(X_2-\bar{X}_2)+\left(\frac{r_{13}-r_{23}r_{12}}{1-r_{12}^2}\right)\left(\frac{s_3}{s_1}\right)(X_1-\bar{X}_1) \qquad (32)$$

From equations (*31*) and (*32*) the coefficients of X_3 and X_1 are, respectively,

$$b_{13.2}=\left(\frac{r_{13}-r_{12}r_{23}}{1-r_{23}^2}\right)\left(\frac{s_1}{s_3}\right) \quad \text{and} \quad b_{31.2}=\left(\frac{r_{13}-r_{23}r_{12}}{1-r_{12}^2}\right)\left(\frac{s_3}{s_1}\right)$$

Thus

$$b_{13.2}b_{31.2}=\frac{(r_{13}-r_{12}r_{23})^2}{(1-r_{23}^2)(1-r_{12}^2)}=r_{13.2}^2$$

15.19 If $r_{12.3}=0$, prove that

$$(a)\quad r_{13.2}=r_{13}\sqrt{\frac{1-r_{23}^2}{1-r_{12}^2}} \qquad (b)\quad r_{23.1}=r_{23}\sqrt{\frac{1-r_{13}^2}{1-r_{12}^2}}$$

SOLUTION

If

$$r_{12.3}=\frac{r_{12}-r_{13}r_{23}}{\sqrt{(1-r_{13}^2)(1-r_{23}^2)}}=0$$

we have $r_{12}=r_{13}r_{23}$.

(*a*)

$$r_{13.2}=\frac{r_{13}-r_{12}r_{23}}{\sqrt{(1-r_{12}^2)(1-r_{23}^2)}}=\frac{r_{13}-(r_{13}r_{23})r_{23}}{\sqrt{(1-r_{12}^2)(1-r_{23}^2)}}=\frac{r_{13}(1-r_{23}^2)}{\sqrt{(1-r_{12}^2)(1-r_{23}^2)}}=r_{13}\sqrt{\frac{1-r_{23}^2}{1-r_{12}^2}}$$

(*b*) Interchange the subscripts 1 and 2 in the result of part (*a*).

MULTIPLE AND PARTIAL CORRELATION INVOLVING FOUR OR MORE VARIABLES

15.20 A college entrance examination consisted of three tests: in mathematics, English, and general knowledge. To test the ability of the examination to predict performance in a statistics course, data concerning a sample of 200 students were gathered and analyzed. Letting

X_1 = grade in statistics course X_3 = score on English test
X_2 = score on mathematics test X_4 = score on general knowledge test

the following calculations were obtained:

$$\bar{X}_1 = 75 \qquad s_1 = 10 \qquad \bar{X}_2 = 24 \qquad s_2 = 5$$
$$\bar{X}_3 = 15 \qquad s_3 = 3 \qquad \bar{X}_4 = 36 \qquad s_4 = 6$$
$$r_{12} = 0.90 \qquad r_{13} = 0.75 \qquad r_{14} = 0.80 \qquad r_{23} = 0.70 \qquad r_{24} = 0.70 \qquad r_{34} = 0.85$$

Find the least-squares regression equation of X_1 on X_2, X_3, and X_4.

SOLUTION

Generalizing the result of Problem 15.8, we can write the least-squares regression equation of X_1 on X_2, X_3, and X_4 in the form

$$x_1 = b_{12.34}x_2 + b_{13.24}x_3 + b_{14.23}x_4 \tag{33}$$

where $b_{12.34}$, $b_{13.24}$, and $b_{14.23}$ can be obtained from the normal equations

$$\begin{aligned} \sum x_1x_2 &= b_{12.34}\sum x_2^2 + b_{13.24}\sum x_2x_3 + b_{14.23}\sum x_2x_4 \\ \sum x_1x_3 &= b_{12.34}\sum x_2x_3 + b_{13.24}\sum x_3^2 + b_{14.23}\sum x_3x_4 \\ \sum x_1x_4 &= b_{12.34}\sum x_2x_4 + b_{13.24}\sum x_3x_4 + b_{14.23}\sum x_4^2 \end{aligned} \tag{34}$$

and where $x_1 = X_1 - \bar{X}_1$, $x_2 = X_2 - \bar{X}_2$, $x_3 = X_3 - \bar{X}_3$, and $x_4 = X_4 - \bar{X}_4$.

From the given data, we find

$$\sum x_2^2 = Ns_2^2 = 5000 \qquad \sum x_1x_2 = Ns_1s_2r_{12} = 9000 \qquad \sum x_2x_3 = Ns_1s_3r_{23} = 2100$$
$$\sum x_3^2 = Ns_3^2 = 1800 \qquad \sum x_1x_3 = Ns_1s_3r_{13} = 4500 \qquad \sum x_2x_4 = Ns_2s_4r_{24} = 4200$$
$$\sum x_4^2 = Ns_4^2 = 7200 \qquad \sum x_1x_4 = Ns_1s_4r_{14} = 9600 \qquad \sum x_3x_4 = Ns_3s_4r_{34} = 3060$$

Putting these results into equations (34) and solving, we obtain

$$b_{12.34} = 1.3333 \qquad b_{13.24} = 0.0000 \qquad b_{14.23} = 0.5556 \tag{35}$$

which, when substituted in equation (33), yield the required regression equation

$$x_1 = 1.3333x_2 + 0.0000x_3 + 0.5556x_4$$

or

$$X_1 - 75 = 1.3333(X_2 - 24) + 0.5556(X_4 - 27) \tag{36}$$

or

$$X_1 = 22.9999 + 1.3333X_2 + 0.5556X_4$$

An exact solution of equations (34) yields $b_{12.34} = \frac{4}{3}$, $b_{13.24} = 0$, and $b_{14.23} = \frac{5}{9}$, so that the regression equation can also be written

$$X_1 = 23 + \tfrac{4}{3}X_2 + \tfrac{5}{9}X_4 \tag{37}$$

It is interesting to note that the regression equation does not involve the score in English, namely, X_3. This does not mean that one's knowledge of English has no bearing on proficiency in statistics. Instead, it means that the need for English, insofar as prediction of the statistics grade is concerned, is amply evidenced by the scores achieved on the other tests.

15.21 Two students taking the college entrance examination of Problem 15.20 receive respective scores of (*a*) 30 in mathematics, 18 in English, and 32 in general knowledge; and (*b*) 18 in mathematics, 20 in English, and 36 in general knowledge. What would be their predicted grades in statistics?

SOLUTION

(*a*) Substituting $X_2 = 30$, $X_3 = 18$, and $X_4 = 32$ in equation (37), the predicted grade in statistics is $X_1 = 81$.

(*b*) Proceeding as in part (*a*) with $X_2 = 18$, $X_3 = 20$, and $X_4 = 36$, we find $X_1 = 67$.

Mathcad **15.22** For the data of Problem 15.20, find the partial correlation coefficients (*a*) $r_{12.34}$, (*b*) $r_{13.24}$, and (*c*) $r_{14.23}$.

SOLUTION

(*a*) and (*b*) $r_{12.4}=\dfrac{r_{12}-r_{14}r_{24}}{\sqrt{(1-r_{14}^2)(1-r_{24}^2)}}$ $r_{13.4}=\dfrac{r_{13}-r_{14}r_{34}}{\sqrt{(1-r_{14}^2)(1-r_{34}^2)}}$ $r_{23.4}=\dfrac{r_{23}-r_{24}r_{34}}{\sqrt{(1-r_{24}^2)(1-r_{34}^2)}}$

Substituting the values from Problem 15.20, we obtain $r_{12.4}=0.7935$, $r_{13.4}=0.2215$, and $r_{23.4}=0.2791$. Thus

$$r_{12.34}=\frac{r_{12.4}-r_{13.4}r_{23.4}}{\sqrt{(1-r_{13.4}^2)(1-r_{23.4}^2)}}=0.7814 \quad\text{and}\quad r_{13.24}=\frac{r_{13.4}-r_{12.4}r_{23.4}}{\sqrt{(1-r_{12.4}^2)(1-r_{23.4}^2)}}=0.0000$$

(*c*) $r_{14.3}=\dfrac{r_{14}-r_{13}r_{34}}{\sqrt{(1-r_{13}^2)(1-r_{34}^2)}}$ $r_{12.3}=\dfrac{r_{12}-r_{13}r_{23}}{\sqrt{(1-r_{13}^2)(1-r_{23}^2)}}$ $r_{24.3}=\dfrac{r_{24}-r_{23}r_{34}}{\sqrt{(1-r_{23}^2)(1-r_{34}^2)}}$

Substituting the values from Problem 15.20, we obtain $r_{14.3}=0.4664$, $r_{12.3}=0.7939$, and $r_{24.3}=0.2791$. Thus

$$r_{14.23}=\frac{r_{14.3}-r_{12.3}r_{24.3}}{\sqrt{(1-r_{12.3}^2)(1-r_{24.3}^2)}}=0.4193$$

15.23 Interpret the partial correlation coefficients (*a*) $r_{12.4}$, (*b*) $r_{13.4}$, (*c*) $r_{12.34}$, (*d*) $r_{14.3}$, and (*e*) $r_{14.23}$ obtained in Problem 15.22.

SOLUTION

(*a*) $r_{12.4}=0.7935$ represents the (linear) correlation coefficient between statistics grades and mathematics scores for students having the same general knowledge scores. In obtaining this coefficient, scores in English (as well as other factors that have not been taken into account) are not considered, as is evidenced by the fact that the subscript 3 is omitted.

(*b*) $r_{13.4}=0.2215$ represents the correlation coefficient between statistics grades and English scores for students having the same general knowledge scores. Here, scores in mathematics have not been considered.

(*c*) $r_{12.34}=0.7814$ represents the correlation coefficient between statistics grades and mathematics scores for students having both the same English scores and general knowledge scores.

(*d*) $r_{14.3}=0.4664$ represents the correlation coefficient between statistics grades and general knowledge scores for students having the same English scores.

(*e*) $r_{14.23}=0.4193$ represents the correlation coefficient between statistics grades and general knowledge scores for students having both the same mathematics scores and English scores.

15.24 (*a*) For the data of Problem 15.20, show that

$$\frac{r_{12.4}-r_{13.4}r_{23.4}}{\sqrt{(1-r_{13.4}^2)(1-r_{23.4}^2)}}=\frac{r_{12.3}-r_{14.3}r_{24.3}}{\sqrt{(1-r_{14.3}^2)(1-r_{24.3}^2)}} \tag{38}$$

(*b*) Explain the significance of the equality in part (*a*).

SOLUTION

(*a*) The left-hand side of equation (*38*) is evaluated in Problem 15.22(*a*), yielding the result 0.7814. To evaluate the right-hand side of equation (*38*), use the results of Problem 15.22(*c*); again, the result is 0.7814. Thus the equality holds in this special case. It can be shown by direct algebraic processes that the equality holds in general.

(*b*) The left side of equation (*38*) is $r_{12.34}$, and the right side is $r_{12.43}$. Since $r_{12.34}$ is the correlation between variables X_1 and X_2 keeping X_3 and X_4 constant, while $r_{12.43}$ is the correlation between X_1 and X_2 keeping X_4 and X_3 constant, it is at once evident why the equality should hold.

Mathcad **15.25** For the data of Problem 15.20, find (*a*) the multiple correlation coefficient $R_{1.234}$ and (*b*) the standard error of estimate $s_{1.234}$.

SOLUTION

(*a*)
$$1 - R_{1.234}^2 = (1 - r_{12}^2)(1 - r_{13.2}^2)(1 - r_{14.23}^2) \qquad \text{or} \qquad R_{1.234} = 0.9310$$

since $r_{12} = 0.90$ from Problem 15.20, $r_{14.23} = 0.4193$ from Problem 15.22(*c*), and

$$r_{13.2} = \frac{r_{13} - r_{12}r_{23}}{\sqrt{(1 - r_{12}^2)(1 - r_{23}^2)}} = \frac{0.75 - (0.90)(0.70)}{\sqrt{[1 - (0.90)^2][1 - (0.70)^2]}} = 0.3855$$

Another method

Interchanging subscripts 2 and 4 in the first equation yields

$$1 - R_{1.234}^2 = (1 - r_{14}^2)(1 - r_{13.4}^2)(1 - r_{12.34}^2) \qquad \text{or} \qquad R_{1.234} = 0.9310$$

where the results of Problem 15.22(*a*) are used directly.

(*b*)
$$R_{1.234} = \sqrt{\frac{1 - s_{1.234}^2}{s_1^2}} \qquad \text{or} \qquad s_{1.234} = s_1\sqrt{1 - R_{1.234}^2} = 10\sqrt{1 - (0.9310)^2} = 3.650$$

Compare with equation (*8*) of this chapter.

Supplementary Problems

REGRESSION EQUATIONS INVOLVING THREE VARIABLES

15.26 Using an appropriate subscript notation, write the regression equations of (*a*) X_3 on X_1 and X_2 and (*b*) X_4 on X_1, X_2, X_3, and X_5.

15.27 Write the normal equations corresponding to the regression equations of (*a*) X_2 on X_1 and X_3 and (*b*) X_5 on X_1, X_2, X_3, and X_4.

15.28 Table 15.4 shows the corresponding values of three variables: X_1, X_2, and X_3.

(*a*) Find the least-squares regression equation of X_3 on X_1 and X_2.

(*b*) Estimate X_3 when $X_1 = 10$ and $X_2 = 6$.

Table 15.4

X_1	3	5	6	8	12	14
X_2	16	10	7	4	3	2
X_3	90	72	54	42	30	12

15.29 An instructor of mathematics wished to determine the relationship of grades on a final examination to grades on two quizzes given during the semester. Calling X_1, X_2, and X_3 the grades of a student on the first quiz, second quiz, and final examination, respectively, he made the following computations for a total of 120 students:

$$\bar{X}_1 = 6.8 \qquad \bar{X}_2 = 7.0 \qquad \bar{X}_3 = 74$$
$$s_1 = 1.0 \qquad s_2 = 0.80 \qquad s_3 = 9.0$$
$$r_{12} = 0.60 \qquad r_{13} = 0.70 \qquad r_{23} = 0.65$$

(a) Find the least-squares regression equation of X_3 on X_1 and X_2.

(b) Estimate the final grades of two students whose respective scores on the two quizzes were (1) 9 and 7 and (2) 4 and 8.

15.30 Work Problem 15.8 by choosing the variables X_2 and X_3 so that $\sum X_2 = \sum X_3 = 0$.

STANDARD ERROR OF ESTIMATE

15.31 For the data of Problem 15.28, find the standard error of estimate of X_3 on X_1 and X_2.

15.32 For the data of Problem 15.29, find the standard error of estimate of (a) X_3 on X_1 and X_2 and (b) X_1 on X_2 and X_3.

COEFFICIENT OF MULTIPLE CORRELATION

15.33 For the data of Problem 15.28, compute the coefficient of linear multiple correlation of X_3 on X_1 and X_2.

15.34 For the data of Problem 15.29, compute (a) $R_{3.12}$, (b) $R_{1.23}$, and (c) $R_{2.13}$.

15.35 (a) If $r_{12} = r_{13} = r_{23} = r \neq 1$, show that

$$R_{1.23} = R_{2.31} = R_{3.12} = \frac{r\sqrt{2}}{\sqrt{1+r}}$$

(b) Discuss the case $r = 1$.

15.36 If $R_{1.23} = 0$, prove that $|r_{23}| \geq |r_{12}|$ and $|r_{23}| \geq |r_{13}|$ and interpret.

PARTIAL CORRELATION

15.37 Compute the coefficients of linear partial correlation (a) $r_{12.3}$, (b) $r_{13.2}$, and (c) $r_{23.1}$ for the data of Problem 15.28 and interpret your answers.

15.38 Work Problem 15.37 for the data of Problem 15.29.

15.39 If $r_{12} = r_{13} = r_{23} = r \neq 1$, show that $r_{12.3} = r_{13.2} = r_{23.1} = r/(1+r)$. Discuss the case $r = 1$.

15.40 If $r_{12.3} = 1$, show that (a) $|r_{13.2}| = 1$, (b) $|r_{23.1}| = 1$, (c) $R_{1.23} = 1$, and (d) $s_{1.23} = 0$.

MULTIPLE AND PARTIAL CORRELATION INVOLVING FOUR OR MORE VARIABLES

15.41 Show that the regression equation of X_4 on X_1, X_2, and X_3 can be written

$$\frac{x_4}{s_4} = a_1\left(\frac{x_1}{s_1}\right) + a_2\left(\frac{x_2}{s_2}\right) + a_3\left(\frac{x_3}{s_3}\right)$$

where a_1, a_2, and a_3 are determined by solving simultaneously the equations

$$a_1 r_{11} + a_2 r_{12} + a_3 r_{13} = r_{14}$$
$$a_1 r_{21} + a_2 r_{22} + a_3 r_{23} = r_{24}$$
$$a_1 r_{31} + a_2 r_{32} + a_3 r_{33} = r_{34}$$

and where $x_j = X_j - \bar{X}_j$, $r_{jj} = 1$, and $j = 1, 2, 3$, and 4. Generalize to the case of more than four variables.

15.42 Given $\bar{X}_1 = 20$, $\bar{X}_2 = 36$, $\bar{X}_3 = 12$, $\bar{X}_4 = 80$, $s_1 = 1.0$, $s_2 = 2.0$, $s_3 = 1.5$, $s_4 = 6.0$, $r_{12} = -0.20$, $r_{13} = 0.40$, $r_{23} = 0.50$, $r_{14} = 0.40$, $r_{24} = 0.30$, and $r_{34} = -0.10$, (a) find the regression equation of X_4 on X_1, X_2, and X_3, and (b) estimate X_4 when $X_1 = 15$, $X_2 = 40$, and $X_3 = 14$.

15.43 Find (a) $r_{41.23}$, (b) $r_{42.13}$, and (c) $r_{43.12}$ for the data of Problem 15.42 and interpret your results.

15.44 For the data of Problem 15.42, find (a) $R_{4.123}$ and (b) $s_{4.123}$.

15.45 A scientist collected data concerning four variables: T, U, V, and W. She believed that an equation of the form $W = aT^bU^cV^d$, where a, b, c, and d are unknown constants, could be found from which she could determine W by knowing T, U, and V. Outline clearly a procedure by means of which this aim may be accomplished. [*Hint:* Take logarithms of both sides of the equation.]

Chapter 16

Analysis of Variance

THE PURPOSE OF ANALYSIS OF VARIANCE

In Chapter 8 we used sampling theory to test the significance of differences between two sampling means. We assumed that the two populations from which the samples were drawn had the same variance. In many situations there is a need to test the significance of differences between three or more sampling means or, equivalently, to test the null hypothesis that the sample means are all equal.

EXAMPLE 1. Suppose that in an agricultural experiment four different chemical treatments of soil produced mean wheat yields of 28, 22, 18, and 24 bushels per acre, respectively. Is there a significant difference in these means, or is the observed spread due simply to chance?

Problems such as this can be solved by using an important technique known as *analysis of variance*, developed by Fisher. It makes use of the F distribution already considered in Chapter 11.

ONE-WAY CLASSIFICATION, OR ONE-FACTOR EXPERIMENTS

In a *one-factor experiment*, measurements (or observations) are obtained for a independent groups of samples, where the number of measurements in each group is b. We speak of a *treatments*, each of which has b *repetitions*, or b *replications*. In Example 1, $a = 4$.

The results of a one-factor experiment can be presented in a table having a rows and b columns, as shown in Table 16.1. Here X_{jk} denotes the measurement in the jth row and kth column, where $j = 1, 2, \ldots, a$ and where $k = 1, 2, \ldots, b$. For example, X_{35} refers to the fifth measurement for the third treatment.

Table 16.1

Treatment 1	$X_{11}, X_{12}, \ldots, X_{1b}$	$\bar{X}_{1.}$
Treatment 2	$X_{21}, X_{22}, \ldots, X_{2b}$	$\bar{X}_{2.}$
$\vdots$	$\vdots$	$\vdots$
Treatment a	$X_{a1}, X_{a2}, \ldots, X_{ab}$	$\bar{X}_{a.}$

We shall denote by $\bar{X}_{j.}$ the mean of the measurements in the jth row. We have

$$\bar{X}_{j.} = \frac{1}{b} \sum_{k=1}^{b} X_{jk} \qquad j = 1, 2, \ldots, a \tag{1}$$

The dot in $\bar{X}_{j.}$ is used to show that the index k has been summed out. The values $\bar{X}_{j.}$ are called *group means, treatment means*, or *row means*. The *grand mean*, or *overall mean*, is the mean of all the measurements in all the groups and is denoted by $\bar{X}$:

$$\bar{X} = \frac{1}{ab} \sum_{j=1}^{a} \sum_{k=1}^{b} X_{jk} \tag{2}$$

TOTAL VARIATION, VARIATION WITHIN TREATMENTS, AND VARIATION BETWEEN TREATMENTS

We define the *total variation*, denoted by V, as the sum of the squares of the deviations of each measurement from the grand mean $\bar{X}$:

$$\text{Total variation} = V = \sum_{j,k} (X_{jk} - \bar{X})^2 \tag{3}$$

By writing the identity

$$X_{jk} - \bar{X} = (X_{jk} - \bar{X}_{j.}) + (\bar{X}_{j.} - \bar{X}) \tag{4}$$

and then squaring and summing over j and k, we have (see Problem 16.1)

$$\sum_{j,k} (X_{jk} - \bar{X})^2 = \sum_{j,k} (X_{jk} - \bar{X}_{j.})^2 + \sum_{j,k} (\bar{X}_{j.} - \bar{X})^2 \tag{5}$$

or

$$\sum_{j,k} (X_{jk} - \bar{X})^2 = \sum_{j,k} (X_{jk} - \bar{X}_{j.})^2 + b \sum_{j} (\bar{X}_{j.} - \bar{X})^2 \tag{6}$$

We call the first summation on the right-hand side of equations (*5*) and (*6*) the *variation within treatments* (since it involves the squares of the deviations of X_{jk} from the treatment means $\bar{X}_{j.}$) and denote it by V_W. Thus

$$V_W = \sum_{j,k} (X_{jk} - \bar{X}_{j.})^2 \tag{7}$$

The second summation on the right-hand side of equations (*5*) and (*6*) is called the *variation between treatments* (since it involves the squares of the deviations of the various treatment means $\bar{X}_{j.}$ from the grand mean $\bar{X}$) and is denoted by V_B. Thus

$$V_B = \sum_{j,k} (\bar{X}_{j.} - \bar{X})^2 = b \sum_{j} (\bar{X}_j - \bar{X})^2 \tag{8}$$

Equations (*5*) and (*6*) can thus be written

$$V = V_W + V_B \tag{9}$$

SHORTCUT METHODS FOR OBTAINING VARIATIONS

To minimize the labor of computing the above variations, the following forms are convenient:

$$V = \sum_{j,k} X_{jk}^2 - \frac{T^2}{ab} \tag{10}$$

$$V_B = \frac{1}{b} \sum_{j} T_{j.}^2 - \frac{T^2}{ab} \tag{11}$$

$$V_W = V - V_B \tag{12}$$

where T is the total of all values X_{jk} and where $T_{j.}$ is the total of all values in the jth treatment:

$$T = \sum_{j,k} X_{jk} \qquad T_{j.} = \sum_{k} X_{jk} \tag{13}$$

In practice, it is convenient to subtract some fixed value from all the data in the table in order to simplify the calculation; this has no effect on the final results.

MATHEMATICAL MODEL FOR ANALYSIS OF VARIANCE

We can consider each row of Table 16.1 to be a random sample of size b from the population for that particular treatment. The X_{jk} will differ from the population mean μ_j for the jth treatment by a *chance error*, or *random error*, which we denote by ε_{jk}; thus

$$X_{jk} = \mu_j + \varepsilon_{jk} \tag{14}$$

These errors are assumed to be normally distributed with mean 0 and variance σ^2. If μ is the mean of the population for all treatments and if we let $\alpha_j = \mu_j - \mu$, so that $\mu_j = \mu + \alpha_j$, then equation (*14*) becomes

$$X_{jk} = \mu + \alpha_j + \varepsilon_{jk} \tag{15}$$

where $\sum_j \alpha_j = 0$ (see Problem 16.9). From equation (*15*) and the assumption that the ε_{jk} are normally distributed with mean 0 and variance σ^2, we conclude that the X_{jk} can be considered random variables that are normally distributed with mean μ and variance σ^2.

The null hypothesis that all treatment means are equal is given by (H_0: $\alpha_j = 0; j = 1, 2, \ldots, a$) or, equivalently, by ($H_0$: $\mu_j = \mu; j = 1, 2, \ldots, a$). If H_0 is true, the treatment populations will all have the same normal distribution (i.e., with the same mean and variance). In such case there is just one treatment population (i.e., all treatments are statistically identical); in other words, there is no significant difference between the treatments.

EXPECTED VALUES OF THE VARIATIONS

It can be shown (see Problem 16.10) that the expected values of V_W, V_B, and V are given by

$$E(V_W) = a(b-1)\sigma^2 \tag{16}$$

$$E(V_B) = (a-1)\sigma^2 + b\sum_j \alpha_j^2 \tag{17}$$

$$E(V) = (ab-1)\sigma^2 + b\sum_j \alpha_j^2 \tag{18}$$

From equation (*16*) it follows that

$$E\left[\frac{V_W}{a(b-1)}\right] = \sigma^2 \tag{19}$$

so that

$$\hat{S}_W^2 = \frac{V_W}{a(b-1)} \tag{20}$$

is always a best (unbiased) estimate of σ^2 regardless of whether H_0 is true. On the other hand, we see from equations (*16*) and (*18*) that only if H_0 is true (i.e., $\alpha_j = 0$) will we have

$$E\left(\frac{V_B}{a-1}\right) = \sigma^2 \qquad \text{and} \qquad E\left(\frac{V}{ab-1}\right) = \sigma^2 \tag{21}$$

so that only in such case will

$$\hat{S}_B^2 = \frac{V_B}{a-1} \qquad \text{and} \qquad \hat{S}^2 = \frac{V}{ab-1} \tag{22}$$

provide unbiased estimates of σ^2. If H_0 is not true, however, then from equation (*16*) we have

$$E(\hat{S}_B^2) = \sigma^2 + \frac{b}{a-1}\sum_j \alpha_j^2 \tag{23}$$

DISTRIBUTIONS OF THE VARIATIONS

Using the additive property of chi-square (page 248), we can prove the following fundamental theorems concerning the distributions of the variations V_W, V_B, and V:

Theorem 1: V_W/σ^2 is chi-square-distributed with $a(b-1)$ degrees of freedom.

> **Theorem 2:** Under the null hypothesis H_0, V_B/σ^2 and V/σ^2 are chi-square-distributed with $a-1$ and $ab-1$ degrees of freedom, respectively.

It is important to emphasize that Theorem 1 is valid whether or not H_0 is assumed, whereas Theorem 2 is valid only if H_0 is assumed.

THE *F* TEST FOR THE NULL HYPOTHESIS OF EQUAL MEANS

If the null hypothesis H_0 is not true (i.e., if the treatment means are not equal), we see from equation (*23*) that we can expect $\hat{S}_B^2$ to be greater than σ^2, with the effect becoming more pronounced as the discrepancy between the means increases. On the other hand, from equations (*19*) and (*20*) we can expect $\hat{S}_W^2$ to be equal to σ^2 regardless of whether the means are equal. It follows that a good statistic for testing hypothesis H_0 is provided by $\hat{S}_B^2/\hat{S}_W^2$. If this statistic is significantly large, we can conclude that there is a significant difference between the treatment means and can thus reject H_0; otherwise, we can either accept H_0 or reserve judgment, pending further analysis.

In order to use the $\hat{S}_B^2/\hat{S}_W^2$ statistic, we must know its sampling distribution. This is provided by Theorem 3.

> **Theorem 3:** The statistic $F = \hat{S}_B^2/\hat{S}_W^2$ has the F distribution with $a-1$ and $a(b-1)$ degrees of freedom.

Theorem 3 enables us to test the null hypothesis at some specified significance level by using a one-tailed test of the F distribution (discussed in Chapter 11).

ANALYSIS-OF-VARIANCE TABLES

The calculations required for the above test are summarized in Table 16.2, which is called an *analysis-of-variance table.* In practice, we would compute V and V_B by using either the long method [equations (*3*) and (*8*)] or the short method [equations (*10*) and (*11*)] and then by computing $V_W = V - V_B$. It should be noted that the degrees of freedom for the total variation (i.e., $ab-1$) are equal to the sum of the degrees of freedom for the between-treatments and within-treatments variations.

Table 16.2

<table>
<tr><th>Variation</th><th>Degrees of Freedom</th><th>Mean Square</th><th>F</th></tr>
<tr><td>Between treatments,
$V_B = b\sum_j (\bar{X}_{j.} - \bar{X})^2$</td><td>$a-1$</td><td>$\hat{S}_B^2 = \dfrac{V_B}{a-1}$</td><td rowspan="2">$\dfrac{\hat{S}_B^2}{\hat{S}_W^2}$
with $a-1$ and $a(b-1)$ degrees of freedom</td></tr>
<tr><td>Within treatments,
$V_W = V - V_B$</td><td>$a(b-1)$</td><td>$\hat{S}_W^2 = \dfrac{V_W}{a(b-1)}$</td></tr>
<tr><td>Total,
$V = V_B + V_W$
$= \sum_{j,k} (X_{jk} - \bar{X})^2$</td><td>$ab-1$</td><td></td><td></td></tr>
</table>

MODIFICATIONS FOR UNEQUAL NUMBERS OF OBSERVATIONS

In case the treatments $1, \ldots, a$ have different numbers of observations—equal to $N_1, \ldots, N_a$, respectively—the above results are easily modified. Thus we obtain

$$V = \sum_{j,k} (X_{jk} - \bar{X})^2 = \sum_{j,k} X_{jk}^2 - \frac{T^2}{N} \tag{24}$$

$$V_B = \sum_{j,k} (\bar{X}_{j.} - \bar{X})^2 = \sum_{j} N_j(\bar{X}_{j.} - \bar{X})^2 = \sum_{j} \frac{T_{j.}^2}{N_j} - \frac{T^2}{N} \tag{25}$$

$$V_W = V - V_B \tag{26}$$

where $\sum_{j,k}$ denotes the summation over k from 1 to N_j and then the summation over j from 1 to a. Table 16.3 is the analysis-of-variance table for this case.

Table 16.3

Variation	Degrees of Freedom	Mean Square	F
Between treatments, $V_B = \sum_j N_j(\bar{X}_{j.} - \bar{X})^2$	$a - 1$	$\hat{S}_B^2 = \dfrac{V_B}{a-1}$	$\dfrac{\hat{S}_B^2}{\hat{S}_W^2}$
Within treatments, $V_W = V - V_B$	$N - a$	$\hat{S}_W^2 = \dfrac{V_W}{N-a}$	with $a-1$ and $N-a$ degrees of freedom
Total, $V = V_B + V_W = \sum_{j,k} (X_{jk} - \bar{X})^2$	$N - 1$		

TWO-WAY CLASSIFICATION, OR TWO-FACTOR EXPERIMENTS

The ideas of analysis of variance for one-way classification, or one-factor experiments, can be generalized. Example 2 illustrates the procedure for *two-way classification*, or *two-factor experiments.*

EXAMPLE 2. Suppose that an agricultural experiment consists of examining the yields per acre of 4 different varieties of wheat, where each variety is grown on 5 different plots of land. Thus a total of $(4)(5) = 20$ plots are needed. It is convenient in such case to combine the plots into *blocks*, say 4 plots to a block, with a different variety of wheat grown on each plot within a block. Thus 5 blocks would be required here.

In this case there are two classifications, or factors, since there may be differences in yield per acre due to (1) the particular type of wheat grown or (2) the particular block used (which may involve different soil fertility, etc.).

By analogy with the agricultural experiment of Example 2, we often refer to the two factors in an experiment as *treatments* and *blocks*, but of course we could simply refer to them as factor 1 and factor 2.

NOTATION FOR TWO-FACTOR EXPERIMENTS

Assuming that we have a treatments and b blocks, we construct Table 16.4, where it is supposed that there is one experimental value (such as yield per acre) corresponding to each treatment and block. For treatment j and block k, we denote this value by X_{jk}. The mean of the entries in the jth row is denoted by $X_{j.}$, where $j = 1, \ldots, a$, while the mean of the entries in the kth column is denoted by $\bar{X}_{.k}$, where $k = 1, \ldots, b$. The overall, or grand, mean is denoted by $\bar{X}$. In symbols,

$$\bar{X}_{j.} = \frac{1}{b}\sum_{k=1}^{b} X_{jk} \qquad \bar{X}_{.k} = \frac{1}{a}\sum_{j=1}^{a} X_{jk} \qquad \bar{X} = \frac{1}{ab}\sum_{j,k} X_{jk} \tag{27}$$

Table 16.4

	Block				
	1	2	$\cdots$	b	
Treatment 1	X_{11}	X_{12}	$\cdots$	X_{1b}	$\bar{X}_{1.}$
Treatment 2	X_{21}	X_{22}	$\cdots$	X_{2b}	$\bar{X}_{2.}$
$\vdots$	$\vdots$	$\vdots$	$\vdots$	$\vdots$	$\vdots$
Treatment a	X_{a1}	X_{a2}	$\cdots$	X_{ab}	$\bar{X}_{a.}$
	$\bar{X}_{.1}$	$\bar{X}_{.2}$		$\bar{X}_{.b}$	

VARIATIONS FOR TWO-FACTOR EXPERIMENTS

As in the case of one-factor experiments, we can define variations for two-factor experiments. We first define the *total variation*, as in equation (*3*), to be

$$V = \sum_{j,k} (X_{jk} - \bar{X})^2 \tag{28}$$

By writing the identity

$$X_{jk} - \bar{X} = (X_{jk} - \bar{X}_{j.} - \bar{X}_{.k} + \bar{X}) + (\bar{X}_{j.} - \bar{X}) + (\bar{X}_{.k} - \bar{X}) \tag{29}$$

and then squaring and summing over j and k, we can show that

$$V = V_E + V_R + V_C \tag{30}$$

where

$$V_E = \text{variation due to error or chance} = \sum_{j,k} (X_{jk} - \bar{X}_{j.} - \bar{X}_{.k} + \bar{X})^2$$

$$V_R = \text{variation between rows (treatments)} = b \sum_{j=1}^{a} (\bar{X}_{j.} - \bar{X})^2$$

$$V_C = \text{variation between columns (blocks)} = a \sum_{k=1}^{b} (\bar{X}_{.k} - \bar{X})^2$$

The variation due to error or chance is also known as the *residual variation* or *random variation.*

The following, analogous to equations (*10*), (*11*), and (*12*), are shortcut formulas for computation:

$$V = \sum_{j,k} X_{jk}^2 - \frac{T^2}{ab} \tag{31}$$

$$V_R = \frac{1}{b}\sum_{j=1}^{a} T_{j.}^2 - \frac{T^2}{ab} \tag{32}$$

$$V_C = \frac{1}{a}\sum_{k=1}^{b} T_{.k}^2 - \frac{T^2}{ab} \tag{33}$$

$$V_E = V - V_R - V_C \tag{34}$$

where $T_{j.}$ is the total of entries in the jth row, $T_{.k}$ is the total of entries in the kth column, and T is the total of all entries.

ANALYSIS OF VARIANCE FOR TWO-FACTOR EXPERIMENTS

The generalization of the mathematical model for one-factor experiments given by equation (*15*) leads us to assume for two-factor experiments that

$$X_{jk} = \mu + \alpha_j + \beta_k + \varepsilon_{jk} \tag{35}$$

where $\sum \alpha_j = 0$ and $\sum \beta_k = 0$. Here μ is the population grand mean, α_j is that part of X_{jk} due to the different treatments (sometimes called the *treatment effects*), β_k is that part of X_{jk} due to the different blocks (sometimes called the *block effects*), and ε_{jk} is that part of X_{jk} due to chance or error. As before, we assume that the ε_{jk} are normally distributed with mean 0 and variance σ^2, so that the X_{jk} are also normally distributed with mean μ and variance σ^2.

Corresponding to results (*16*), (*17*), and (*18*), we can prove that the expectations of the variations are given by

$$E(V_E) = (a-1)(b-1)\sigma^2 \tag{36}$$

$$E(V_R) = (a-1)\sigma^2 + b\sum_j \alpha_j^2 \tag{37}$$

$$E(V_C) = (b-1)\sigma^2 + a\sum_k \beta_k^2 \tag{38}$$

$$E(V) = (ab-1)\sigma^2 + b\sum_j \alpha_j^2 + a\sum_k \beta_k^2 \tag{39}$$

There are two null hypotheses that we would want to test:

$H_0^{(1)}$: All treatment (row) means are equal; that is, $\alpha_j = 0$, and $j = 1, \ldots, a$.

$H_0^{(2)}$: All block (column) means are equal; that is, $\beta_k = 0$, and $k = 1, \ldots, b$.

We see from equation (*38*) that, without regard to $H_0^{(1)}$ or $H_0^{(2)}$, a best (unbiased) estimate of σ^2 is provided by

$$\hat{S}_E^2 = \frac{V_E}{(a-1)(b-1)} \qquad \text{that is,} \qquad E(\hat{S}_E^2) = \sigma^2 \tag{40}$$

Also, if hypotheses $H_0^{(1)}$ and $H_0^{(2)}$ are true, then

$$\hat{S}_R^2 = \frac{V_R}{a-1} \qquad \hat{S}_C^2 = \frac{V_C}{b-1} \qquad \hat{S}^2 = \frac{V}{ab-1} \tag{41}$$

will be unbiased estimates of σ^2. If $H_0^{(1)}$ and $H_0^{(2)}$ are not true, however, then from equations (*36*) and (*37*), respectively, we have

$$E(\hat{S}_R^2) = \sigma^2 + \frac{b}{a-1}\sum_j \alpha_j^2 \tag{42}$$

$$E(\hat{S}_C^2) = \sigma^2 + \frac{a}{b-1}\sum_k \beta_k^2 \tag{43}$$

The following theorems are similar to Theorems 1 and 2:

> **Theorem 4:** V_E/σ^2 is chi-square-distributed with $(a-1)(b-1)$ degrees of freedom, without regard to $H_0^{(1)}$ or $H_0^{(2)}$.

> **Theorem 5:** Under hypothesis $H_0^{(1)}$, V_R/σ^2 is chi-square-distributed with $a-1$ degrees of freedom. Under hypothesis $H_0^{(2)}$, V_C/σ^2 is chi-square-distributed with $b-1$ degrees of freedom. Under both hypotheses, $H_0^{(1)}$ and $H_0^{(2)}$, V/σ^2 is chi-square-distributed with $ab-1$ degrees of freedom.

To test hypothesis $H_0^{(1)}$, it is natural to consider the statistic $\hat{S}_R^2/\hat{S}_E^2$ since we can see from equation (*42*) that $\hat{S}_R^2$ is expected to differ significantly from σ^2 if the row (treatment) means are significantly different. Similarly, to test hypothesis $H_0^{(2)}$, we consider the statistic $\hat{S}_C^2/\hat{S}_E^2$. The distributions of $\hat{S}_R^2/\hat{S}_E^2$ and $\hat{S}_C^2/\hat{S}_E^2$ are given in Theorem 6, which is analogous to Theorem 3.

> **Theorem 6:** Under hypothesis $H_0^{(1)}$, the statistic $\hat{S}_R^2/\hat{S}_E^2$ has the F distribution with $a-1$ and $(a-1)(b-1)$ degrees of freedom. Under hypothesis $H_0^{(2)}$, the statistic $\hat{S}_C^2/\hat{S}_E^2$ has the F distribution with $b-1$ and $(a-1)(b-1)$ degrees of freedom.

Theorem 6 enables us to accept or reject $H_0^{(1)}$ or $H_0^{(2)}$ at specified significance levels. For convenience, as in the one-factor case, an analysis-of-variance table can be constructed as shown in Table 16.5.

Table 16.5

Variation	Degrees of Freedom	Mean Square	F
Between treatments, $V_R = b\sum_j (\bar{X}_{j.}-\bar{X})^2$	$a-1$	$\hat{S}_R^2 = \dfrac{V_R}{a-1}$	$\hat{S}_R^2/\hat{S}_E^2$ with $a-1$ and $(a-1)(b-1)$ degrees of freedom
Between blocks, $V_C = a\sum_k (\bar{X}_{.k}-\bar{X})^2$	$b-1$	$\hat{S}_C^2 = \dfrac{V_C}{b-1}$	$\hat{S}_C^2/\hat{S}_E^2$ with $b-1$ and $(a-1)(b-1)$ degrees of freedom
Residual or random, $V_E = V - V_R - V_C$	$(a-1)(b-1)$	$\hat{S}_E^2 = \dfrac{V_E}{(a-1)(b-1)}$	
Total, $V = V_R + V_C + V_E = \sum_{j,k}(X_{jk}-\bar{X})^2$	$ab-1$		

TWO-FACTOR EXPERIMENTS WITH REPLICATION

In Table 16.4 there is only one entry corresponding to a given treatment and a given block. More information regarding the factors can often be obtained by repeating the experiment, a process called *replication.* In such case there will be more than one entry corresponding to a given treatment and a given block. We shall suppose that there are c entries for every position; appropriate changes can be made when the replication numbers are not all equal.

Because of replication, an appropriate model must be used to replace that given by equation (*35*). We use

$$X_{jkl} = \mu + \alpha_j + \beta_k + \gamma_{jk} + \varepsilon_{jkl} \tag{44}$$

where the subscripts j, k, and l of X_{jkl} correspond to the jth row (or treatment), the kth column (or block), and the lth repetition (or replication), respectively. In equation (*44*) the μ, α_j, and β_k are defined as before; ε_{jkl} is a chance or error term, while the γ_{jk} denote the row-column (or treatment-block) *interaction effects*, often simply called *interactions.* We have the restrictions

$$\sum_j \alpha_j = 0 \qquad \sum_k \beta_k = 0 \qquad \sum_j \gamma_{jk} = 0 \qquad \sum_k \gamma_{jk} = 0 \tag{45}$$

and the X_{jkl} are assumed to be normally distributed with mean μ and variance σ^2.

As before, the total variation V of all the data can be broken up into variations due to rows V_R, columns V_C, interaction V_I, and random or residual error V_E:

$$V = V_R + V_C + V_I + V_E \tag{46}$$

where
$$V = \sum_{j,k,l} (X_{jkl} - \bar{X})^2 \tag{47}$$

$$V_R = bc \sum_{j=1}^{a} (\bar{X}_{j..} - \bar{X})^2 \tag{48}$$

$$V_C = ac \sum_{k=1}^{b} (\bar{X}_{.k.} - \bar{X})^2 \tag{49}$$

$$V_I = c \sum_{j,k} (\bar{X}_{jk.} - \bar{X}_{j..} - \bar{X}_{.k.} + \bar{X})^2 \tag{50}$$

$$V_E = \sum_{j,k,l} (X_{jkl} - \bar{X}_{jk.})^2 \tag{51}$$

In these results the dots in the subscripts have meanings analogous to those given before (page 340); thus, for example,

$$\bar{X}_{j..} = \frac{1}{bc} \sum_{k,l} X_{jkl} = \frac{1}{b} \sum_{k} \bar{X}_{jk.} \tag{52}$$

The expected values of the variations can be found as before. Using the appropriate number of degrees of freedom for each source of variation, we can set up the analysis-of-variance table as shown in Table 16.6. The F ratios in the last column of Table 16.6 can be used to test the null hypotheses:

$H_0^{(1)}$: All treatment (row) means are equal; that is, $\alpha_j = 0$.

$H_0^{(2)}$: All block (column) means are equal; that is, $\beta_k = 0$.

$H_0^{(3)}$: There are no interactions between treatments and blocks; that is, $\gamma_{jk} = 0$.

Table 16.6

Variation	Degrees of Freedom	Mean Square	F
Between treatments, V_R	$a-1$	$\hat{S}_R^2 = \frac{V_R}{a-1}$	$\hat{S}_R^2/\hat{S}_E^2$ with $a-1$ and $ab(c-1)$ degrees of freedom
Between blocks, V_C	$b-1$	$\hat{S}_C^2 = \frac{V_C}{b-1}$	$\hat{S}_C^2/\hat{S}_E^2$ with $b-1$ and $ab(c-1)$ degrees of freedom
Interaction, V_I	$(a-1)(b-1)$	$\hat{S}_I^2 = \frac{V_I}{(a-1)(b-1)}$	$\hat{S}_I^2/\hat{S}_E^2$ with $(a-1)(b-1)$ and $ab(c-1)$ degrees of freedom
Residual or random, V_E	$ab(c-1)$	$\hat{S}_E^2 = \frac{V_E}{ab(c-1)}$	
Total, V	$abc-1$		

From a practical point of view we should first decide whether or not $H_0^{(3)}$ can be rejected at an appropriate level of significance by using the F ratio $\hat{S}_I^2/\hat{S}_E^2$ of Table 16.6. Two possible cases then arise:

1. **$H_0^{(3)}$ Cannot Be Rejected.** In this case we can conclude that the interactions are not too large. We can then test $H_0^{(1)}$ and $H_0^{(2)}$ by using the F ratios $\hat{S}_R^2/\hat{S}_E^2$ and $\hat{S}_C^2/\hat{S}_E^2$, respectively, as shown in Table 16.6. Some statisticians recommend pooling the variations in this case by taking the total of $V_I + V_E$ and dividing it by the total corresponding degrees of freedom $(a-1)(b-1) + ab(c-1)$ and using this value to replace the denominator $\hat{S}_E^2$ in the F test.

2. **$H_0^{(3)}$ Can Be Rejected.** In this case we can conclude that the interactions are significantly large. Differences in factors would then be of importance only if they were large compared with such interactions. For this reason, many statisticians recommend that $H_0^{(1)}$ and $H_0^{(2)}$ be tested by using the F ratios $\hat{S}_R^2/\hat{S}_I^2$ and $\hat{S}_C^2/\hat{S}_I^2$ rather than those given in Table 16.6. We, too, shall use this alternative procedure.

The analysis of variance with replication is most easily performed by first totaling the replication values that correspond to particular treatments (rows) and blocks (columns). This produces a two-factor table with single entries, which can be analyzed as in Table 16.5. This procedure is illustrated in Problem 16.16.

EXPERIMENTAL DESIGN

The techniques of analysis of variance discussed above are employed after the results of an experiment have been obtained. However, in order to gain as much information as possible, the design of an experiment must be planned carefully in advance; this is often referred to as the *design of the experiment.* The following are some important examples of experimental design:

1. **Complete Randomization.** Suppose that we have an agricultural experiment as in Example 1. To design such an experiment, we could divide the land into $4 \times 4 = 16$ plots (indicated in Fig. 16-1 by squares, although physically any shape can be used) and assign each treatment (indicated by A, B, C, and D) to four blocks chosen completely at random. The purpose of the randomization is to eliminate various sources of error, such as soil fertility.

D	A	C	C
B	D	B	A
D	C	B	D
A	B	C	A

Complete Randomization

Fig. 16-1

I	C	B	A	D
II	A	B	D	C
III	B	C	D	A
IV	A	D	C	B

Randomized Blocks

Fig. 16-2

D	B	C	A
B	D	A	C
C	A	D	B
A	C	B	D

Latin Square

Fig. 16-3

B_γ	A_β	D_δ	C_α
A_δ	B_α	C_γ	D_β
D_α	C_δ	B_β	A_γ
C_β	D_γ	A_α	B_δ

Graeco-Latin Square

Fig. 16-4

2. **Randomized Blocks.** When, as in Example 2, it is necessary to have a complete set of treatments for each block, the treatments A, B, C, and D are introduced in random order within each block: I, II, III, and IV (i.e., the rows in Fig. 16-2), and for this reason the blocks are referred to as *randomized blocks.* This type of design is used when it is desired to control *one source of error or variability*: namely, the difference in blocks.

3. **Latin Squares.** For some purposes it is necessary to control *two sources of error or variability* at the same time, such as the difference in rows and the difference in columns. In the experiment of Example 1, for instance, errors in different rows and columns could be due to changes in soil fertility in different parts of the land. In such case it is desirable that each treatment occur once in each row and once in each column, as in Fig. 16-3. The arrangement is called a *Latin square* from the fact that the Latin letters A, B, C, and D are used.

4. **Graeco-Latin Squares.** If it is necessary to control *three sources of error or variability*, a *Graeco-Latin square* is used, as shown in Fig. 16-4. Such a square is essentially two Latin squares superimposed on each other, with the Latin letters A, B, C, and D used for one square and the Greek letters α, β, γ, and δ used for the other square. The additional requirement that must be met is that each Latin letter must be used once and only once with each Greek letter; when this requirement is met, the square is said to be *orthogonal.*

Solved Problems

ONE-WAY CLASSIFICATION, OR ONE-FACTOR EXPERIMENTS

16.1 Prove that $V = V_W + V_B$; that is,

$$\sum_{j,k} (X_{jk} - \bar{X})^2 = \sum_{j,k} (X_{jk} - \bar{X}_{j.})^2 + \sum_{j,k} (\bar{X}_{j.} - \bar{X})^2$$

SOLUTION

We have $$X_{jk} - \bar{X} = (X_{jk} - \bar{X}_{j.}) + (\bar{X}_{j.} - \bar{X})$$

Then, squaring and summing over j and k, we obtain

$$\sum_{j,k} (X_{jk} - \bar{X})^2 = \sum_{j,k} (X_{jk} - \bar{X}_{j.})^2 + \sum_{j,k} (\bar{X}_{j.} - \bar{X})^2 + 2\sum_{j,k} (X_{jk} - \bar{X}_{j.})(\bar{X}_{j.} - \bar{X})$$

To prove the required result, we must show that the last summation is zero. In order to do this, we proceed as follows:

$$\sum_{j,k} (X_{jk} - \bar{X}_{j.})(\bar{X}_{j.} - \bar{X}) = \sum_{j=1}^{a} (\bar{X}_{j.} - \bar{X}) \left[\sum_{k=1}^{b} (X_{jk} - \bar{X}_{j.}) \right]$$

$$= \sum_{j=1}^{a} (\bar{X}_{j.} - \bar{X}) \left[\left(\sum_{k=1}^{b} X_{jk} \right) - b\bar{X}_{j.} \right] = 0$$

since $$\bar{X}_{j.} = \frac{1}{b} \sum_{k=1}^{b} X_{jk}$$

16.2 Verify that (a) $T = ab\bar{X}$, (b) $T_{j.} = b\bar{X}_{j.}$, and (c) $\sum_j T_{j.} = ab\bar{X}$, using the notation on page 340.

SOLUTION

(a) $$T = \sum_{j,k} X_{jk} = ab\left(\frac{1}{b} \sum_{j,k} X_{jk} \right) = ab\bar{X}$$

(b) $$T_{j.} = \sum_{k} X_{jk} = b\left(\frac{1}{b} \sum_{k} X_{jk} \right) = b\bar{X}_{j.}$$

(c) Since $T_{j.} = \sum_k X_{jk}$, by part (a) we have

$$\sum_j T_{j.} = \sum_j \sum_k X_{jk} = T = ab\bar{X}$$

16.3 Verify the shortcut formulas (*10*), (*11*), and (*12*) of this chapter.

SOLUTION

We have $$V = \sum_{j,k} (X_{jk} - \bar{X})^2 = \sum_{j,k} (X_{jk}^2 - 2\bar{X}X_{jk} + \bar{X}^2)$$

$$= \sum_{j,k} X_{jk}^2 - 2\bar{X} \sum_{j,k} X_{jk} + ab\bar{X}^2$$

$$= \sum_{j,k} X_{jk}^2 - 2\bar{X}(ab\bar{X}) + ab\bar{X}^2$$

$$= \sum_{j,k} X_{jk}^2 - ab\bar{X}^2$$

$$= \sum_{j,k} X_{jk}^2 - \frac{T^2}{ab}$$

using Problem 16.2(a) in the third and last lines above. Similarly,

$$\begin{aligned} V_B &= \sum_{j,k} (\bar{X}_{j.} - \bar{X})^2 = \sum_{j,k} (\bar{X}_{j.}^2 - 2\bar{X}\bar{X}_{j.} + \bar{X}^2) \\ &= \sum_{j,k} \bar{X}_{j.}^2 - 2\bar{X} \sum_{j,k} \bar{X}_{j.} + ab\bar{X}^2 \\ &= \sum_{j,k} \left(\frac{T_{j.}}{b}\right)^2 - 2\bar{X} \sum_{j,k} \frac{T_{j.}}{b} + ab\bar{X}^2 \\ &= \frac{1}{b^2} \sum_{j=1}^{a} \sum_{k=1}^{b} T_{j.}^2 - 2\bar{X}(ab\bar{X}) + ab\bar{X}^2 \\ &= \frac{1}{b} \sum_{j=1}^{a} T_{j.}^2 - ab\bar{X}^2 \\ &= \frac{1}{b} \sum_{j=1}^{a} T_{j.}^2 - \frac{T^2}{ab} \end{aligned}$$

using Problem 16.2(b) in the third line and Problem 16.2(a) in the last line. Finally, equation (*12*) follows from the fact that $V = V_W + V_B$, or $V_W = V - V_B$.

16.4 Table 16.7 shows the yields in bushels per acre of a certain variety of wheat grown in a particular type of soil treated with chemicals A, B, or C. Find (a) the mean yields for the different treatments, (b) the grand mean for all treatments, (c) the total variation, (d) the variation between treatments, and (e) the variation within treatments. Use the long method.

Table 16.7

A	48	49	50	49
B	47	49	48	48
C	49	51	50	50

Table 16.8

3	4	5	4
2	4	3	3
4	6	5	5

SOLUTION

To simplify the arithmetic, we may subtract some suitable number, say 45, from all the data without affecting the values of the variations. We then obtain the data of Table 16.8.

(a) The treatment (row) means for Table 16.8 are given, respectively, by

$$\bar{X}_{1.} = \tfrac{1}{4}(3+4+5+4) = 4 \qquad \bar{X}_{2.} = \tfrac{1}{4}(2+4+3+3) = 3 \qquad \bar{X}_{3.} = \tfrac{1}{4}(4+6+5+5) = 5$$

Thus the mean yields, obtained by adding 45 to these, are 49, 48, and 50 bushels per acre for A, B, and C, respectively.

(b) The grand mean for all treatments is

$$\bar{X} = \tfrac{1}{12}(3+4+5+4+2+4+3+3+4+6+5+5) = 4$$

Thus the grand mean for the original set of data is $45 + 4 = 49$ bushels per acre.

(c) The total variation is

$$V = \sum_{j,k} (X_{jk} - X)^2 = (3-4)^2 + (4-4)^2 + (5-4)^2 + (4-4)^2 + (2-4)^2 + (4-4)^2$$
$$+ (3-4)^2 + (3-4)^2 + (4-4)^2 + (6-4)^2 + (5-4)^2 + (5-4)^2 = 14$$

(d) The variation between treatments is

$$V_B = b \sum_{j} (\bar{X}_{j.} - \bar{X})^2 = 4[(4-4)^2 + (3-4)^2 + (5-4)^2] = 8$$

(*e*) The variation within treatments is

$$V_W = V - V_B = 14 - 8 = 6$$

Another method

$$V_W = \sum_{j,k} (X_{jk} - \bar{X}_{j.})^2 = (3-4)^2 + (4-4)^2 + (5-4)^2 + (4-4)^2 + (2-3)^2 + (4-3)^2$$
$$+ (3-3)^2 + (3-3)^2 + (4-5)^2 + (6-5)^2 + (5-5)^2 + (5-5)^2 = 6$$

Note: Table 16.9 is the analysis-of-variance table for Problems 16.4, 16.5, and 16.6.

Table 16.9

Variation	Degree of Freedom	Mean Square	F
Between treatments, $V_B = 8$	$a - 1 = 2$	$\hat{S}_B^2 = \frac{8}{2} = 4$	$\frac{\hat{S}_B^2}{\hat{S}_W^2} = \frac{4}{2/3} = 6$ with 2 and 9 degrees of freedom
Within treatments, $V_W = V - V_B = 14 - 8 = 6$	$a(b-1) = (3)(3) = 9$	$\hat{S}_W^2 = \frac{6}{9} = \frac{2}{3}$	
Total, $V = 14$	$ab - 1 = (3)(4) - 1 = 11$		

16.5 Referring to Problem 16.4, find an unbiased estimate of the population variance σ^2 from (*a*) the variation between treatments under the null hypothesis of equal treatment means and (*b*) the variation within treatments.

SOLUTION

(*a*)
$$\hat{S}_B^2 = \frac{V_B}{a-1} = \frac{8}{3-1} = 4$$

(*b*)
$$\hat{S}_W^2 = \frac{V_W}{a(b-1)} = \frac{6}{3(4-1)} = \frac{2}{3}$$

16.6 Referring to Problem 16.4, can we reject the null hypothesis of equal means at significance levels of (*a*) 0.05 and (*b*) 0.01?

SOLUTION

We have
$$F = \frac{\hat{S}_B^2}{\hat{S}_W^2} = \frac{4}{2/3} = 6$$

with $a - 1 = 3 - 1 = 2$ degrees of freedom and $a(b-1) = 3(4-1) = 9$ degrees of freedom.

(*a*) Referring to Appendix V, with $\nu_1 = 2$ and $\nu_2 = 9$, we see that $F_{.95} = 4.26$. Since $F = 6 > F_{.95}$, we can reject the null hypothesis of equal means at the 0.05 level.

(*b*) Referring to Appendix VI, with $\nu_1 = 2$ and $\nu_2 = 9$, we see that $F_{.99} = 8.02$. Since $F = 6 < F_{.99}$, we cannot reject the null hypothesis of equal means at the 0.01 level.

16.7 Use the shortcut formulas (*10*), (*11*), and (*12*) to obtain the results of Problem 16.4.

SOLUTION

It is convenient to arrange the data as in Table 16.10.

Table 16.10

		$T_{j.}$	$T_{j.}^2$
A	3 4 5 4	16	256
B	2 4 3 3	12	144
C	4 6 5 5	20	400
	$\sum_{j,k} X_{jk}^2 = 206$	$T = \sum_j T_{j.} = 48$	$\sum_j T_{j.}^2 = 800$

(a) Using formula (10), we have

$$\sum_{j,k} X_{jk}^2 = 9+16+25+16+4+16+9+9+16+36+25+25 = 206$$

and
$$T = 3+4+5+4+2+4+3+3+4+6+5+5 = 48$$

Thus
$$V = \sum_{j,k} X_{jk}^2 - \frac{T^2}{ab} = 206 - \frac{(48)^2}{(3)(4)} = 206 - 192 = 14$$

(b) The totals of the rows are

$$T_{1.} = 3+4+5+4 = 16 \qquad T_{2.} = 2+4+3+3 = 12 \qquad T_{3.} = 4+6+5+5 = 20$$

and
$$T = 16+12+20 = 48$$

Thus, using formula (11), we have

$$V_B = \frac{1}{b}\sum_j T_{j.}^2 - \frac{T^2}{ab} = \frac{1}{4}(16^2+12^2+20^2) - \frac{(48)^2}{(3)(4)} = 200 - 192 = 8$$

(c) Using formula (12), we have

$$V_W = V - V_B = 14 - 8 = 6$$

The results agree with those obtained in Problem 16.4, and from this point on the analysis proceeds as before.

16.8 A company wishes to purchase one of five different machines: A, B, C, D, or E. In an experiment designed to test whether there is a difference in the machines' performance, each of five experienced operators works on each of the machines for equal times. Table 16.11 shows the numbers of units produced per machine. Test the hypothesis that there is no difference between the machines at significance levels of (a) 0.05 and (b) 0.01.

SOLUTION

Subtract a suitable number, say 60, from all the data to obtain Table 16.12. Then

$$V = 2658 - \frac{(54)^2}{(5)(4)} = 2658 - 145.8 = 2512.2$$

and
$$V_B = \frac{1}{5}(3874) - \frac{(54)^2}{(5)(4)} = 774.8 - 145.8 = 629.0$$

We now form Table 16.13. For 4 and 20 degrees of freedom, we have $F_{.95} = 2.87$. Thus we cannot reject the null hypothesis at the 0.05 level and therefore certainly cannot reject it at the 0.01 level.

Table 16.11

A	68	72	77	42	53
B	72	53	63	53	48
C	60	82	64	75	72
D	48	61	57	64	50
E	64	65	70	68	53

Table 16.12

						$T_{j.}$	$T_{j.}^2$
A	8	12	17	−18	−7	12	144
B	12	−7	3	−7	−12	−11	121
C	0	22	4	15	12	53	2809
D	−12	1	−3	4	−10	−20	400
E	4	5	10	8	−7	20	400
	$\sum X_{jk}^2 = 2658$					54	3874

Table 16.13

Variation	Degrees of Freedom	Mean Square	F
Between treatments, $V_B = 629.0$	$a-1=4$	$\hat{S}_B^2 = \dfrac{629.0}{4} = 157.25$	$\dfrac{\hat{S}_B^2}{\hat{S}_W^2} = 1.67$
Within treatments, $V_W = 1883.8$	$a(b-1)=(5)(4)=20$	$\hat{S}_W^2 = \dfrac{1883.2}{(5)(4)} = 94.16$	
Total, $V = 2512.2$	$ab-1=24$		

MODIFICATIONS FOR UNEQUAL NUMBERS OF OBSERVATIONS

16.9 Table 16.14 shows the lifetimes in hours of samples from three different types of television tubes manufactured by a company. Using the long method, determine whether there is a difference between the three types at significance levels of (a) 0.05 and (b) 0.01.

Table 16.14

Sample 1	407	411	409		
Sample 2	404	406	408	405	402
Sample 3	410	408	406	408	

SOLUTION

It is convenient to subtract a suitable number from the data, say 400, obtaining Table 16.15. This table shows the row totals, the sample (or group) means, and the grand mean. Thus we have

$$V = \sum_{j,k} (X_{jk} - \bar{X})^2 = (7-7)^2 + (11-7)^2 + \cdots + (8-7)^2 = 72$$

$$V_B = \sum_{j,k} (\bar{X}_{j.} - \bar{X})^2 = \sum_j N_j(\bar{X}_{j.} - \bar{X})^2 = 3(9-7)^2 + 5(7-5)^2 + 4(8-7)^2 = 36$$

$$V_W = V - V_B = 72 - 36 = 36$$

Table 16.15

		Total	Mean
Sample 1	7 11 9	27	9
Sample 2	4 6 8 5 2	25	5
Sample 3	10 8 6 8	32	8
	$\bar{X} = \text{grand mean} = \frac{84}{12} = 7$		

We can also obtain V_W directly by observing that it is equal to

$$(7-9)^2+(11-9)^2+(9-9)^2+(4-5)^2+(6-5)^2+(8-5)^2+(5-5)^2$$
$$+(2-5)^2+(10-8)^2+(8-8)^2+(6-8)^2+(8-8)^2$$

The data can be summarized as in Table 16.16, the analysis-of-variance table. Now for 2 and 9 degrees of freedom, we find from Appendix V that $F_{.95} = 4.26$ and from Appendix VI that $F_{.99} = 8.02$. Thus we can reject the hypothesis of equal means (i.e., no difference between the three types of tubes) at the 0.05 level but not at the 0.01 level.

Table 16.16

Variation	Degree of Freedom	Mean Square	F
$V_B = 36$	$a-1=2$	$\hat{S}_B^2 = \dfrac{36}{2} = 18$	$\dfrac{\hat{S}_B^2}{\hat{S}_W^2} = \dfrac{18}{4}$ $= 4.5$
$V_W = 36$	$N-a=9$	$\hat{S}_W^2 = \dfrac{36}{9} = 4$	

Mathcad **16.10** Work Problem 16.9 by using the shortcut formulas included in equations (*24*), (*25*), and (*26*).

SOLUTION

From Table 16.15 we have $N_1 = 3$, $N_2 = 5$, $N_3 = 4$, $N = 12$, $T_{1.} = 27$, $T_{2.} = 25$, $T_{3.} = 32$, and $T = 84$. Thus we have

$$V = \sum_{j,k} X_{jk}^2 - \frac{T^2}{N} = 7^2 + 11^2 + \cdots + 6^2 + 8^2 - \frac{(84)^2}{12} = 72$$

$$V_B = \sum_j \frac{T_{j.}^2}{N_j} - \frac{T^2}{N} = \frac{(27)^2}{3} + \frac{(25)^2}{5} + \frac{(32)^2}{4} - \frac{(84)^2}{12} = 36$$

$$V_W = V - V_B = 36$$

Using these, the analysis of variance then proceeds as in Problem 16.9.

TWO-WAY CLASSIFICATION, OR TWO-FACTOR EXPERIMENTS

Mathcad **16.11** Table 16.17 shows the yields per acre of four different plant crops grown on lots treated with three different types of fertilizer. Using the long method, determine at the 0.01 significance level whether there is a difference in yield per acre (*a*) due to the fertilizers and (*b*) due to the crops.

Table 16.17

	Crop I	Crop II	Crop III	Crop IV
Fertilizer *A*	4.5	6.4	7.2	6.7
Fertilizer *B*	8.8	7.8	9.6	7.0
Fertilizer *C*	5.9	6.8	5.7	5.2

SOLUTION

Compute the row totals, the row means, the column totals, the column means, the grand total, and the grand mean, as shown in Table 16.18. From this table we obtain:

Table 16.18

	Crop I	Crop II	Crop III	Crop IV	Row Total	Row Mean
Fertilizer *A*	4.5	6.4	7.2	6.7	24.8	6.2
Fertilizer *B*	8.8	7.8	9.6	7.0	33.2	8.3
Fertilizer *C*	5.9	6.8	5.7	5.2	23.6	5.9
Column total	19.2	21.0	22.5	18.9	Grand total = 81.6	
Column mean	6.4	7.0	7.5	6.3	Grand mean = 6.8	

The variation of row means from the grand mean is

$$V_R = 4[(6.2-6.8)^2+(8.3-6.8)^2+(5.9-6.8)^2] = 13.68$$

The variation of column means from the grand mean is

$$V_C = 3[(6.4-6.8)^2+(7.0-6.8)^2+(7.5-6.8)^2+(6.3-6.8)^2] = 2.82$$

The total variation is

$$\begin{aligned} V = {} & (4.5-6.8)^2+(6.4-6.8)^2+(7.2-6.8)^2+(6.7-6.8)^2 \\ & +(8.8-6.8)^2+(7.8-6.8)^2+(9.6-6.8)^2+(7.0-6.8)^2 \\ & +(5.9-6.8)^2+(6.8-6.8)^2+(5.7-6.8)^2+(5.2-6.8)^2 = 23.08 \end{aligned}$$

The random variation is

$$V_E = V - V_R - V_C = 6.58$$

This leads to the analysis of variance in Table 16.19.

At the 0.05 significance level with 2 and 6 degrees of freedom, $F_{.95} = 5.14$. Then, since $6.24 > 5.14$, we can reject the hypothesis that the row means are equal and conclude that at the 0.05 level there is a significant difference in yield due to the fertilizers.

Since the F value corresponding to the differences in column means is less than 1, we can conclude that there is no significant difference in yield due to the crops.

Table 16.19

Variation	Degree of Freedom	Mean Square	F
$V_R = 13.68$	2	$\hat{S}_R^2 = 6.84$	$\hat{S}_R^2/\hat{S}_E^2 = 6.24$ with 2 and 6 degrees of freedom
$V_C = 2.82$	3	$\hat{S}_C^2 = 0.94$	$\hat{S}_C^2/\hat{S}_E^2 = 0.86$ with 3 and 6 degrees of freedom
$V_E = 6.58$	6	$\hat{S}_E^2 = 1.097$	
$V = 23.08$	11		

16.12 Use the short computational formulas to obtain the results of Problem 16.11.

SOLUTION

From Table 16.18 we have

$$\sum_{j,k} X_{jk}^2 = (4.5)^2 + (6.4)^2 + \cdots + (5.2)^2 = 577.96$$

$$T = 24.8 + 33.2 + 23.6 = 81.6$$

$$\sum T_{j.}^2 = (24.8)^2 + (33.2)^2 + (23.6)^2 = 2274.24$$

$$\sum T_{.k}^2 = (19.2)^2 + (21.0)^2 + (22.5)^2 + (18.9)^2 = 1673.10$$

Then

$$V = \sum_{j,k} X_{jk}^2 - \frac{T^2}{ab} = 577.96 - 554.88 = 23.08$$

$$V_R = \frac{1}{b}\sum T_{j.}^2 - \frac{T^2}{ab} = \frac{1}{4}(2274.24) - 554.88 = 13.68$$

$$V_C = \frac{1}{a}\sum T_{.k}^2 - \frac{T^2}{ab} = \frac{1}{3}(1673.10) - 554.88 = 2.82$$

$$V_E = V - V_R - V_C = 23.08 - 13.68 - 2.82 = 6.58$$

in agreement with Problem 16.11.

TWO-FACTOR EXPERIMENTS WITH REPLICATION

16.13 A manufacturer wishes to determine the effectiveness of four types of machines (A, B, C, and D) in the production of bolts. To accomplish this, the numbers of defective bolts produced by each machine in the days of a given week are obtained for each of two shifts; the results are shown in Table 16.20. Perform an analysis of variance to determine at the 0.05 significance level whether this is a difference (a) between the machines and (b) between the shifts.

SOLUTION

The data can be equivalently organized as in Table 16.21. In this table the two main factors are indicated: the machine and the shift. Note that two shifts have been indicated for each machine. The days of the week can be considered to be replicates (or repetitions) of performance for each machine for the

Table 16.20

Machine	First Shift Mon.	Tue.	Wed.	Thu.	Fri.	Second Shift Mon.	Tue.	Wed.	Thu.	Fri.
A	6	4	5	5	4	5	7	4	6	8
B	10	8	7	7	9	7	9	12	8	8
C	7	5	6	5	9	9	7	5	4	6
D	8	4	6	5	5	5	7	9	7	10

Table 16.21

Factor I: Machine	Factor II: Shift	Replicates Mon.	Tue.	Wed.	Thu.	Fri.	Total
A	1	6	4	5	5	4	24
	2	5	7	4	6	8	30
B	1	10	8	7	7	9	41
	2	7	9	12	8	8	44
C	1	7	5	6	5	9	32
	2	9	7	5	4	6	31
D	1	8	4	6	5	5	28
	2	5	7	9	7	10	38
	Total	57	51	54	47	59	268

two shifts. The total variation for all the data of Table 16.21 is

$$V = 6^2 + 4^2 + 5^2 + \cdots + 7^2 + 10^2 - \frac{(268)^2}{40} = 1946 - 1795.6 = 150.4$$

In order to consider the two main factors (the machine and the shift), we limit our attention to the total of replication values corresponding to each combination of factors. These are arranged in Table 16.22, which is thus a two-factor table with single entries. The total variation for Table 16.22, which we shall call the *subtotal variation* V_S, is given by

$$V_S = \frac{(24)^2}{5} + \frac{(41)^2}{5} + \frac{(32)^2}{5} + \frac{(28)^2}{5} + \frac{(30)^2}{5} + \frac{(44)^2}{5} + \frac{(31)^2}{5} + \frac{(38)^2}{5} - \frac{(268)^2}{40}$$

$$= 1861.2 - 1795.6 = 65.6$$

The variation between rows is given by

$$V_R = \frac{(54)^2}{10} + \frac{(85)^2}{10} + \frac{(63)^2}{10} + \frac{(66)^2}{10} - \frac{(268)^2}{40} = 1846.6 - 1795.6 = 51.0$$

The variation between columns is given by

$$V_C = \frac{(125)^2}{20} + \frac{(143)^2}{20} - \frac{(268)^2}{40} = 1803.7 - 1795.6 = 8.1$$

Table 16.22

Machine	First Shift	Second Shift	Total
A	24	30	54
B	41	44	85
C	32	31	63
D	28	38	66
Total	125	143	268

If we now subtract from the subtotal variation V_S the sum of the variations between the rows and columns $(V_R + V_C)$, we obtain the variation due to the *interaction* between the rows and columns. This is given by

$$V_I = V_S - V_R - V_C = 65.6 - 51.0 - 8.1 = 6.5$$

Finally, the residual variation, which we can think of as the random or error variation V_E (provided that we believe that the various days of the week do not provide any important differences), is found by subtracting the subtotal variation (i.e., the sum of the row, column, and interaction variations) from the total variation V. This yields

$$V_E = V - (V_R + V_C + V_I) = V - V_S = 150.4 - 65.6 = 84.8$$

These variations are shown in Table 16.23, the analysis of variance. The table also gives the number of degrees of freedom corresponding to each type of variation. Thus, since there are four rows in Table 16.22, the variation due to rows has $4 - 1 = 3$ degrees of freedom, while the variation due to the two columns has $2 - 1 = 1$ degree of freedom. To find the degrees of freedom due to interaction, we note that there are eight entries in Table 16.22; thus the total degrees of freedom are $8 - 1 = 7$. Since 3 of these 7 degrees of freedom are due to rows and 1 is due to columns, the remainder $[7 - (3 + 1) = 3]$ are due to interaction. Since there are 40 entries in the original Table 16.21, the total degrees of freedom are $40 - 1 = 39$. Thus the degrees of freedom due to random or residual variation are $39 - 7 = 32$.

Table 16.23

Variation	Degrees of Freedom	Mean Square	F
Rows (machines), $V_R = 51.0$	3	$\hat{S}_R^2 = 17.0$	$\dfrac{17.0}{2.65} = 6.42$
Columns (shifts), $V_C = 8.1$	1	$\hat{S}_C^2 = 8.1$	$\dfrac{8.1}{2.65} = 3.06$
Interaction, $V_I = 6.5$	3	$\hat{S}_I^2 = 2.167$	$\dfrac{2.167}{2.65} = 0.817$
Subtotal, $V_S = 65.6$	7		
Random or residual, $V_E = 84.8$	32	$\hat{S}_E^2 = 2.65$	
Total, $V = 150.4$	39		

To proceed further, we must first determine whether there is any significant interaction between the basic factors (i.e., the rows and columns of Table 16.22). From Table 16.23 we see that for interaction we have $F = 0.817$, which shows that the interaction is not significant; that is, we cannot reject hypothesis $H_0^{(3)}$ of page 348. Following the rules on page 348, we see that the computed F for the rows is 6.42. Since $F_{.95} = 2.90$ for 3 and 32 degrees of freedom, we can reject hypothesis $H_0^{(1)}$ that the rows have equal means. This is equivalent to saying that at the 0.05 level we can conclude that the machines are not equally effective.

For 1 and 32 degrees of freedom, $F_{.95} = 4.15$. Then since the computed F for columns is 3.06, we *cannot* reject the hypothesis $H_0^{(2)}$ that the columns have equal means. This is equivalent to saying that at the 0.05 level there is no significant difference between the shifts.

If we choose to analyze the results by pooling the interaction and residual variations, as recommended by some statisticians, we find that $V_I + V_E = 6.5 + 84.8 = 91.3$ for the pooled variation and that $V_I + V_E = 3 + 32 = 35$ for the pooled degrees of freedom, giving us a pooled variance of $91.3/35 = 2.61$. Using this value instead of 2.65 for the denominator of F in Table 16.23 does not affect the conclusions reached above.

16.14 Work Problem 16.13 if the 0.01 level is used.

SOLUTION

At this level there is still no appreciable interaction, so we can proceed further.

Since $F_{.99} = 4.47$ for 3 and 32 degrees of freedom and since the computed F for rows is 6.42, we can conclude that even at the 0.01 level the machines are not equally effective.

Since $F_{.99} = 7.51$ for 1 and 32 degrees of freedom and since the computed F for columns is 3.06, we can conclude that at the 0.01 level there is no significant difference in the shifts.

LATIN SQUARES

16.15 A farmer wishes to test the effects of four different fertilizers (A, B, C, and D) on the yield of wheat. In order to eliminate sources of error due to variability in soil fertility, he uses the fertilizers in a Latin-square arrangement, as shown in Table 16.24, where the numbers indicate yields in bushels per unit area. Perform an analysis of variance to determine whether there is a difference between the fertilizers at significance levels of (a) 0.05 and (b) 0.01.

SOLUTION

We first obtain totals for the rows and columns, as shown in Table 16.25. We also obtain total yields for each of the fertilizers, as shown in Table 16.26. The total variation and the variations for the rows, columns and treatments are then obtained as usual. We find:

The total variation is

$$V = (18)^2 + (21)^2 + (25)^5 + \cdots + (10)^2 + (17)^2 - \frac{(295)^2}{16}$$

$$= 5769 - 5439.06 = 329.94$$

Table 16.24

A 18	C 21	D 25	B 11
D 22	B 12	A 15	C 19
B 15	A 20	C 23	D 24
C 22	D 21	B 10	A 17

Table 16.25

					Total
	A 18	C 21	D 25	B 11	75
	D 22	B 12	A 15	C 19	68
	B 15	A 20	C 23	D 24	82
	C 22	D 21	B 10	A 17	70
Total	77	74	73	71	295

Table 16.26

	A	*B*	*C*	*D*	
Total	70	48	85	92	295

The variation between rows is

$$V_R = \frac{(75)^2}{4} + \frac{(68)^2}{4} + \frac{(82)^2}{4} + \frac{(70)^2}{4} - \frac{(295)^2}{16}$$

$$= 5468.25 - 5439.06 = 29.19$$

The variation between columns is

$$V_C = \frac{(77)^2}{4} + \frac{(74)^2}{4} + \frac{(73)^2}{4} + \frac{(71)^2}{4} - \frac{(295)^2}{16}$$

$$= 5443.75 - 5439.06 = 4.69$$

The variation between treatments is

$$V_B = \frac{(70)^2}{4} + \frac{(48)^2}{4} + \frac{(85)^2}{4} + \frac{(92)^2}{4} - \frac{(295)^2}{16}$$

$$= 5723.25 - 5439.06 = 284.19$$

Table 16.27 shows the analysis of variance.

Table 16.27

Variation	Degrees of Freedom	Mean Square	*F*
Rows, 29.19	3	9.73	4.92
Columns, 4.69	3	1.563	0.79
Treatments, 284.19	3	94.73	47.9
Residuals, 11.87	6	1.978	
Total, 329.94	15		

(*a*) Since $F_{.95,3,6} = 4.76$, we can reject at the 0.05 level the hypothesis that there are equal row means. It follows that at the 0.05 level there is a difference in the fertility of the soil from one row to another.

Since the F value for columns is less than 1, we conclude that there is no difference in soil fertility in the columns.

Since the F value for treatments is $47.9 > 4.76$, we can conclude that there is a difference between fertilizers.

(*b*) Since $F_{.99,3,6} = 9.78$, we can accept the hypothesis that there is no difference in soil fertility in the rows (or the columns) at the 0.01 level. However, we must still conclude that there is a difference between fertilizers at the 0.01 level.

GRAECO-LATIN SQUARES

16.16 It is of interest to determine whether there is any significant difference in mileage per gallon between gasolines *A*, *B*, *C*, and *D*. Design an experiment that uses four different drivers, four different cars, and four different roads.

SOLUTION

Since the same number of gasolines, drivers, cars, and roads is involved (four), we can use a Graeco-Latin square. Suppose that the different cars are represented by the rows and that the different drivers are represented by the columns, as shown in Table 16.28. We now assign the different gasolines (A, B, C, and D) to the rows and columns at random, subject only to the requirement that each letter appear just once in each row and just once in each column. Thus each driver will have an opportunity to drive each car and to use each type of gasoline, and no car will be driven twice with the same gasoline.

We now assign at random the four roads to be used, denoted by α, β, γ, and δ, subjecting them to the same requirement imposed on the Latin squares. Thus each driver will also have the opportunity to drive along each of the roads. Table 16.28 shows one possible arrangement.

Table 16.28

	Driver			
	1	2	3	4
Car 1	B_γ	A_β	D_δ	C_α
Car 2	A_δ	B_α	C_γ	D_β
Car 3	D_α	C_δ	B_β	A_γ
Car 4	C_β	D_γ	A_α	B_δ

16.17 Suppose that in carrying out the experiment of Problem 16.16 the numbers of miles per gallon are as given in Table 16.29. Use analysis of variance to determine whether there are any differences at the 0.05 significance level.

Table 16.29

	Driver			
	1	2	3	4
Car 1	B_γ 19	A_β 16	D_δ 16	C_α 14
Car 2	A_δ 15	B_α 18	C_γ 11	D_β 15
Car 3	D_α 14	C_δ 11	B_β 21	A_γ 16
Car 4	C_β 16	D_γ 16	A_α 15	B_δ 23

SOLUTION

We first obtain the row and column totals, as shown in Table 16.30. We then obtain the totals for each Latin letter and for each Greek letter, as follows:

$$
\begin{aligned}
A \text{ total:} &\quad 15+16+15+16=62\\
B \text{ total:} &\quad 19+18+21+23=81\\
C \text{ total:} &\quad 16+11+11+14=52\\
D \text{ total:} &\quad 14+16+16+15=61\\
\alpha \text{ total:} &\quad 14+18+15+14=61\\
\beta \text{ total:} &\quad 16+16+21+15=68\\
\gamma \text{ total:} &\quad 19+16+11+16=62\\
\delta \text{ total:} &\quad 15+11+16+23=65
\end{aligned}
$$

Table 16.30

					Total
	B_γ 19	A_β 16	D_δ 16	C_α 14	65
	A_δ 15	B_α 18	C_γ 11	D_β 15	59
	D_α 14	C_δ 11	B_β 21	A_γ 16	62
	C_β 16	D_γ 16	A_α 15	B_δ 23	70
Total	64	61	63	68	256

We now compute the variations corresponding to all of these, using the shortcut method:

Rows: $$\frac{(65)^2}{4}+\frac{(59)^2}{4}+\frac{(62)^2}{4}+\frac{(70)^2}{4}-\frac{(256)^2}{16}=4112.50-4096=16.50$$

Columns: $$\frac{(64)^2}{4}+\frac{(61)^2}{4}+\frac{(63)^2}{4}+\frac{(68)^2}{4}-\frac{(256)^2}{16}=4102.50-4096=6.50$$

Gasolines (A, B, C, D): $$\frac{(62)^2}{4}+\frac{(81)^2}{4}+\frac{(52)^2}{4}+\frac{(61)^2}{4}-\frac{(256)^2}{16}=4207.50-4096=111.50$$

Roads ($\alpha, \beta, \gamma, \delta$): $$\frac{(61)^2}{4}+\frac{(68)^2}{4}+\frac{(62)^2}{4}+\frac{(65)^2}{4}-\frac{(256)^2}{16}=4103.50-4096=7.50$$

The total variation is

$$(19)^2+(16)^2+(16)^2+\cdots+(15)^2+(23)^2-\frac{(256)^2}{16}=4244-4096=148.00$$

so that the variation due to error is

$$148.00-16.50-6.50-111.50-7.50=6.00$$

The results are shown in Table 16.31, the analysis of variance. The total number of degrees of freedom is N^2-1 for an $N \times N$ square. Each of the rows, columns, Latin letters, and Greek letters has $N-1$ degrees of freedom. Thus the degrees of freedom for error are $N^2-1-4(N-1)=(N-1)(N-3)$. In our case, $N=4$.

We have $F_{.95,3,3}=9.28$ and $F_{.99,3,3}=29.5$. Thus we can reject the hypothesis that the gasolines are the same at the 0.05 level but not at the 0.01 level.

MISCELLANEOUS PROBLEMS

16.18 Prove [as in equation (*15*) of this chapter] that $\sum_j \alpha_j = 0$.

SOLUTION

The treatment population means μ_j and the total population mean μ are related by

$$\mu = \frac{1}{a}\sum_j \mu_j \tag{53}$$

Then, since $\alpha_j = \mu_j - \mu$, we have, using equation (*53*),

$$\sum_j \alpha_j = \sum_j (\mu_j - \mu) = \sum_j \mu_j - a\mu = 0 \tag{54}$$

Table 16.31

Variation	Degrees of Freedom	Mean Square	F
Rows (cars), 16.50	3	5.500	$\frac{5.500}{2.000} = 2.75$
Columns (drivers), 6.50	3	2.167	$\frac{2.167}{2.000} = 1.08$
Gasolines (*A, B, C, D*), 111.50	3	37.167	$\frac{37.167}{2.000} = 18.6$
Roads ($\alpha, \beta, \gamma, \delta$), 7.50	3	2.500	$\frac{2.500}{2.000} = 1.25$
Error, 6.00	3	2.000	
Total, 148.00	15		

16.19 Derive (*a*) equation (*16*) and (*b*) equation (*17*) of this chapter.

SOLUTION

(*a*) By definition, we have

$$V_W = \sum_{j,k} (X_{jk} - \bar{X}_{j.})^2 = b \sum_{j=1}^{a} \left[\frac{1}{b} \sum_{k=1}^{b} (X_{jk} - \bar{X}_{j.})^2 \right] = b \sum_{j=1}^{a} S_j^2$$

where S_j^2 is the sample variance for the *j*th treatment. Then, since the sample size is *b*,

$$E(V_W) = b \sum_{j=1}^{a} E(S_j^2) = b \sum_{j=1}^{a} \left(\frac{b-1}{b} \sigma^2 \right) = a(b-1)\sigma^2$$

(*b*) By definition,

$$V_B = b \sum_{j=1}^{a} (\bar{X}_{j.} - \bar{X})^2 = b \sum_{j=1}^{a} \bar{X}_{j.}^2 - 2b\bar{X} \sum_{j=1}^{a} \bar{X}_{j.} + ab\bar{X}^2 = b \sum_{j=1}^{a} \bar{X}_{j.}^2 - ab\bar{X}^2$$

since $\bar{X} = (\sum_j X_{jk})/a$. Then, omitting the summation index, we have

$$E(V_B) = b \sum E(\bar{X}_{j.}^2) - abE(\bar{X}^2) \tag{55}$$

Now for any random variable *U*, $E(U^2) = \text{var}(U) + [E(U)]^2$, where var (*U*) denotes the variance of *U*. Thus

$$E(\bar{X}_{j.}^2) = \text{var}(\bar{X}_{j.}) + [E(\bar{X}_{j.})]^2 \tag{56}$$

$$E(\bar{X}^2) = \text{var}(\bar{X}) + [E(\bar{X})]^2 \tag{57}$$

But since the treatment populations are normal with mean $\mu_j = \mu + \alpha_j$, we have

$$\text{var}(\bar{X}_{j.}) = \frac{\sigma^2}{b} \tag{58}$$

$$\text{var}(\bar{X}) = \frac{\sigma^2}{ab} \tag{59}$$

$$E(\bar{X}_{j.}) = \mu_j = \mu + \alpha_j \tag{60}$$

$$E(\bar{X}) = \mu \tag{61}$$

Using results (*56*) to (*61*) together with result (*53*), we have

$$E(V_B) = b\sum\left[\frac{\sigma^2}{b} + (\mu + \alpha_j)^2\right] - ab\left[\frac{\sigma^2}{ab} + \mu^2\right]$$
$$= a\sigma^2 + b\sum(\mu + \alpha_j)^2 - \sigma^2 - ab\mu^2$$
$$= (a-1)\sigma^2 + ab\mu^2 + 2b\mu\sum\alpha_j + b\sum\alpha_j^2 + ab\mu^2$$
$$= (a-1)\sigma^2 + b\sum\alpha_j^2$$

16.20 Prove Theorem 1 in this chapter.

SOLUTION

As shown in Problem 16.19,

$$V_W = b\sum_{j=1}^{a} S_j^2 \quad \text{or} \quad \frac{V_W}{\sigma^2} = \sum_{j=1}^{a} \frac{bS_j^2}{\sigma^2}$$

where S_j^2 is the sample variance for samples of size b drawn from the population of treatment j. From page 232 we see that bS_j^2/σ^2 has a chi-square distribution with $b-1$ degrees of freedom. Thus, since the variances S_j^2 are independent, we conclude from page 248 that V_W/σ^2 is chi-square-distributed with $a(b-1)$ degrees of freedom.

Supplementary Problems

ONE-WAY CLASSIFICATION, OR ONE-FACTOR EXPERIMENTS

16.21 An experiment is performed to determine the yields of five different varieties of wheat: *A*, *B*, *C*, *D*, and *E*. Four plots of land are assigned to each variety, and the yields (in bushels per acre) are as shown in Table 16.32. Assuming that the plots are of similar fertility and that the varieties are assigned to the plots at random, determine whether there is a difference between the yields at significance levels of (*a*) 0.05 and (*b*) 0.01.

Table 16.32

A	20	12	15	19
B	17	14	12	15
C	23	16	18	14
D	15	17	20	12
E	21	14	17	18

16.22 A company wishes to test four different types of tires: *A*, *B*, *C*, and *D*. The tires' lifetimes, as determined from their treads, are given (in thousands of miles) in Table 16.33, where each type has been tried on six similar automobiles assigned at random to the tires. Determine whether there is a significant difference between the tires at the (*a*) 0.05 and (*b*) 0.01 levels.

16.23 A teacher wishes to test three different teaching methods: I, II, and III. To do this, three groups of five students each are chosen at random, and each group is taught by a different method. The same examination is then given to all the students, and the grades in Table 16.34 are obtained. Determine whether there is a difference between the teaching methods at significance levels of (*a*) 0.05 and (*b*) 0.01.

Table 16.33

A	33	38	36	40	31	35
B	32	40	42	38	30	34
C	31	37	35	33	34	30
D	29	34	32	30	33	31

Table 16.34

Method I	75	62	71	58	73
Method II	81	85	68	92	90
Method III	73	79	60	75	81

MODIFICATIONS FOR UNEQUAL NUMBERS OF OBSERVATIONS

16.24 Table 16.35 gives the numbers of miles to the gallon obtained by similar automobiles using five different brands of gasoline. Determine whether there is a difference between the brands at significance levels of (a) 0.05 and (b) 0.01.

Table 16.35

Brand A	12	15	14	11	15
Brand B	14	12	15		
Brand C	11	12	10	14	
Brand D	15	18	16	17	14
Brand E	10	12	14	12	

Table 16.36

Mathematics	72	80	83	75	
Science	81	74	77		
English	88	82	90	87	80
Economics	74	71	77	70	

16.25 During one semester a student received grades in various subjects, as shown in Table 16.36. Determine whether there is a significant difference between the student's grades at the (a) 0.05 and (b) 0.01 levels.

TWO-WAY CLASSIFICATION, OR TWO-FACTOR EXPERIMENTS

16.26 Articles manufactured by a company are produced by three operators using three different machines. The manufacturer wishes to determine whether there is a difference (a) between the operators and (b) between the machines. An experiment is performed to determine the number of articles per day produced by each operator using each machine; the results are shown in Table 16.37. Provide the desired information, using a significance level of 0.05.

Table 16.37

	Operator		
	1	2	3
Machine A	23	27	24
Machine B	34	30	28
Machine C	28	25	27

Table 16.38

	Type of Corn			
	I	II	III	IV
Block A	12	15	10	14
Block B	15	19	12	11
Block C	14	18	15	12
Block D	11	16	12	16
Block E	16	17	11	14

16.27 Work Problem 16.26 at the 0.01 significance level.

16.28 Seeds of four different types of corn are planted in five blocks. Each block is divided into four plots, which are then randomly assigned to the four types. Determine at the 0.05 significance level whether the yields in bushels per acre, as shown in Table 16.38, vary significantly with differences in (*a*) the soil (i.e., the five blocks) and (*b*) the type of corn.

16.29 Work Problem 16.28 at the 0.01 significance level.

16.30 Suppose that in Problem 16.22 the first observation for each type of tire is made using one particular kind of automobile, the second observation is made using a second particular kind, and so on. Determine at the 0.05 significance level whether there is a difference (*a*) between the types of tires and (*b*) between the kinds of automobiles.

16.31 Work Problem 16.30 at the 0.01 significance level.

16.32 Suppose that in Problem 16.23 the first entry for each teaching method corresponds to a student at one particular school, the second method corresponds to a student at another school, and so on. Test the hypothesis at the 0.05 significance level that there is a difference (*a*) between the teaching methods and (*b*) between the schools.

16.33 An experiment is performed to test whether the hair color and heights of adult female students in the United States have any bearing on scholastic achievement. The results are given in Table 16.39, where the numbers indicate individuals in the top 10% of those graduating. Analyze the experiment at a significance level of 0.05.

Table 16.39

	Redhead	Blonde	Brunette
Tall	75	78	80
Medium	81	76	79
Short	73	75	77

Table 16.40

A	16	18	20	23
B	15	17	16	19
C	21	19	18	21
D	18	22	21	23
E	17	18	24	20

16.34 Work Problem 16.33 at the 0.01 significance level.

TWO-FACTOR EXPERIMENTS WITH REPLICATION

16.35 Suppose that the experiment of Problem 16.21 was carried out in the southern part of the United States and that the columns of Table 16.32 now indicate four different types of fertilizer, while a similar experiment performed in the western part gives the results shown in Table 16.40. Determine at the 0.05 significance level whether there is a difference in yields due to (*a*) the fertilizers and (*b*) the locations.

16.36 Work Problem 16.35 at the 0.01 significance level.

16.37 Table 16.41 gives the number of articles produced by four different operators working on two different types of machines, I and II, on different days of the week. Determine at the 0.05 level whether there are significant differences (*a*) between the operators and (*b*) between the machines.

Table 16.41

	Machine I					Machine II				
	Mon.	Tue.	Wed.	Thu.	Fri.	Mon.	Tue.	Wed.	Thu.	Fri.
Operator *A*	15	18	17	20	12	14	16	18	17	15
Operator *B*	12	16	14	18	11	11	15	12	16	12
Operator *C*	14	17	18	16	13	12	14	16	14	11
Operator *D*	19	16	21	23	18	17	15	18	20	17

LATIN SQUARES

16.38 An experiment is performed to test the effect on corn yield of four different fertilizer treatments (*A*, *B*, *C*, and *D*) and of soil variations in two perpendicular directions. The Latin square of Table 16.42 is obtained, where the numbers show the corn yield per unit area. Test at the 0.01 significance level the hypothesis that there is no difference between (*a*) the fertilizers and (*b*) the soil variations.

Table 16.42

C 8	*A* 10	*D* 12	*B* 11
A 14	*C* 12	*B* 11	*D* 15
D 10	*B* 14	*C* 16	*A* 10
B 7	*D* 16	*A* 14	*C* 12

Table 16.43

E 75	*W* 78	*M* 80
M 81	*E* 76	*W* 79
W 73	*M* 75	*E* 77

16.39 Work Problem 16.38 at the 0.05 significance level.

16.40 Referring to Problem 16.33, suppose that we introduce an additional factor—giving the section *E*, *M*, or *W* of the United States in which a student was born, as shown in Table 16.43. Determine at the 0.05 level whether there is a significant difference in the scholastic achievements of female students due to differences in (*a*) height, (*b*) hair color, and (*c*) birthplace.

GRAECO-LATIN SQUARES

16.41 In order to produce a superior type of chicken feed, four different quantities of each of two chemicals are added to the basic ingredients. The different quantities of the first chemical are indicated by *A*, *B*, *C*, and *D*, while those of the second chemical are indicated by α, β, γ, and δ. The feed is given to baby chicks arranged in groups according to four different initial weights (W_1, W_2, W_3, and W_4) and four different species (S_1, S_2, S_3, and S_4). The increases in weight per unit time are given in the Graeco-Latin square of Table 16.44. Perform an analysis of variance of the experiment at the 0.05 significance level, stating any conclusions that can be drawn.

Table 16.44

	W_1	W_2	W_3	W_4
S_1	C_γ 8	B_β 6	A_α 5	D_δ 6
S_2	A_δ 4	D_α 3	C_β 7	B_γ 3
S_3	D_β 5	A_γ 6	B_δ 5	C_α 6
S_4	B_α 6	C_δ 10	D_γ 10	A_β 8

16.42 Four different types of cable (T_1, T_2, T_3, and T_4) are manufactured by each of four companies (C_1, C_2, C_3, and C_4). Four operators (A, B, C, and D) using four different machines (α, β, γ, and δ) measure the cable strengths. The average strengths obtained are given in the Graeco-Latin square of Table 16.45. Perform an analysis of variance at the 0.05 significance level, stating any conclusions that can be drawn.

Table 16.45

	C_1	C_2	C_3	C_4
T_1	A_β 164	B_γ 181	C_α 193	D_δ 160
T_2	C_δ 171	D_α 162	A_γ 183	B_β 145
T_3	D_γ 198	C_β 212	B_δ 207	A_α 188
T_4	B_α 157	A_δ 172	D_β 166	C_γ 136

Table 16.46

A	3	5	4	4
B	4	2	3	3
C	6	4	5	5

MISCELLANEOUS PROBLEMS

16.43 Table 16.46 gives data on the accumulated rust on iron that has been treated with chemical A, B, or C, respectively. Determine at the (a) 0.05 and (b) 0.01 levels whether there is a significant difference in the treatments.

16.44 An experiment measures the intelligence quotients (IQs) of adult male students of tall, short, and medium stature. The results are given in Table 16.47. Determine at the (a) 0.05 and (b) 0.01 significance levels whether there is any difference in the IQ scores relative to the height differences.

Table 16.47

Tall	110	105	118	112	90	
Short	95	103	115	107		
Medium	108	112	93	104	96	102

16.45 Prove results (*10*), (*11*), and (*12*) of this chapter.

16.46 An examination is given to determine whether veterans or nonveterans of different IQs performed better. The scores obtained are shown in Table 16.48. Determine at the 0.05 significance level whether there is a difference in scores due to differences in (a) veteran status and (b) IQ.

Table 16.48

	Test Score		
	High IQ	Medium IQ	Low IQ
Veteran	90	81	74
Nonveteran	85	78	70

16.47 Work Problem 16.46 at the 0.01 significance level.

16.48 Table 16.49 shows test scores for a sample of college students who are from different parts of the country and who have different IQs. Analyze the table at the 0.05 significance level and state your conclusions.

Table 16.49

	Test Score		
	High IQ	Medium IQ	Low IQ
East	88	80	72
West	84	78	75
South	86	82	70
North and central	80	75	79

16.49 Work Problem 16.48 at the 0.01 significance level.

16.50 In Problem 16.37, can you determine whether there is a significant difference in the number of articles produced on different days of the week? Explain.

16.51 In analysis-of-variance calculations it is known that a suitable constant can be added or subtracted from each entry without affecting the conclusions. Is this also true if each entry is multiplied or divided by a suitable constant? Justify your answer.

16.52 Derive results (*24*), (*25*), and (*26*) for unequal numbers of observations.

16.53 Suppose that the results in Table 16.46 of Problem 16.43 hold for the northeastern part of the United States, while the corresponding results for the western part are those given in Table 16.50. Determine at the 0.05 significance level whether there are differences due to (a) chemicals and (b) location.

Table 16.50

A	5	4	6	3
B	3	4	2	3
C	5	7	4	6

Table 16.51

A	17	14	18	12
B	20	10	20	15
C	18	15	16	17
D	12	11	14	11
E	15	12	19	14

16.54 Referring to Problems 16.21 and 16.35, suppose that an additional experiment performed in the northeastern part of the United States produced the results given in Table 16.51. Determine at the 0.05 significance level whether there is a difference in yields due to (a) the fertilizers and (b) the three locations.

16.55 Work Problem 16.54 at the 0.01 significance level.

16.56 Perform an analysis of variance on the Latin square of Table 16.52 at the 0.05 significance level and state your conclusions.

16.57 Make up an experiment leading to the Latin square of Table 16.52.

Table 16.52

Factor 1

Factor 2			
	B 16	*C* 21	*A* 15
	A 18	*B* 23	*C* 14
	C 15	*A* 18	*B* 12

16.58 Perform an analysis of variance on the Graeco-Latin square of Table 16.53 at the 0.05 significance level and state your conclusions.

Table 16.53

Factor 1

Factor 2				
	A_γ 6	B_β 12	C_δ 4	D_α 18
	B_δ 3	A_α 8	D_γ 15	C_β 14
	D_β 15	C_γ 20	B_α 9	A_δ 5
	C_α 16	D_δ 6	A_β 17	B_γ 7

16.59 Make up an experiment leading to the Graeco-Latin square of Table 16.53.

16.60 Describe how to use analysis-of-variance techniques for three-factor experiments with replications.

16.61 Make up and solve a problem that illustrates the procedure in Problem 16.60.

16.62 Prove (*a*) equation (*30*) and (*b*) results (*31*) to (*34*) of this chapter.

16.63 In practice, would you expect to find (*a*) a 2×2 Latin square and (*b*) a 3×3 Graeco-Latin square? Explain.

Chapter 17

Nonparametric Tests

INTRODUCTION

Most tests of hypotheses and significance (or decision rules) considered in previous chapters require various assumptions about the distribution of the population from which the samples are drawn. For example, on page 176 the population distributions are required to be normal or nearly normal.

Situations arise in practice in which such assumptions may not be justified or in which there is doubt that they apply, as in the case where a population may be highly skewed. Because of this, statisticians have devised various tests and methods that are independent of population distributions and associated parameters. These are called *nonparametric tests.*

Nonparametric tests can be used as shortcut replacements for more complicated tests. They are especially valuable in dealing with nonnumerical data, such as arise when consumers rank cereals or other products in order of preference.

THE SIGN TEST

Consider Table 17.1, which shows the numbers of defective bolts produced by two different types of machines (I and II) on 12 consecutive days and which assumes that the machines have the same total output per day. We wish to test the hypothesis H_0 that there is no difference between the machines: that the observed differences between the machines in terms of the numbers of defective bolts they produce are merely the result of chance, which is to say that the samples come from the same population.

A simple nonparametric test in the case of such paired samples is provided by the *sign test.* This test consists of taking the difference between the numbers of defective bolts for each day and writing only the *sign* of the difference; for instance, for day 1 we have $47-71$, which is negative. In this way we obtain from Table 17.1 the sequence of signs

$$- \quad - \quad + \quad - \quad - \quad - \quad + \quad - \quad + \quad - \quad - \quad - \tag{1}$$

(i.e., 3 pluses and 9 minuses). Now if it is just as likely to get a + as a −, we would expect to get 6 of each. The test of H_0 is thus equivalent to that of whether a coin is fair if 12 tosses result in 3 heads (+) and 9 tails (−). This involves the binomial distribution of Chapter 7. Problem 17.1 shows that by using a two-tailed test of this distribution at the 0.05 significance level, we cannot reject H_0; that is, there is no difference between the machines at this level.

Table 17.1

Day	1	2	3	4	5	6	7	8	9	10	11	12
Machine I	47	56	54	49	36	48	51	38	61	49	56	52
Machine II	71	63	45	64	50	55	42	46	53	57	75	60

Remark 1: If on some day the machines produced the same number of defective bolts, a difference of *zero* would appear in sequence (*1*). In such case we can omit these sample values and use 11 instead of 12 observations.

Remark 2: A normal approximation to the binomial distribution, using a correction for continuity, can also be used (see Problem 17.2).

Although the sign test is particularly useful for paired samples, as in Table 17.1, it can also be used for problems involving single samples (see Problems 17.3 and 17.4).

THE MANN–WHITNEY *U* TEST

Consider Table 17.2, which shows the strengths of cables made from two different alloys, I and II. In this table we have two samples: 8 cables of alloy I and 10 cables of alloy II. We would like to decide whether or not there is a difference between the samples or, equivalently, whether or not they come from the same population. Although this problem can be worked by using the t test of Chapter 11, a nonparametric test called the *Mann–Whitney U test*, or briefly the *U test*, is useful. This test consists of the following steps:

Table 17.2

Alloy I				Alloy II				
18.3	16.4	22.7	17.8	12.6	14.1	20.5	10.7	15.9
18.9	25.3	16.1	24.2	19.6	12.9	15.2	11.8	14.7

Step 1. Combine all sample values in an array from the smallest to the largest, and assign ranks (in this case from 1 to 18) to all these values. If two or more sample values are identical (i.e., there are *tie scores*, or briefly *ties*), the sample values are each assigned a rank equal to the *mean* of the ranks that would otherwise be assigned. If the entry 18.9 in Table 17.2 were 18.3, two identical values 18.3 would occupy ranks 12 and 13 in the array so that the rank assigned to each would be $\frac{1}{2}(12+13) = 12.5$.

Step 2. Find the sum of the ranks for each of the samples. Denote these sums by R_1 and R_2, where N_1 and N_2 are the respective sample sizes. For convenience, choose N_1 as the smaller size if they are unequal, so that $N_1 \le N_2$. A significant difference between the rank sums R_1 and R_2 implies a significant difference between the samples.

Step 3. To test the difference between the rank sums, use the statistic

$$U = N_1N_2 + \frac{N_1(N_1+1)}{2} - R_1 \tag{2}$$

corresponding to sample 1. The sampling distribution of U is symmetrical and has a mean and variance given, respectively, by the formulas

$$\mu_U = \frac{N_1N_2}{2} \qquad \sigma_U^2 = \frac{N_1N_2(N_1+N_2+1)}{12} \tag{3}$$

If N_1 and N_2 are both at least equal to 8, it turns out that the distribution of U is nearly normal, so that

$$z = \frac{U - \mu_U}{\sigma_U} \tag{4}$$

is normally distributed with mean 0 and variance 1. Using Appendix II, we can then decide whether the samples are significantly different. Problem 17.5 shows that there is a significant difference between the cables at the 0.05 level.

Remark 3: A value corresponding to sample 2 is given by the statistic

$$U = N_1N_2 + \frac{N_2(N_2+1)}{2} - R_2 \tag{5}$$

and has the same sampling distribution as statistic (*2*), with the mean and variance of formulas (*3*). Statistic (*5*) is related to statistic (*2*), for if U_1 and U_2 are the values corresponding to statistics (*2*) and (*5*), respectively, then we have the result

$$U_1 + U_2 = N_1 N_2 \tag{6}$$

We also have

$$R_1 + R_2 = \frac{N(N+1)}{2} \tag{7}$$

where $N = N_1 + N_2$. Result (*7*) can provide a check for calculations.

Remark 4: The statistic U in equation (*2*) is the total number of times that sample 1 values precede sample 2 values when all sample values are arranged in increasing order of magnitude. This provides an alternative *counting method* for finding U.

THE KRUSKAL–WALLIS H TEST

The U test is a nonparametric test for deciding whether or not two samples come from the same population. A generalization of this for k samples is provided by the *Kruskal-Wallis H test*, or briefly the *H test.*

This test may be described thus: Suppose that we have k samples of sizes $N_1, N_2, \ldots, N_k$, with the total size of all samples taken together being given by $N = N_1 + N_2 + \cdots + N_k$. Suppose further that the data from all the samples taken together are ranked and that the sums of the ranks for the k samples are $R_1, R_2, \ldots, R_k$, respectively. If we define the statistic

$$H = \frac{12}{N(N+1)} \sum_{j=1}^{k} \frac{R_j^2}{N_j} - 3(N+1) \tag{8}$$

then it can be shown that the sampling distribution of H is very nearly a *chi-square distribution* with $k-1$ degrees of freedom, provided that $N_1, N_2, \ldots, N_k$ are all at least 5.

The H test provides a nonparametric method in the *analysis of variance* for one-way classification, or one-factor experiments, and generalizations can be made.

THE H TEST CORRECTED FOR TIES

In case there are too many ties among the observations in the sample data, the value of H given by statistic (*8*) is smaller than it should be. The corrected value of H, denoted by H_c, is obtained by dividing the value given in statistic (*8*) by the correction factor

$$1 - \frac{\sum (T^3 - T)}{N^3 - N} \tag{9}$$

where T is the number of ties corresponding to each observation and where the sum is taken over all the observations. If there are no ties, then $T = 0$ and factor (*9*) reduces to 1, so that no correction is needed. In practice, the correction is usually negligible (i.e., it is not enough to warrant a change in the decision).

THE RUNS TEST FOR RANDOMNESS

Although the word "random" has been used many times in this book (such as in "random sampling" and "tossing a coin at random"), no previous chapter has given any test for randomness. A nonparametric test for randomness is provided by the *theory of runs.*

To understand what a run is, consider a sequence made up of two symbols, a and b, such as

$$a \quad a \mid b \quad b \quad b \mid a \mid b \quad b \mid a \quad a \quad a \quad a \quad a \mid b \quad b \quad b \mid a \quad a \quad a \quad a \mid \tag{10}$$

In tossing a coin, for example, a could represent "heads" and b could represent "tails." Or in sampling the bolts produced by a machine, a could represent "defective" and b could represent "nondefective."

A *run* is defined as a set of identical (or related) symbols contained between two different symbols or no symbol (such as at the beginning or end of the sequence). Proceeding from left to right in sequence (*10*), the first run, indicated by a vertical bar, consists of two a's; similarly, the second run consists of three b's, the third run consists of one a, etc. There are seven runs in all.

It seems clear that some relationship exists between randomness and the number of runs. Thus for the sequence

$$a \mid b \mid a \mid b \mid a \mid b \mid a \mid b \mid a \mid b \mid a \mid b \mid \tag{11}$$

there is a *cyclic pattern*, in which we go from a to b, back to a again, etc., which we could hardly believe to be random. In such case we have *too many* runs (in fact, we have the maximum number possible for the given number of a's and b's).

On the other hand, for the sequence

$$a \quad a \quad a \quad a \quad a \quad a \mid b \quad b \quad b \quad b \mid a \quad a \quad a \quad a \quad a \mid b \quad b \quad b \mid \tag{12}$$

there seems to be a *trend pattern*, in which the a's and b's are grouped (or clustered) together. In such case there are *too few* runs, and we would not consider the sequence to be random.

Thus a sequence would be considered nonrandom if there are either too many or too few runs, and random otherwise. To quantify this idea, suppose that we form all possible sequences consisting of N_1 a's and N_2 b's, for a total of N symbols in all ($N_1 + N_2 = N$). The collection of all these sequences provides us with a sampling distribution. Each sequence has an associated number of runs, denoted by V. In this way we are led to the sampling distribution of the statistic V. It can be shown that this sampling distribution has a mean and variance given, respectively, by the formulas

$$\mu_V = \frac{2N_1N_2}{N_1 + N_2} + 1 \qquad \sigma_V^2 = \frac{2N_1N_2(2N_1N_2 - N_1 - N_2)}{(N_1 + N_2)^2(N_1 + N_2 - 1)} \tag{13}$$

By using formulas (*13*), we can test the hypothesis of randomness at appropriate levels of significance. It turns out that if both N_1 and N_2 are at least equal to 8, then the sampling distribution of V is very nearly a normal distribution. Thus

$$z = \frac{V - \mu_V}{\sigma_V} \tag{14}$$

is normally distributed with mean 0 and variance 1, and thus Appendix II can be used.

FURTHER APPLICATIONS OF THE RUNS TEST

The following are other applications of the runs test to statistical problems:

1. **Above- and Below-Median Test for Randomness of Numerical Data.** To determine whether numerical data (such as collected in a sample) are random, first place the data in the *same order* in which they were collected. Then find the median of the data and replace each entry with the letter a or b according to whether its value is *above* or *below* the median. If a value is the same as the median, omit it from the sample. The sample is random or not according to whether the sequence of a's and b's is random or not. (See Problem 17.20.)
2. **Differences in Populations from Which Samples Are Drawn.** Suppose that two samples of sizes m and n are denoted by $a_1, a_2, \ldots, a_m$ and $b_1, b_2, \ldots, b_n$, respectively. To decide whether the samples do or do not come from the same population, first arrange all $m + n$ sample values in a sequence

of increasing values. If some values are the same, they should be ordered by a random process (such as by using random numbers). If the resulting sequence is random, we can conclude that the samples are not really different and thus come from the same population; if the sequence is not random, no such conclusion can be drawn. This test can provide an alternative to the Mann-Whitney U test. (See Problem 17.21.)

SPEARMAN'S RANK CORRELATION

Nonparametric methods can also be used to measure the correlation of two variables, X and Y. Instead of using precise values of the variables, or when such precision is unavailable, the data may be ranked from 1 to N in order of size, importance, etc. If X and Y are ranked in such a manner, the *coefficient of rank correlation*, or *Spearman's formula for rank correlation* (as it is often called), is given by

$$r_S = 1 - \frac{6 \sum D^2}{N(N^2 - 1)} \qquad (15)$$

where D denotes the differences between the ranks of corresponding values of X and Y, and where N is the number of pairs of values (X, Y) in the data.

Solved Problems

THE SIGN TEST

17.1 Referring to Table 17.1, test the hypothesis H_0 that there is no difference between machines I and II against the alternative hypothesis H_1 that there is a difference at the 0.05 significance level.

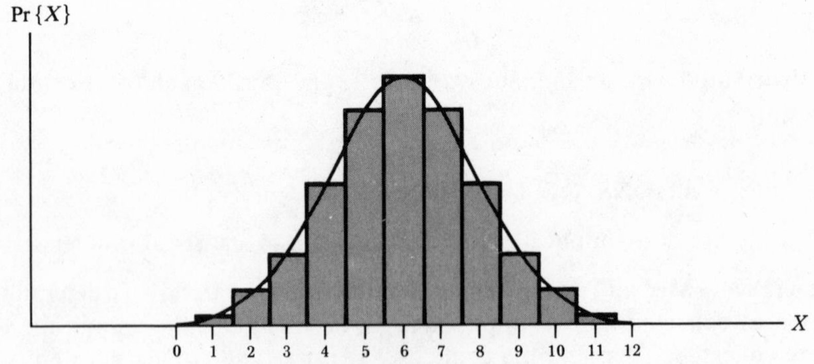

Fig. 17-1

SOLUTION

Figure 17-1 is a graph of the binomial distribution (and a normal approximation to it) that gives the probabilities of X heads in 12 tosses of a fair coin, where $X = 0, 1, 2, \ldots, 12$. From Chapter 7 the probability of X heads is

$$\Pr\{X\} = \binom{12}{X}\left(\frac{1}{2}\right)^X\left(\frac{1}{2}\right)^{12-X} = \binom{12}{X}\left(\frac{1}{2}\right)^{12}$$

whereby $\Pr\{0\} = 0.00024$, $\Pr\{1\} = 0.00293$, $\Pr\{2\} = 0.01611$, and $\Pr\{3\} = 0.05371$.

Since H_1 is the hypothesis that there is a *difference* between the machines, rather than the hypothesis that machine I is *better* than machine II, we use a two-tailed test. For the 0.05 significance level, each tail has the associated probability $\frac{1}{2}(0.05) = 0.025$. We now add the probabilities in the left-hand tail until the sum exceeds 0.025. Thus

$$\Pr\{0, 1, \text{ or } 2 \text{ heads}\} = 0.00024 + 0.00293 + 0.01611 = 0.01928$$

$$\Pr\{0, 1, 2, \text{ or } 3 \text{ heads}\} = 0.00024 + 0.00293 + 0.01611 + 0.05371 = 0.07299$$

Since 0.025 is greater than 0.01928 but less than 0.07299, we can reject hypothesis H_0 if the number of heads is 2 or less (or, by symmetry, if the number of heads is 10 or more); however, the number of heads [the + signs in sequence (*1*) of this chapter] is 3. Thus we cannot reject H_0 at the 0.05 level and must conclude that there is no difference between the machines at this level.

17.2 Work Problem 17.1 by using a normal approximation to the binomial distribution.

SOLUTION

For a normal approximation to the binomial distribution, we use the fact that the z score corresponding to the number of heads is

$$z = \frac{X - \mu}{\sigma} = \frac{X - Np}{\sqrt{Npq}}$$

(see page 152). Because the variable X for the binomial distribution is discrete while that for a normal distribution is continuous, we make a *correction for continuity* (for example, 3 heads are really a value between 2.5 and 3.5 heads). This amounts to decreasing X by 0.5 if $X > Np$ and to increasing X by 0.5 if $X < Np$. Now $N = 12$, $\mu = Np = (12)(0.5) = 6$, and $\sigma = \sqrt{Npq} = \sqrt{(12)(0.5)(0.5)} = 1.73$, so that

$$z = \frac{(3 + 0.5) - 6}{1.73} = -1.45$$

Since this is greater than -1.96 (the value of z for which the area in the left-hand tail is 0.025), we arrive at the same conclusion in Problem 17.1.

Note that $\Pr\{z \leq -1.45\} = 0.0735$, which agrees very well with the $\Pr\{X \leq 3 \text{ heads}\} = 0.07299$ of Problem 17.1.

Mathcad **17.3** The PQR Company claims that the lifetime of a type of battery that it manufactures is more than 250 hours (h). A consumer advocate wishing to determine whether the claim is justified measures the lifetimes of 24 of the company's batteries; the results are listed in Table 17.3. Assuming the sample to be random, determine whether the company's claim is justified at the 0.05 significance level.

SOLUTION

Let H_0 be the hypothesis that the company's batteries have a lifetime equal to 250 h, and let H_1 be the hypothesis that they have a lifetime greater than 250 h. To test H_0 against H_1, we can use the sign test. To do this, we subtract 250 from each entry in Table 17.3 and record the signs of the differences, as shown in Table 17.4. We see that there are 15 plus signs and 9 minus signs.

Table 17.3

271	230	198	275	282	225	284	219
253	216	262	288	236	291	253	224
264	295	211	252	294	243	272	268

Table 17.4

+	−	−	+	+	−	+	−
+	−	+	+	−	+	+	−
+	+	−	+	+	−	+	+

Using a one-tailed test at the 0.05 significance level, we would reject H_0 if the z score were greater than 1.645 (Fig. 17-2). Since the z score, using a correction for continuity, is

$$z = \frac{(15-0.5)-(24)(0.5)}{\sqrt{(24)(0.5)(0.5)}} = 1.02$$

the company's claim cannot be justified at the 0.05 level.

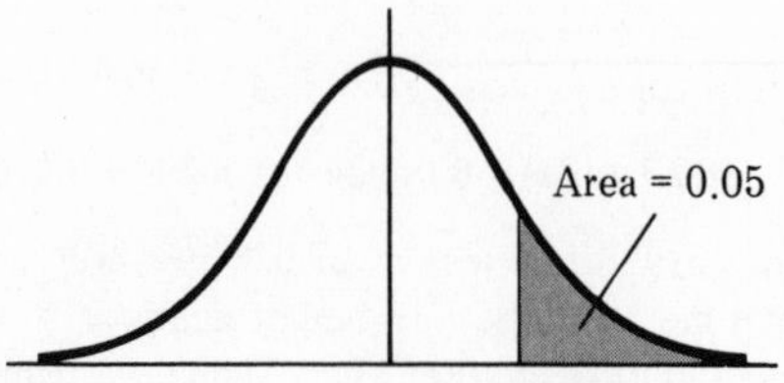

Fig. 17-2

17.4 A sample of 40 grades from a statewide examination is shown in Table 17.5. Test the hypothesis at the 0.05 significance level that the median grade for all participants is (a) 66 and (b) 75.

SOLUTION

(a) Subtracting 66 from all the entries of Table 17.5 and retaining only the associated signs gives us Table 17.6, in which we see that there are 23 pluses, 15 minuses, and 2 zeros. Discarding the 2 zeros, our sample consists of 38 signs: 23 pluses and 15 minuses. Using a two-tailed test of the normal distribution with probabilities $\frac{1}{2}(0.05) = 0.025$ in each tail (Fig. 17-3), we adopt the following decision rule:

Table 17.5

71	67	55	64	82	66	74	58	79	61
78	46	84	93	72	54	78	86	48	52
67	95	70	43	70	73	57	64	60	83
73	40	78	70	64	86	76	62	95	66

Table 17.6

+	+	−	−	+	0	+	−	+	−
+	−	+	+	+	−	+	+	−	−
+	+	+	−	+	+	−	−	−	+
+	−	+	+	−	+	+	−	+	0

Table 17.7

−	−	−	−	+	−	−	−	+	−
+	−	+	+	−	−	+	+	−	−
−	+	−	−	−	−	−	−	−	+
−	−	+	−	−	+	+	−	+	−

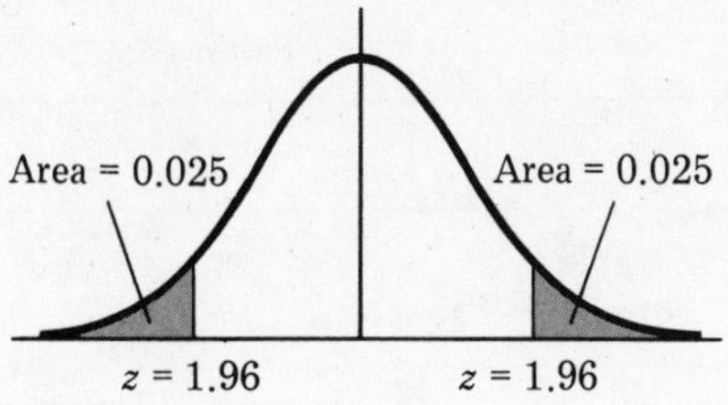

Fig. 17-3

Accept the hypothesis if $-1.96 \leq z \leq 1.96$.

Reject the hypothesis otherwise.

Since
$$z = \frac{X - Np}{\sqrt{Npq}} = \frac{(23 - 0.5) - (38)(0.5)}{\sqrt{(38)(0.5)(0.5)}} = 1.14$$

we accept the hypothesis that the median is 66 at the 0.05 level.

Note that we could also have used 15, the number of minus signs. In this case

$$z = \frac{(15 + 0.5) - (38)(0.5)}{\sqrt{(38)(0.5)(0.5)}} = -1.14$$

with the same conclusion.

(*b*) Subtracting 75 from all the entries in Table 17.5 gives us Table 17.7, in which there are 13 pluses and 27 minuses. Since

$$z = \frac{(13 + 0.5) - (40)(0.5)}{\sqrt{(40)(0.5)(0.5)}} = -2.06$$

we reject the hypothesis that the median is 75 at the 0.05 level.

Using this method, we can arrive at a 95% confidence interval for the median grade on the examination. (See Problem 17.30.)

THE MANN-WHITNEY U TEST

Mathcad **17.5** Referring to Table 17.2, determine whether there is a difference at the 0.05 significance level between cables made of alloy I and alloy II.

SOLUTION

We organize the work in accordance with steps 1, 2, and 3 (described earlier in this chapter):

Step 1. Combining all 18 sample values in an array from the smallest to the largest gives us the first line of Table 17.8. These values are numbered 1 to 18 in the second line, which gives us the ranks.

Step 2. To find the sum of the ranks for each sample, rewrite Table 17.2 by using the associated ranks from Table 17.8; this gives us Table 17.9. The sum of the ranks is 106 for alloy I and 65 for alloy II.

Table 17.8

10.7	11.8	12.6	12.9	14.1	14.7	15.2	15.9	16.1	16.4	17.8	18.3	18.9	19.6	20.5	22.7	24.2	25.3
1	2	3	4	5	6	7	8	9	10	11	12	13	14	15	16	17	18

Step 3. Since the alloy I sample has the smaller size, $N_1 = 8$ and $N_2 = 10$. The corresponding sums of the ranks are $R_1 = 106$ and $R_2 = 65$. Then

$$U = N_1 N_2 + \frac{N_1(N_1 + 1)}{2} - R_1 = (8)(10) + \frac{(8)(9)}{2} - 106 = 10$$

$$\mu_U = \frac{N_1 N_2}{2} = \frac{(8)(10)}{2} = 40 \qquad \sigma_U^2 = \frac{N_1 N_2 (N_1 + N_2 + 1)}{12} = \frac{(8)(10)(19)}{12} = 126.67$$

Table 17.9

Alloy I		Alloy II	
Cable Strength	Rank	Cable Strength	Rank
18.3	12	12.6	3
16.4	10	14.1	5
22.7	16	20.5	15
17.8	11	10.7	1
18.9	13	15.9	8
25.3	18	19.6	14
16.1	9	12.9	4
24.2	17	15.2	7
	Sum 106	11.8	2
		14.7	6
			Sum 65

Thus $\sigma_U = 11.25$ and

$$z = \frac{U - \mu_U}{\sigma_U} = \frac{10 - 40}{11.25} = -2.67$$

Since the hypothesis H_0 that we are testing is whether there is *no* difference between the alloys, a two-tailed test is required. For the 0.05 significance level, we have the decision rule:

Accept H_0 if $-1.96 \le z \le 1.96$.

Reject H_0 otherwise.

Because $z = -2.67$, we reject H_0 and conclude that there is a difference between the alloys at the 0.05 level.

17.6 Verify results (*6*) and (*7*) of this chapter for the data of Problem 17.5.

SOLUTION

(*a*) Since samples 1 and 2 yield values for U given by

$$U_1 = N_1 N_2 + \frac{N_1(N_1+1)}{2} - R_1 = (8)(10) + \frac{(8)(9)}{2} - 106 = 10$$

$$U_2 = N_1 N_2 + \frac{N_2(N_2+1)}{2} - R_2 = (8)(10) + \frac{(10)(11)}{2} - 65 = 70$$

we have $U_1 + U_2 = 10 + 70 = 80$, and $N_1 N_2 = (8)(10) = 80$.

(*b*) Since $R_1 = 106$ and $R_2 = 65$, we have $R_1 + R_2 = 106 + 65 = 171$ and

$$\frac{N(N+1)}{2} = \frac{(N_1+N_2)(N_1+N_2+1)}{2} = \frac{(18)(19)}{2} = 171$$

17.7 Work Problem 17.5 by using the statistic U for the alloy II sample.

SOLUTION

For the alloy II sample,

$$U = N_1 N_2 + \frac{N_2(N_2+1)}{2} - R_2 = (8)(10) + \frac{(10)(11)}{2} - 65 = 70$$

so that

$$z = \frac{U - \mu_U}{\sigma_U} = \frac{70 - 40}{11.25} = 2.67$$

This value of z is the *negative* of the z in Problem 17.5, and the right-hand tail of the normal distribution is used instead of the left-hand tail. Since this value of z also lies outside $-1.96 \le z \le 1.96$, the conclusion is the same as that for Problem 17.5.

17.8 A professor has two classes in psychology: a morning class of 9 students, and an afternoon class of 12 students. On a final examination scheduled at the same time for all students, the classes received the grades shown in Table 17.10. Can one conclude at the 0.05 significance level that the morning class performed worse than the afternoon class?

Table 17.10

Morning class	73	87	79	75	82	66	95	75	70			
Afternoon class	86	81	84	88	90	85	84	92	83	91	53	84

SOLUTION

Step 1. Table 17.11 shows the array of grades and ranks. Note that the rank for the two grades of 75 is $\frac{1}{2}(5+6) = 5.5$, while the rank for the three grades of 84 is $\frac{1}{3}(11+12+13) = 12$.

Step 2. Rewriting Table 17.10 in terms of ranks gives us Table 17.12.

Check: $R_1 = 73$, $R_2 = 158$, and $N = N_1 + N_2 = 9 + 12 = 21$; thus $R_1 + R_2 = 73 + 158 = 231$ and

$$\frac{N(N+1)}{2} = \frac{(21)(22)}{2} = 231 = R_1 + R_2$$

Table 17.11

53	66	70	73	75	75	79	81	82	83	84	84	84	85	86	87	88	90	91	92	95
1	2	3	4	5.5		7	8	9	10		12		14	15	16	17	18	19	20	21

Table 17.12

													Sum of Ranks
Morning class	4	16	7	5.5	9	2	21	5.5	3				73
Afternoon class	15	8	12	17	18	14	12	20	10	19	1	12	158

Step 3.

$$U = N_1 N_2 + \frac{N_1(N_1+1)}{2} - R_1 = (9)(12) + \frac{(9)(10)}{2} - 73 = 80$$

$$\mu_U = \frac{N_1 N_2}{2} = \frac{(9)(12)}{2} = 54 \qquad \sigma_U^2 = \frac{N_1 N_2 (N_1 + N_2 + 1)}{12} = \frac{(9)(12)(22)}{12} = 198$$

Thus
$$z = \frac{U - \mu_U}{\sigma_U} = \frac{80 - 54}{14.07} = 1.85$$

Since we wish to test the hypothesis H_1 that the morning class performs worse than the afternoon class against the hypothesis H_0 that there is no difference at the 0.05 level, a one-tailed test is needed. Referring to Fig. 17-2, which applies here, we have the decision rule:

Accept H_0 if $z \le 1.645$.

Reject H_0 if $z > 1.645$.

Since the actual value of $z = 1.85 > 1.645$, we reject H_0 and conclude that the morning class performed worse than the afternoon class at the 0.05 level. This conclusion cannot be reached, however, for the 0.01 level (see Problem 17.33).

17.9 Find U for the data of Table 17.13 by using (*a*) formula (*2*) of this chapter and (*b*) the counting method (as described in Remark 4 of this chapter).

SOLUTION

(*a*) Arranging the data from both samples in an array in increasing order of magnitude and assigning ranks from 1 to 5 gives us Table 17.14. Replacing the data of Table 17.13 with the corresponding ranks gives us Table 17.15, from which the sums of the ranks are $R_1 = 5$ and $R_2 = 10$. Since $N_1 = 2$ and $N_2 = 3$, the value of U for sample 1 is

$$U = N_1 N_2 + \frac{N_1(N_1+1)}{2} - R_1 = (2)(3) + \frac{(2)(3)}{2} - 5 = 4$$

The value of U for sample 2 can be found similarly to be $U = 2$.

Table 17.13

Sample 1	22	10	
Sample 2	17	25	14

Table 17.14

Data	10	14	17	22	25
Rank	1	2	3	4	5

Table 17.15

				Sum of Ranks
Sample 1	4	1		5
Sample 2	3	5	2	10

(*b*) Let us replace the sample values in Table 17.14 with I or II, depending on whether the value belongs to sample 1 or 2. Then the first line of Table 17.14 becomes

Data	I	II	II	I	II

From this we see that

Number of sample 1 values preceding first sample 2 value $= 1$

Number of sample 1 values preceding second sample 2 value $= 1$

Number of sample 1 values preceding third sample 2 value $= \underline{2}$

Total $= 4$

Thus the value of U corresponding to the first sample is 4.

Similarly, we have

$$\begin{aligned}\text{Number of sample 2 values preceding first sample 1 value} &= 0\\ \text{Number of sample 2 values preceding second sample 1 value} &= \underline{2}\\ \text{Total} &= 2\end{aligned}$$

Thus the value of U corresponding to the second sample is 2.

Note that since $N_1 = 2$ and $N_2 = 3$, these values satisfy $U_1 + U_2 = N_1 N_2$; that is, $4 + 2 = (2)(3) = 6$.

17.10 A population consists of the values 7, 12, and 15. Two samples are drawn without replacement from this population: sample 1, consisting of one value, and sample 2, consisting of two values. [Between them, the two samples exhaust the population.]

(*a*) Find the sampling distribution of U and its graph.

(*b*) Find the mean and variance of the distribution in part (*a*).

(*c*) Verify the results found in part (*b*) by using formulas (*3*) of this chapter.

SOLUTION

(*a*) We choose sampling without replacement to avoid ties—which would occur if, for example, the value 12 were to appear in both samples.

There are $3 \cdot 2 = 6$ possibilities for choosing the samples, as shown in Table 17.16. It should be noted that we could just as easily use ranks 1, 2, and 3 instead of 7, 12, and 15. The value U in Table 17.16 is that found for sample 1, but if U for sample 2 were used, the distribution would be the same.

Table 17.16

Sample 1	Sample 2	U
7	12 15	2
7	15 12	2
12	7 15	1
12	15 7	1
15	7 12	0
15	12 7	0

A graph of this distribution is shown in Fig. 17-4, where f is the frequency. The probability distribution of U can also be graphed; in this case $\Pr\{U=0\} = \Pr\{U=1\} = \Pr\{U=2\} = \frac{1}{3}$. The required graph is the same as that shown in Fig. 17-4, but with ordinates 1 and 2 replaced by $\frac{1}{6}$ and $\frac{1}{3}$, respectively.

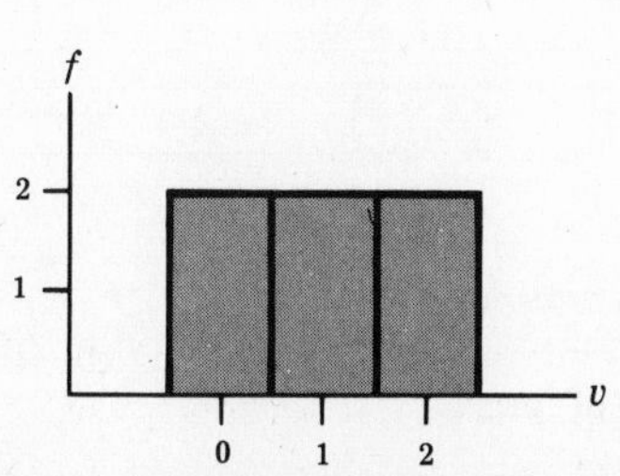

Fig. 17-4

(*b*) The mean and variance found from Table 17.15 are given by

$$\mu_U = \frac{2+2+1+1+0+0}{6} = 1$$

$$\sigma_U^2 = \frac{(2-1)^2+(2-1)^2+(1-1)^2+(1-1)^2+(0-1)^2+(0-1)^2}{6} = \frac{2}{3}$$

(*c*) By formulas (*3*),

$$\mu_U = \frac{N_1 N_2}{2} = \frac{(1)(2)}{2} = 1$$

$$\sigma_U^2 = \frac{N_1 N_2(N_1+N_2+1)}{12} = \frac{(1)(2)(1+2+1)}{12} = \frac{2}{3}$$

showing agreement with part (*a*).

17.11 (*a*) Find the sampling distribution of U in Problem 17.9 and graph it.
(*b*) Graph the corresponding probability distribution of U.
(*c*) Obtain the mean and variance of U directly from the results of part (*a*).
(*d*) Verify part (*c*) by using formulas (*3*) of this chapter.

SOLUTION

(*a*) In this case there are $5 \cdot 4 \cdot 3 \cdot 2 = 120$ possibilities for choosing values for the two samples and the method of Problem 17.9 is too laborious. To simplify the procedure, let us concentrate on the smaller sample (of size $N_1 = 2$) and the possible sums of the ranks, R_1. The sum of the ranks for sample 1 is the *smallest* when the sample consists of the two lowest-ranking numbers (1, 2); then $R_1 = 1+2 = 3$. Similarly, the sum of the ranks for sample 1 is the *largest* when the sample consists of the two highest-ranking numbers (4, 5); then $R_1 = 4+5 = 9$. Thus R_1 varies from 3 to 9.

Column 1 of Table 17.17 lists these values of R_1 (from 3 to 9), and column 2 shows the corresponding sample 1 values, whose sum is R_1. Column 3 gives the frequency (or number) of samples with sum R_1; for example, there are $f = 2$ samples with $R_1 = 5$. Since $N_1 = 2$ and $N_2 = 3$, we have

$$U = N_1 N_2 + \frac{N_1(N_1+1)}{2} - R_1 = (2)(3) + \frac{(2)(3)}{2} - R_1 = 9 - R_1$$

Table 17.17

R_1	Sample 1 Values	f	U	$\Pr\{U = R_1\}$
3	(1, 2)	1	6	0.1
4	(1, 3)	1	5	0.1
5	(1, 4), (2, 3)	2	4	0.2
6	(1, 5), (2, 4)	2	3	0.2
7	(2, 5), (3, 4)	2	2	0.2
8	(3, 5)	1	1	0.1
9	(4, 5)	1	0	0.1

From this we find the corresponding values of U in column 4 of the table; note that as R_1 varies from 3 to 9, U varies from 6 to 0. The sampling distribution is provided by columns 3 and 4, and the graph is shown in Fig. 17-5.

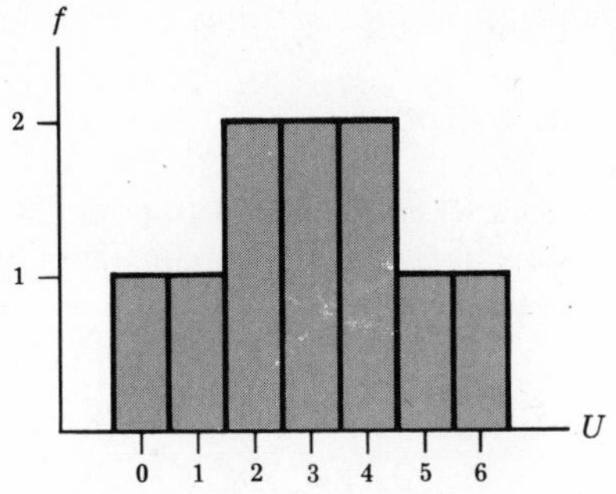

Fig. 17.5

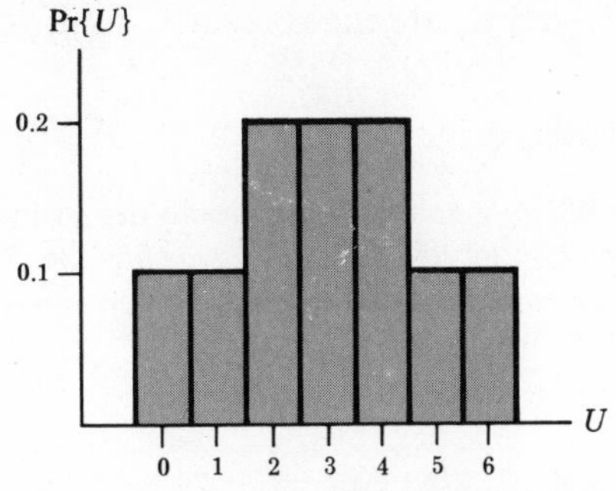

Fig. 17-6

(*b*) The probability that $U = R_1$ (i.e., $\Pr\{U = R_1\}$) is shown in column 5 of Table 17.17 and is obtained by finding the relative frequency. The relative frequency is found by dividing each frequency f by the sum of all the frequencies, or 10; for example, $\Pr\{U = 5\} = \frac{2}{10} = 0.2$. The graph of the probability distribution is shown in Fig. 17-6.

(*c*) From columns 3 and 4 of Table 17.17 we have

$$\mu_U = \bar{U} = \frac{\sum fU}{\sum f} = \frac{(1)(6)+(1)(5)+(2)(4)+(2)(3)+(2)(2)+(1)(1)+(1)(0)}{1+1+2+2+2+1+1} = 3$$

$$\sigma_U^2 = \frac{\sum f(U-\bar{U})^2}{\sum f}$$

$$= \frac{(1)(6-3)^2+(1)(5-3)^2+(2)(4-3)^2+(2)(3-3)^2+(2)(2-3)^2+(1)(1-3)^2+(1)(0-3)^2}{10} = 3$$

Another method

$$\sigma_U^2 = \overline{U^2} - \bar{U}^2 = \frac{(1)(6)^2+(1)(5)^2+(2)(4)^2+(2)(3)^2+(2)(2)^2+(1)(1)^2+(1)(0)^2}{10} - (3)^2 = 3$$

(*d*) By formulas (*3*), using $N_1 = 2$ and $N_2 = 3$, we have

$$\mu_U = \frac{N_1 N_2}{2} = \frac{(2)(3)}{2} = 3 \qquad \sigma_U^2 = \frac{N_1 N_2 (N_1 + N_2 + 1)}{12} = \frac{(2)(3)(6)}{12} = 3$$

17.12 If N numbers in a set are ranked from 1 to N, prove that the sum of the ranks is $[N(N+1)]/2$.

SOLUTION

Let R be the sum of the ranks. Then we have

$$R = 1 + 2 + 3 + \cdots + (N-1) + N \qquad (16)$$

$$R = N + (N-1) + (N-2) + \cdots + 2 + 1 \qquad (17)$$

where the sum in equation (*17*) is obtained by writing the sum in (*16*) backward. Adding equations (*16*) and (*17*) gives

$$2R = (N+1)+(N+1)+(N+1)+\cdots+(N+1)+(N+1) = N(N+1)$$

since $(N+1)$ occurs N times in the sum; thus $R = [N(N+1)]/2$. This can also be obtained by using a result from elementary algebra on arithmetic progressions and series.

17.13 If R_1 and R_2 are the respective sums of the ranks for samples 1 and 2 in the U test, prove that $R_1 + R_2 = [N(N+1)]/2$.

SOLUTION

We assume that there are no ties in the sample data. Then R_1 must be the sum of some of the ranks (numbers) in the set $1, 2, 3, \ldots, N$, while R_2 must be the sum of the remaining ranks in the set. Thus the sum $R_1 + R_2$ must be the sum of all the ranks in the set; that is, $R_1 + R_2 = 1 + 2 + 3 + \cdots + N = [N(N+1)]/2$ by Problem 17.12.

THE KRUSKAL–WALLIS *H* TEST

17.14 A company wishes to purchase one of five different machines: *A*, *B*, *C*, *D*, or *E*. In an experiment designed to determine whether there is a performance difference between the machines, five experienced operators each work on the machines for equal times. Table 17.18 shows the number of units produced by each machine. Test the hypothesis that there is no difference between the machines at the (*a*) 0.05 and (*b*) 0.01 significance levels.

Table 17.18

A	68	72	77	42	53
B	72	53	63	53	48
C	60	82	64	75	72
D	48	61	57	64	50
E	64	65	70	68	53

Table 17.19

						Sum of Ranks
A	17.5	21	24	1	6.5	70
B	21	6.5	12	6.5	2.5	48.5
C	10	25	14	23	21	93
D	2.5	11	9	14	4	40.5
E	14	16	19	17.5	6.5	73

SOLUTION

Since there are five samples (*A*, *B*, *C*, *D*, and *E*), $k = 5$. And since each sample consists of five values, we have $N_1 = N_2 = N_3 = N_4 = N_5 = 5$, and $N = N_1 + N_2 + N_3 + N_4 + N_5 = 25$. By arranging all the values in increasing order of magnitude and assigning appropriate ranks to the ties, we replace Table 17.18 with Table 17.19, the right-hand column of which shows the sum of the ranks. We see from Table 17.19 that $R_1 = 70$, $R_2 = 48.5$, $R_3 = 93$, $R_4 = 40.5$, and $R_5 = 73$. Thus

$$H = \frac{12}{N(N+1)} \sum_{j=1}^{k} \frac{R_j^2}{N_j} - 3(N+1)$$

$$= \frac{12}{(25)(26)} \left[\frac{(70)^2}{5} + \frac{(48.5)^2}{5} + \frac{(93)^2}{5} + \frac{(40.5)^2}{5} + \frac{(73)^2}{5} \right] - 3(26) = 6.44$$

For $k - 1 = 4$ degrees of freedom at the 0.05 significance level, from Appendix IV we have $\chi^2_{.95} = 9.49$. Since $6.44 < 9.49$, we cannot reject the hypothesis of no difference between the machines at the 0.05 level and therefore certainly cannot reject it at the 0.01 level. In other words, we can accept the hypothesis (or reserve judgment) that there is no difference between the machines at both levels.

Note that we have already worked this problem by using analysis of variance (see Problem 16.8) and have arrived at the same conclusion.

17.15 Work Problem 17.14 if a correction for ties is made.

SOLUTION

Table 17.20 shows the number of ties corresponding to each of the tied observations. For example, 48 occurs two times, whereby $T = 2$, and 53 occurs four times, whereby $T = 4$. By calculating $T^3 - T$ for each of these values of T and adding, we find that $\sum (T^3 - T) = 6 + 60 + 24 + 6 + 24 = 120$, as shown in Table 17.20. Then, since $N = 25$, the correction factor is

$$1 - \frac{\sum (T^3 - T)}{N^3 - N} = 1 - \frac{120}{(25)^3 - 25} = 0.9923$$

and the corrected value of H is

$$H_c = \frac{6.44}{0.9923} = 6.49$$

This correction is not sufficient to change the decision made in Problem 17.14.

Table 17.20

Observation	48	53	64	68	72	
Number of ties (T)	2	4	3	2	3	
$T^3 - T$	6	60	24	6	24	$\sum (T^3 - T) = 120$

17.16 Three samples are chosen at random from a population. Arranging the data according to rank gives us Table 17.21. Determine whether there is any difference between the samples at the (*a*) 0.05 and (*b*) 0.01 significance levels.

SOLUTION

Here $k = 3$, $N_1 = 4$, $N_2 = 3$, $N_3 = 5$, $N = N_1 + N_2 + N_3 = 12$, $R_1 = 7 + 4 + 6 + 10 = 27$, $R_2 = 11 + 9 + 12 = 32$, and $R_3 = 5 + 1 + 3 + 8 + 2 = 19$. Thus

$$H = \frac{12}{N(N+1)} \sum_{j=1}^{k} \frac{R_j^2}{N_j} - 3(N+1) = \frac{12}{(12)(13)} \left[\frac{(27)^2}{4} + \frac{(32)^2}{3} + \frac{(19)^2}{5} \right] - 3(13) = 6.83$$

(*a*) For $k - 1 = 3 - 1 = 2$ degrees of freedom, $\chi^2_{.95} = 5.99$. Thus, since $6.83 > 5.99$, we can conclude that there is a significant difference between the samples at the 0.05 level.

(*b*) For 2 degrees of freedom, $\chi^2_{.95} = 9.21$. Thus, since $6.83 < 9.21$, we cannot conclude that there is a difference between the samples at the 0.01 level.

Table 17.21

Sample 1	7	4	6	10	
Sample 2	11	9	12		
Sample 3	5	1	3	8	2

THE RUNS TEST FOR RANDOMNESS

17.17 In 30 tosses of a coin the following sequence of heads (H) and tails (T) is obtained:

H T T H T H H H T H H T T H T
H T H H T H T T H T H H T H T

(*a*) Determine the number of runs, V.

(*b*) Test at the 0.05 significance level whether the sequence is random.

SOLUTION

(*a*) Using a vertical bar to indicate a run, we see from

H | T T | H | T | H H H | T | H H | T T | H | T |
H | T | H H | T | H | T T | H | T | H H | T | H | T |

that the number of runs is $V = 22$.

(*b*) There are $N_1 = 16$ heads and $N_2 = 14$ tails in the given sample of tosses, and from part (*a*) the number of runs is $V = 22$. Thus from formulas (*13*) of this chapter we have

$$\mu_V = \frac{2(16)(14)}{16+14} + 1 = 15.93 \qquad \sigma_V^2 = \frac{2(16)(14)[2(16)(14) - 16 - 14]}{(16+14)^2(16+14-1)} = 7.175$$

or $\sigma_V = 2.679$. The z score corresponding to $V = 22$ runs is therefore

$$z = \frac{V - \mu_V}{\sigma_V} = \frac{22 - 15.93}{2.679} = 2.27$$

Now for a two-tailed test at the 0.05 significance level, we would accept the hypothesis H_0 of randomness if $-1.96 \le z \le 1.96$ and would reject it otherwise (see Fig. 17-7). Since the calculated value of z is $2.27 > 1.96$, we conclude that the tosses are not random at the 0.05 level. The test shows that there are *too many* runs, indicating a *cyclic pattern* in the tosses.

If a correction for continuity is used, the above z score is replaced by

$$z = \frac{(22 - 0.5) - 15.93}{2.679} = 2.08$$

and the same conclusion is reached.

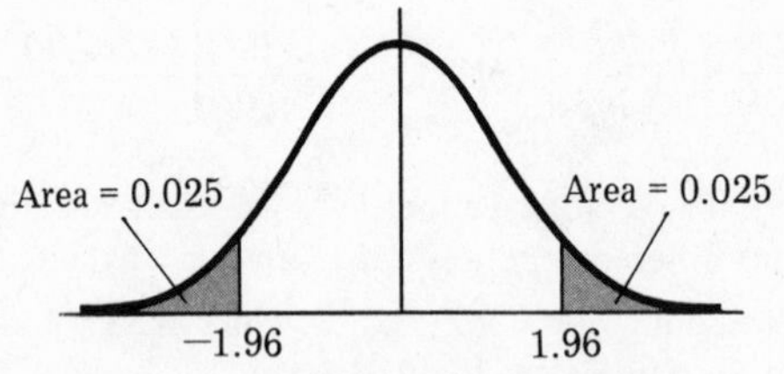

Fig. 17-7

Mathcad **17.18** A sample of 48 tools produced by a machine shows the following sequence of good (G) and defective (D) tools:

G G G G G G D D G G G G G G G G
G G D D D D G G G G G G D G G G
G G G G G G D D G G G G G G D G G

Test the randomness of the sequence at the 0.05 significance level.

SOLUTION

The numbers of D's and G's are $N_1 = 10$ and $N_2 = 38$, respectively, and the number of runs is $V = 11$. Thus the mean and variance are given by

$$\mu_V = \frac{2(10)(38)}{10+38} + 1 = 16.83 \qquad \sigma_V^2 = \frac{2(10)(38)[2(10)(38) - 10 - 38]}{(10+38)^2(10+38-1)} = 4.997$$

so that $\sigma_V = 2.235$.

For a two-tailed test at the 0.05 level, we would accept the hypothesis H_0 of randomness if $-1.96 \leq z \leq 1.96$ (see Fig. 17-7) and would reject it otherwise. Since the z score corresponding to $V = 11$ is

$$z = \frac{V - \mu_V}{\sigma_V} = \frac{11 - 16.83}{2.235} = -2.61$$

and $-2.61 < -1.96$, we can reject H_0 at the 0.05 level.

The test shows that there are *too few* runs, indicating a clustering (or bunching) of defective tools. In other words, there seems to be a *trend pattern* in the production of defective tools. Further examination of the production process is warranted.

17.19 (*a*) Form all possible sequences consisting of three *a*'s and two *b*'s and give the numbers of runs, *V*, corresponding to each sequence.

(*b*) Obtain the sampling distribution of *V* and its graph.

(*c*) Obtain the probability distribution of *V* and its graph.

SOLUTION

(*a*) The number of possible sequences consisting of three *a*'s and two *b*'s is

$$\binom{5}{2} = \frac{5!}{2!3!} = 10$$

These sequences are shown in Table 17.22, along with the number of runs corresponding to each sequence.

(*b*) The sampling distribution of *V* is given in Table 17.23 (obtained from Table 17.21), where *V* denotes the number of runs and *f* denotes the frequency. For example, Table 17.23 shows that there is one 5, four 4's, etc. The corresponding graph is shown in Fig. 17-8.

Table 17.22

Sequence	Runs (*V*)
a a a b b	2
a a b a b	4
a a b b a	3
a b a b a	5
a b b a a	3
a b a a b	4
b b a a a	2
b a b a a	4
b a a a b	3
b a a b a	4

Table 17.23

V	*f*
2	2
3	3
4	4
5	1

(*c*) The probability distribution of *V*, graphed in Fig. 17-9, is obtained from Table 17.23 by dividing each frequency by the total frequency $2+3+4+1=10$. For example, $\Pr\{V=5\} = \frac{1}{10} = 0.1$.

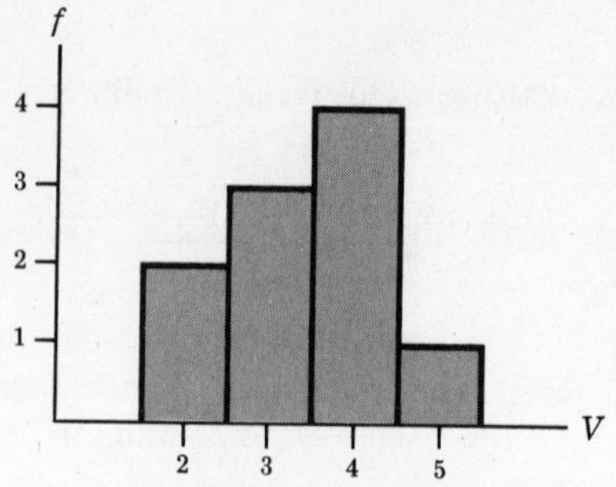

Fig. 17-8

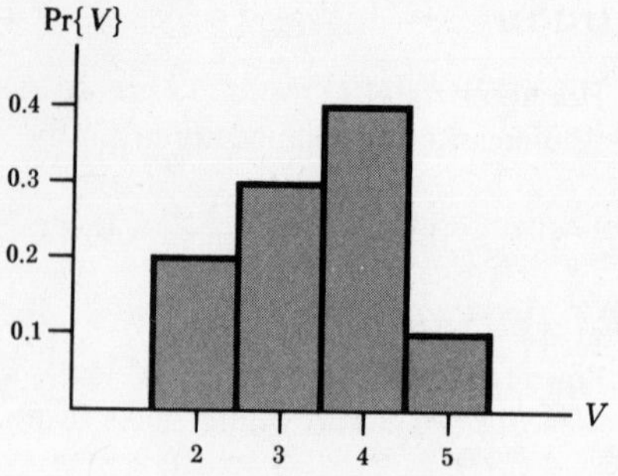

Fig. 17-9

17.20 Find (*a*) the mean and (*b*) the variance of the number of runs in Problem 17.19 directly from the results obtained there.

SOLUTION

(*a*) From Table 17.22 we have

$$\mu_V = \frac{2+4+3+5+3+4+2+4+3+4}{10} = \frac{17}{5}$$

Another method

From Table 17.22 the grouped-data method gives

$$\mu_V = \frac{\sum fV}{\sum f} = \frac{(2)(2)+(3)(3)+(4)(4)+(1)(5)}{2+3+4+1} = \frac{17}{5}$$

(*b*) Using the grouped-data method for computing the variance, from Table 17.23 we have

$$\sigma_V^2 = \frac{\sum f(V-\bar{V})^2}{\sum f} = \frac{1}{10}\left[(2)\left(2-\frac{17}{5}\right)^2 + (3)\left(3-\frac{17}{5}\right)^2 + (4)\left(4-\frac{17}{5}\right)^2 + (1)\left(5-\frac{17}{5}\right)^2\right] = \frac{21}{25}$$

Another method

As in Chapter 3, the variance is given by

$$\sigma_V^2 = \overline{V^2} - \bar{V}^2 = \frac{(2)(2)^2+(3)(3)^2+(4)(4)^2+(1)(5)^2}{10} - \left(\frac{17}{5}\right)^2 = \frac{21}{25}$$

17.21 Work Problem 17.20 by using formulas (*13*) of this chapter.

SOLUTION

Since there are three *a*'s and two *b*'s, we have $N_1 = 3$ and $N_2 = 2$. Thus

(*a*) $$\mu_V = \frac{2N_1N_2}{N_1+N_2} + 1 = \frac{2(3)(2)}{3+2} + 1 = \frac{17}{5}$$

(*b*) $$\sigma_V^2 = \frac{2N_1N_2(2N_1N_2 - N_1 - N_2)}{(N_1+N_2)^2(N_1+N_2-1)} = \frac{2(3)(2)[2(3)(2)-3-2]}{(3+2)^2(3+2-1)} = \frac{21}{25}$$

FURTHER APPLICATIONS OF THE RUNS TEST

Mathcad **17.22** Referring to Problem 17.3, and assuming a significance level of 0.05, determine whether the sample lifetimes of the batteries produced by the PQR Company are random.

SOLUTION

Table 17.24 shows the batteries' lifetimes in increasing order of magnitude. Since there are 24 entries in the table, the median is obtained from the middle two entries, 253 and 262, as $\frac{1}{2}(253+262)=257.5$. Rewriting the data of Table 17.3 by using an a if the entry is above the median and a b if it is below the median, we obtain Table 17.25, in which we have 12 a's, 12 b's, and 15 runs. Thus $N_1=12$, $N_2=12$, $N=24$, $V=15$, and we have

$$\mu_V=\frac{2N_1N_2}{N_1+N_2}+1=\frac{2(12)(12)}{12+12}+1=13 \qquad \sigma_V^2=\frac{2(12)(12)(264)}{(24)^2(23)}=5.739$$

so that

$$z=\frac{V-\mu_V}{\sigma_V}=\frac{15-13}{2.396}=0.835$$

Using a two-tailed test at the 0.05 significance level, we would accept the hypothesis of randomness if $-1.96\leq z\leq 1.96$. Since 0.835 falls within this range, we conclude that the sample is random.

Table 17.24

198	211	216	219	224	225	230	236
243	252	253	253	262	264	268	271
272	275	282	284	288	291	294	295

Table 17.25

a	b	b	a	a	b	a	b
b	b	a	a	b	a	b	b
a	a	b	b	a	b	a	a

17.23 Work Problem 17.5 by using the runs test for randomness.

SOLUTION

The arrangement of all values from both samples already appears in line 1 of Table 17.8. Using the symbols a and b for the data from samples I and II, respectively, the arrangement becomes

$$b\ b\ b\ b\ b\ b\ b\ b\ a\ a\ a\ a\ a\ b\ b\ a\ a\ a$$

Since there are four runs, we have $V=4$, $N_1=8$, and $N_2=10$. Then

$$\mu_V=\frac{2N_1N_2}{N_1+N_2}+1=\frac{2(8)(10)}{18}+1=9.889$$

$$\sigma_V^2=\frac{2N_1N_2(2N_1N_2-N_1-N_2)}{(N_1+N_2)^2(N_1+N_2-1)}=\frac{2(8)(10)(142)}{(18)^2(17)}=4.125$$

so that

$$z=\frac{V-\mu_V}{\sigma_V}=\frac{4-9.889}{2.031}=-2.90$$

If H_0 is the hypothesis that there is no difference between the alloys, it is also the hypothesis that the above sequence is random. We would accept this hypothesis if $-1.96\leq z\leq 1.96$ and would reject it otherwise. Since $z=-2.90$ lies outside this interval, we reject H_0 and reach the same conclusion as for Problem 17.5.

Note that if a correction is made for continuity,

$$z=\frac{V-\mu_V}{\sigma_V}=\frac{(4+0.5)-9.889}{2.031}=-2.65$$

and we reach the same conclusion.

RANK CORRELATION

17.24 Table 17.26 shows how 10 students, arranged in alphabetical order, were ranked according to their achievements in both the laboratory and lecture sections of a biology course. Find the coefficient of rank correlation.

Table 17.26

Laboratory	8	3	9	2	7	10	4	6	1	5
Lecture	9	5	10	1	8	7	3	4	2	6

SOLUTION

The difference in ranks, D, in the laboratory and lecture sections for each student is given in Table 17.27, which also gives D^2 and $\sum D^2$. Thus

$$r_S = 1 - \frac{6\sum D^2}{N(N^2-1)} = 1 - \frac{6(24)}{10(10^2-1)} = 0.8545$$

indicating that there is a marked relationship between the achievements in the course's laboratory and lecture sections.

Table 17.27

Difference of ranks (D)	−1	−2	−1	1	−1	3	1	2	−1	−1	
D^2	1	4	1	1	1	9	1	4	1	1	$\sum D^2 = 24$

17.25 Table 17.28 shows the heights of a sample of 12 fathers and their oldest adult sons. Find the coefficient of rank correlation.

Table 17.28

Height of father (inches)	65	63	67	64	68	62	70	66	68	67	69	71
Height of son (inches)	68	66	68	65	69	66	68	65	71	67	68	70

SOLUTION

Arranged in ascending order of magnitude, the fathers' heights are

$$62 \quad 63 \quad 64 \quad 65 \quad 66 \quad 67 \quad 67 \quad 68 \quad 68 \quad 69 \quad 71 \tag{18}$$

Since the sixth and seventh places in this array represent the same height (67 inches), we assign a mean rank $\frac{1}{2}(6+7) = 6.5$ to these places. Similarly, the eighth and ninth places are assigned the rank $\frac{1}{2}(8+9) = 8.5$. Thus the fathers' heights are assigned the ranks

$$1 \quad 2 \quad 3 \quad 4 \quad 5 \quad 6.5 \quad 6.5 \quad 8.5 \quad 8.5 \quad 10 \quad 11 \quad 12 \tag{19}$$

Similarly, arranged in ascending order of magnitude, the sons' heights are

$$65 \quad 65 \quad 66 \quad 66 \quad 67 \quad 68 \quad 68 \quad 68 \quad 68 \quad 69 \quad 70 \quad 71 \tag{20}$$

and since the sixth, seventh, eighth, and ninth places represent the same height (68 inches), we assign the mean rank $\frac{1}{4}(6+7+8+9) = 7.5$ to these places. Thus the sons' heights are assigned the ranks

$$1.5 \quad 1.5 \quad 3.5 \quad 3.5 \quad 5 \quad 7.5 \quad 7.5 \quad 7.5 \quad 7.5 \quad 10 \quad 11 \quad 12 \tag{21}$$

Using the correspondences (*18*) and (*19*), and (*20*) and (*21*), we can replace Table 17.28 with Table 17.29. Table 17.30 shows the difference in ranks, D, and the computations of D^2 and $\sum D^2$, whereby

$$r_S = 1 - \frac{6\sum D^2}{N(N^2-1)} = 1 - \frac{6(72.50)}{12(12^2-1)} = 0.7465$$

This result agrees well with the correlation coefficient obtained by other methods (see Problems 14.9, 14.14, 14.16, and 14.23).

Table 17.29

Rank of father	4	2	6.5	3	8.5	1	11	5	8.5	6.5	10	12
Rank of son	7.5	3.5	7.5	1.5	10	3.5	7.5	1.5	12	5	7.5	11

Table 17.30

D	−3.5	−1.5	−1.0	.1.5	−1.5	−2.5	3.5	3.5	−3.5	1.5	2.5	1.0	
D^2	12.25	2.25	1.00	2.25	2.25	6.25	12.25	12.25	12.25	2.25	6.25	1.00	$\sum D^2 = 72.50$

Supplementary Problems

THE SIGN TEST

17.26 A company claims that if its product is added to an automobile's gasoline tank, the mileage per gallon will improve. To test the claim, 15 different automobiles are chosen and the mileage per gallon with and without the additive is measured; the results are shown in Table 17.31. Assuming that the driving conditions are the same, determine whether there is a difference due to the additive at significance levels of (*a*) 0.05 and (*b*) 0.01.

Table 17.31

With additive	34.7	28.3	19.6	25.1	15.7	24.5	28.7	23.5	27.7	32.1	29.6	22.4	25.7	28.1	24.3
Without additive	31.4	27.2	20.4	24.6	14.9	22.3	26.8	24.1	26.2	31.4	28.8	23.1	24.0	27.3	22.9

17.27 Can one conclude at the 0.05 significance level that the mileage per gallon achieved in Problem 17.26 is *better* with the additive than without it?

17.28 A weight-loss club advertises that a special program that it has designed will produce a weight loss of at least 6% in 1 month if followed precisely. To test the club's claim, 36 adults undertake the program. Of these, 25 realize the desired loss, 6 gain weight, and the rest remain essentially unchanged. Determine at the 0.05 significance level whether the program is effective.

17.29 A training manager claims that by giving a special course to company sales personnel, the company's annual sales will increase. To test this claim, the course is given to 24 people. Of these 24, the sales of 16 increase, those of 6 decrease, and those of 2 remain unchanged. Test at the 0.05 significance level the hypothesis that the course increased the company's sales.

17.30 The MW Soda Company sets up "taste tests" in 27 locations around the country in order to determine the public's relative preference for two brands of cola, *A* and *B*. In eight locations brand *A* is preferred over brand *B*, in 17 locations brand *B* is preferred over brand *A*, and in the remaining locations there is indifference. Can one conclude at the 0.05 significance level that brand *B* is preferred over brand *A*?

17.31 The breaking strengths of a random sample of 25 ropes made by a manufacturer are given in Table 17.32. On the basis of this sample, test at the 0.05 significance level the manufacturer's claim that the breaking strength of a rope is (*a*) 25, (*b*) 30, (*c*) 35, and (*d*) 40.

Table 17.32

41	28	35	38	23
37	32	24	46	30
25	36	22	41	37
43	27	34	27	36
42	33	28	31	24

17.32 Show how to obtain 95% confidence limits for the data in Problem 17.4.

17.33 Make up and solve a problem involving the sign test.

THE MANN–WHITNEY *U* TEST

17.34 Instructors *A* and *B* both teach a first course in chemistry at XYZ University. On a common final examination, their students received the grades shown in Table 17.33. Test at the 0.05 significance level the hypothesis that there is no difference between the two instructors' grades.

Table 17.33

A	88	75	92	71	63	84	55	64	82	96				
B	72	65	84	53	76	80	51	60	57	85	94	87	73	61

17.35 Referring to Problem 17.34, can one conclude at the 0.01 significance level that the students' grades in the morning class are worse than those in the afternoon class?

17.36 A farmer wishes to determine whether there is a difference in yields between two different varieties of wheat, I and II. Table 17.34 shows the production of wheat per unit area using the two varieties. Can the farmer conclude at significance levels of (*a*) 0.05 and (*b*) 0.01 that a difference exists?

Table 17.34

Wheat I	15.9	15.3	16.4	14.9	15.3	16.0	14.6	15.3	14.5	16.6	16.0
Wheat II	16.4	16.8	17.1	16.9	18.0	15.6	18.1	17.2	15.4		

17.37 Can the farmer of Problem 17.36 conclude at the 0.05 level that wheat II produces a larger yield than wheat I?

17.38 A company wishes to determine whether there is a difference between two brands of gasoline, *A* and *B*. Table 17.35 shows the distances traveled per gallon for each brand. Can we conclude at the 0.05 significance level (*a*) that there is a difference between the brands and (*b*) that brand *B* is better than brand *A*?

Table 17.35

A	30.4	28.7	29.2	32.5	31.7	29.5	30.8	31.1	30.7	31.8
B	33.5	29.8	30.1	31.4	33.8	30.9	31.3	29.6	32.8	33.0

17.39 Can the U test be used to determine whether there is a difference between machines I and II of Table 17.1? Explain.

17.40 Make up and solve a problem using the U test.

17.41 Find U for the data of Table 17.36, using (*a*) the formula method and (*b*) the counting method.

17.42 Work Problem 17.41 for the data of Table 17.37.

Table 17.36

Sample 1	15	25
Sample 2	20	32

Table 17.37

Sample 1	40	27	30	56
Sample 2	10	35		

17.43 A population consists of the values 2, 5, 9, and 12. Two samples are drawn from this population, the first consisting of one of these values and the second consisting of the other three values.

(*a*) Obtain the sampling distribution of U and its graph.

(*b*) Obtain the mean and variance of this distribution, both directly and by formula.

17.44 Prove that $U_1 + U_2 = N_1 N_2$.

17.45 Prove that $R_1 + R_2 = [N(N+1)]/2$ for the case where the number of ties is (*a*) 1, (*b*) 2, and (*c*) any number.

17.46 If $N_1 = 14$, $N_2 = 12$, and $R_1 = 105$, find (*a*) R_2, (*b*) U_1, and (*c*) U_2.

17.47 If $N_1 = 10$, $N_2 = 16$, and $U_2 = 60$, find (*a*) R_1, (*b*) R_2, and (*c*) U_1.

17.48 What is the largest number of the values N_1, N_2, R_1, R_2, U_1, and U_2 that can be determined from the remaining ones? Prove your answer.

THE KRUSKAL–WALLIS H TEST

17.49 An experiment is performed to determine the yields of five different varieties of wheat: *A*, *B*, *C*, *D*, and *E*. Four plots of land are assigned to each variety. The yields (in bushels per acre) are shown in Table 17.38. Assuming that the plots have similar fertility and that the varieties are assigned to the plots at random, determine whether there is a significant difference between the yields at the (*a*) 0.05 and (*b*) 0.01 levels.

Table 17.38

A	20	12	15	19
B	17	14	12	15
C	23	16	18	14
D	15	17	20	12
E	21	14	17	18

Table 17.39

A	33	38	36	40	31	35
B	32	40	42	38	30	34
C	31	37	35	33	34	30
D	27	33	32	29	31	28

17.50 A company wishes to test four different types of tires: A, B, C, and D. The lifetimes of the tires, as determined from their treads, are given (in thousands of miles) in Table 17.39; each type has been tried on six similar automobiles assigned to the tires at random. Determine whether there is a significant difference between the tires at the (a) 0.05 and (b) 0.01 levels.

17.51 A teacher wishes to test three different teaching methods: I, II, and III. To do this, the teacher chooses at random three groups of five students each and teaches each group by a different method. The same examination is then given to all the students, and the grades in Table 17.40 are obtained. Determine at the (a) 0.05 and (b) 0.01 significance levels whether there is a difference between the teaching methods.

Table 17.40

Method I	78	62	71	58	73
Method II	76	85	77	90	87
Method III	74	79	60	75	80

Table 17.41

Mathematics	72	80	83	75	
Science	81	74	77		
English	88	82	90	87	80
Economics	74	71	77	70	

17.52 During one semester a student received in various subjects the grades shown in Table 17.41. Test at the (a) 0.05 and (b) 0.01 significance levels whether there is a difference between the grades in these subjects.

17.53 Using the H test, work (a) Problem 16.9, (b) Problem 16.21, and (c) Problem 16.22.

17.54 Using the H test, work (a) Problem 16.23, (b) Problem 16.24, and (c) Problem 16.25.

THE RUNS TEST FOR RANDOMNESS

17.55 Determine the number of runs, V, for each of these sequences:

(a) A B A B B A A A B B A B

(b) H H T H H H T T T T H H T H H T H T

17.56 Twenty-five individuals were sampled as to whether they liked or did not like a product (indicated by Y and N, respectively). The resulting sample is shown by the following sequence:

Y Y N N N N Y Y Y N Y N N Y N N N N N Y Y Y Y N N

(a) Determine the number of runs, V.

(b) Test at the 0.05 significance level whether the responses are random.

17.57 Use the runs test on sequences (*10*) and (*11*) in this chapter, and state any conclusions about randomness.

17.58 (a) Form all possible sequences consisting of two a's and one b, and give the number of runs, V, corresponding to each sequence.

(b) Obtain the sampling distribution of V and its graph.

(c) Obtain the probability distribution of V and its graph.

17.59 In Problem 17.58, find the mean and variance of V (a) directly from the sampling distribution and (b) by formula.

17.60 Work Problems 17.58 and 17.59 for the cases in which there are (a) two a's and two b's, (b) one a and three b's, and (c) one a and four b's.

17.61 Work Problems 17.58 and 17.59 for the cases in which there are (*a*) two *a*'s and four *b*'s and (*b*) three *a*'s and three *b*'s.

FURTHER APPLICATIONS OF THE RUNS TEST

17.62 Assuming a significance level of 0.05, determine whether the sample of 40 grades in Table 17.5 is random.

17.63 The closing prices of a stock on 25 successive days are given in Table 17.42. Determine at the 0.05 significance level whether the prices are random.

Table 17.42

10.375	11.125	10.875	10.625	11.500
11.625	11.250	11.375	10.750	11.000
10.875	10.750	11.500	11.250	12.125
11.875	11.375	11.875	11.125	11.750
11.375	12.125	11.750	11.500	12.250

17.64 The first digits of $\sqrt{2}$ are 1.41421 35623 73095 0488 · · · . What conclusions can you draw concerning the randomness of the digits?

17.65 What conclusions can you draw concerning the randomness of the following digits?

(*a*) $\sqrt{3} = 1.73205\ 08075\ 68877\ 2935 \cdots$

(*b*) $\pi = 3.14159\ 26535\ 89793\ 2643 \cdots$

17.66 Work Problem 17.30 by using the runs test for randomness.

17.67 Work Problem 17.32 by using the runs test for randomness.

17.68 Work Problem 17.34 by using the runs test for randomness.

RANK CORRELATION

17.69 In a contest, two judges were asked to rank eight candidates (numbered 1 through 8) in order of preference. The judges submitted the choices shown in Table 17.43.

(*a*) Find the coefficient of rank correlation.

(*b*) Decide how well the judges agreed in their choices.

Table 17.43

First judge	5	2	8	1	4	6	3	7
Second judge	4	5	7	3	2	8	1	6

17.70 Use rank correlation to work (*a*) Problem 14.26, (*b*) Problem 14.42, (*c*) Problem 14.46, and (*d*) Problem 14.63.

17.71 The rank correlation coefficient is derived by using the ranked data in the product-moment formula of Chapter 14. Illustrate this by using both methods to work a problem.

17.72 Can the rank correlation coefficient be found for grouped data? Explain this, and illustrate your answer with an example.

Chapter 18

Analysis of Time Series

TIME SERIES

A *time series* is a set of observations taken at specific times, usually at equal intervals. Examples of time series are the total annual production of steel in the United States over a number of years, the daily closing price of a share on the stock exchange, the hourly temperatures announced by a city's weather bureau, and the total monthly sales receipts in a department store.

Mathematically, a time series is defined by the values $Y_1, Y_2, \ldots$ of a variable Y (temperature, closing price of a share, etc.) at times $t_1, t_2, \ldots$. Thus Y is a function of t; this is symbolized by $Y = F(t)$.

GRAPHS OF TIME SERIES

A time series involving a variable Y is represented pictorially by constructing a graph of Y versus t, as done many times in previous chapters. For example, Fig. 18-1 is the graph of a time series showing the cattle population of the United States during the years 1870–1980.

CHARACTERISTIC MOVEMENTS OF TIME SERIES

It is interesting to think of a time-series graph (such as that shown in Fig. 18-1) as a graph that describes a point moving with the passage of time, in many ways analogous to the path of a physical particle moving under the influence of physical forces. Rather than resulting from physical forces, however, the motion may result from a combination of economic, sociological, psychological, and other forces.

Experience with many examples of time series has revealed certain *characteristic movements,* or *variations,* some or all of which are present to varying degrees. Analysis of such movements is of great value in many connections, one of which is the problem of *forecasting* future movements. It should thus come as no surprise that many industries and government agencies are vitally concerned with this important subject.

CLASSIFICATION OF TIME-SERIES MOVEMENTS

The characteristic movements of time series may be classified into four main types, often called the *components* of a time series:

1. **Long-Term, or Secular, Movements.** These refer to the general direction in which the graph of a time series appears to be going over a long interval of time. In Fig. 18-1 this secular movement (or *secular variation* or *secular trend,* as it is sometimes called) is indicated by a *trend curve,* shown dashed. For some time series a *trend line* may be appropriate. The determination of such trend lines and curves by the least-squares method has been considered in Chapter 13. Other methods are discussed later in this chapter.
2. **Cyclic Movements, or Cyclic Variations.** These refer to the long-term oscillations, or swings, about a trend line or curve. These *cycles,* as they are sometimes called, may or may not be *periodic*; that is, they may or may not follow exactly similar patterns after equal intervals of time. In business and economic activities, movements are considered cyclic only if they recur after time intervals of more than 1 year. An important example of cyclic movements are the so-called *business cycles* representing intervals of prosperity, recession, depression, and recovery. The cyclic movements about the trend curve are quite apparent in Fig. 18-1.

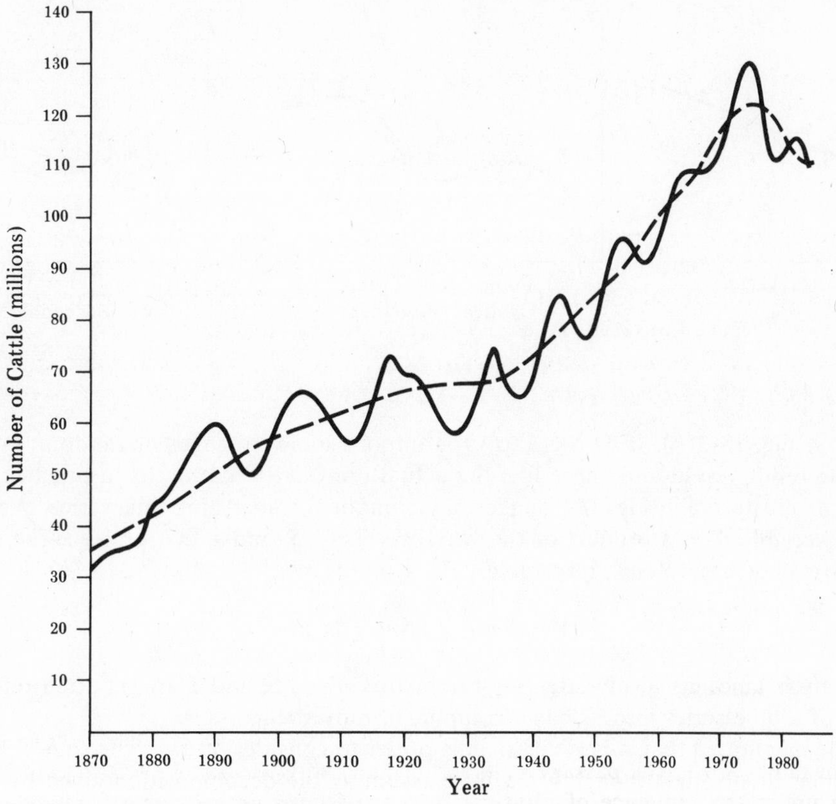

Fig. 18-1. Cattle population of the United States, 1870–1980 (*Source:* U.S. Department of Agriculture)

3. **Seasonal Movements, or Seasonal Variations.** These refer to the identical or almost identical patterns that a time series appears to follow during corresponding months of successive years. Such movements are due to recurring events that take place annually, such as the sudden increase of department-store sales before Christmas. In Fig. 18-1 no seasonal movements are present, since the graph was obtained only from annual figures.

   Although seasonal movements generally refer in business or economic theory to *annual* periodicity, the ideas involved can be extended to include periodicity over any interval of time (such as days, hours, or weeks), depending on the type of data available.

4. **Irregular, or Random, Movements.** These refer to the sporadic motions of time series due to chance events, such as floods, strikes, and elections. Although it is ordinarily assumed that such events produce variations lasting only a short time, it is conceivable that they may be so intense as to result in new cyclic or other movements.

TIME-SERIES ANALYSIS

Time-series analysis consists of a description (generally mathematical) of the component movements present. To understand the procedures involved in such a description, consider Fig. 18-2, which shows *ideal* time series. Figure 18-2(a) shows the graph of a long-term, or secular, trend line (rather than a trend curve, which could have been used instead), Fig. 18-2(b) shows this long-term trend line with a superimposed cyclic movement (assumed to be periodic), and Fig. 18-2(c) shows a seasonal movement

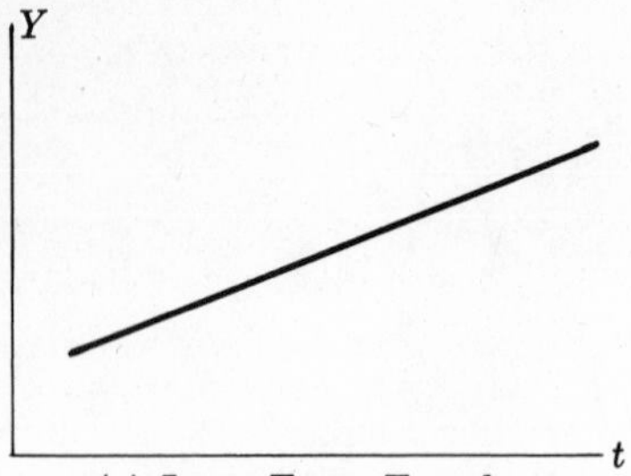

(a) Long-Term Trend

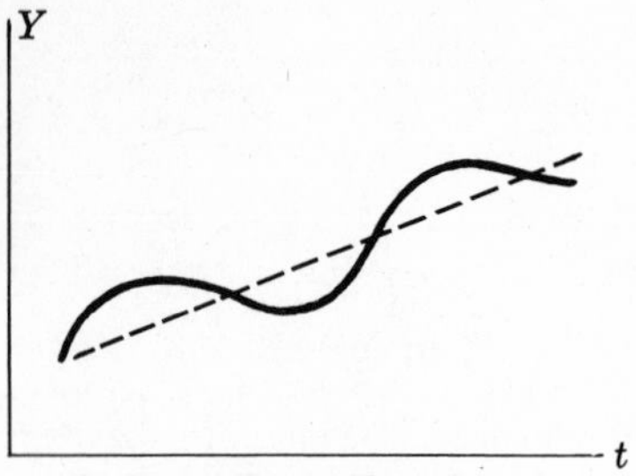

(b) Long-Term Trend and Cyclical Movement

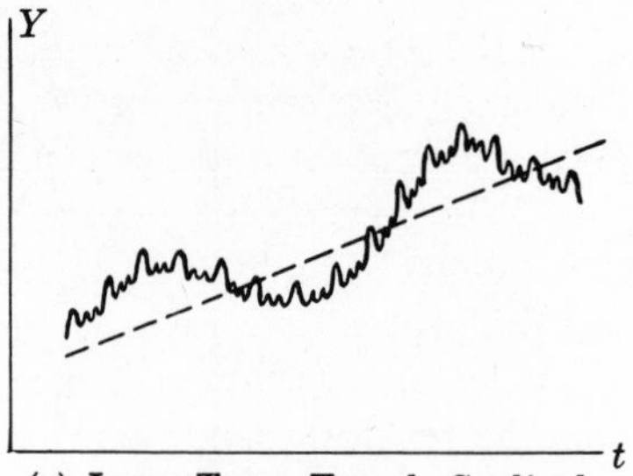

(c) Long-Term Trend, Cyclical and Seasonal Movements

Fig. 18-2

superimposed on Fig. 18-2(*b*). If we were to superimpose some irregular, or random, movements on Fig. 18-2(*c*), the result would look more like the actual time series that occur in practice.

The concepts illustrated in Fig. 18-2 suggest a technique for analyzing time series. We assume that the time-series variable Y is a product of the variables T, C, S, and I that produce the trend, cyclic, seasonal, and irregular movements, respectively. In symbols,

$$Y = T \times C \times S \times I = TCSI \tag{1}$$

Time-series analysis amounts to investigating the factors T, C, S, and I and is often referred to as a *decomposition* of a time series into its basic component movements.

It should be mentioned that some statisticians prefer to consider Y to be the sum $T+C+S+I$ of the basic variables involved. Although we will be assuming the decomposition given by equation (*1*) as we examine the methods discussed in this chapter, analogous procedures are available when a sum is assumed. In practice, deciding which method of decomposition should be assumed depends on the degree of success achieved in applying the assumption.

MOVING AVERAGES; THE SMOOTHING OF TIME SERIES

Given a set of numbers

$$Y_1, Y_2, Y_3, \ldots \tag{2}$$

we define a *moving average of order N* to be the sequence of arithmetic means:

$$\frac{Y_1+Y_2+\cdots+Y_N}{N}, \quad \frac{Y_2+Y_3+\cdots+Y_{N+1}}{N}, \quad \frac{Y_3+Y_4+\cdots+Y_{N+2}}{N}, \quad \ldots \tag{3}$$

The sums in the numerators of sequence (*3*) are called *moving totals of order N.*

EXAMPLE 1. Given the numbers 2, 6, 1, 5, 3, 7, and 2, a moving average of order 3 is given by the sequence

$$\frac{2+6+1}{3}, \quad \frac{6+1+5}{3}, \quad \frac{1+5+3}{3}, \quad \frac{5+3+7}{3}, \quad \frac{3+7+2}{3} \qquad \text{or} \qquad 3, 4, 3, 5, 4$$

It is customary to locate each number in the moving average at its appropriate position relative to the original data. In this example we would write

Original data	2, 6, 1, 5, 3, 7, 2
Moving average of order 3	3, 4, 3, 5, 4

each number in the moving average being the mean of the three numbers immediately above it.

If the data are given annually or monthly, a moving average of order N is called, respectively, an *N-year moving average* or an *N-month moving average*. Thus we speak of 5-year moving averages, 12-month moving averages, etc. Clearly, any other unit of time can also be used.

Moving averages have the property that they tend to reduce the amount of variation present in a set of data. In the case of time series, this property is often used to eliminate unwanted fluctuations, and the process is called the *smoothing of time series*.

If weighted arithmetic means are used in sequence (*3*), the weights being specified in advance, then the resulting sequence is called a *weighted moving average of order N*.

EXAMPLE 2. If the weights 1, 4, and 1 are used in Example 1, a weighted moving average of order 3 is given by the sequence

$$\frac{1(2)+4(6)+1(1)}{1+4+1}, \quad \frac{1(6)+4(1)+1(5)}{1+4+1}, \quad \frac{1(1)+4(5)+1(3)}{1+4+1}, \quad \frac{1(5)+4(3)+1(7)}{1+4+1}, \quad \frac{1(3)+4(7)+1(2)}{1+4+1}$$

or 4.5, 2.5, 4.0, 4.0, 5.5.

ESTIMATION OF TREND

A trend can be estimated in any of several ways:

1. **The Least-Squares Method.** This method, described in Chapter 13, can be used to find the equation of an appropriate trend line or trend curve. From this equation we can compute the trend values T.
2. **The Freehand Method.** This method, which consists of fitting a trend line or curve simply by looking at the graph, can be used to estimate T. However, it has the obvious disadvantage of depending too much on individual judgment.
3. **The Moving-Average Method.** By using moving averages of appropriate orders, we can eliminate cyclic, seasonal, and irregular patterns, thus leaving only the trend movement.

   One disadvantage of this method is that the data at the beginning and end of a series are lost: for instance, in Example 1 we began with seven numbers, and with a moving average of order 3 we arrived at five numbers. Another disadvantage is that moving averages may generate cycles or other movements that were not present in the original data. A third disadvantage is that moving averages are strongly affected by extreme values. To overcome this somewhat, a weighted moving average with appropriate weights is sometimes used; in such case the central item or items are given the largest weight, and extreme values are given small weights.
4. **The Method of Semiaverages.** This consists of separating the data into two parts (preferably equal) and averaging the data in each part, thus obtaining two points on the graph of the time series. A trend line is then drawn between these two points, and the trend values are determined from the trend line. The trend values can also be determined directly, without a graph (see Problem 18.6).

   Although this method is simple to apply, it may lead to poor results when used indiscriminately. Also, it is applicable only where the trend is linear or approximately linear, although it can be extended to cases where the data can be broken up into several parts in each of which the trend is linear.

ESTIMATION OF SEASONAL VARIATIONS; THE SEASONAL INDEX

To determine the seasonal factor S in equation (*1*), we must estimate how the data in the time series vary from month to month throughout a typical year. A set of numbers showing the relative values of a variable during the months of the year is called a *seasonal index* for the variable. For example, if we know that sales during January, February, March, etc., are 50, 120, 90, ... percent of the average monthly sales for the whole year, then the numbers 50, 120, 90, ... provide the seasonal index for the year, they are sometimes called *seasonal index numbers*. The average (mean) seasonal index for the whole year should be 100%; that is, the sum of the 12 months' index numbers should be 1200%.

Various methods are available for computing a seasonal index:

1. **The Average-Percentage Method.** In this method we express the data for each month as percentages of the average for the year. The percentages for corresponding months of different years are then averaged, using either a mean or a median; if the mean is used, it is best to avoid any extreme values that may occur. The resulting 12 percentages give the seasonal index. If their mean is not 100% (i.e., if the sum is not 1200%), they should be adjusted—which is done by multiplying them by a suitable factor.

2. **The Percentage Trend, or Ratio-to-Trend, Method.** In this methou we express the data for each month as percentages of monthly trend values. An appropriate average of the percentages for corresponding months then gives the required index. As in method 1, we adjust these if they do not average to 100%..

   Note that dividing each monthly value Y by the corresponding trend value T yields $Y/T = CSI$, from equation (*1*), and that the subsequent averaging of Y/T produces the seasonal indexes. Insofar as these indexes include cyclic and irregular variations, this may be an important disadvantage of the method, especially if the variations are large.

3. **The Percentage Moving-Average, or Ratio-to-Moving-Average, Method.** In this method we compute a 12-month moving average. Since the results thus obtained fall between successive months instead of in the middle of the month (which is where the original data fall), we compute a 2-month moving average of this 12-month moving average. The result is often called a *12-month centered moving average.*

   After doing this, we express the original data for each month as a percentage of the 12-month centered moving average that corresponds to the original data. The percentages for the corresponding months are then averaged, giving the required index. As before, we adjust these if they do not average to 100%.

   Note that the logical reasoning behind this method follows from equation (*1*). A 12-month centered moving average of Y serves to eliminate the seasonal and irregular movements S and I and is thus equivalent to the values given by TC. Dividing the original data by TC thus yields SI. The subsequent averages over corresponding months serve to eliminate the irregularity I and thus result in a suitable index S.

4. **The Link-Relative Method.** In this method we express the data for each month as a percentage of the data for the previous month; these monthly percentages are called *link relatives* because they link each month to the preceding one. We then take an appropriate average of the link relatives for the corresponding months. From these 12 average link relatives we then obtain the relative percentages of each month with respect to January, which is considered to be 100%.

   After doing this, we will usually find that the next January has an associated percentage that is either higher or lower than 100%, depending on whether there has been an increase or a decrease in the trend. Using this next-January percentage, we then adjust the various months' relative percentages (obtained above) for this trend. These final percentages, adjusted so that they average to 100%, provide the required seasonal index.

DESEASONALIZATION OF DATA

If the original monthly data are divided by the corresponding seasonal index numbers, the resulting data are said to be *deseasonalized,* or *adjusted for seasonal variation.* Such data still include trend, cyclic, and irregular movements.

ESTIMATION OF CYCLIC VARIATIONS

After the data have been deseasonalized, they can also be adjusted for trend simply by dividing the data by the corresponding trend values. According to equation (*1*), the process of adjusting for seasonal variation and trend corresponds to dividing Y by ST, which yields CI (the cyclic and irregular variations). An appropriate moving average of a few months' duration (such as 3, 5, or 7 months, so that subsequent centering is not necessary) then serves to smooth out the irregular variations I and to leave only the cyclic variations C. Once these cyclic variations have thus been isolated, they can be studied in detail. If a periodicity or approximate periodicity of cycles occurs, *cyclic indexes* can be constructed in much the same manner as seasonal indexes.

ESTIMATION OF IRREGULAR VARIATIONS

Irregular (or random) variations can be estimated by adjusting the data for the trend, seasonal, and cyclic variations. This amounts to dividing the original data Y by T, S, and C, which [by equation (*1*)] yields I. In practice it is found that irregular movements tend to have a small magnitude and often tend to follow the pattern of a normal distribution; that is, small deviations occur with large frequency, and large deviations occur with small frequency.

COMPARABILITY OF DATA

When comparing data, one must always be careful that such comparison is justified. For example, in comparing March data with February data, we must realize that March has 31 days, while February has 28 or 29 days; and in comparing February data for different years, we must remember that in a leap year February has 29 rather than 28 days. To take another example, the number of working days during various months of the same or different years may differ because of holidays, strikes, layoffs, and so forth.

In practice, no definite rule is followed in making adjustments for such variations. The need for such adjustment is left to the discretion of the investigator.

FORECASTING

The above methods and principles are used in the important work of forecasting time series. One must realize, of course, that the mathematical treatment of data does not in itself solve all problems. Nevertheless, when coupled with an investigator's common sense, experience, ingenuity, and good judgment, mathematical analysis has proved valuable both in long-range and short-range forecasting.

SUMMARY OF THE FUNDAMENTAL STEPS IN TIME-SERIES ANALYSIS

1. Collect data for the time series, making every effort to ensure that these data are reliable. Always keep in mind the eventual purpose of the time-series analysis; for example, if one wishes to forecast a given time series, it may be helpful to obtain related time series (as well as other information). If necessary, adjust the data for comparability, such as for leap years and holidays.
2. Graph the time series, noting qualitatively the presence of seasonal variations and of long-term trend and cyclic variations.
3. Construct the long-term trend curve or line, and obtain the appropriate trend values by using the least-squares, freehand, moving-averages, or semiaverages method.
4. If seasonal variations are present, obtain a seasonal index and deseasonalize the data (i.e., adjust the data for the seasonal variations).
5. Adjust the deseasonalized data for trend. The resulting data contain (theoretically) only the cyclic and irregular variations. A moving average of 3, 5, or 7 months will serve to remove the irregular variations, revealing the cyclic variations.
6. Graph the cyclic variations obtained in step 5, noting any periodicities or approximate periodicities that may be present.

7. If a forecast is desired, make the forecast by combining the results of steps 1 through 6 and by using any other available information as well. Identify and evaluate all possible sources of error and their magnitude.

Solved Problems

CHARACTERISTIC MOVEMENTS OF TIME SERIES

18.1 With which characteristic movement of a time series would you mainly associate (*a*) a fire in a factory that delays the factory's production for 3 weeks, (*b*) an era of prosperity, (*c*) an after-Easter sale in a department store, (*d*) a need for increased wheat production due to a constant increase in population, and (*e*) the monthly number of inches of rainfall in a city over a 5-year period?

SOLUTION

The characteristic movements are (*a*) irregular, (*b*) cyclic, (*c*) seasonal, (*d*) long-term, and (*e*) seasonal.

MOVING AVERAGES; THE SMOOTHING OF TIME SERIES

18.2 Table 18.1 shows the U.S. farm population (in millions) for the years 1973–1983. Construct (*a*) a 5-year moving average and (*b*) a 4-year moving average.

Table 18.1

Year	1973	1974	1975	1976	1977	1978	1979	1980	1981	1982	1983
Farm population (millions)	9.47	9.26	8.86	8.25	7.81	8.01	7.55	7.24	7.01	6.88	7.03

Source: U.S. Department of Agriculture.

SOLUTION

(*a*) Refer to Table 18.2. In column 3 the first moving total, 43.65, is the sum of the first through fifth entries of column 2; the second moving total, 42.19, is the sum of the second through sixth entries in column 2; etc.

In practice, after obtaining the first moving total (43.65), we can easily obtain the second moving total by subtracting 9.47 (the first entry of column 2) from it and adding 8.01 (the sixth entry of column 2), for a result of 42.19. Succeeding moving totals are obtained similarly.

Dividing each moving total by 5 yields the required moving average (column 4).

(*b*) Refer to Table 18.3. The 4-year moving totals are obtained as in part (*a*), except that instead of adding five entries of column 2, we add four entries. Note that, unlike the method in part (*a*), the moving totals are centered *between* successive years. This is always the case when an *even* number of years is taken as the moving average. For example, if we consider that 1974 stands for July 1, 1974, then the first 4-year moving total is centered at Jan. 1, 1975, or Dec. 31, 1974.

The 4-year moving averages are obtained by dividing the 4-year moving totals by 4.

18.3 Construct a 4-year centered moving average for the data of Problem 18.2.

Table 18.2

Year	Data	5-Year Moving Total	5-Year Moving Average
1973	9.47		
1974	9.26		
1975	8.86	43.65	8.73
1976	8.25	42.19	8.44
1977	7.81	40.48	8.10
1978	8.01	38.86	7.77
1979	7.55	37.62	7.52
1980	7.24	36.69	7.34
1981	7.01	35.71	7.14
1982	6.88		
1983	7.03		

Table 18.3

Year	Data	4-Year Moving Total	4-Year Moving Average
1973	9.47		
1974	9.26		
		35.84	8.96
1975	8.86		
		34.18	8.55
1976	8.25		
		32.93	8.23
1977	7.81		
		31.62	7.91
1978	8.01		
		30.61	7.65
1979	7.55		
		29.81	7.45
1980	7.24		
		28.68	7.17
1981	7.01		
		28.16	7.04
1982	6.88		
1983	7.03		

SOLUTION

First method

First we compute a 4-year moving average, as in Problem 18.2(*b*); these values are centered between successive years, as shown in Table 18.4. If we now compute a 2-year moving total of these 4-year moving averages, the results are centered at the required years. Dividing the results in column 4 by 2 yields the required *centered* moving average (column 5).

Table 18.4

Year	Data	4-Year Moving Average	2-Year Moving Total of Column 3	4-Year Centered Moving Average (Column 4 ÷ 2)
1973	9.47			
1974	9.26			
		8.96		
1975	8.86		17.51	8.76
		8.55		
1976	8.25		16.78	8.39
		8.23		
1977	7.81		16.14	8.07
		7.91		
1978	8.01		15.56	7.78
		7.65		
1979	7.55		15.10	7.55
		7.45		
1980	7.24		14.62	7.31
		7.17		
1981	7.01		14.21	7.11
		7.04		
1982	6.88			
1983	7.03			

Second method

First we compute a 4-year moving total, as in Problem 18.2(*b*); these values are centered between successive years, as shown in Table 18.5. If we now compute a 2-year moving total of these 4-year moving totals, the results become centered at the required years. Dividing the results in column 4 by 8 (2×4) yields the required moving average. For the year 1975, the slight difference between 8.76 and 8.75 in Tables 18.4 and 18.5, respectively, is due to rounding errors.

Table 18.5

Year	Data	4-Year Moving Total	2-Year Moving Total of Column 3	4-Year Centered Moving Average (Column 4÷8)
1973	9.47			
1974	9.26			
		35.84		
1975	8.86		70.02	8.75
		34.18		
1976	8.25		67.11	8.39
		32.93		
1977	7.81		64.55	8.07
		31.62		
1978	8.01		62.23	7.78
		30.61		
1979	7.55		60.42	7.55
		29.81		
1980	7.24		58.49	7.31
		28.68		
1981	7.01		56.84	7.11
		28.16		
1982	6.88			
1983	7.03			

18.4 Show that the 4-year centered moving average of Problem 18.3 is equivalent to a 5-year weighted moving average with weights 1, 2, 2, 2, and 1, respectively.

SOLUTION

Let $Y_1, Y_2, \ldots, Y_{11}$ denote the values corresponding to the years 1973, 1974, ..., 1983, respectively. Then, proceeding as in the second method of Problem 18.3, we obtain Table 18.6, from the right-hand column of which it follows that the 4-year centered moving average is a 5-year weighted moving average with weights 1, 2, 2, 2, and 1, respectively. Note that the sum of these weights is $1+2+2+2+1=8$.

This method can be used to obtain the results of Problem 18.3. For example, the first entry (corresponding to 1975) is

$$\frac{(1)(9.47)+2(9.26)+2(8.86)+2(8.25)+1(7.81)}{8}=8.75$$

Table 18.6

Year	Y	4-Year Moving Total	2-Year Moving Total of Column 3	4-Year Centered Moving Average (Column 4÷8)
1948	Y_1			
1949	Y_2			
		$Y_1+Y_2+Y_3+Y_4$		
1950	Y_3		$Y_1+2Y_2+2Y_3+2Y_4+2Y_5$	$\frac{1}{8}(Y_1+2Y_2+2Y_3+2Y_4+Y_5)$
		$Y_2+Y_3+Y_4+Y_5$		
1951	Y_4		$Y_2+2Y_3+2Y_4+2Y_5+2Y_6$	$\frac{1}{8}(Y_2+2Y_3+2Y_4+2Y_5+Y_6)$
		$Y_3+Y_4+Y_5+Y_6$		
1952	Y_5		$Y_3+2Y_4+2Y_5+2Y_6+Y_7$	$\frac{1}{8}(Y_3+2Y_4+2Y_5+2Y_6+Y_7)$
		$Y_4+Y_5+Y_6+Y_7$		
1953	Y_6			
...	...	....	....	....
1958	Y_{11}			

18.5 Graph both the moving average of Problem 18.2(a) and the original data (from Table 18.1).

SOLUTION

The graph of the original data is shown by the solid line in Fig. 18-3, in which the graph of the moving average is shown dashed. Note how the moving average has smoothed the graph of the original data, showing the trend line clearly.

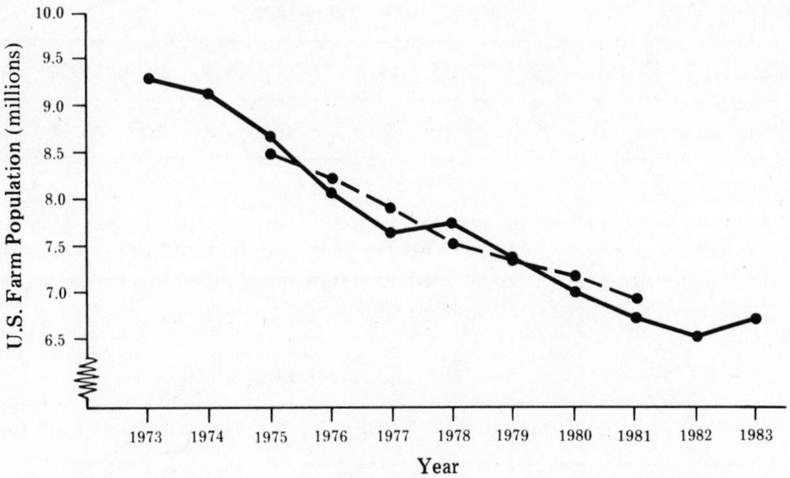

Fig. 18-3

A disadvantage of the moving average is that data is lost at the end and the beginning of the time series. This can be serious when the amount of data is not very large.

ESTIMATION OF TREND

18.6 Using the method of semiaverages, obtain the trend values for the data of Problem 18.2 by taking the average as (a) the mean and (b) the median.

SOLUTION

(a) Divide the data into two equal parts (omitting the middle year, 1978), as shown in Table 18.7. Then compute the mean of the data in each part. From the results obtained it follows that in 6 years (1975 to 1981) there has been a *decrease* of $8.73 - 7.14 = 1.59$ million, for a decrease of $1.59/6 = 0.265$ million per year. By knowing this, we can compute the trend values. Thus the trend values for 1976 and 1977 are, respectively, $8.73 - 0.265 = 8.47$ and $8.73 - 2(0.265) = 8.20$; the trend values for 1974 and 1973 are, respectively, $8.73 + 0.265 = 9.00$ and $8.73 + 2(0.265) = 9.26$; and so forth, as shown in Table 18.8.

The results can also be obtained by drawing the graph of a line connecting the points (1975, 8.73) and (1981, 7.14) and reading the trend values from the graph.

Table 18.7

1973	9.47	1979	7.55
1974	9.26	1980	7.24
1975	8.86	1981	7.01
1976	8.25	1982	6.88
1977	7.81	1983	7.03
	Total 43.65		Total 35.71

Mean = $43.65/5 = 8.73$ (corresponding to 1975)

Mean = $35.71/5 = 7.14$ (corresponding to 1981)

Table 18.8

Year	1973	1974	1975	1976	1977	1978	1979	1980	1981	1982	1983
Trend value	9.26	9.00	8.73	8.47	8.20	7.94	7.67	7.41	7.14	6.88	6.61

(*b*) The medians for each of the two equal parts in part (*a*) are 8.86 and 7.03, respectively. Thus there is a decrease of $(8.86-7.03)/6=0.305$ per year, and the trend values are as shown in Table 18.9.

When medians are used, the method is sometimes called the method of *semimedians.* If the type of average is not specified, the mean is implied.

Table 18.9

Year	1973	1974	1975	1976	1977	1978	1979	1980	1981	1982	1983
Trend value	9.47	9.17	8.86	8.56	8.25	7.95	7.64	7.34	7.03	6.73	6.42

18.7 Describe how to use (*a*) the freehand method and (*b*) the moving-averages method to compute the trend values for the data of Problem 18.2.

SOLUTION

(*a*) Using the freehand method, we simply construct a line or curve that closely approximates the graph in Fig. 18-3, and then we read the trend values from this line or curve.

(*b*) We saw in Problem 18.5 that the 5-year moving average smoothed the time-series data considerably. We can use the averages obtained as the trend values for the years 1975–1981. Thus from Problem 18.2(*a*) we see that the trend values corresponding to 1975, 1976, 1977, etc., are 8.73, 8.44, 8.10, etc. However, using this method makes the trend values unavailable for the years 1973, 1974, 1982, and 1983; if desired, these could be obtained by extrapolation from Fig. 18-3 (the graph of Problem 18.5).

Mathcad **18.8** (*a*) Use the least-squares method to fit a line to the data of Problem 18.2.

(*b*) From the result in part (*a*), find the trend values.

SOLUTION

(*a*) Since the data involve an odd number of years, we use the second method of Problem 13.19, whereby we obtain Table 18.10. Thus the required least-squares line is

$$Y=\bar{Y}+\left(\frac{\sum XY}{\sum X^2}\right)X=\frac{87.37}{11}+\left(\frac{-29.55}{110}\right)X \qquad \text{or} \qquad Y=7.94-0.269X$$

where the origin $X=0$ is the year 1978 and the unit of X is 1 year.

(*b*) Setting $X=-5, -4, -3, \ldots, 5$ in the least-squares equation of part (*a*), we obtain the trend values shown in Table 18.11. The results compare favorably with those of Problem 18.6.

ESTIMATION OF SEASONAL VARIATIONS; THE SEASONAL INDEX

18.9 Table 18.12 shows the monthly electric energy production, in billions of kilowatt-hours (kWh), of utilities in the United States for the years 1976–1981.

(*a*) Construct a graph of the data.

(*b*) Obtain a seasonal index by using the average-percentage method.

Table 18.10

Year	X	Y	X^2	XY
1973	−5	9.47	25	−47.35
1974	−4	9.26	16	−37.04
1975	−3	8.86	9	−26.58
1976	−2	8.25	4	−16.50
1977	−1	7.81	1	−7.81
1978	0	8.01	0	0
1979	1	7.55	1	7.55
1980	2	7.24	4	14.48
1981	3	7.01	9	21.03
1982	4	6.88	16	27.52
1983	5	7.03	25	35.15
		$\sum Y = 87.37$	$\sum X^2 = 110$	$\sum XY = -29.55$

Table 18.11

Year	1973	1974	1975	1976	1977	1978	1979	1980	1981	1982	1983
Trend value	9.28	9.01	8.74	8.47	8.20	7.93	7.66	7.39	7.12	6.85	6.58

Table 18.12

	Jan	Feb	Mar	Apr	May	June	July	Aug	Sep	Oct	Nov	Dec
1976	178.2	156.7	164.2	153.2	157.5	172.6	185.9	185.8	165.0	163.6	169.0	183.1
1977	196.3	162.8	168.6	156.9	168.2	180.2	197.9	195.9	176.0	166.4	166.3	183.9
1978	197.3	173.7	173.2	159.7	175.2	187.4	202.6	205.6	185.6	175.6	176.3	191.7
1979	209.5	186.3	183.0	169.5	178.2	186.7	202.4	204.9	180.6	179.8	177.4	188.9
1980	200.0	188.7	187.5	168.6	175.7	189.4	216.1	215.4	191.5	178.5	178.6	195.6
1981	205.2	179.6	185.4	172.4	177.7	202.7	220.2	210.2	186.9	181.4	175.6	195.6

Source: Survey of Current Business.

SOLUTION

(*a*) See Fig. 18-4.

(*b*) Table 18.13 shows the totals and monthly averages (means) for the years 1976–1981. Dividing the monthly data from Table 18.12 by the corresponding monthly averages for each year from Table 18.13 and expressing the result as a percentage yields the entries in Table 18.14; for example, the first entry is given by $178.2/169.6 = 105.1\%$. The bottom row of Table 18.14 shows the mean percentage for each month; since the total of these percentages is 1200%, no adjustment is necessary, and thus the numbers in this bottom row represent the required seasonal index.

This seasonal index shows that, on average, the electric energy production required is the least in April and the greatest in the summer months, July and August (when air conditioning creates extra demands). The actual production figures for various regions of the country help these regions' utility companies provide sufficient energy for their consumers' needs.

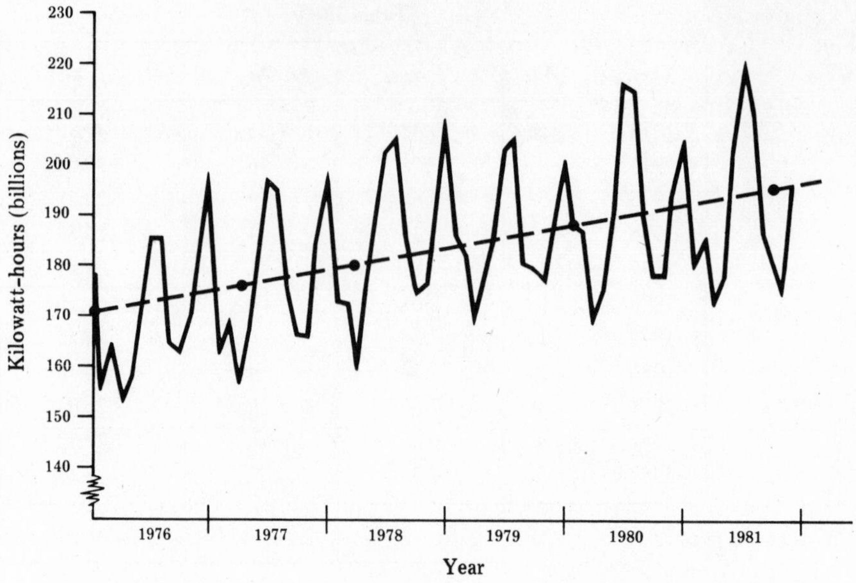

Fig. 18-4. Electric power production by United States utilities, 1976–1981

Table 18.13

Year	1976	1977	1978	1979	1980	1981
Total	2034.8	2119.4	2203.9	2247.2	2285.6	2292.9
Monthly average	169.6	176.6	183.7	187.3	190.5	191.1

Table 18.14

	Jan	Feb	Mar	Apr	May	June	July	Aug	Sep	Oct	Nov	Dec
1976	105.1	92.4	96.8	90.3	92.9	101.8	109.6	109.6	97.3	96.5	99.6	108.0
1977	111.2	92.2	95.5	88.8	95.2	102.0	112.1	110.9	99.7	94.2	94.2	104.1
1978	107.4	94.6	94.3	86.9	95.4	102.0	110.3	111.9	101.0	95.6	96.0	104.4
1979	111.9	99.5	97.7	90.5	95.1	99.7	108.1	109.4	96.4	96.0	94.7	100.9
1980	105.0	99.1	98.4	88.5	92.2	99.4	113.4	113.1	100.5	93.7	93.8	102.7
1981	107.4	94.0	97.0	90.2	93.0	106.1	115.2	110.0	97.8	94.9	91.9	102.4
Total	648.0	571.8	579.7	535.2	563.8	611.0	668.7	664.9	592.7	570.9	570.2	622.5
Mean	108.0	95.3	96.6	89.2	94.0	101.8	111.5	110.8	98.8	95.2	95.0	103.8

18.10 Obtain the seasonal index for Problem 18.9 by using the median instead of the mean.

SOLUTION

The numbers in the January column of Table 18.14, when arranged in increasing order of magnitude, are 105.0, 105.1, 107.4, 107.4, 111.2, and 111.9, whereby the median is $\frac{1}{2}(107.4+107.4) = 107.4$. The medians for the other months are obtained similarly and are shown in the second row of Table 18.15. Since these medians add up to 1198.2, we adjust them by multiplying each number by 1200/1198.2. This yields the numbers in the third row of Table 18.15, which gives the required seasonal index. The results compare favorably with the index obtained by using the mean (in Problem 18.9). In practice, whenever the mean results differ from the median results, it is often best to use the median so that extreme values are eliminated.

Table 18.15

	Jan	Feb	Mar	Apr	May	June	July	Aug	Sep	Oct	Nov	Dec
Median	107.4	94.3	96.9	90.0	94.0	101.9	111.2	110.5	98.8	95.3	94.5	103.4
Seasonal Index	107.6	94.4	97.0	90.1	94.1	102.1	111.4	110.7	98.9	95.4	94.6	103.6

18.11 Obtain a seasonal index for the data of Problem 18.9 by using the percentage trend (or ratio-to-trend) method. In applying this method, use the least-squares method to obtain the monthly trend values.

SOLUTION

From the graph of the actual data (Fig. 18-4) it appears that the long-term trend can be suitably approximated by a straight line. Instead of obtaining this line from the monthly data of Table 18.12, we shall obtain it from the monthly averages for the years 1976–1981, as shown in Table 18.16 (which is taken from Table 18.13). Let us assume that the monthly figures in Table 18.12 correspond to the middle of the month; thus the averages in Table 18.16 correspond to June 30 or July 1 of the corresponding year.

Since there is an even number of years, we use the second method of Problem 13.20, whereby we obtain Table 18.17. The required least-squares line is

$$Y = \bar{Y} + \left(\frac{\sum XY}{\sum X^2}\right)X = \frac{1098.8}{6} + \left(\frac{152.8}{70}\right)X = 183.13 + 2.183X$$

Table 18.16

Year	1976	1977	1978	1979	1980	1981
Monthly average	169.6	176.6	183.7	187.3	190.5	191.1

Table 18.17

Year	X	Y	X^2	XY
1976	−5	169.6	25	−848.0
1977	−3	176.6	9	−529.8
1978	−1	183.7	1	−183.7
1979	1	187.3	1	187.3
1980	3	190.5	9	571.5
1981	5	191.1	25	955.5
		$\sum Y = 1098.8$	$\sum X^2 = 70$	$\sum XY = 152.8$

where X is measured in half-years and the origin is Dec. 31, 1978, or Jan. 1, 1979. From this equation it follows that the values of Y increase by 2.183 every half-year, or by $2.183/6 = 0.3638$ every month. Thus when $X = 0$ (Jan. 1, 1978), $Y = 183.13$. A half-month later (Jan. 15, 1978) the value of Y is $183.13 + \frac{1}{2}(0.3638) = 183.31$. By successively adding 0.3638 to 183.31, we find the trend values for February 1978, March 1978, etc., to be $183.31 + 0.3638 = 183.7$, $183.31 + 2(0.3638) = 184.0$, etc. Similarly, by successively subtracting 0.3638 from 183.31, we find the trend values for December 1977, November 1977, etc., to be $183.13 - 0.3638 = 182.8$, $183.13 - 2(0.3638) = 182.4$, etc. In this manner we obtain the monthly trend values shown in Table 18.18. The least-squares line is shown dashed in Fig. 18-4.

Table 18.18

	Jan	Feb	Mar	Apr	May	June	July	Aug	Sep	Oct	Nov	Dec
1976	170.2	170.6	170.9	171.3	171.7	172.0	172.4	172.8	173.1	173.5	173.9	174.2
1977	174.6	174.9	175.3	175.7	176.0	176.4	176.8	177.1	177.5	177.9	178.2	178.6
1978	178.9	179.3	179.7	180.0	180.4	180.8	181.1	181.5	181.9	182.9	182.6	182.9
1979	183.3	183.7	184.0	184.4	184.8	185.1	185.5	185.9	186.2	186.6	186.9	187.3
1980	187.7	188.0	188.4	188.8	189.1	189.5	189.9	190.2	190.6	190.9	191.3	191.7
1981	192.0	192.4	192.8	193.1	193.5	193.9	194.2	194.6	195.0	195.3	195.7	196.0

Table 18.19

	Jan	Feb	Mar	Apr	May	June	July	Aug	Sep	Oct	Nov	Dec
1976	104.7	91.9	96.1	89.4	91.7	100.3	107.8	107.5	95.3	94.3	97.2	105.1
1977	112.4	93.1	96.2	89.3	95.6	102.2	111.9	110.8	99.2	93.5	93.3	103.0
1978	110.3	96.9	96.4	88.7	97.1	103.7	111.9	113.3	102.0	96.4	96.5	104.8
1979	114.6	101.4	99.5	91.9	96.4	100.9	109.1	110.2	97.0	96.4	94.9	100.9
1980	106.6	100.4	99.7	89.3	92.9	99.9	113.8	113.2	100.5	93.5	93.4	102.0
1981	106.9	93.3	96.2	89.3	91.8	104.5	113.4	108.0	95.8	92.9	89.7	99.8
Mean	109.3	96.2	97.4	89.7	94.3	101.9	111.3	110.5	98.3	94.5	94.2	102.6
Median	108.6	95.1	96.3	89.3	94.3	101.6	111.9	110.5	98.1	93.9	94.2	102.5
Adjusted median	108.9	95.4	96.6	89.6	94.6	101.9	112.2	110.8	98.4	94.2	94.5	102.8

We now divide each of the given monthly values in Table 18.12 by the corresponding trend values in Table 18.18. The results, expressed as percentages, are shown in Table 18.19; for example, the first entry of the table is given by $178.2/170.2 = 104.7\%$.

Since the total of the means in Table 18.19 is 1200.2, which is very close to the required 1200%, no adjustment is needed; consequently, the third row from the bottom of the table represents the seasonal index as determined by the mean. Since the total of the medians is 1196.6, we must adjust them; to do this, we multiply each one by 1200/1196.6, thus obtaining the bottom row of Table 18.19, which shows the required seasonal index as determined by the median. We see that there is good agreement in Table 18.19 between the means and the adjusted medians. These results also agree well with those of Problems 18.9(b) and 18.10.

Mathcad **18.12** Obtain a seasonal index for the data of Problem 18.9 by using the percentage moving-average (or ratio-to-moving-average) method.

SOLUTION

Using the second method of Problem 18.3, we first obtain a 12-month centered moving average, as shown in Table 18.20. These results are graphed in Fig. 18-5; note that the seasonal pattern has been removed, thus smoothing the graph considerably.

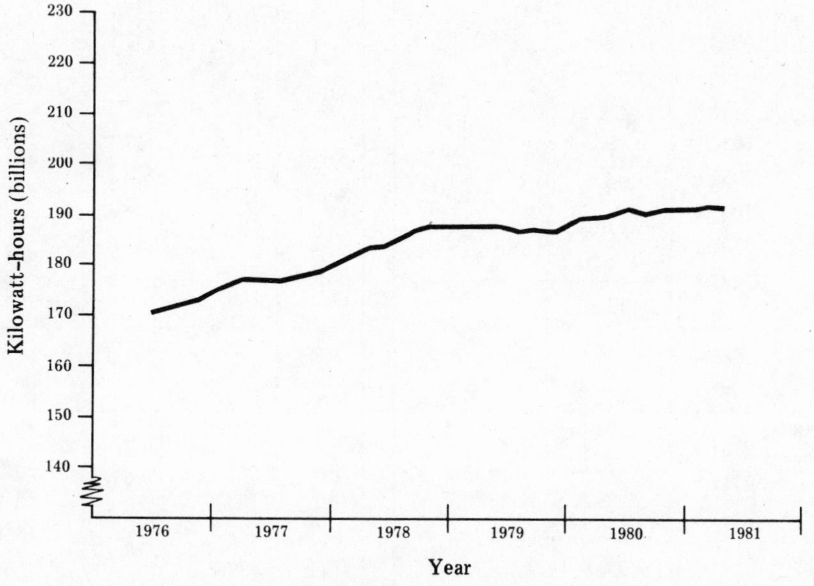

Fig. 18-5. 12-month centered moving average

We now divide each of the actual monthly values by the corresponding 12-month centered moving average and express each result as a percentage; for July 1976, for example, we obtain $185.9/170.3 = 109.2\%$. The results are shown in Table 18.21. Note that the entries for the first 6 months of 1976 and for the last 6 months of 1981 are not available by this method.

Table 18.21 gives the average percentage for each month in terms of both the mean and the median. Whereas the means (which total 1200.2) have not been adjusted in the table, the medians (which total 1198.9) have been. Thus the first and third of the table's bottom three rows represent the seasonal indexes obtained by using the mean and the median, respectively. These indexes agree well with each other and with the indexes obtained by other methods in the previous problems.

18.13 Obtain a seasonal index for the data of Problem 18.9 by using the link-relative method.

SOLUTION

We first express the data for each month as a percentage of the data for the previous month, as shown in Table 18.22. Each of these percentages is called a *link relative.* For example, to obtain the entries for

Table 18.20

Year and Month	Data	12-Month Moving Total	2-Month Moving Total of Column 3	12-Month Centered Moving Average (Col. 4 ÷ 24)
1976				
Jan	178.2			
Feb	156.7			
Mar	164.2			
Apr	153.2			
May	157.5			
June	172.6			
		2034.8		
July	185.9		4087.7	170.3
		2052.9		
Aug	185.8		4111.9	171.3
		2059.0		
Sep	165.0		4122.4	171.8
		2063.4		
Oct	163.6		4130.5	172.1
		2067.1		
Nov	169.0		4144.9	172.7
		2077.8		
Dec	183.1		4163.2	173.5
1977		2085.4		
Jan	196.3		4182.8	174.3
		2097.4		
Feb	162.8		4204.9	175.2
		2107.5		
Mar	168.6		4226.0	176.1
		2118.5		
Apr	156.9		4239.8	176.7
		2121.3		
May	168.2		4239.9	176.7
		2118.6		
June	180.2		4238.0	176.6
		2119.4		
July	197.9		4239.8	176.7
		2120.4		
Aug	195.9		4251.7	177.2
		2131.3		
Sep	176.0		4267.2	177.8
		2135.9		
Oct	166.4		4274.6	178.1
		2138.7		
Nov	166.3		4284.4	178.5
		2145.7		
Dec	183.9		4298.6	179.1
1978		2152.9		
Jan	197.3		4310.5	179.6
		2157.6		
Feb	173.7		4324.9	180.2
		2167.3		
Mar	173.2		4344.2	181.0
		2176.9		
Apr	159.7		4363.0	181.8
		2186.1		
May	175.2		4382.2	182.6
		2196.1		
June	187.4		4400.0	183.3
		2203.9		
July	202.6		4420.0	184.2
		2216.1		
Aug	205.6		4444.8	185.2
		2228.7		
Sep	185.6		4467.2	186.1
		2238.5		
Oct	175.6		4486.8	187.0
		2248.3		
Nov	176.3		4499.6	187.5
		2251.3		
Dec	191.7		4501.9	187.6
1979		2250.6		
Jan	209.5		4501.0	187.5
		2250.4		
Feb	186.3		4500.1	187.5
		2249.7		
Mar	183.0		4494.4	187.3
		2244.7		
Apr	169.5		4493.6	187.2
		2248.9		
May	178.2		4498.9	187.5
		2250.0		
June	186.7		4497.2	187.4
		2247.2		
July	202.4		4484.9	186.9
		2237.7		
Aug	204.9		4477.8	186.6
		2240.1		
Sep	180.6		4484.7	186.9
		2244.6		
Oct	179.8		4488.3	187.0
		2243.7		
Nov	177.4		4484.9	186.9
		2241.2		
Dec	188.9		4485.1	186.9
1980		2243.9		
Jan	200.0		4501.5	187.6
		2257.6		
Feb	188.7		4525.7	188.6
		2268.1		
Mar	187.5		4547.1	189.5
		2279.0		
Apr	168.6		4556.7	189.9
		2277.7		
May	175.7		4556.6	189.9
		2278.9		
June	189.4		4564.5	190.2
		2285.6		
July	216.1		4576.4	190.7
		2290.8		
Aug	215.4		4572.5	190.5
		2281.7		
Sep	191.5		4561.3	190.1
		2279.6		
Oct	178.5		4563.0	190.1
		2283.4		
Nov	178.6		4568.8	190.4
		2285.4		
Dec	195.6		4584.1	191.0
1981		2298.7		
Jan	205.2		4601.5	191.7
		2302.8		
Feb	179.6		4600.4	191.7
		2297.6		
Mar	185.4		4590.6	191.3
		2293.0		
Apr	172.4		4588.9	191.2
		2295.9		
May	177.7		4588.8	191.2
		2292.9		
June	202.7		4585.8	191.1
		2292.9		
July	202.2			
Aug	210.2			
Sep	186.9			
Oct	181.4			
Nov	175.6			
Dec	195.6			

Table 18.21

	Jan	Feb	Mar	Apr	May	June	July	Aug	Sep	Oct	Nov	Dec
1976							109.2	108.5	96.0	95.1	97.9	105.5
1977	112.6	92.9	95.7	88.8	95.2	102.0	112.0	110.6	99.0	93.4	93.2	102.7
1978	109.9	96.4	95.7	87.8	95.9	102.2	110.0	111.0	99.7	93.9	94.0	102.2
1979	111.7	99.4	97.7	90.5	95.0	99.6	108.3	109.8	96.6	96.1	94.9	101.1
1980	106.6	100.1	98.9	88.8	92.5	99.6	113.3	113.1	100.7	93.9	93.8	102.4
1981	107.0	93.7	96.9	90.2	92.9	106.1						
Mean	109.6	96.5	97.0	89.2	94.3	101.9	110.6	110.6	98.4	94.5	94.8	102.8
Median	109.9	96.4	96.9	88.8	95.0	102.0	110.0	110.6	99.0	93.9	94.0	102.4
Adjusted Median	110.0	96.5	97.0	88.9	95.1	102.1	110.1	110.7	99.1	94.0	94.1	102.5

February and March 1976, we use the data from Problem 18.9 to get

$$\text{Link relative for February 1976} = \frac{\text{value for February 1976}}{\text{value for January 1976}} = \frac{156.7}{178.2} = 87.9\%$$

$$\text{Link relative for March 1976} = \frac{\text{value for March 1976}}{\text{value for February 1976}} = \frac{164.2}{156.7} = 104.8\%$$

The bottom two rows of Table 18.22 show the averages of the link relatives for each month that we obtain by using the mean and the median, respectively, we see that these mean and median results agree very well.

Table 18.22

	Jan	Feb	Mar	Apr	May	June	July	Aug	Sep	Oct	Nov	Dec
1976		87.9	104.8	93.3	102.8	109.6	107.7	99.9	88.8	99.2	103.3	108.3
1977	107.2	82.9	103.6	93.1	107.2	107.1	109.8	99.0	89.8	94.5	99.9	110.6
1978	107.3	88.0	99.7	92.2	109.7	107.0	108.1	101.5	90.3	94.6	100.4	108.7
1979	109.3	88.9	98.2	92.6	105.1	104.8	108.4	101.2	88.1	99.6	98.7	106.5
1980	105.9	94.4	99.4	89.9	104.2	107.8	114.1	99.7	88.9	93.2	100.1	109.5
1981	104.9	87.5	103.2	93.0	103.1	114.1	108.6	95.5	88.9	97.1	96.8	111.4
Mean	106.9	88.3	101.5	92.4	105.4	108.4	109.5	99.5	89.1	96.4	99.9	109.2
Median	107.2	88.0	101.5	92.8	104.7	107.5	108.5	99.8	88.9	95.9	100.0	109.1

Consider January as having the value 100% (see Table 18.23). Since the average link relative for February is 88.0 (using the median value in Table 18.22), the data for February are, on the average, 88.0% of the data for January (i.e., 88.0% of 100.0 = 88.0); similarly, the average link relative for March is 101.5% of that for February (i.e., 101.5% of 88.0 = 89.3); etc. Continuing in this manner, we obtain Table 18.23, whose entries are sometimes called *chain relatives.*

At the right-hand side of Table 18.23, the result for the second January is 100.7, an increase of 0.7

over that of the first January. This increase is due to the long-term trend in the data. To adjust for this trend, we must subtract $(12/12)(0.7) = 0.7$ from the second January's 100.7 (making it 100.0), subtract $(11/12)(0.7) = 0.64$ from the December value, subtract $(10/12)(0.7) = 0.58$ from the November value, etc. The values adjusted for trend are shown in Table 18.24. [Strictly speaking, we should *multiply* the entries from right to left, respectively, by $(100.0/100.7)^{12/12}$, $(100.0/100.7)^{11/12}$, $(100.0/100.7)^{10/12}$, etc.; this, however, yields practically the same results as in Table 18.24.] Since the percentages in Table 18.24 total 1094.5, we adjust them by multiplying each percentage by 1200/1094.5, and we thus obtain the seasonal index shown in Table 18.25.

Table 18.23

Jan	Feb	Mar	Apr	May	June	July	Aug	Sep	Oct	Nov	Dec	Jan
100.0	88.0	89.3	82.9	86.8	93.3	101.2	101.0	89.8	86.1	86.1	93.9	100.7

Table 18.24

Jan	Feb	Mar	Apr	May	June	July	Aug	Sep	Oct	Nov	Dec
100.0	87.9	89.2	82.7	86.6	93.0	100.8	100.6	89.3	85.6	85.5	93.3

Table 18.25

	Jan	Feb	Mar	Apr	May	June	July	Aug	Sep	Oct	Nov	Dec
Seasonal index	109.6	96.4	97.8	90.7	94.9	102.0	110.5	110.3	97.9	93.9	93.7	102.3

18.14 Construct a table comparing the seasonal indexes obtained by all the methods of Problems 18.9, 18.11, 18.12, and 18.13.

SOLUTION

See Table 18.26, which shows the seasonal indexes obtained by using the median.

Table 18.26

Method	Jan	Feb	Mar	Apr	May	June	July	Aug	Sep	Oct	Nov	Dec
Average percentage (Problem 18.9)	107.6	94.4	97.0	90.1	94.1	102.1	111.4	110.7	98.9	95.4	94.6	103.6
Ratio to trend (Problem 18.11)	108.9	95.4	96.6	89.6	94.6	101.9	112.2	110.8	98.4	94.2	94.5	102.8
Ratio to moving average (Problem 18.12)	110.0	96.5	97.0	88.9	95.1	102.1	110.1	110.7	99.1	94.0	94.1	102.5
Link relative (Problem 18.13)	109.6	96.4	97.8	90.7	94.9	102.0	110.5	110.3	97.9	93.9	93.7	102.3

DESEASONALIZATION OF DATA

Mathcad **18.15** Adjust the data of Problem 18.9 for seasonal variation; that is, deseasonalize the data.

SOLUTION

To adjust the data for seasonal variation, we must divide every entry in the original data of Problem 18.9 by the seasonal index of the corresponding month, as found by any of the above methods. For example, if we used the seasonal index of Problem 18.12 (i.e., the ratio-to-moving-average method), we would divide all January values by 110.0% (i.e., 1.100), all February values by 96.5% (i.e., 0.965), etc. The resulting deseasonalized data are shown in Table 18.27.

Table 18.27

	Jan	Feb	Mar	Apr	May	June	July	Aug	Sep	Oct	Nov	Dec
1976	160.5	162.4	169.3	172.3	165.6	169.0	168.8	167.8	166.5	174.0	179.6	178.6
1977	178.5	168.7	173.8	176.5	176.9	176.5	179.7	177.0	177.6	177.0	176.7	179.4
1978	179.4	180.0	178.6	179.6	184.2	183.5	184.0	185.7	187.3	186.8	187.4	187.0
1979	190.5	193.1	188.7	190.7	187.4	182.9	183.8	185.1	182.2	191.3	188.5	184.3
1980	181.8	195.5	193.3	189.7	184.8	185.5	196.3	194.6	193.2	189.9	189.8	190.8
1981	186.5	186.1	191.1	193.9	186.9	198.5	200.0	189.9	188.6	193.0	186.6	190.8

18.16 (*a*) Graph the deseasonalized data obtained in Problem 18.15.
(*b*) Compare this graph with Fig. 18-4 of Problem 18.9(*a*).

SOLUTION

(*a*) See Fig. 18-6.

(*b*) The graph of the seasonally adjusted data shows the long-term trend, which, apart from its fluctuations, approximates a straight line. If we denote the data of Problem 18.9 by $Y = TCSI$, then the graph in Fig. 18-6 is that of the variable $Y/S = TCI$ plotted against time t and thus contains the long-term trend, cyclic, and irregular movements. Since the graph indicates a long-term trend with little cyclic and irregular patterning, it appears that the product CI of the cyclic and irregular factors must be nearly 100%. (Problem 18.18 confirms that this is indeed the case.)

ESTIMATION OF CYCLIC AND IRREGULAR VARIATIONS

Mathcad **18.17** Adjust the data of Problem 18.16 for trend.

SOLUTION

To remove the trend from the data of Problem 18.16, divide each entry by the corresponding monthly trend value computed by any of the above methods. Let's use the monthly trend values obtained in Problem 18.12 by the moving-averages method. The results are shown in Table 18.28. To obtain the entry for July 1976, for example, we divide the corresponding entry in Table 18.27, which is 168.8, by the value 170.3 (see the first entry in column 5 of Table 18.20), which gives us $168.8/170.3 = 99.1\%$. The remaining entries are obtained in a similar manner. A disadvantage of this method, as with all methods involving moving averages, is that the data at both ends of the time series are lost.

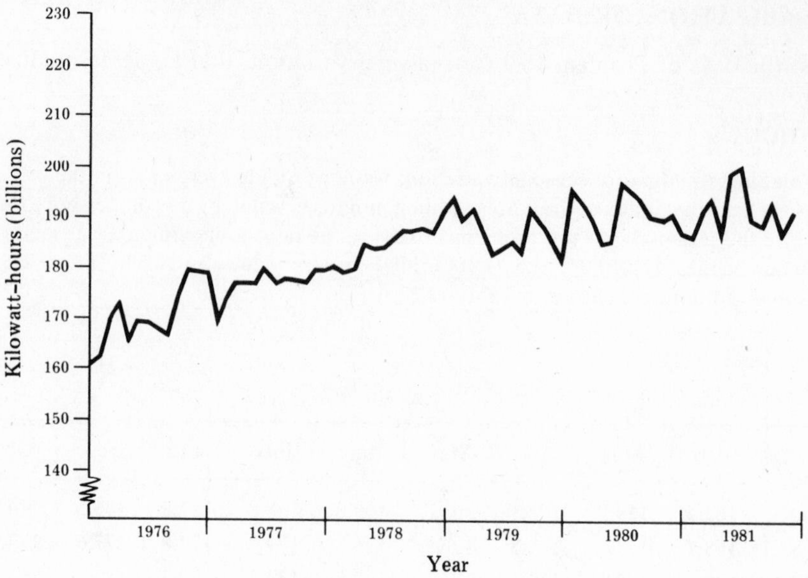

Fig. 18-6. Seasonally adjusted data

18.18 (*a*) Graph the data obtained in Problem 18.17.

(*b*) Explain the significance of this graph.

SOLUTION

(*a*) It is convenient to subtract 100(%) from the data of Problem 18.17 and to graph the resulting deviations. This graph, using a greatly magnified vertical scale, is shown in Fig. 18-7.

(*b*) The original data are represented by $Y = TCSI$. Adjusting for seasonal variation (as in Problem 18.15) amounts to dividing both sides by the seasonal index S, thus obtaining $Y/S = TCI$. Subsequent adjustment for trend amounts to dividing by T, thus obtaining $Y/ST = CI$. Subtracting 100(%) gives $(Y/ST) - 100 = CI - 100$. Thus the dependent variable in Fig. 18-7 is $(Y/ST) - 100$, and the independent variable is time t.

The graph of Fig. 18-7 is theoretically composed only of the cyclic and irregular movements C and I. Note that the product CI varies between 96% and 104%, confirming the conclusion reached in Problem 18.16(*b*).

Table 18.28

	Jan	Feb	Mar	Apr	May	June	July	Aug	Sep	Oct	Nov	Dec
1976							99.1	98.0	96.9	101.1	104.0	102.9
1977	102.4	96.3	98.7	99.9	100.1	100.0	101.7	99.9	99.9	99.4	99.0	100.2
1978	99.9	99.9	98.7	98.8	100.9	100.1	99.9	100.3	100.6	99.6	99.9	99.7
1979	101.6	103.0	100.7	101.9	99.9	97.6	98.3	99.2	97.5	102.3	100.9	98.6
1980	96.9	103.7	102.0	99.9	97.3	97.5	102.9	102.2	101.6	99.9	99.7	99.9
1981	97.3	97.1	99.9	101.4	97.8	103.9						

18.19 (*a*) Obtain the 3-month and 7-month moving averages of the data in Problem 18.17.

(*b*) Construct the graphs of the moving averages of part (*a*).

(*c*) Interpret the graphs.

SOLUTION

(*a*) The required moving averages are shown in Table 18.29.

(*b*) The graphs of the 3- and 7-month moving averages are shown in Figs. 18-8 and 18-9, respectively.

Table 18.29

Year and Month	Data	3-Month Moving Total	3-Month Moving Average	7-Month Moving Total	7-Month Moving Average
1976					
July	91.1				
Aug	98.0	294.0	98.0		
Sep	96.9	296.0	98.7		
Oct	101.1	302.0	100.7	704.4	100.6
Nov	104.0	308.0	102.7	701.6	100.2
Dec	102.9	309.3	103.1	702.3	100.3
1977					
Jan	102.4	301.6	100.5	705.3	100.8
Feb	96.3	297.4	99.1	704.3	100.6
Mar	98.7	294.9	98.3	700.3	100.0
Apr	99.9	298.7	99.6	699.1	99.9
May	100.1	300.0	100.0	704.7	100.7
June	100.0	301.8	100.6	700.2	100.0
July	101.7	301.6	100.5	700.9	100.1
Aug	99.9	301.5	100.5	700.0	100.0
Sep	99.9	299.2	99.7	700.1	100.0
Oct	99.4	298.3	99.4	700.0	100.0
Nov	99.0	298.6	99.5	698.2	99.7
Dec	100.2	299.1	99.7	697.0	99.6
1978					
Jan	99.9	300.0	100.0	695.9	99.4
Feb	99.9	298.5	99.5	697.4	99.6
Mar	98.7	297.4	99.1	698.5	99.8
Apr	98.8	298.4	99.5	698.2	99.7
May	100.9	299.8	99.9	698.6	99.8
June	100.1	300.9	100.3	699.3	99.9
July	99.9	300.3	100.1	700.5	100.1
Aug	100.3	300.8	100.3	701.6	100.2
Sep	100.6	300.8	100.3	700.4	100.1
Oct	99.9	300.4	100.1	701.9	100.3
Nov	99.9	299.5	99.8	705.0	100.7
Dec	99.7	301.2	100.4	705.4	100.8

Table 18.29 (continued)

Year and Month	Data	3-Month Moving Total	3-Month Moving Average	7-Month Moving Total	7-Month Moving Average
1979					
Jan	101.6	304.3	101.4	706.7	101.0
Feb	103.0	305.3	101.8	706.7	101.0
Mar	100.7	305.6	101.9	704.4	100.6
Apr	101.9	302.5	100.8	703.0	100.4
May	99.9	299.4	99.8	700.6	100.1
June	97.6	295.8	98.6	695.1	99.3
July	98.3	295.1	98.4	696.7	99.5
Aug	99.2	295.0	98.3	695.7	99.4
Sep	97.5	299.0	99.7	694.4	99.2
Oct	102.3	300.7	100.2	693.7	99.1
Nov	100.9	301.8	100.6	699.1	99.9
Dec	98.6	296.4	98.8	701.9	100.3
1980					
Jan	96.9	299.2	99.7	704.3	100.6
Feb	103.7	302.6	100.9	699.3	99.9
Mar	102.0	305.6	101.9	695.9	99.4
Apr	99.9	299.2	99.7	700.2	100.0
May	97.3	294.7	98.2	705.5	100.8
June	97.5	297.7	99.2	703.4	100.5
July	102.9	302.6	100.9	701.3	100.2
Aug	102.2	306.7	102.2	701.1	100.2
Sep	101.6	303.7	101.2	703.7	100.5
Oct	99.9	301.2	100.4	703.5	100.5
Nov	99.7	299.5	99.8	697.7	99.7
Dec	99.9	296.9	99.0	695.4	99.3
1981					
Jan	97.3	294.3	98.1	695.2	99.3
Feb	97.1	294.3	98.1	693.1	99.0
Mar	99.9	298.4	99.5	696.8	99.5
Apr	101.4	299.1	99.7		
May	97.8	303.1	101.0		
June	103.9				

(*c*) As is to be expected, the moving averages serve to smooth out the irregularities in the data of Problem 18.17, as we can see by comparing Figs. 18-8 and 18-9 with Fig. 18-7. It is also clear from the graphs that the 7-month moving average provides better smoothing of the data in this case than does the 3-month moving average. All the fluctuations for the 3-month moving average are less than about 3%, while those for the 7-month average are less than 1%.

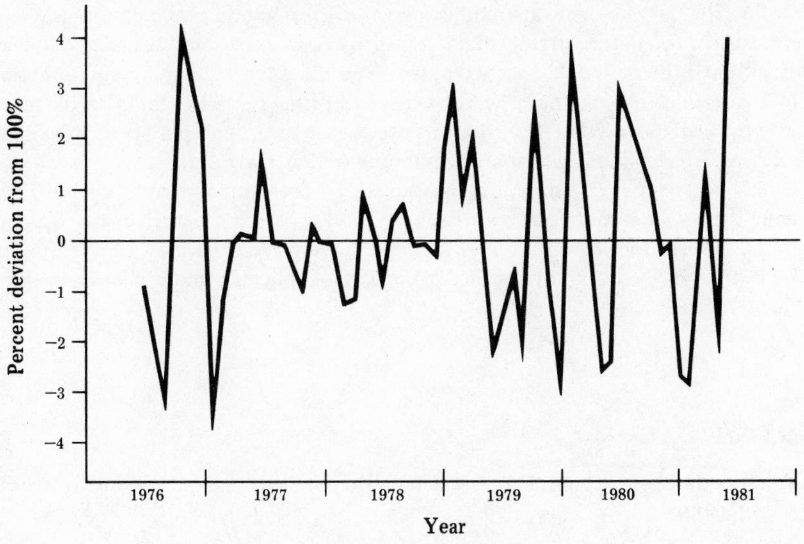

Fig. 18-7. Cyclical and irregular variations

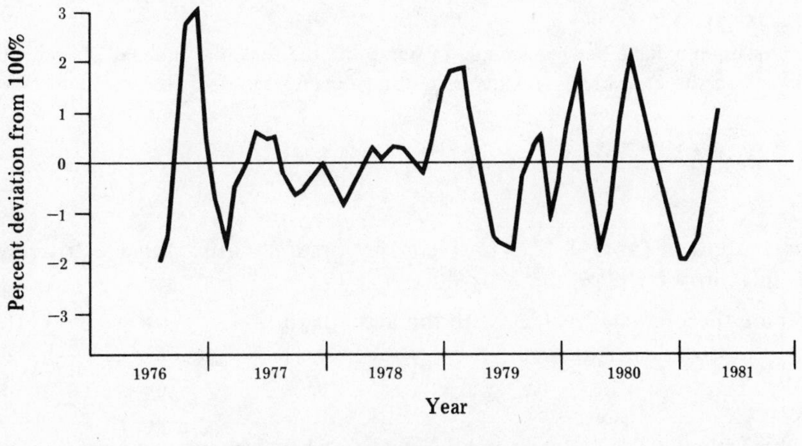

Fig. 18-8. 3-Month moving average

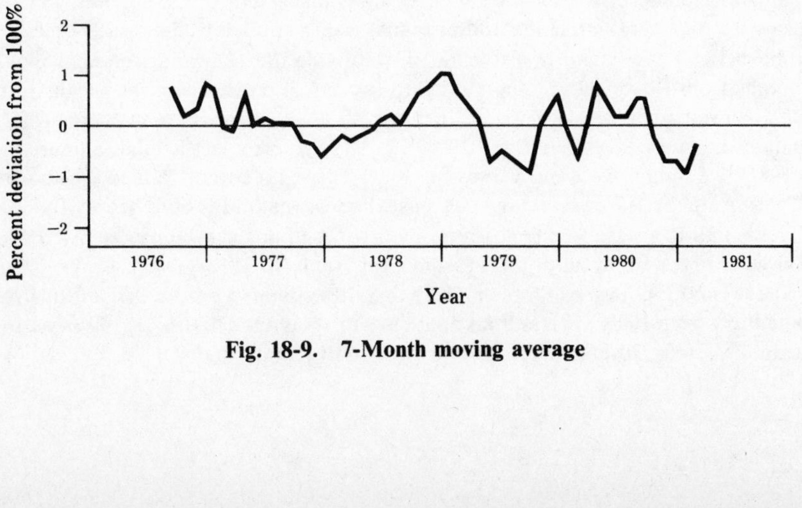

Fig. 18-9. 7-Month moving average

Ordinarily, this problem's method is used for investigating cyclic patterns. We would expect this to be the case, for if the original data (given by $Y = TCSI$) are adjusted for trend and seasonal variations, then the new data that we obtain would (at least theoretically) contain only cyclic and irregular variations. A suitable moving average can thus serve to eliminate irregularities and reveal whatever cyclic pattern exists. For this purpose, a 12-month centered moving average is perhaps best, since it eliminates residual seasonal variation as well as irregularities.

In this problem no cyclic effect appears to be present; or if it is present, it is negligible. In economic theory we often require as much as 20 years of data before cycles make their appearance (see Fig. 18-1). The fact that the 3- and 7-month moving averages show peaks around December 1978 and December 1979—but a low in December 1980—indicates that a change in the seasonal pattern may be taking place.

COMPARABILITY OF DATA

18.20 How should the data of Problem 18.9 be modified in order to make allowances for the leap years 1976 and 1980?

SOLUTION

In a leap year, February has 29 days instead of the usual 28 days. To achieve comparability, we would multiply the data for a leap-year February by 28/29. Thus in Table 18.12 of Problem 18.9 we would replace the value for February 1976 with $(28/29)(156.7) = 151.3$ and would replace the value for February 1980 with $(28/29)(188.7) = 182.2$.

These adjustments have not been made in obtaining the seasonal indexes of Problems 18.9 to 18.13, but their effects on these problems' results would have been negligible (see Problem 18.54).

FORECASTING

Mathcad **18.21** (*a*) Using the data in Table 18.12 of Problem 18.9, predict the monthly electric energy production of utilities in the United States for the year 1982.

(*b*) Compare the predicted values with the actual values.

SOLUTION

(*a*) The future monthly values are given by $Y = TCSI$, where we must estimate T, C, S, and I.

We can estimate the trend T by any of several methods. From Fig. 18-6 of Problem 18.16 it appears that we should be able to get fairly accurate estimates of future trend values by fitting a straight line to the trend values for the last 2 years, for example. This could be done by using the least-squares method or any of the other methods discussed in this chapter. Let's obtain the trend values by the relatively simple method of semiaverages applied to the results obtained in Table 18.20 of Problem 18.12. As shown in Table 18.30, we divide the 12-month centered moving averages for the months from July 1979 to June 1981 into two equal parts. From the means of the data in each part, it follows that there has been an increase of $190.9 - 188.1 = 2.8$ in 12 months, or $2.8/12 = 0.23$ per month; by successively adding 0.23 to 191.1 (the table's last available figure, corresponding to June 1981), we obtain the trend values for 1982. These 1982 trend values are shown in Table 18.31.

To estimate the seasonal factor S, let's use the seasonal index obtained in Table 18.21 of Problem 18.12 (although the seasonal index found by other methods can be used as well). For convenience, this seasonal index from Table 18.21 is shown in Table 18.31.

We see from Fig. 18-8 of Problem 18.19 that the estimated product CI of the cyclic and irregular factors differs from 100% by less than 5%. Thus if we assume that $CI = 100\% = 1$ (i.e., $Y = TS$), the cyclic and irregular factors should not throw us off by more than 5% in Y.

Table 18.30

July 1979	186.9	July 1980	190.7
Aug 1979	186.6	Aug 1980	190.5
Sep 1979	186.9	Sep 1980	190.1
Oct 1979	187.0	Oct 1980	190.1
Nov 1979	186.9	Nov 1980	190.4
Dec 1979	186.9	Dec 1980	191.0
Jan 1980	187.6	Jan 1981	191.7
Feb 1980	188.6	Feb 1981	191.7
Mar 1980	189.5	Mar 1981	191.3
Apr 1980	189.9	Apr 1981	191.2
May 1980	189.9	May 1981	191.2
June 1980	190.2	June 1981	191.1
Total	2256.9	Total	2291.0
Mean	188.1	Mean	190.9

Table 18.31

	Jan	Feb	Mar	Apr	May	June	July	Aug	Sep	Oct	Nov	Dec
1981 trend value (T)						191.1	191.3	191.6	191.8	192.0	192.3	192.5
1982 trend value (T)	192.7	193.0	193.2	193.4	193.6	193.9	194.1	194.3	194.6	194.8	195.0	195.2
Seasonal index (S%)	110.0	96.5	97.0	88.9	95.1	102.1	110.1	110.7	99.1	94.0	94.1	102.5
1982 predicted energy (TS)	212.0	186.2	187.4	171.9	184.1	198.0	213.7	215.1	192.8	183.1	183.5	200.1

Finally, multiplying the values of T for 1982 by the corresponding values of S (expressed as percentages, remember), we obtain the predicted monthly values, or *projections*, for 1982; these are shown in the bottom row of Table 18.31. For example, the predicted value for June 1982 is $(193.9)(102.1\%) = (193.9)(1.021) = 198.0$.

(*b*) The predicted monthly values for the year 1982 (shown in the bottom row of Table 18.31) agree well with the actual values shown in Table 18.32 for the early part of 1982, but for the latter part of 1982 they do not agree well. These discrepancies can be attributed to our assumption in part (*a*) that we should be able to use a straight line to estimate the trend values for 1982, whereas Fig. 18-5 shows that there seems to be a downtrend. Another potential source of error is a possible change in the seasonal pattern (see the remark at the end of Problem 18.19).

Table 18.32

	Jan	Feb	Mar	Apr	May	June	July	Aug	Sep	Oct	Nov	Dec
1982 actual energy	210.1	180.3	187.7	172.6	177.1	186.1	210.6	205.7	180.7	173.0	173.4	184.7

Source: Survey of Current Business.

We can improve the forecast's accuracy by using a *least-squares parabola* (see Problems 18.40 and 18.67) to fit the monthly averages in Table 18.13 of Problem 18.9. Table 18.33 shows both the actual values for 1982 and the predicted values obtained by using a least-squares parabola. The results are better than those given in Table 18.31, for as the bottom row of Table 18.33 shows, the percentage errors do not exceed 5%.

Table 18.33

	Jan	Feb	Mar	Apr	May	June	July	Aug	Sep	Oct	Nov	Dec
1982 actual power	210.1	180.3	187.7	172.6	177.1	186.1	210.6	205.7	180.7	173.0	173.4	184.7
1982 predicted power	210.1	184.3	185.0	169.6	181.3	194.5	209.6	210.6	188.4	178.2	178.3	194.0
Percentage error	0.0%	2.2%	1.4%	1.7%	2.4%	4.5%	0.5%	2.4%	4.3%	3.2%	3.0%	5.0%

Supplementary Problems

CHARACTERISTIC MOVEMENTS OF TIME SERIES

18.22 With which characteristic movements of a time series would you mainly associate (*a*) a recession, (*b*) an increase in employment during the summer months, (*c*) the decline in the death rate due to advances in science, (*d*) a steel strike, and (*e*) a continually increasing demand for smaller automobiles?

MOVING AVERAGES

18.23 Given the numbers 1, 0, −1, 0, 1, 0, −1, 0, and 1, determine a moving average of order (*a*) 2, (*b*) 3, (*c*) 4, and (*d*) 5.

18.24 Prove that if a sequence of numbers has period N (i.e., the sequence repeats itself after N terms), then every moving average of an order less than N has period N. Illustrate this with reference to Problem 18.23.

18.25 (*a*) In Problem 18.24, what happens in the case of a moving average of order N?

(*b*) What happens if the order is greater than N? Illustrate this with reference to Problem 18.23.

18.26 Prove that if every number in a sequence is increased (or decreased) by a constant, the moving average is also increased (or decreased) by this constant.

18.27 Prove that if every number in a sequence is multiplied (or divided) by a nonzero constant, the moving average is also multiplied (or divided) by this constant.

18.28 Find the weighted moving average of the numbers in Problem 18.23, parts (*b*), (*c*), and (*d*), if the respective weights are (*b*) 1, 2, and 1; (*c*) 1, 2, 2, and 1; and (*d*) 1, 2, 2, 2, and 1. Compare these results with those of Problem 18.23.

18.29 (*a*) Prove the properties in Problems 18.26 and 18.27 for weighted moving averages.

(*b*) Does the result of Problem 18.24 hold for weighted moving averages?

18.30 A sequence has (*a*) 24, (*b*) 25, and (*c*) 200 numbers. How many numbers will there be in a moving average of order 5?

18.31 A sequence has M numbers.

(*a*) Prove that in a moving average of order N there will be $M-N+1$ numbers. Illustrate this with several examples, using different values of M and N.

(*b*) Discuss the case where $M=N$.

18.32 Table 18.34 shows the average monthly U.S. production (in thousands) of new passenger cars for the years 1976–1985. Construct (*a*) a 2-year moving average, (*b*) a 2-year centered moving average, (*c*) a 3-year moving average, (*d*) a 4-year centered moving average, and (*e*) a 6-year centered moving average.

Table 18.34

Year	1976	1977	1978	1979	1980	1981	1982	1983	1984	1985
Average monthly U.S. production of new cars (thousands)	708	767	764	702	533	521	421	562	635	667

Source: Survey of Current Business.

18.33 Graph the moving averages of Problem 18.32 together with the original data, and discuss the results obtained.

18.34 (*a*) Show that the 2-year centered moving average of Problem 18.32(*b*) is equivalent to a 3-year weighted moving average with weights 1, 2, and 1, respectively. Illustrate this by direct numerical calculation.

(*b*) Show that the 6-year centered moving average of Problem 18.32(*e*) is equivalent to a suitable weighted moving average.

18.35 (*a*) For the data of Problem 18.32, determine a weighted moving average of order 3 if the weights 1, 4, and 1 are used.

(*b*) Graph this moving average, and compare the results obtained with those of Problem 18.32(*c*).

18.36 Table 18.35 shows the total monthly U.S. production (in millions of pounds) of all kinds of cheese during the years 1983–1985. Construct (*a*) a 12-month moving average, (*b*) a 12-month centered moving average, and (*c*) a 6-month centered moving average. In parts (*b*) and (*c*), graph the moving average together with the original data, and compare the results.

Table 18.35

	Jan	Feb	Mar	Apr	May	June	July	Aug	Sep	Oct	Nov	Dec
1983	375	353	417	408	429	436	401	381	375	392	388	420
1984	387	369	413	415	437	420	388	369	349	378	372	392
1985	391	355	412	430	456	442	439	423	400	428	412	438

Source: Survey of Current Business.

ESTIMATION OF TREND

18.37 Using the method of semiaverages, obtain the trend values for the data of Problem 18.32 by taking the average as (*a*) the mean and (*b*) the median. Construct a graph illustrating the results obtained.

18.38 Work Problem 18.32 by using (*a*) the freehand method and (*b*) a moving average of suitable order. Compare the results obtained with those of Problem 18.37.

18.39 (*a*) Use the least-squares method to fit a line to the data of Problem 18.32.

(*b*) From the result in part (*a*), find the trend values, and compare these with the results in Problems 18.35 and 18.36.

18.40 (*a*) Fit a parabola $Y = a_0 + a_1X + a_2X^2$ to the data of Problem 18.9, using the monthly averages in Table 18.13 of Problem 8.10.

(*b*) Compare the result in part (*a*) with the least-squares line of Problem 18.10, and compute the trend values.

18.41 Obtain trend values for the data of Problem 18.36 by using (*a*) the method of semiaverages, (*b*) the freehand method, (*c*) a 12-month centered moving average, and (*d*) a suitable least-squares curve (to determine this, use the graph of the original data constructed in Problem 18.36). Discuss the advantages and disadvantages of each method.

ESTIMATION OF SEASONAL VARIATIONS; THE SEASONAL INDEX

18.42 Table 18.36 shows the monthly U.S. production (in thousands) of room air conditioners during the years 1980–1985.

(*a*) Graph the data.

(*b*) Construct a seasonal index by using the average-percentage method. Before obtaining this index, adjust the data for leap years.

Table 18.36

	Jan	Feb	Mar	Apr	May	June	July	Aug	Sep	Oct	Nov	Dec
1980	203	342	434	416	344	316	566	94	66	90	125	203
1981	222	366	623	603	477	653	283	64	52	90	94	163
1982	191	361	572	517	419	289	145	61	17	31	71	84
1983	88	130	309	259	300	265	306	108	58	32	52	98
1984	168	262	504	459	588	648	187	47	40	36	51	113
1985	209	277	530	524	632	416	171	68	49	24	39	113

Source: Survey of Current Business.

18.43 Obtain a seasonal index for the data of Problem 18.42 by using the percentage trend (or ratio-to-trend) method. To obtain the trend values, fit a suitable least-squares curve to the monthly averages of the given years.

18.44 Obtain a seasonal index for the data of Problem 18.42 by using the percentage moving-average (or ratio-to-moving-average) method.

18.45 Obtain a seasonal index for the data of Problem 18.42 by using the link-relative method.

18.46 Compare the results obtained in Problems 18.42 to 18.45.

18.47 Table 18.37 shows the U.S. production of newsprint (in thousands of short tons) for the years 1980–1985.

(*a*) Construct a graph of the data.

(*b*) Obtain a seasonal index by using the average-percentage method.

Table 18.37

	Jan	Feb	Mar	Apr	May	June	July	Aug	Sep	Oct	Nov	Dec
1980	343	334	358	339	368	356	341	374	353	377	358	338
1981	379	356	399	391	402	404	405	426	400	420	412	359
1982	415	378	420	396	385	383	363	372	353	406	373	330
1983	403	378	406	364	399	372	378	419	377	406	414	372
1984	417	410	434	422	436	424	409	426	415	426	417	389
1985	425	406	443	387	418	408	416	414	405	407	397	398

Source: Survey of Current Business.

18.48 Work Problem 18.47 by the ratio-to-trend method.

18.49 Work Problem 18.47 by the ratio-to-moving-average method.

18.50 Work Problem 18.47 by the link-relative method.

18.51 Compare the seasonal indexes obtained in Problems 18.47 to 18.50.

18.52 Obtain a seasonal index for Problem 18.36 by using two methods, and compare the results.

18.53 (*a*) For the data of Problem 18.9, calculate a seasonal index for the last 3 years and the first 3 years, using any method.

(*b*) Compare the two indexes obtained in part (*a*).

18.54 Adjusting their data for leap years, rework Problems 18.42 to 18.45. Determine whether the adjustment has any significant bearing on the final seasonal index obtained.

DESEASONALIZATION OF DATA

18.55 (*a*) Deseasonalize the data of Problem 18.42, using any of the seasonal indexes obtained in Problems 18.42 to 18.45.

(*b*) Graph the deseasonalized data and explain the results obtained.

18.56 (*a*) Adjust the data of Problem 18.47 for seasonal variation, using any of the results of Problems 18.47 to 18.51.

(*b*) Graph the seasonally adjusted data and explain the results obtained.

18.57 (*a*) Deseasonalize the data of Problem 18.36, using the two seasonal indexes obtained in Problem 18.52.

(*b*) Graph the seasonally adjusted data and explain the results obtained.

ESTIMATION OF CYCLIC AND IRREGULAR VARIATIONS

18.58 (*a*) Adjust the data of Problem 18.55 for trend, using any method.

(*b*) Graph the data obtained.

(*c*) Take 3- and 7-month moving averages of the data in part (*a*).

(*d*) Graph the results of part (*c*) and explain the variation observed. In particular, identify any cyclic movements that may be present.

18.59 Work Problem 18.58 for the data of Problem 18.56.

18.60 Work Problem 18.58 for the data of Problem 18.57.

18.61 Table 18.38 shows the average monthly U.S. production of newsprint (in thousands of short tons) for the years 1960–1985.

(*a*) Graph the data.

(*b*) Having analyzed the data, discuss whether cycles may possibly be evident in the data.

Table 18.38

Year	1960	1961	1962	1963	1964	1965	1966	1967	1968	1969	1970	1971	1972
Monthly average	170	174	179	185	188	182	201	218	245	269	276	275	285

Year	1973	1974	1975	1976	1977	1978	1979	1980	1981	1982	1983	1984	1985
Monthly average	286	290	297	307	323	317	342	353	396	381	391	419	410

Source: Survey of Current Business.

18.62 In adjusting data for trend and seasonal variations, does it make any difference which is done first? Include in your answer (*a*) a theoretical discussion and (*b*) an illustration that employs the time series in Problem 18.42, 18.47, or 18.53.

18.63 (*a*) Work Problem 18.19 by using a 12-month centered moving average, and construct the graph.

(*b*) What conclusions do you draw from the results in part (*a*)?

18.64 (*a*) Obtain a frequency distribution for the magnitudes of the irregular variations found in Problems 18.17 and 18.18.

(*b*) Does the frequency distribution found in part (*a*) approximate a normal distribution? If so, give a possible reason for this.

FORECASTING

18.65 (*a*) Use the results of Problem 18.42 to forecast the U.S. production of room air conditioners during the year 1986.

(*b*) Discuss possible sources of error.

(*c*) Compare your predictions with the actual values for 1986 shown in Table 18.39.

Table 18.39

Jan	Feb	Mar	Apr	May	June	July	Aug	Sep	Oct	Nov	Dec
131	175	422	456	451	427	361	89	89	53	56	77

Source: Survey of Current Business.

18.66 (*a*) Use the results of Problem 18.47 to forecast the U.S. production of newsprint during the year 1986.

(*b*) Discuss possible sources of error.

(*c*) Compare your predictions with the actual values for 1986 shown in Table 18.40.

(*d*) Does it help to use the extra data of Problem 18.61? Explain.

Table 18.40

Jan	Feb	Mar	Apr	May	June	July	Aug	Sep	Oct	Nov	Dec
420	394	444	409	446	420	433	441	420	426	429	428

Source: Survey of Current Business.

18.67 Use the least-squares parabola of Problem 18.40 to obtain the data for 1982 in Problem 18.9, and compare your predicted values with the actual values given in Table 18.32 of Problem 18.21.

18.68 Table 18.41 shows the monthly U.S. factory production (in millions of pounds) of creamery butter during the years 1979–1983. In 1982, however, the data were reported for the second, third, and fourth quarters instead of for the months. The total for each of these quarters is shown in boldface in Table 18.41. Use methods of time-series analysis to obtain estimates for the missing monthly values. Discuss possible sources of error.

Table 18.41

	Jan	Feb	Mar	Apr	May	June	July	Aug	Sep	Oct	Nov	Dec
1979	97.4	86.6	89.3	92.4	99.2	83.0	72.5	64.3	60.5	78.0	75.8	84.0
1980	103.8	99.1	101.7	112.3	116.6	93.9	83.7	75.3	77.0	91.4	84.7	103.6
1981	121.3	110.1	116.7	116.9	115.5	95.9	82.7	82.3	85.2	99.5	93.4	109.5
1982	128.3	116.8	123.4		**332.9**			**262.2**			**295.1**	
1983	133.9	120.7	126.1	126.5	121.1	104.6	94.7	83.9	84.2	98.3	98.8	108.5

Source: Survey of Current Business.

18.69 Omit some data from Table 18.12 of Problem 18.9 and see whether you can recover the data by using methods of time-series analysis.

18.70 Work Problem 18.69 by using the data of Problems 18.42 and 18.47.

MISCELLANEOUS PROBLEMS

18.71 Analyze each of the time series, (*a*) through (*e*), in Tables 18.42 and 18.43, which give U.S. data for the years 1960–1986 and 1979–1986, respectively. If you wish, use only the data for the years through 1985 and forecast the 1986 results for columns (*a*) through (*e*); then compare these forecasts to the actual data for 1986. Note that Table 18.42 shows the *monthly averages* for each year, while Table 18.43 shows the *monthly values* for each year.

18.72 Table 18.44 shows the total monthly sales (in millions of dollars) of U.S. manufacturers of electric machinery for the years 1979–1986.

(*a*) Analyze the time series for seasonal and cyclic patterns.

(*b*) Identify and discuss the difficulties involved in the analysis because of price inflation.

Table 18.42

Year	(*a*) New Housing Units Started, Public and Private (thousands)	(*b*) Production of Bituminous Coal (millions of short tons)	(*c*) Factory Sales of New Cars (thousands)	(*d*) Production of Lumber (millions of board feet)	(*e*) Production of Primary Aluminum (thousands of short tons)
1960	106.6	32.72	556		167.9
1961	113.8	33.58	462	2654	158.6
1962	123.5	35.25	578	2740	176.5
1963	136.7	38.24	637	2879	192.7
1964	132.1	40.17	646	2951	212.7
1965	128.6	42.67	776	3075	229.6
1966	104.3	44.33	717	3011	247.3
1967	110.2	46.05	620	2940	272.4
1968	129.0	44.99	735	3089	271.3
1969	125.0	46.71	685	3162	316.1
1970	122.1	49.17	546	3050	331.3
1971	173.7	46.02	715	3051	327.1
1972	198.2	49.62	735	3239	343.5
1973	171.5	49.17	805	3191	377.5
1974	112.7	49.26	611	2872	408.6
1975	97.7	53.19	560	2654	323.3
1976	129.0	55.42	708	3045	354.3
1977	165.8	56.00	767	3125	378.1
1978	152.6	53.94	764	3128	400.2
1979	145.8	64.17	702	3084	418.5
1980	109.3	69.17	533	2613	427.5
1981	91.7	68.67	521	2435	412.3
1982	89.3	69.15	421	2224	300.8
1983	142.7	64.85	562	2610	281.6
1984	146.3	74.15	635	2830	341.6
1985	145.4	73.52	667	3050	291.6
1986	150.6	73.70	626	3363	253.0

Source: Survey of Current Business.

Table 18.43

Year	(*a*) New Housing Units Started, Public and Private (thousands)	(*b*) Production of Bituminous Coal (millions of short tons)	(*c*) Factory Sales of New Cars (thousands)	(*d*) Production of Lumber (millions of board feet)	(*e*) Production of Primary Aluminum (thousands of short tons)
1979					
Jan	88.4	56.49	737	2877	418
Feb	84.7	53.63	709	2877	379
Mar	153.3	65.49	883	3306	419
Apr	161.3	62.79	761	3119	402
May	189.1	67.93	922	3219	423
June	192.0	69.40	820	3143	410
July	165.0	54.50	587	3018	429
Aug	171.4	72.10	449	3355	430
Sep	163.8	63.90	630	3131	419
Oct	169.0	75.91	787	3412	435
Nov	119.2	67.56	641	2914	423
Dec	91.8	60.32	494	2631	435
1980					
Jan	73.4	67.81	513	2798	431
Feb	80.6	64.33	619	2835	406
Mar	86.1	69.87	649	2879	434
Apr	96.6	69.87	572	2257	421
May	93.0	70.40	518	2307	438
June	117.8	71.36	544	2486	425
July	121.5	60.70	432	2479	427
Aug	131.7	70.24	299	2783	426
Sep	147.0	72.06	529	2818	419
Oct	153.7	75.75	675	2903	437
Nov	113.5	65.51	560	2480	427
Dec	96.3	72.12	490	2329	439
1981					
Jan	85.2	66.16	439	2523	445
Feb	72.5	69.79	475	2542	404
Mar	108.9	77.27	620	2818	448
Apr	124.0	38.02	645	2780	431
May	110.6	37.28	670	2651	441
June	107.0	61.90	712	2588	420
July	101.0	73.35	513	2483	426
Aug	87.3	78.20	345	2554	416
Sep	90.9	81.30	522	2307	393
Oct	88.1	84.78	520	2379	396
Nov	64.9	76.03	425	1831	364
Dec	59.7	79.97	370	1765	364

Table 18.43 (continued)

Year	(*a*) New Housing Units Started, Public and Private (thousands)	(*b*) Production of Bituminous Coal (millions of short tons)	(*c*) Factory Sales of New Cars (thousands)	(*d*) Production of Lumber (millions of board feet)	(*e*) Production of Primary Aluminum (thousands of short tons)
1982					
Jan	47.6	65.72	273	1810	351
Feb	52.0	69.62	320	1891	311
Mar	78.7	82.93	469	2148	336
Apr	85.1	73.16	488	2281	319
May	99.2	70.66	510	2251	321
June	91.9	71.23	561	2338	300
July	107.2	59.87	439	2376	297
Aug	97.2	72.09	356	2560	287
Sep	108.4	67.60	429	2445	271
Oct	111.5	70.48	431	2333	275
Nov	109.9	63.68	407	2247	266
Dec	83.4	62.73	366	2004	275
1983					
Jan	92.9	61.85	457	2484	279
Feb	96.7	60.26	474	2481	223
Mar	135.8	68.13	575	2682	248
Apr	136.4	61.27	529	2623	245
May	175.5	62.94	587	2645	265
June	173.8	62.23	644	2718	261
July	162.0	55.03	461	2585	284
Aug	177.7	73.11	492	2714	297
Sep	156.8	70.44	627	2748	299
Oct	159.9	71.34	678	2787	320
Nov	136.4	68.27	636	2504	318
Dec	108.5	63.35	581	2345	340
1984					
Jan	109.2	67.87	647	2740	342
Feb	130.4	73.68	682	2678	324
Mar	138.1	81.59	772	3104	350
Apr	173.0	71.71	665	2983	348
May	182.2	79.83	699	2828	365
June	184.3	75.29	676	2968	351
July	163.1	73.92	517	2685	349
Aug	147.8	90.37	519	2933	344
Sep	149.6	78.54	538	2776	329
Oct	152.7	69.42	686	3154	338
Nov	126.5	64.04	668	2814	325
Dec	99.0	63.48	553	2295	334

Table 18.43 (continued)

Year	(*a*) New Housing Units Started, Public and Private (thousands)	(*b*) Production of Bituminous Coal (millions of short tons)	(*c*) Factory Sales of New Cars (thousands)	(*d*) Production of Lumber (millions of board feet)	(*e*) Production of Primary Aluminum (thousands of short tons)
1985					
Jan	105.4	67.98	733	2727	329
Feb	95.8	67.04	659	2718	289
Mar	145.2	77.66	736	3085	312
Apr	176.0	76.54	744	3296	295
May	170.5	78.24	760	3256	304
June	163.4	73.02	677	3101	288
July	161.0	69.01	565	3034	292
Aug	161.1	79.48	554	3299	289
Sep	148.6	73.82	638	3196	280
Oct	173.2	80.12	739	3387	285
Nov	124.1	69.29	658	2851	265
Dec	120.5	70.01	540	2649	271
1986					
Jan	115.9	78.28	713	3092	273
Feb	107.2	72.69	675	3046	251
Mar	151.1	77.57	655	3347	281
Apr	188.3	74.89	713	3362	275
May	186.7	73.14	685	3405	284
June	183.6	72.67	706	3355	241
July	172.2	67.82	505	2967	231
Aug	163.8	76.55	426	3441	235
Sep	154.3	75.02	637	3397	231
Oct	154.9	76.83	684	3820	243
Nov	115.7	68.67	556	3496	239
Dec	113.1	70.26	561	3623	252

Source: Survey of Current Business.

Table 18.44

	Jan	Feb	Mar	Apr	May	June	July	Aug	Sep	Oct	Nov	Dec
1979	8,128	9,107	9,562	8,873	8,990	9,851	8,178	9,029	9,877	9,790	9,614	9,720
1980	9,204	10,617	10,778	9,909	9,838	10,714	9,150	10,263	11,169	11,459	11,201	10,596
1981	9,986	11,293	11,812	11,301	11,338	12,452	10,463	11,465	12,397	11,988	11,725	11,125
1982	10,410	11,689	12,094	11,831	11,949	12,588	10,843	11,327	12,301	11,908	11,496	11,421
1983	11,042	12,214	13,028	12,462	12,526	13,890	11,481	12,416	14,398	14,066	14,059	14,330
1984	13,129	14,435	15,791	14,646	14,980	16,549	13,700	15,009	16,718	15,605	15,372	16,572
1985	13,557	15,288	16,352	14,612	14,796	16,844	13,586	15,064	16,565	16,104	16,509	16,237
1986	13,614	15,887	17,024	15,549	15,504	17,537	14,643	16,375	18,362	17,240	17,614	17,845

Source: Survey of Current Business.

Chapter 19

Index Numbers

INDEX NUMBER

An *index number* is a statistical measure designed to show changes in a variable or a group of related variables with respect to time, geographic location, income, or any other characteristic. A collection of index numbers for different years, locations, etc., is sometimes called an *index series.*

APPLICATIONS OF INDEX NUMBERS

Index numbers are used for making comparisons. For example, with index numbers we can compare food or other living costs in a city during one year with those of a previous year, or we can compare steel production during a given year in one part of a country with that in another part. Although used mainly in business and economics, index numbers can be applied in many other fields. In education, for example, we can use index numbers to compare the relative intelligence of students in different locations or for different years.

Many government and private agencies are engaged in computing index numbers—or *indexes,* as they are often called—for purposes of forecasting business and economic conditions, providing general information, and so forth. Thus we have wage indexes, production indexes, unemployment indexes, and many others. Perhaps the best-known is the *cost-of-living index,* or *consumer price index,* prepared by the U.S. Bureau of Labor Statistics. In many labor contracts there appear certain *escalator clauses* that provide automatic increases in wages corresponding to increases in the cost-of-living index.

In this chapter we shall mainly be interested in index numbers that show changes with respect to time, although the methods described in this chapter can certainly be applied to other cases.

PRICE RELATIVES

One of the simplest examples of an index number is a *price relative,* which is the ratio of the price of a single commodity in a *given period* to its price in another period, called the *base period,* or *reference period.* For simplicity, let us assume that the prices in any one period are constant. If they are not, we can take an appropriate average for the period in order to make this assumption valid.

If p_n and p_o denote the commodity prices during the given period and the base period, respectively, then by definition

$$\text{Price relative} = \frac{p_n}{p_o} \qquad (1)$$

The price relative is usually expressed as a percentage by multiplying it by 100.

More generally, if p_a and p_b are the prices of a commodity during periods a and b, respectively, then *the price relative in period b with respect to period a is defined as* p_b/p_a and is denoted by $p_{a|b}$, a notation that will be found useful. With this notation, the price relative in equation (*1*) is denoted by $p_{o|n}$.

EXAMPLE 1. Suppose that the consumer prices of a quart of milk in the years 1970 and 1980 were 45¢ and 54¢, respectively. Taking 1970 as the *base year* and 1980 as the *given year,* we have

$$\text{Price relative} = p_{1970|1980} = \frac{\text{price in 1980}}{\text{price in 1970}} = \frac{54¢}{45¢} = 1.2 = 120\%$$

or briefly 120, omitting the % sign (as is often done in statistical literature). This result simply means that in 1980 the price of milk was 120% of that in 1970; that is, it *increased* by 20%.

EXAMPLE 2. Taking 1980 as the base year and 1970 as the given year in Example 1, we have

$$\text{Price relative} = p_{1980|1970} = \frac{\text{price in 1970}}{\text{price in 1980}} = \frac{45¢}{54¢} = \frac{5}{6} = 83\tfrac{1}{3}\%$$

or briefly $83\frac{1}{3}$. This means that in 1970 the price of milk was $83\frac{1}{3}\%$ of that in 1980; that is, it was $16\frac{2}{3}\%$ less than in 1980.

Note that the price relative for a given period with respect to the *same* period is always 100%, or 100. In particular, the price relative corresponding to a base period is always 100. This accounts for the notation (often found in statistical literature) of writing, for example, "1970 = 100" to indicate that the year 1970 is taken as the base period.

PROPERTIES OF PRICE RELATIVES

If $p_a, p_b, p_c, \ldots$ denote the prices in periods $a, b, c, \ldots$, respectively, then we have the following properties for the associated price relatives. The proofs follow directly from the definitions.

1. **Identity Property:** $p_{a|a} = 1$. This simply states that the price relative for a given period with respect to the same period is 1, or 100%.
2. **Time-Reversal Property:** $p_{a|b}p_{b|a} = 1$, or $p_{a|b} = 1/p_{b|a}$. This states that if two periods are interchanged, the corresponding price relatives are reciprocals of each other (see Examples 1 and 2).
3. **Cyclic, or Circular, Property:** $p_{a|b}p_{b|c}p_{c|a} = 1$, $p_{a|b}p_{b|c}p_{c|d}p_{d|a} = 1$, etc.
4. **Modified Cyclic (or Circular) Property:** $p_{a|b}p_{b|c} = p_{a|c}$, $p_{a|b}p_{b|c}p_{c|d} = p_{a|d}$, etc. This property follows directly from Properties 2 and 3.

QUANTITY, OR VOLUME, RELATIVES

Instead of comparing the prices of a commodity, we may be interested in comparing the quantities (or volumes) of the commodity, such as the quantity (or volume) of production, consumption, and exports. In such cases we speak of *quantity relatives*, or *volume relatives*. For simplicity, as in the case of prices, we assume that the quantities are constant in any period. If they are not, we can take an appropriate average for the period in order to make this assumption valid.

If q_o denotes the quantity (or volume) of a commodity produced, consumed, exported, etc., during a base period, while q_n denotes the corresponding quantity produced, consumed, etc., during a given period, we define

$$\text{Quantity or volume relative} = \frac{q_n}{q_o} \tag{2}$$

which is generally expressed as a percentage.

As in the case of price relatives, we use the notation $q_{a|b} = q_b/q_a$ to denote the quantity relative in period b with respect to period a. The same remarks and properties pertaining to price relatives are applicable to quantity relatives.

VALUE RELATIVES

If p is the price of a commodity during a period and q is the quantity (or volume) produced, sold, etc., during the period, then pq is called the *total value*. Thus if 1000 quarts of milk are sold at 56¢ per quart, the total value is $pq = (\$0.56)(1000) = \$560$.

If p_o and q_o denote the price and quantity of a commodity during a base period, while p_n and q_n denote the corresponding price and quantity during a given period, the total values during these periods are given by v_o and v_n, respectively, and we define

$$\text{Value relative} = \frac{v_n}{v_o} = \frac{p_n q_n}{p_o q_o} = \left(\frac{p_n}{p_o}\right)\left(\frac{q_n}{q_o}\right)$$

$$= \text{price relative} \times \text{quantity relative} \qquad (3)$$

The same remarks, notation, and properties pertaining to price and quantity relatives can be applied to value relatives. In particular, if $p_{a|b}$, $q_{a|b}$, and $v_{a|b}$ denote the price, quantity, and value relatives of period b with respect to period a, then, as in equation (3),

$$v_{a|b} = p_{a|b} q_{a|b}$$

which is called the *factor-reversal property.*

LINK AND CHAIN RELATIVES

If $p_1, p_2, p_3, \ldots$ represent the prices during successive intervals of time $1, 2, 3, \ldots,$ then $p_{1|2}, p_{2|3}, p_{3|4}, \ldots$ represent the price relatives of each time interval relative to the preceding time interval, and they are called *link relatives.*

EXAMPLE 3. If the prices of a commodity during 1983, 1984, 1985, and 1986 are 8¢, 12¢, 15¢, and 18¢, respectively, then the link relatives are $p_{1983|1984} = \frac{12}{8} = 150\ (\%)$, $p_{1984|1985} = \frac{15}{12} = 125\ (\%)$, and $p_{1985|1986} = \frac{18}{15} = 120\ (\%)$.

The price relative for a given period with respect to any other period taken as the base period can always be expressed in terms of link relatives. This is a consequence of the *cyclic*, or *circular*, property of relatives. Thus, for example, $p_{5|2} = p_{5|4} p_{4|3} p_{3|2}$.

EXAMPLE 4. From Example 3 the price relative for 1986 with respect to the base year 1983 is

$$p_{1983|1986} = p_{1983|1984} p_{1984|1985} p_{1985|1986} = \frac{12}{8} \cdot \frac{15}{12} \cdot \frac{18}{15} = \frac{18}{8} = 225\ (\%)$$

The price relatives with respect to a *fixed* base period, which as we have seen can be obtained by using link relatives, are sometimes called the *chain relatives* with respect to this base, or the relatives *chained* to the fixed base.

EXAMPLE 5. In Examples 3 and 4, the collection of chain relatives for the years 1984, 1985, and 1986 with respect to the base 1983 are given by

$$p_{1983|1984} = \frac{12}{8} = 150\ (\%)$$

$$p_{1983|1985} = p_{1983|1984} p_{1984|1985} = \frac{12}{8} \cdot \frac{15}{12} = 187.5\ (\%)$$

$$p_{1983|1986} = p_{1983|1984} p_{1984|1985} p_{1985|1986} = \frac{12}{8} \cdot \frac{15}{12} \cdot \frac{18}{15} = 225\ (\%)$$

The above ideas are also applicable to quantity and value relatives.

PROBLEMS INVOLVED IN THE COMPUTATION OF INDEX NUMBERS

In actual practice we are less interested in comparing the prices, quantities, or values of single commodities than in comparing the prices (etc.) of large groups of related commodities. For example, in computing a cost-of-living index we not only wish to compare the prices of milk in one period with respect to another, but we also want to compare the prices of eggs, meat, bread, rent, clothes, etc., so as to obtain some general picture. Of course, we could merely list the price relatives of *all* commodities. This, however, would not be satisfactory. What we would like is a *single* price index number that would compare prices in the two periods *on the average.*

It is not difficult to see that computations of index numbers involving groups of commodities involve many problems that must be resolved. In computing a cost-of-living index, for example, we must decide what commodities should be included as well as how to weight their relative importance; we must collect data concerning the prices and quantities of such commodities; we must determine what to do insofar as different *qualities* of the same type of commodity are concerned, and what to do when certain appliances or materials are available during a given year that were not available during the base year; finally, we must decide how to put all this information together and come up with a single cost-of-living index number that has practical significance.

THE USE OF AVERAGES

Since we must arrive at a single index number summarizing a large amount of information, it is easy to realize that averages (discussed in Chapter 3) play an important role in computing index numbers.

Just as many methods exist for computing averages, so there are many methods for computing index numbers, each with its own advantages and disadvantages.

In the following we shall examine a few methods commonly employed in practice, using various types of averaging procedures. Although we restrict ourselves to price indexes at first, we shall see how suitable modifications are easily made for quantity or value indexes.

THEORETICAL TESTS FOR INDEX NUMBERS

It is desirable from a theoretical point of view that index numbers for groups of commodities have the properties satisfied by relatives (index numbers for single commodities). Any index number that has such a property is said to meet the *test* associated with the property. Thus, for example, index numbers having the time-reversal property are said to satisfy the *time-reversal test*, etc.

No index number yet discovered meets *all* tests, although in many instances the tests are satisfied approximately. Fisher's ideal index (page 439), which in particular satisfies the *time-reversal test* and *factor-reversal test,* comes closer than any other useful index number in satisfying the properties considered important (hence the name "ideal").

From a practical point of view however, other index numbers serve as well, and we shall examine some of these.

NOTATION

It is customary to let $p_n^{(1)}, p_n^{(2)}, p_n^{(3)}, \ldots$ denote the prices of a first, second, third, ... commodity during a given period n. The corresponding prices during a base period are denoted by $p_o^{(1)}, p_o^{(2)}, p_o^{(3)}$, etc. The numbers $1, 2, 3, \ldots$ are *superscripts* and should not be confused with exponents. With this notation, the price of commodity j during period n is denoted by $p_n^{(j)}$.

As in previous chapters, we can use the summation notation by summing over the index j. For example, assuming that there is a total of N commodities, the sum of their prices during the period n could be written $\sum_{j=1}^{N} p_n^{(j)}$ or $\sum p_n^{(j)}$. It is simpler, however, to omit the superscript altogether and to write $\sum p_n$, which we shall do when no confusion can result; do remember that the more complete symbolism is implied. With this notation, $\sum p_o$ would denote the sum of the prices of all commodities during the base period.

A similar notation is used for quantities and values.

THE SIMPLE AGGREGATE METHOD

In this method of computing a price index, we express the total commodity prices in the given year as a percentage of the total commodity prices in the base year. In symbols, we have

$$\text{Simple aggregate price index} = \frac{\sum p_n}{\sum p_o} \tag{4}$$

where $\sum p_o$ = sum of all commodity prices in the base year
$\sum p_n$ = sum of corresponding commodity prices in the given year

and where the result is expressed as a percentage, as are index numbers in general.

Although this method has the advantage of being easy to apply, it has two great disadvantages that make it unsatisfactory:

1. It does not take into account the relative importance of the various commodities. Thus, according to this method, equal weight (or importance) would be attached to milk and shaving cream in computing a cost-of-living index.
2. The particular units in price quotations (such as gallons, bushels, and pounds) affect the value of the index. (See Problem 19.12.)

THE SIMPLE AVERAGE-OF-RELATIVES METHOD

The index produced by this method depends on the procedure used to average the price relatives; the procedures include taking the arithmetic mean, geometric mean, harmonic mean, and median. Using the arithmetic mean, for example, we would have

$$\text{Simple arithmetic mean of relative price index} = \frac{\sum p_n/p_o}{N} \tag{5}$$

where $\sum p_n/p_o$ = sum of all commodity price relatives
N = number of commodity price relatives used

For indexes using other types of averages, see Problems 19.14 and 19.15.

Although this method does not have the second disadvantage of the simple aggregate method, it still has the first disadvantage.

THE WEIGHTED AGGREGATE METHOD

To overcome the disadvantages of the simple aggregate method, we *weight* the price of each commodity by a suitable factor. This factor is often taken to be the quantity (or volume) of the commodity sold during the base year, the given year, or some typical year (which may involve an average over several years). Such weights indicate the importance of the particular commodity. Depending on whether we use base-year, given-year, or typical-year quantities (denoted by q_o, q_n, and q_t, respectively), we use one of the following formulas:

1. **Laspeyres' Index, or the Base-Year Method:**

$$\text{Weighted aggregate price index with base-year quantity weights} = \frac{\sum p_n q_o}{\sum p_o q_o} \tag{6}$$

2. **Paasche's Index, or the Given-Year Method:**

$$\text{Weighted aggregate price index with given-year quantity weights} = \frac{\sum p_n q_n}{\sum p_o q_n} \tag{7}$$

3. **The Typical-Year Method.** If we let q_t denote the quantity weight during some typical period t, then we define

$$\text{Weighted aggregate price index with typical-year quantity weights} = \frac{\sum p_n q_t}{\sum p_o q_t} \qquad (8)$$

For $t = o$ and $t = n$, this reduces to equations (*6*) and (*7*), respectively.

FISHER'S IDEAL INDEX

We define

$$\text{Fisher's ideal price index} = \sqrt{\left(\frac{\sum p_n q_o}{\sum p_o q_o}\right)\left(\frac{\sum p_n q_n}{\sum p_o q_n}\right)} \qquad (9)$$

This index is the geometric mean of the Laspeyres and Paasche index numbers given in equations (*6*) and (*7*). As already noted, Fisher's ideal index satisfies both the *time-reversal* and *factor-reversal tests*, which gives it certain theoretical advantages over other index numbers.

THE MARSHALL–EDGEWORTH INDEX

The Marshall–Edgeworth index uses the weighted aggregate typical-year method, in which the weights are taken as the arithmetic mean of the base-year and given-year quantities; that is, $q_t = \frac{1}{2}(q_0 + q_n)$. Substituting this value of q_t into equation (*8*), we have

$$\text{Marshall–Edgeworth price index} = \frac{\sum p_n(q_o + q_n)}{\sum p_o(q_o + q_n)} \qquad (10)$$

THE WEIGHTED AVERAGE-OF-RELATIVES METHOD

To overcome the disadvantages of the simple average-of-relatives method, we can use a *weighted average of relatives.* The weighted average most often used in this connection is the *weighted arithmetic mean,* although other weighted averages, such as the weighted geometric mean (Chapter 3), can be used as well.

In this method we weight each price relative by the total value of the commodity in terms of some monetary unit, such as the dollar. Since the value of a commodity is obtained by multiplying the price p of the commodity by the quantity q, the weights are given by pq.

Depending on whether we use base-year, given-year, or typical-year values (denoted by $p_o q_o$, $p_n q_n$, and $p_t q_t$, respectively), we use one of the following formulas:

Weighted arithmetic mean of price relatives, using base-year value weights:

$$\frac{\sum (p_n/p_o)(p_o q_o)}{\sum p_o q_o} = \frac{\sum p_n q_o}{\sum p_o q_o} \qquad (11)$$

Weighted arithmetic mean of price relatives, using given-year value weights:

$$\frac{\sum (p_n/p_o)(p_n q_n)}{\sum p_n q_n} \qquad (12)$$

Weighted arithmetic mean of price relatives, using typical-year value weights:

$$\frac{\sum (p_n/p_o)(p_t q_t)}{\sum p_t q_t} \qquad (13)$$

Note that formula (*11*) yields the same result as Laspeyres' formula given in (*6*).

QUANTITY, OR VOLUME, INDEX NUMBERS

The formulas described above for obtaining price index numbers are easily modified to obtain quantity (or volume) index numbers by simply interchanging p and q. For example, replacing p with q in equation (5) gives

$$\text{Simple arithmetic mean of relatives volume index} = \frac{\sum q_n/q_o}{N} \tag{14}$$

where $\sum q_n/q_o$ = sum of all commodity quantity relatives
N = number of commodity quantity relatives used

Similarly, formulas (6) and (7) become

$$\text{Weighted aggregate volume index with base-year price weights} = \frac{\sum q_n p_o}{\sum q_o p_o} \tag{15}$$

$$\text{Weighted aggregate volume index with given-year price weights} = \frac{\sum q_n p_n}{\sum q_o p_n} \tag{16}$$

Formula (15) is sometimes called a *Laspeyres volume index*, and formula (16) is sometimes called a *Paasche volume index*. In these formulas the weights used are prices. However, any other suitable weights can be used instead.

Formulas (8) to (13) could be modified in the same manner.

VALUE INDEX NUMBERS

Just as we have obtained formulas for price and volume indexes, so we can obtain formulas for *value indexes*. The simplest such index is

$$\text{Value index} = \frac{\sum p_n q_n}{\sum p_o q_o} \tag{17}$$

where $\sum p_o q_o$ = total value of all commodities in the base period
$\sum p_n q_n$ = total value of all commodities in the given period

This is a *simple aggregate index*, since the values have not been weighted. Other formulas in which we use weights to indicate the relative importance of the items can be formulated.

CHANGING THE BASE PERIOD OF INDEX NUMBERS

In practice it is desirable that the base period chosen for comparison purposes be a period of economic stability that is not too far distant in the past. From time to time it may therefore be necessary to change this base period.

One possibility is to recompute all index numbers in terms of the new base period. A simpler approximate method is to divide all index numbers for the various years corresponding to the old base period by the index number corresponding to the new base period, expressing the results as percentages. These results represent the new index numbers, the index number for the new base period being 100 (%), as it should be.

Mathematically speaking, this method is strictly applicable only if the index numbers satisfy the *circular test* (see Problem 19.37). However, for many types of index numbers the method fortunately yields results which in practice are close enough to those which would be obtained theoretically.

DEFLATION OF TIME SERIES

Although the incomes of individuals may theoretically be rising over a period of years, their *real incomes* may actually be declining because of increases in living costs—insofar as these increases in living costs amount to decreases in *purchasing power.* We calculate the real incomes by dividing the *apparent*, or *physical, incomes* for the various years by the cost-of-living index numbers for the years, using an appropriate base period. For example, if an individual's income in 1980 is 150% of his income in 1970 (i.e., it has increased by 50%) and the cost-of-living index has doubled over the same period, then the individual's real income in 1980 is only $\frac{150}{2} = 75\%$ of what it was in 1970.

The above paragraph describes the process of deflating a time series involving income. A similar procedure may be used to deflate other time series. For instance, in Chapter 18 we used an analogous procedure to *deseasonalize* data by using seasonal index numbers.

Mathematically speaking, this method of deflating time series is strictly applicable only if the index numbers satisfy the *factor-reversal test*, and for this reason Fisher's ideal index is appropriate. However, other index numbers can be used since they yield results that are correct for most practical purposes.

Solved Problems

PRICE RELATIVES

19.1 The average retail prices (in cents per pound) of zinc sold in the United States during the years 1978–1984 are shown in Table 19.1.

(*a*) Using 1978 as the base, find the price relatives corresponding to the years 1983 and 1984.

(*b*) Using 1980 as the base, find the price relatives corresponding to all the given years.

(*c*) Using 1978–1980 as the base, find the price relatives corresponding to all the given years.

Table 19.1

Year	1978	1979	1980	1981	1982	1983	1984
Average retail price of zinc	31.0	37.3	37.4	44.6	38.5	41.4	48.6

Source: U.S. Bureau of Mines.

SOLUTION

(*a*) The price relative for 1982 with 1978 as the base is

$$p_{1978|1982} = \frac{\text{price in 1982}}{\text{price in 1978}} = \frac{38.5}{31.0} = 1.242 = 124.2\%$$

The price relative for 1984 with 1978 as the base is

$$p_{1978|1984} = \frac{\text{price in 1984}}{\text{price in 1978}} = \frac{48.6}{31.0} = 1.568 = 156.8\%$$

In statistical literature it is the custom to omit the % signs when quoting index numbers, although these signs are understood. Using this convention, we quote the above price relatives as 124.2 and 156.8, respectively.

(*b*) Divide each retail price in Table 19.1 by 37.4 (cents per pound), the price for the year 1980; thus the required price relatives, expressed in percentage form, are as shown in Table 19.2. These price relatives represent the *index numbers* of zinc retail prices for the years 1978–1984, and the entire collection is called an *index series.* Note that the price relative (or price index number) corresponding to the year 1980 is in its percentage form equal to 100.0, as is always true for a base period. This is often written symbolically in statistical literature as 1980 = 100.

Table 19.2

Year	1978	1979	1980	1981	1982	1983	1984
Price relative (1980 = 100)	82.9	99.7	100.0	119.3	102.9	110.7	129.9

(*c*) The arithmetic mean of the prices for the years 1978–1980 is $\frac{1}{3}(31.0+37.3+37.4)=35.2$. Divide each retail price in Table 19.1 by this average base-period price of 35.2 (cents per pound); thus the required price relatives, expressed in percentage form, are as shown in Table 19.3. These represent the index numbers of zinc retail prices for the years 1978–1984 with 1978–1980 as the base period. Note that the arithmetic mean of the index numbers corresponding to base period 1978–1980 is $\frac{1}{3}(88.1+106.0+106.3)=100.1$, or 100.0 (the slight discrepancy is due to rounding errors), as is always true for a base period. This is often written symbolically in statistical literature as 1978–1980 = 100.

Table 19.3

Year	1978	1979	1980	1981	1982	1983	1984
Price relative (1978–1980 = 100)	88.1	106.0	106.3	126.7	109.4	117.6	138.1

19.2 Prove (*a*) that $p_{a|b}p_{b|c}=p_{a|c}$ and (*b*) that $p_{a|b}p_{b|a}=1$.

SOLUTION

By definition, the proofs are

(*a*)
$$p_{a|b}p_{b|c}=\frac{p_b}{p_a}\cdot\frac{p_c}{p_b}=\frac{p_c}{p_a}=p_{a|c}$$

(*b*)
$$p_{a|b}p_{b|a}=\frac{p_b}{p_a}\cdot\frac{p_a}{p_b}=1$$

19.3 Using Table 19.3, which uses 1978–1980 as the base, obtain the price relatives with 1980 as the base.

SOLUTION

Divide each price relative in Table 19.3 by the price relative 106.3. The resulting numbers, expressed as percentages, are the required price relatives. They are shown (apart from rounding errors) in Table 19.2.

This solution demonstrates that, given an index series corresponding to one base period, we can obtain the index series corresponding to another base period without using the original price data. The method involved is known as *changing the base period,* or *shifting the base.* For a proof of this method, see Problem 19.36.

19.4 In 1986 the average price of a commodity was 20% more than in 1985, 20% less than in 1984, and 50% more than in 1987. Reduce the data to price relatives by using (*a*) 1985, (*b*) 1986, and (*c*) 1984–1985 as the base.

SOLUTION

(a) The price relative (or index number) with 1985 as the base is 100. (Symbolically, 1985 = 100, or 100%.)

Since the price in 1986 is 20% more than in 1985, the price relative corresponding to 1986 is $100+20=120$; that is, the price in 1986 is 120% of the price in 1985.

Since the price in 1986 is 20% less than in 1984, it must be $100-20=80\%$ of the 1984 price. Thus the 1984 price is $1/0.80=\frac{5}{4}=125\%$ of the 1986 price; that is,

$$\begin{aligned}\text{1984 price relative} &= 125\% \text{ of the 1986 price relative}\\ &= 125\% \text{ of } 120 = 150\end{aligned}$$

Since the price in 1986 is 50% more than in 1987, it must be $100+50=150\%$ of the 1987 price. Thus the 1987 price is $1/1.50=\frac{2}{3}$ of the 1986 price; that is,

$$\begin{aligned}\text{1987 price relative} &= \tfrac{2}{3} \text{ of the 1986 price relative}\\ &= \tfrac{2}{3} \text{ of } 120 = 80\end{aligned}$$

Thus the required price relatives with 1985 as the base year are as shown in Table 19.4.

(b) We use the method of changing the base period, as described in Problem 19.3. Divide each price relative in Table 19.4 by 120 (the price relative corresponding to the new base year 1986) and express the result as a percentage. Thus the required price relatives with 1986 as the base year are as shown in Table 19.5.

(c) **First method** [using part (a)]

From Table 19.4 the arithmetic mean of the price relatives for 1984 and 1985 is $\frac{1}{2}(150+100)=125$. Dividing each price relative in Table 19.4 by 125, we obtain the required price relatives, which are shown in Table 19.6.

Second method [using part (b)]

From Table 19.5 the arithmetic mean of the price relatives for 1984 and 1985 is $\frac{1}{2}(125+83.3)=104.2$. Dividing each price relative in Table 19.5 by 104.2, we obtain the same results as in the first method.

Table 19.4

Year	1984	1985	1986	1987
Price relative (1985 = 100)	150	100	120	80

Table 19.5

Year	1984	1985	1986	1987
Price relative (1986 = 100)	125	83.3	100	66.7

Table 19.6

Year	1984	1985	1986	1987
Price relative (1984–1985 = 100)	120	80	96	64

QUANTITY, OR VOLUME, RELATIVES

19.5 Table 19.7 shows the U.S. production of wheat (in millions of bushels) for the years 1977–1985. Reduce the table's data to quantity relatives by using (a) 1982 and (b) 1977–1980 as the base.

SOLUTION

(a) Divide the production figures for each year by 2765 (the production figure for the base year 1982). Thus the required quantity relatives (or quantity index numbers), expressed in percentage form, are as shown in Table 19.8.

Table 19.7

Year	1977	1978	1979	1980	1981	1982	1983	1984	1985
Production of wheat	2046	1776	2134	2380	2785	2765	2420	2595	2425

Source: U.S. Department of Agriculture.

Table 19.8

Year	1977	1978	1979	1980	1981	1982	1983	1984	1985
Quantity relative (1982 = 100)	74.0	64.2	77.2	86.1	100.7	100.0	87.5	93.9	87.7

(*b*) The arithmetic mean of production for the years 1977–1980 is $\frac{1}{4}(2046+1776+2134+2380)=2084$. Dividing the production figure for each year by 2084, we obtain the required quantity relatives expressed in percentage form, as shown in Table 19.9. Note that $\frac{1}{4}(98.2+85.2+102.4+114.2)=100.0$, which serves as a check.

Table 19.9

Year	1977	1978	1979	1980	1981	1982	1983	1984	1985
Quantity relative (1977–1980 = 100)	98.2	85.2	102.4	114.2	133.6	132.7	116.1	124.5	116.4

19.6 While the quantity relative for the year 1986 is 105 when we use 1977 as the base, it is 140 when we use 1980 as the base. Find the quantity relative for 1980 with 1977 as the base.

SOLUTION

First method

From the properties of quantity relatives, we have $q_{a|b}q_{b|c}=q_{a|c}$. Letting $a=1977$, $b=1980$, and $c=1986$, we have $q_{1977|1980}=q_{1977|1986}q_{1986|1980}=(1.05)(1/1.40)=0.75=75\%$. Thus the required quantity relative is 75.

Second method

Let q_{1977}, q_{1980}, and q_{1986} denote the actual quantities in 1977, 1980, and 1986, respectively; thus

$$\text{Quantity relative for 1986 with base 1977}=\frac{q_{1986}}{q_{1977}}=105\%=1.05$$

$$\text{Quantity relative for 1986 with base 1980}=\frac{q_{1986}}{q_{1980}}=140\%=1.40$$

Thus the quantity relative for 1980 with 1977 as the base is

$$\frac{q_{1980}}{q_{1977}}=\frac{q_{1980}/q_{1986}}{q_{1977}/q_{1986}}=\frac{1/1.40}{1/1.05}=\frac{1.05}{1.40}=75\%$$

Third method

Since $q_{1986}=1.05q_{1977}=1.40q_{1980}$, we have $q_{1980}/q_{1977}=1.05/1.40=75\%$. Thus the required quantity relative is 75.

VALUE RELATIVES

19.7 In January 1980 a factory paid out a total of \$80,000 to 120 employees on the payroll. In July of the same year the factory had 30 more employees on the payroll and paid out \$12,000 more than in January.

(*a*) Using January 1980 as the base, find the employment index number (quantity relative) for July.

(*b*) Using January 1980 as the base, find the labor-expense index number (value relative) for July.

(*c*) Using the result *price relative* × *quantity relative* = *value relative*, what interpretation can be given to the price relative in this case?

SOLUTION

(*a*) The employment index number is

$$\text{Quantity relative} = \frac{120+30}{120} = 1.25 = 125\% \qquad \text{or} \qquad 125$$

(*b*) The labor-expense index number is

$$\text{Value relative} = \frac{\$80{,}000+\$12{,}000}{\$80{,}000} = 1.15 = 115\% \qquad \text{or} \qquad 115$$

(*c*) The price relative is

$$\frac{\text{Value relative}}{\text{Quantity relative}} = \frac{115}{125} = 0.92 = 92\% \qquad \text{or} \qquad 92$$

We can interpret this as a *cost-per-employee index number.* The significance is that in July 1980 the cost per employee was 92% of that in the base period, January 1980. Sometimes this is called a *per capita* labor-cost index number.

19.8 A company expects its sales of a commodity to increase by 50% in the coming year. By what percentage should it increase the commodity's selling price in order to double its gross income from this commodity?

SOLUTION

Given $$\text{Price relative} \times \text{quantity relative} = \text{value relative}$$

we have $$\text{Price relative} \times 150\% = 200\%$$

Thus $$\text{Price relative} = \tfrac{200}{150} = \tfrac{4}{3} = 133\tfrac{1}{3}\%$$

The company should therefore increase the commodity's selling price by $133\frac{1}{3} - 100 = 33\frac{1}{3}\%$.

LINK AND CHAIN RELATIVES

19.9 Given that the link relatives for prices in the years 1981, 1982, . . . , 1985 are 125, 120, 135, 150, and 175, respectively, (*a*) find the price relative for 1982 with 1980 as the base, and (*b*) chain the link relatives to a 1981 base.

SOLUTION

We have $p_{1980|1981} = 1.25$, $p_{1981|1982} = 1.20$, $p_{1982|1983} = 1.35$, $p_{1983|1984} = 1.50$, and $p_{1984|1985} = 1.75$. Thus:

(*a*) $$p_{1980|1982} = p_{1980|1981}\, p_{1981|1982} = (1.25)(1.20) = 1.50 = 150\%$$

(*b*)

$$p_{1981|1980} = \frac{1}{p_{1980|1981}} = \frac{1}{1.25} = 80\%$$
$$p_{1981|1981} = 100\%$$
$$p_{1981|1982} = 120\%$$
$$p_{1981|1983} = p_{1981|1982}\,p_{1982|1983} = (1.20)(1.35) = 1.62 = 162\%$$
$$p_{1981|1984} = p_{1981|1982}\,p_{1982|1983}\,p_{1983|1984} = (1.20)(1.35)(1.50) = 2.43 = 243\%$$
$$p_{1981|1985} = p_{1981|1982}\,p_{1982|1983}\,p_{1983|1984}\,p_{1984|1985} = (1.20)(1.35)(1.50)(1.75) = 425\%$$

INDEX NUMBERS; THE SIMPLE AGGREGATE METHOD

Mathcad

19.10 For milk, butter, and cheese, Table 19.10 shows the U.S. average wholesale prices and production for the years 1980, 1981, and 1985. Compute a single aggregate wholesale price index of these dairy products for the year 1985, using (*a*) 1980 and (*b*) 1980–1981 as the base.

Table 19.10

	Price (cents per pound)			Quantity (millions of pounds)		
	1980	1981	1985	1980	1981	1985
Milk	13.23	13.95	12.90	128,500	132,800	143,700
Butter	139.3	148.0	141.1	1,145	1,228	1,248
Cheese	156.2	167.2	162.0	2,381	2,664	2,854

Source: Survey of Current Business.

SOLUTION

(*a*) The simple aggregate price index is

$$\frac{\sum p_n}{\sum p_o} = \frac{\text{sum of prices in given year (1985)}}{\text{sum of prices in base year (1980)}} = \frac{12.90 + 141.1 + 162.0}{13.23 + 139.3 + 156.2} = 102.4\ (\%)$$

That is, the average wholesale price of the three dairy products in 1985 is 102.4% of that in 1980 (or 2.4% greater).

(*b*) The average (mean) price of milk in the base period 1980–1981 is

$$\tfrac{1}{2}(13.23 + 13.95) = 13.59¢/\text{lb}$$

the average (mean) price of butter in the base period 1980–1981 is

$$\tfrac{1}{2}(139.3 + 148.0) = 143.7¢/\text{lb}$$

the average (mean) price of cheese in the base period 1980–1981 is

$$\tfrac{1}{2}(156.2 + 167.2) = 161.7¢/\text{lb}$$

and thus the simple aggregate price index is

$$\frac{\sum p_n}{\sum p_o} = \frac{\text{sum of prices in given year (1985)}}{\text{sum of prices in base year (1980–1981)}} = \frac{12.90 + 141.1 + 162.0}{13.59 + 143.7 + 161.7} = 99.1\ (\%)$$

Note that this method does not make use of the *quantities* produced, but only of the commodities' prices.

For illustrative purposes, only three commodities have been used here to compute an index number. In actual practice many more commodities would be included.

19.11 Explain why the index numbers obtained in Problem 19.10 may be inappropriate measures of price changes in the given commodities.

SOLUTION

The index computed in Problem 19.10 does not take into account the relative importance of the commodities—as would be determined, for example, by *how much* is used by the consumer or by *how much* is produced for consumption purposes. These considerations are addressed in later problems.

19.12 Table 19.11 shows the average U.S. prices and production of cotton and wheat for the years 1980 and 1986. Explain why a simple aggregate price index for 1986 with 1980 as the base year is an inappropriate measure of price changes in the given commodities.

Table 19.11

	Price		Quantity*	
	1980	1986	1980	1986
Cotton	74.4¢ (per pound)	56.8¢ (per pound)	11.122 (million bales)	13.432 (million bales)
Wheat	\$3.91 (per bushel)	\$3.16 (per bushel)	511.4 (million bushels)	487.1 (million bushels)

* 1 bale = 480 lb; 1 bushel = 60 lb.
Source: Survey of Current Business.

SOLUTION

If a simple aggregate price index is used, the result is

$$\frac{\sum p_n}{\sum p_o} = \frac{\text{sum of prices in given year (1986)}}{\text{sum of prices in base year (1980)}} = \frac{56.8¢ + 316¢}{74.4¢ + 391¢} = 0.801 = 80.1\ (\%)$$

indicating that the average price of these commodities was about 80% as great in 1986 as in 1980.

If we express the price of wheat in cents per pound, it is \$3.91/60 = 6.52¢/lb for 1980 and \$3.16/60 = 5.27¢/lb for 1986. In this case the simple aggregate price index is

$$\frac{\sum p_n}{\sum p_o} = \frac{56.8¢ + 5.27¢}{74.4¢ + 6.52¢} = 76.7\ (\%)$$

This illustrates the fact that the simple aggregate price index can be very sensitive to units used in price quotations; therefore, it is clearly an inappropriate measure for such cases. This fact and the disadvantage noted in Problem 19.11 give us good reasons for not using the simple aggregate index in practice.

The remark at the end of Problem 19.10 applies to this problem as well.

THE SIMPLE AVERAGE-OF-RELATIVES METHOD

19.13 Use the method of the simple average (mean) of relatives to compute a wholesale price index for the dairy products in Table 19.10 for the year 1985, using (*a*) 1980 and (*b*) 1980–1981 as the base.

SOLUTION

(*a*) The price relatives for milk, butter, and cheese in 1985 with 1980 as the base are as follows:

$$\text{Price relative for milk} = \frac{\text{price of milk in 1985}}{\text{price of milk in 1980}} = \frac{12.90}{13.23} = 97.5\ (\%)$$

$$\text{Price relative for butter} = \frac{\text{price of butter in 1985}}{\text{price of butter in 1980}} = \frac{141.1}{139.3} = 101.3\ (\%)$$

$$\text{Price relative for cheese} = \frac{\text{price of cheese in 1985}}{\text{price of cheese in 1980}} = \frac{162.0}{156.2} = 103.7\ (\%)$$

$$\text{Average (mean) of price relatives} = \frac{\sum p_n/p_o}{N} = \frac{97.5 + 101.3 + 103.7}{3} = 100.8\ (\%)$$

19.14 Work Problem 19.13 by using the median instead of the mean.

SOLUTION

(*a*) Required index number = median of price relatives 97.5, 101.3, and 103.7 = 101.3.

(*b*) Required index number = median of price relatives 94.9, 98.2, and 100.2 = 98.2.

19.15 Work Problem 19.13 by using the geometric mean instead of the mean.

SOLUTION

(*a*) Required index number = geometric mean of price relatives 97.5, 101.3, and 103.7 = $\sqrt[3]{(97.5)(101.3)(103.7)} = 100.8$.

(*b*) Required index number = geometric mean of price relatives 94.9, 98.2, and 100.2 = $\sqrt[3]{(94.9)(98.2)(100.2)} = 97.7$.

19.16 Use the simple average (mean) of the price relatives to obtain a price index number for the commodities in Table 19.11, using 1980 as the base year and 1986 as the given year.

SOLUTION

$$\text{Price relative for cotton} = \frac{\text{price of cotton in 1986}}{\text{price of cotton in 1980}} = \frac{56.8¢}{74.4¢} = 76.3\ (\%)$$

$$\text{Price relative for wheat} = \frac{\text{price of wheat in 1986}}{\text{price of wheat in 1980}} = \frac{\$3.16}{\$3.91} = 80.8\ (\%)$$

$$\text{Simple average (mean) of price relatives} = \frac{\sum p_n/p_o}{N} = \frac{76.3 + 80.8}{2} = 78.6\ (\%)$$

Note that the result is *independent* of the units used in price quotations (compare Problem 19.12).

19.17 Work Problem 19.16 by using the geometric mean.

SOLUTION

Required index number = geometric mean of price relatives 76.3 and 78.6 = $\sqrt{(76.3)(78.6)} = 77.4\ (\%)$.

THE WEIGHTED AGGREGATE METHOD; LASPEYRES' AND PAASCHE'S INDEXES

Mathcad **19.18** Using the data of Table 19.10, compute a Laspeyres price index number for the year 1985 with (*a*) 1980 and (*b*) 1980–1981 as the base.

SOLUTION

(*a*) Laspeyres' index, the weighted aggregate price index with base-period quantity weights, is

$$\frac{\sum p_n q_o}{\sum p_o q_o} = \frac{\sum (\text{prices in 1985})(\text{quantities in 1980})}{\sum (\text{prices in 1980})(\text{quantities in 1980})}$$

$$= \frac{(12.90)(128{,}500) + (141.1)(1145) + (162.0)(2381)}{(13.23)(128{,}500) + (139.3)(1145) + (156.2)(2381)} = 0.9881 = 98.8\ (\%)$$

(*b*) The average quantities of milk, butter, and cheese produced in 1980–1981 are $\frac{1}{2}(128{,}500 + 132{,}800) = 130{,}650$, $\frac{1}{2}(1145 + 1228) = 1186.5$, and $\frac{1}{2}(2381 + 2664) = 2522.5$, respectively; the average prices in 1980–1981 are shown in Problem 19.10(*b*). Thus Laspeyres' index is

$$\frac{\sum p_n q_o}{\sum p_o q_o} = \frac{\sum (\text{prices in 1985})(\text{average quantities in 1980–1981})}{\sum (\text{prices in 1980–1981})(\text{average quantities in 1980–1981})}$$

$$= \frac{(12.90)(130{,}650) + (141.1)(1186.5) + (162.0)(2522.5)}{(13.59)(130{,}650) + (143.7)(1186.5) + (161.7)(2522.5)} = 0.9607 = 96.1\ (\%)$$

Mathcad **19.19** Using the data of Table 19.10, compute a Paasche price index number for the year 1985 with (*a*) 1980 and (*b*) 1980–1981 as the base.

SOLUTION

(*a*) Paasche's index, the weighted aggregate price index with given-year quantity weights, is

$$\frac{\sum p_n q_n}{\sum p_o q_n} = \frac{\sum (\text{prices in 1985})(\text{quantities in 1985})}{\sum (\text{prices in 1980})(\text{quantities in 1985})}$$

$$= \frac{(12.90)(143{,}700) + (141.1)(1248) + (162.0)(2854)}{(13.23)(143{,}700) + (139.3)(1248) + (156.2)(2854)} = 0.9886 = 98.9\ (\%)$$

(*b*) Paasche's index is

$$\frac{\sum p_n q_n}{\sum p_o q_n} = \frac{\sum (\text{prices in 1985})(\text{quantities in 1985})}{\sum (\text{prices in 1980–1981})(\text{quantities in 1985})}$$

$$= \frac{(12.90)(143{,}700) + (141.1)(1248) + (162.0)(2854)}{(13.59)(143{,}700) + (143.65)(1248) + (161.7)(2854)} = 0.9609 = 96.1\ (\%)$$

19.20 (*a*) Find the Laspeyres index numbers for the data of Table 19.11.

(*b*) Find the Paasche index numbers for the data of Table 19.11.

(*c*) In the event that revisions of an index number are to be made from year to year, state an advantage of Laspeyres' index over Paasche's index.

SOLUTION

(*a*) Laspeyres' index is

$$\frac{\sum p_n q_o}{\sum p_o q_o} = \frac{\sum (\text{prices in 1986})(\text{quantities in 1980})}{\sum (\text{prices in 1980})(\text{quantities in 1980})}$$

$$= \frac{(56.8¢/\text{lb})(11.122 \times 500 \text{ million lb}) + (316¢/\text{bu})(511.4 \text{ million bu})}{(74.4¢/\text{lb})(11.122 \times 500 \text{ million lb}) + (391¢/\text{bu})(511.4 \text{ million bu})} = 87.2\ (\%)$$

(*b*) Paasche's index is

$$\frac{\sum p_n q_n}{\sum p_o q_n} = \frac{\sum \text{(prices in 1986)(quantities in 1986)}}{\sum \text{(prices in 1980)(quantities in 1986)}}$$

$$= \frac{(56.8¢/\text{lb})(13.432 \times 500 \text{ million lb}) + (316¢/\text{bu})(487.1 \text{ million bu})}{(74.4¢/\text{lb})(13.432 \times 500 \text{ million lb}) + (391¢/\text{bu})(487.1 \text{ million bu})} = 77.6\ (\%)$$

Note: In practice, where an index number is to be computed for many commodities, it is advisable to arrange the computations in a suitable tabular form (see Problem 19.31, for example).

(*c*) In computing a Laspeyres index, the weights (or the quantities produced or consumed in the base year, if a price index is computed) do not change from year to year, therefore, the only information that one needs is a list of the latest prices. In computing a Paasche index, one needs the latest information both about the prices and the weights (or quantities); therefore, computing a Paasche index involves more labor in terms of collecting the data.

19.21 Present an interpretation of the (*a*) Laspeyres and (*b*) Paasche price index numbers in terms of the total value (or total cost) of commodities.

SOLUTION

(*a*) In computing a Laspeyres price index, $\sum p_o q_o$ represents the total value (or total cost) of a set of goods and services of commodities (sometimes called a *market basket*) in the base year or period. The quantity $\sum p_n q_o$ represents the total value of *this same market basket* in the given year or period. Thus a Laspeyres price index serves to measure the total costs in any given year of a *fixed market basket* of commodities purchased in the base year.

(*b*) In computing a Paasche price index, $\sum p_o q_n$ is the total value (or total cost) of commodities purchased in the given year, assuming base-year prices, while $\sum p_n q_n$ is the total value of commodities purchased in the given year at given-year prices. Thus a Paasche price index serves to measure the total cost of a *given-year market basket* relative to what the cost would have been if the purchase had been made in the base year.

19.22 It is sometimes stated that the Laspeyres price index tends to *overestimate* price changes, while the Paasche price index tends to *underestimate* them. Present a possible reason to substantiate this statement.

SOLUTION

According to the economic *law of supply and demand*, people tend to purchase *less* when prices are *high* and to purchase *more* when prices are *low*. This is the so-called *elastic demand*, which is valid if the need for commodities is not absolutely essential.

In the case of the Laspeyres index, $\sum p_n q_o$ will be somewhat higher than it should be, since according to the law of supply and demand people tend to purchase fewer high-priced commodities and more lower-priced commodities, so that the total cost would be less than predicted by $\sum p_n q_o$. Thus the Laspeyres index $(\sum p_n q_o)/\sum p_o q_o)$ tends to be higher than it should be.

In the case of the Paasche index, the roles played by the base-year and given-year quantities are interchanged from what they were in the case of the Laspeyres index. This interchange tends to make the Paasche index lower than it should be.

The above reasoning does not imply that the Laspeyres index is *always* higher than the Paasche index, but only that it *tends* to be higher. In practice, the Laspeyres index can be greater than, less than, or equal to the Paasche index. (See Problems 19.18 and 19.19, in which the Laspeyres index is in fact *less* than the Paasche index.)

19.23 Prove that weighted aggregate price index numbers with fixed (quantity) weights satisfy the circular test.

SOLUTION

Letting q_o denote the fixed weights, we have for any periods a, b, and c the index numbers

$$I_{a|b} = \frac{\sum p_b q_o}{\sum p_a q_o} \quad \text{and} \quad I_{b|c} = \frac{\sum p_c q_o}{\sum p_b q_o}$$

Then

$$I_{a|b} I_{b|c} = \frac{\sum p_b q_o}{\sum p_a q_o} \cdot \frac{\sum p_c q_o}{\sum p_b q_o} = \frac{\sum p_c q_o}{\sum p_a q_o} = I_{a|c}$$

which shows that the circular test is satisfied.

The Laspeyres and Paasche index numbers do not satisfy the circular test.

FISHER'S IDEAL INDEX

19.24 Show that Fisher's ideal index is the geometric mean of the Laspeyres and Paasche index numbers.

SOLUTION

Letting F, L, and P denote Fisher's, Laspeyres', and Paasche's index numbers, respectively, we have

$$F = \sqrt{\left(\frac{\sum p_n q_o}{\sum p_o q_o}\right)\left(\frac{\sum p_n q_n}{\sum p_o q_n}\right)} = \sqrt{LP}$$

using the definition of L and P. Since $\sqrt{LP}$ is the geometric mean of L and P, the required result follows.

19.25 Prove that Fisher's ideal index lies between the Laspeyres and Paasche index numbers.

SOLUTION

This follows at once from the fact that $F = \sqrt{LP}$ lies between L and P, since L and P are positive numbers. Note that if $L = P$, then $F = L = P$.

Since by Problem 19.22, L has a tendency to *overestimate* price changes while P has a tendency to *underestimate* them, it follows that F, which lies between L and P, should provide a better estimate than L or P.

19.26 Determine Fisher's ideal price index for the dairy products in Table 19.10 for the year 1985, using (a) 1980 and (b) 1980–1981 as the base.

SOLUTION

(a) By Problems 19.18(a) and 19.19(a),

$$F = \sqrt{LP} = \sqrt{(0.9881)(0.9886)} = 0.9883 = 98.8\ (\%)$$

(b) By Problems 19.18(b) and 19.19(b),

$$F = \sqrt{LP} = \sqrt{(0.9607)(0.9609)} = 0.9608 = 96.1\ (\%)$$

19.27 Determine Fisher's ideal price index for the data of Table 19.11.

SOLUTION

From Problem 19.20, $F = \sqrt{LP} = \sqrt{(0.872)(0.776)} = 0.823 = 82.3\ (\%)$. Note that a good approximation to $\sqrt{LP}$ when L and P are approximately equal is given by $\frac{1}{2}(L + P)$. This arithmetic mean of L and P can be used as the definition of a new index number lying between L and P.

19.28 Prove that Fisher's ideal index satisfies the time-reversal test.

SOLUTION

Let $F_{o|n}$ denote Fisher's ideal index number for a given year with respect to a base year, and let $F_{n|o}$ denote Fisher's ideal index when the base year and given year are interchanged. Then the time-reversal test is satisfied if $F_{o|n} = 1/F_{n|o}$ or $F_{o|n}F_{n|o} = 1$. By definition,

$$F_{o|n} = \sqrt{\left(\frac{\sum p_n q_o}{\sum p_o q_o}\right)\left(\frac{\sum p_n q_n}{\sum p_o q_n}\right)}$$

Then

$$F_{n|o} = \sqrt{\left(\frac{\sum p_o q_n}{\sum p_n q_n}\right)\left(\frac{\sum p_o q_o}{\sum p_n q_o}\right)}$$

and

$$F_{o|n}F_{n|o} = \sqrt{\left(\frac{\sum p_n q_o}{\sum p_o q_o}\right)\left(\frac{\sum p_n q_n}{\sum p_o q_n}\right)\left(\frac{\sum p_o q_n}{\sum p_n q_n}\right)\left(\frac{\sum p_o q_o}{\sum p_n q_o}\right)} = 1$$

THE MARSHALL–EDGEWORTH INDEX

19.29 Calculate the Marshall-Edgeworth price index for the data of Problem 19.10.

SOLUTION

The Marshall-Edgeworth index is

$$\frac{\sum p_n(q_o + q_n)}{\sum p_o(q_o + q_n)} = \frac{\sum \text{(prices in 1985)(sum of quantities in 1980 and 1985)}}{\sum \text{(prices in 1980)(sum of quantities in 1980 and 1985)}}$$

$$= \frac{(12.90)(128{,}500 + 143{,}700) + (141.1)(1145 + 1228) + (162.0)(2381 + 2854)}{(13.23)(128{,}500 + 143{,}700) + (139.3)(1145 + 1228) + (156.2)(2381 + 2854)}$$

$$= 0.9884 = 98.8\ (\%)$$

Note that this lies between the Laspeyres and Paasche index numbers (see Problem 19.20). For a proof that this is always the case, see Problem 19.30.

19.30 (*a*) Prove that if $X_1/X_2 < Y_1/Y_2$, then $X_1/X_2 < (X_1 + Y_1)/(X_2 + Y_2) < Y_1/Y_2$, where X_1, X_2, Y_1, and Y_2 are any positive numbers.

(*b*) Use the result in part (*a*) to prove that the Marshall-Edgeworth index number lies between the Laspeyres and Paasche index numbers.

SOLUTION

(*a*) If $X_1/X_2 < Y_1/Y_2$, then $$X_1Y_2 < X_2Y_1 \qquad (18)$$

Adding X_1X_2 to both sides of equation (*18*), we have

$$X_1X_2 + X_1Y_2 < X_1X_2 + X_2Y_1 \qquad \text{or} \qquad X_1(X_2 + Y_2) < X_2(X_1 + Y_1)$$

or

$$\frac{X_1}{X_2} < \frac{X_1 + Y_1}{X_2 + Y_2} \qquad (19)$$

on dividing both sides by $X_2(X_2 + Y_2)$. Adding Y_1Y_2 to both sides of equation (*18*), we have

$$X_1Y_2 + Y_1Y_2 < X_2Y_1 + Y_1Y_2 \qquad \text{or} \qquad Y_2(X_1 + Y_1) < Y_1(X_2 + Y_2)$$

or

$$\frac{X_1 + Y_1}{X_2 + Y_2} < \frac{Y_1}{Y_2} \qquad (20)$$

on dividing both sides by $Y_1(X_1 + Y_1)$.

The required result follows from equations (*19*) and (*20*).

(*b*) **Case 1** (Laspeyres' index is less than Paasche's index)

Let $X_1 = \sum p_n q_o$, $X_2 = \sum p_o q_o$, $Y_1 = \sum p_n q_n$, and $Y_2 = \sum p_o q_n$. Thus $X_1/X_2 < Y_1/Y_2$, and thus from part (*a*) we have

$$\frac{\sum p_n q_o}{\sum p_o q_o} < \frac{\sum p_n q_o + \sum p_n q_n}{\sum p_o q_o + \sum p_o q_n} < \frac{\sum p_n q_n}{\sum p_o q_n}$$

or

$$\frac{\sum p_n q_o}{\sum p_o q_o} < \frac{\sum p_n (q_o + q_n)}{\sum p_o (q_o + q_n)} < \frac{\sum p_n q_n}{\sum p_o q_n}$$

or Laspeyres index < Marshall-Edgeworth index < Paasche index

Case 2 (Paasche's index is less than Laspeyres' index)

Let $X_1 = \sum p_n q_n$, $X_2 = \sum p_o q_n$, $Y_1 = \sum p_n q_o$, and $Y_2 = \sum p_o q_o$. Thus $X_1/X_2 < Y_1/Y_2$, and thus from part (*a*) we have

$$\frac{\sum p_n q_n}{\sum p_o q_n} < \frac{\sum p_n q_n + \sum p_n q_o}{\sum p_o q_n + \sum p_o q_o} < \frac{\sum p_n q_o}{\sum p_o q_o}$$

or

$$\frac{\sum p_n q_n}{\sum p_o q_n} < \frac{\sum p_n (q_o + q_n)}{\sum p_o (q_o + q_n)} < \frac{\sum p_n q_n}{\sum p_o q_n}$$

or Paasche index < Marshall-Edgeworth index < Laspeyres index

It follows from Cases 1 and 2 that regardless of whether Laspeyres' index is larger or smaller than Paasche's index, the Marshall-Edgeworth index will lie between them.

THE WEIGHTED AVERAGE-OF-RELATIVES METHOD

19.31 Compute a weighted arithmetic mean of the price relatives for the data of Table 19.11 by using (*a*) given-year value weights and (*b*) base-year value weights, where the given year is 1985 and the base year is 1980.

SOLUTION

(*a*) Using given-year value weights, the weighted arithmetic mean of the price relatives is

$$\frac{\sum (p_n/p_o)(p_n q_n)}{\sum p_n q_n} = \frac{\sum \text{(price relatives)(given-year values)}}{\sum \text{(given-year values)}}$$

The calculations involved can be organized as in Table 19.12, where the subscript n stands for the given year, 1985; where the subscript o stands for the base year, 1980; and where p and q stand for

Table 19.12

	p_o	p_n	q_n	p_n/p_o	$p_n q_n$ (millions of dollars)	$(p_n/p_o)(p_n q_n)$ (millions of dollars)
Cotton	74.4¢ (per pound)	56.8¢ (per pound)	13.432 × 480 (million pounds)	0.7634	3662.1	2795.6
Wheat	$3.91 (per bushel)	$3.16 (per bushel)	487.1 (million bushels)	0.8082	1539.2	1244.0
					$\sum p_n q_n = 5201.3$	$\sum (p_n/p_o)(p_n q_n) = 4039.6$

the prices and quantities, respectively. Thus the required index number is

$$\frac{\sum (p_n/p_o)(p_n q_n)}{\sum p_n q_n} = \frac{4039.6}{5201.3} = 77.7\ (\%)$$

(*b*) Using base-year value weights, the weighted arithmetic mean of the price relatives is

$$\frac{\sum (p_n/p_o)(p_o q_o)}{\sum p_o q_o} = \frac{\sum p_n q_o}{\sum p_o q_o} = \text{Laspeyres' index of Problem 19.20}(a) = 87.2\ (\%)$$

We can also proceed by making a table, as in part (*a*).

QUANTITY, OR VOLUME, INDEX NUMBERS

19.32 Use the data of Table 19.11 to compute a volume index for 1986 with base year 1980 by using (*a*) a simple arithmetic mean of volume relatives, (*b*) a weighted aggregate volume index with base-year price weights, and (*c*) a weighted aggregate volume index with given-year price weights.

SOLUTION

(*a*) The simple arithmetic-mean-of-relatives volume index is

$$\frac{\sum (q_n/q_o)}{N} = \frac{13.432/11.122 + 487.1/511.4}{2} = \frac{120.8\ (\%) + 95.2\ (\%)}{2} = 108.0\ (\%)$$

(*b*) The weighted aggregate volume index with base-year price weights is

$$\frac{\sum q_n p_o}{\sum q_o p_o} = \frac{\sum \text{(quantities in 1986)(prices in 1980)}}{\sum \text{(quantities in 1980)(prices in 1980)}}$$

$$= \frac{(13.432 \times 480 \text{ million lb})(74.4¢/\text{lb}) + (487.1 \text{ million bu})(391¢/\text{bu})}{(11.122 \times 480 \text{ million lb})(74.4¢/\text{lb}) + (511.4 \text{ million bu})(391¢/\text{bu})} = 112.2\ (\%)$$

This is sometimes called *Laspeyres' quantity* (*or volume*) *index number.*

(*c*) The weighted aggregate volume index with given-year price weights is

$$\frac{\sum q_n p_n}{\sum q_o p_n} = \frac{\sum \text{(quantities in 1986)(prices in 1986)}}{\sum \text{(quantities in 1980)(prices in 1986)}}$$

$$= \frac{(13.432 \times 480 \text{ million lb})(56.8¢/\text{lb}) + (487.1 \text{ million bu})(316¢/\text{bu})}{(11.122 \times 480 \text{ million lb})(56.8¢/\text{lb}) + (511.4 \text{ million bu})(316¢/\text{bu})} = 111.9\ (\%)$$

19.33 From the results of Problem 19.32, determine Fisher's ideal volume (or quantity) index number.

SOLUTION

Like Fisher's ideal price index, Fisher's ideal volume index is given by the geometric mean of the Laspeyres and Paasche volume index numbers. Thus, from Problem 19.32,

$$\text{Fisher's ideal volume index number} = \sqrt{(112.2)(111.9)} = 112.0\ (\%)$$

VALUE INDEX NUMBERS

19.34 Prove that Fisher's ideal index satisfies the factor-reversal test.

SOLUTION

The factor-reversal test is satisfied if the index is such that

$$\text{Value index} = \text{(price index)(quantity index)}$$

Let F_P and F_Q be Fisher's ideal price and quantity indexes, respectively. Then

$$\text{Value index} = F_P F_Q = \sqrt{\left(\frac{\sum p_n q_o}{\sum p_o q_o}\right)\left(\frac{\sum p_n q_n}{\sum p_o q_n}\right)}\sqrt{\left(\frac{\sum q_n p_o}{q_o p_o}\right)\left(\frac{\sum q_n p_n}{\sum q_o p_n}\right)} = \frac{\sum p_n q_n}{\sum p_o q_o}$$

and thus Fisher's ideal index satisfies the factor-reversal test.

19.35 Calculate the value index in Problem 19.34 for the data of Table 19.11.

SOLUTION

Since the result

$$\text{Value index} = (\text{price index})(\text{quantity index})$$

holds exactly when Fisher's ideal indexes are used, from Problems 19.27 and 19.33 we obtain

$$\text{Value index} = (82.3\%)(112.0\%) = 92.2\%$$

This result can also be obtained by direct substitution in $\sum p_n q_n / \sum p_o q_o$.

CHANGING THE BASE PERIOD OF INDEX NUMBERS

19.36 Establish the validity of the method in Problem 19.3 for obtaining price relatives for a new base period.

SOLUTION

Assume the periods to be numbered consecutively from 1 to N, as in the first row of Table 19.13, and let $p_1, p_2, \ldots, p_N$ denote the prices for these periods, as in the second row of the table. The price relatives corresponding to the periods j and k, which we call the old and new periods, respectively, are indicated in the third and fourth rows of the table; here $p_{j|1} = p_1/p_j$, $p_{j|2} = p_2/p_j$, etc. It is clear that the fourth row can be obtained from the third row by dividing each entry in the third row by $p_{j|k}$ (i.e., the price relative of the kth period with respect to the jth period as base); for example,

$$\frac{p_{j|1}}{p_{j|k}} = \frac{p_1/p_j}{p_k/p_j} = \frac{p_1}{p_k} = p_{k|1} \qquad \text{etc.}$$

The results clearly apply to quantity and value relatives as well as to price relatives.

Table 19.13

Period	1	2	3	...	j	...	k	...	N
Price	p_1	p_2	p_3	...	p_j	...	p_k	...	p_N
Price relative corresponding to old period j	$p_{j\|1}$	$p_{j\|2}$	$p_{j\|3}$	...	100%	...	$p_{j\|k}$	...	$p_{j\|N}$
Price relative corresponding to new period k	$p_{k\|1}$	$p_{k\|2}$	$p_{k\|3}$	...	$p_{k\|j}$	...	100%	...	$p_{k\|N}$

19.37 Prove that the method of Problem 19.36 for changing the base period of index numbers is applicable if and only if the index numbers satisfy the circular test.

SOLUTION

If we denote the index numbers for the various periods with the jth period as base by

$$I_{j|1}, I_{j|2}, \ldots, I_{j|N} \tag{21}$$

and the corresponding index numbers with the kth period as base by

$$I_{k|1}, I_{k|2}, \ldots, I_{k|N} \tag{22}$$

we will obtain sequence (*22*) by dividing each member of sequence (*21*) by $I_{j|k}$ if and only if

$$\frac{I_{j|1}}{I_{j|k}} = I_{k|1}, \frac{I_{j|2}}{I_{j|k}} = I_{k|2}, \ldots$$

or

$$I_{j|1} = I_{j|k}I_{k|1}, I_{j|2} = I_{j|k}I_{k|2}, \ldots$$

which implies that the index numbers satisfy the circular test.

Since the Laspeyres, Paasche, Fisher, and Marshall-Edgeworth index numbers do not satisfy the circular test, the method for changing the base does not apply exactly. However, it does apply approximately in practice.

Weighted aggregate index numbers with fixed-year weights do satisfy the circular test (see Problem 19.23). For index numbers computed in this manner, the method given for changing the base does apply exactly.

19.38 Table 19.14 shows the index of industrial production for all U.S. manufacturers for the years 1974–1985 with 1977 as the base period. Obtain a new index with (*a*) 1979 and (*b*) 1974–1976 as the base.

Table 19.14

Year	1974	1975	1976	1977	1978	1979	1980	1981	1982	1983	1984	1985
Index of industrial production (1977 = 100)	93	85	93	100	107	111	109	111	103	109	122	125

Source: Survey of Current Business.

SOLUTION

(*a*) Divide each index in Table 19.14 by 111 (the index corresponding to 1979) and express the result as a percentage. The required index numbers, with 1979 as the base, are shown in Table 19.15.

(*b*) The average (mean) index for the years 1974–1985 with 1974–1976 as the base is $\frac{1}{3}(93+85+93) = 90.33$. Dividing each index in Table 19.14 by 90.33 and expressing the result as a percentage, we obtain the required index numbers, which are shown in Table 19.16. Note that the average index for the new base period, 1974–1976, is $\frac{1}{3}(103+94+103) = 100$, as it should be.

Table 19.15

Year	1974	1975	1976	1977	1978	1979	1980	1981	1982	1983	1984	1985
Index of industrial production (1979 = 100)	84	77	84	90	96	100	98	100	93	98	110	113

Table 19.16

Year	1974	1975	1976	1977	1978	1979	1980	1981	1982	1983	1984	1985
Index of industrial production (1974–1976 = 100)	103	94	103	111	118	123	121	123	114	121	135	138

DEFLATION OF TIME SERIES

19.39 Table 19.17 shows the average weekly wage of U.S. production workers in the retail trade for the years 1973-1983. It also shows the consumer price index for these years, with 1972 as the base. In terms of the workers' average weekly wage in 1973, determine their real wages during the years 1973-1983.

Table 19.17

Year	1973	1974	1975	1976	1977	1978	1979	1980	1981	1982	1983
Average weekly wage of production workers (dollars)	96.32	102.68	108.86	114.60	121.66	130.20	138.62	147.38	158.03	163.85	171.05
Consumer price index (1972 = 100)	106.2	117.9	128.7	136.1	144.9	155.9	173.5	197.0	217.4	230.7	238.1

Source: U.S. Department of Labor.

SOLUTION

We first form a new consumer price index with 1973 as the base year by dividing all the numbers in the bottom row of Table 19.17 by 106.2 and expressing the result as a percentage. The results are shown in the middle row of Table 19.18. We then divide each average wage for the given years (middle row of Table 19.17) by the corresponding index number (middle row of Table 19.18) to obtain the real wages (bottom row of Table 19.18).

Thus, for example, the real wage corresponding to 1983 is $171.05/224.2(\%) = \$76.29$. It follows that although the apparent wages almost doubled from 1973 to 1983, the real wages actually decreased over the years; in fact, the real wage in 1983 was about \$20 less than 1973. In other words, the workers' purchasing power decreased by approximately $20/96.32 = 21\%$.

Table 19.18

Year	1973	1974	1975	1976	1977	1978	1979	1980	1981	1982	1983
Consumer price index (1973 = 100)	100.0	111.0	121.2	128.2	136.4	146.8	163.4	185.5	204.7	217.2	224.2
Real weekly wage of production workers (dollars)	96.32	92.50	89.82	89.39	89.19	88.69	84.83	79.45	77.20	75.44	76.29

19.40 Use the consumer price index in Table 19.18 to determine the dollar's purchasing power for the various years, assuming that in 1973 the dollar was actually worth a dollar in purchasing power.

SOLUTION

Dividing \$1.00 by each price index in the middle row of Table 19.18, we obtain Table 19.19, which shows the purchasing power of the 1973 dollar in each of the given years. In 1983, for example, the entry 0.45 means that a 1983 dollar could buy only 45% of what a 1973 dollar could buy; that is, the dollar was worth \$0.45 in terms of the 1973 dollar.

Data expressed in terms of the value of a dollar at some specified period of time are said to be expressed in *constant dollars* (with the given period as the reference period, or base).

Table 19.19

Year	1973	1974	1975	1976	1977	1978	1979	1980	1981	1982	1983
Purchasing power of the dollar in 1973 dollars	1.00	0.90	0.83	0.78	0.73	0.68	0.61	0.54	0.49	0.46	0.45

For each \$1.00 earned in 1973, in 1983 a worker would have to earn \$1.00/0.45 = \$2.22 just to stay even with (or "keep up" with) inflation. Another way of saying this is that in *constant 1973 dollars* the workers earned \$96.32 in 1973, \$92.50 in 1974, \$89.82 in 1975, . . . , and \$76.29 in 1983, as seen from Table 19.18.

Supplementary Problems

PRICE RELATIVES

19.41 Table 19.20 shows the average U.S. wholesale prices of eggs for the years 1978–1985. Find the price relative (*a*) for the year 1984 with 1978 as the base, (*b*) for the years 1983 and 1985 with 1981 as the base, and (*c*) for the years 1978–1985 with 1978–1980 = 100.

Table 19.20

Year	1978	1979	1980	1981	1982	1983	1984	1985
Average price of eggs (cents per dozen)	60.3	66.2	62.8	69.0	66.8	72.7	78.6	63.4

Source: U.S. Department of Agriculture.

19.42 Prove (*a*) that $p_{a|b}p_{b|c}p_{c|a} = 1$ and (*b*) that $p_{a|b}p_{b|c}p_{c|d} = p_{a|d}$.

19.43 Prove that $p_{0|n} = p_{0|1}\,p_{1|2}\,p_{2|3}\cdots p_{(n-1)|n}$.

19.44 Prove that the modified circular property follows directly from the circular property and the time-reversal property.

19.45 Table 19.21 shows the price relatives of a commodity with 1977–1979 = 100. Determine the price relatives with (*a*) 1980 = 100 and (*b*) 1983–1984 = 100.

Table 19.21

Year	1980	1981	1982	1983	1984	1985
Price relative (1977–1979 = 100)	127	134	118	125	137	141

19.46 The price relative for the year 1984 with 1986 as the base is $62\frac{1}{2}$, while the price relative for the year 1985 with 1984 as the base is $133\frac{1}{3}$. Find the price relative for the year 1986 with (*a*) 1985 and (*b*) 1984–1985 as the base.

19.47 In 1980 the average price of a commodity decreased by 25% of its 1976 value but increased by 50% of its 1972 value. Find the price relative for (*a*) 1976 and (*b*) 1980 with 1972 as the base.

QUANTITY, OR VOLUME, RELATIVES

19.48 Table 19.22 shows the electric energy in billions of kilowatt-hours (kWh) sold to U.S. residential (or domestic) customers during the years 1975–1986. Reduce the data to quantity relatives with (*a*) 1981 and (*b*) 1975–1977 as the base.

Table 19.22

Year	1975	1976	1977	1978	1979	1980	1981	1982	1983	1984	1985	1986
Electric energy (billions of kWh)	1.918	2.038	2.124	2.206	2.247	2.286	2.295	2.241	2.310	2.416	2.470	2.512

Source: Survey of Current Business.

19.49 In 1984 the production of a metal ore increased by 40% over that of 1983. In 1985 the production was 20% below that of 1984 but $16\frac{2}{3}$% above that of 1986. Find the price relatives for the years 1983–1986 with (*a*) 1983, (*b*) 1986, and (*c*) 1983–1986 as the base.

19.50 If the production of metal ore in Problem 19.49 was 3.20 million short tons for the year 1985, determine the production for the years (*a*) 1983, (*b*) 1984, and (*c*) 1986.

VALUE RELATIVES

19.51 In 1985 the price of a commodity increased by 50% over that in 1978, while the production of the commodity decreased by 30%. In 1985, by what percentage did the total dollar value of the commodity increase or decrease with respect to the 1978 value?

19.52 Table 19.23 shows the price and the value relatives of a commodity for the years 1982–1986, with the base periods as indicated. Find the quantity relatives for the commodity with (*a*) 1982 and (*b*) 1982–1984 as the base. Interpret the results.

Table 19.23

Year	1982	1983	1984	1985	1986
Price relative (1982 = 100)	100	125	150	175	200
Value relative (1973–1975 = 100)	150	180	207	231	252

LINK AND CHAIN RELATIVES

19.53 The link relatives for the consumption of a commodity during the years 1982–1985 are 90, 120, 125, and 80, respectively.

(*a*) Find the price relative for 1983 with 1985 as the base.

(*b*) Chain the link relatives to a 1984 base.

(*c*) Chain the link relatives to a 1982–1983 base.

19.54 At the end of the first of n successive years, the production of a commodity was A units. In each successive year the production increased by $r\%$ over that of the previous year.

(a) Show that the production during the nth year was $A(1+r/100)^{n-1}$ units.

(b) Show that the total production for all n years was $(100A/r)[(1+r/100)^n-1]$ units.

INDEX NUMBERS; THE SIMPLE AGGREGATE METHOD

19.55 Table 19.24 shows the U.S. prices and quantities of consumption of various nonferrous metals for the years 1975 and 1984. Taking 1975 as the base year, calculate a price index for the year 1984 by using the simple aggregate method.

19.56 Prove that the simple aggregate index number satisfies the time-reversal and circular tests but does not satisfy the factor-reversal test.

THE SIMPLE AVERAGE-OF-RELATIVES METHOD

19.57 From the data in Table 19.24 of Problem 19.55, use a simple average (mean) of the price relatives to obtain a price index of nonferrous metals for 1984 with 1975 as the base year, and compare the results with those of Problem 19.55.

Table 19.24

	Price (cents per pound)		Quantity (millions of pounds)	
	1975	1984	1975	1984
Copper	64.2	66.8	3440	2406
Lead	21.5	25.6	1144	710
Tin	339.8	623.8	49.4	42.8
Zinc	39.0	48.6	1068	558

Source: U.S. Department of the Interior, Bureau of Mines.

19.58 Work Problem 19.57 by using the median.

19.59 Work Problem 19.57 by using the geometric mean.

19.60 Work Problem 19.57 by using the harmonic mean.

THE WEIGHTED AGGREGATE METHOD; LASPEYRES' AND PAASCHE'S INDEXES

19.61 From the data in Table 19.24, obtain a Laspeyres price index for 1984 with 1975 as the base year.

19.62 From the data in Table 19.24, obtain a Paasche price index for 1984 with 1975 as the base year.

19.63 Show that (a) Laspeyres' and (b) Paasche's indexes do not satisfy the time-reversal and factor-reversal tests.

FISHER'S IDEAL INDEX

19.64 From the data in Table 19.24, obtain Fisher's ideal price index for 1984 with 1975 as the base year.

19.65 Show that Fisher's ideal index does not satisfy the circular test.

THE MARSHALL–EDGEWORTH INDEX

19.66 From the data in Table 19.24, obtain the Marshall-Edgeworth price index for 1984 with 1975 as the base year.

19.67 Show that the Marshall-Edgeworth index satisfies the time-reversal test but not the factor-reversal test.

THE WEIGHTED AVERAGE-OF-RELATIVES METHOD

19.68 From the data in Table 19.24, obtain the weighted average-of-relatives index number for 1984 with 1975 as the base year, using as weights the (*a*) given-year values and (*b*) base-year values.

QUANTITY, OR VOLUME, INDEX NUMBERS

19.69 From the data in Table 19.24, calculate quantity indexes for 1984 with 1975 as the base year by using (*a*) the simple arithmetic mean of the quantity relatives, (*b*) the simple geometric mean of the quantity relatives, (*c*) a weighted aggregate quantity index with base-year price weights (Laspeyres' quantity index number), (*d*) a weighted aggregate quantity index with given-year price weights (Paasche's quantity index number), (*e*) Fisher's ideal quantity index, and (*f*) the Marshall-Edgeworth quantity index.

VALUE INDEX NUMBERS

19.70 (*a*) Using 1975 as the base year in the data of Table 19.24, calculate the value index for 1984.
(*b*) Verify that the value index in part (*a*) is the same as that obtained from the product of Fisher's ideal price and quantity indexes.

19.71 With 1975 as the base year in the data of Table 19.24, calculate the price index × quantity index for the year 1984, using (*a*) Laspeyres' and (*b*) Paasche's index numbers. Compare the results with the true value index.

19.72 Prove that simple aggregate value index numbers satisfy the time-reversal and circular tests.

CHANGING THE BASE PERIOD OF INDEX NUMBERS

19.73 Table 19.25 shows the wholesale (or producer) price index of all commodities in the United States for the years 1973–1983 with base period 1967. Obtain the price index with (*a*) 1973 and (*b*) 1976–1978 as the base.

Table 19.25

Year	1973	1974	1975	1976	1977	1978	1979	1980	1981	1982	1983
Wholesale price index (1967 = 100)	134.7	160.1	174.9	183.0	194.2	209.3	235.6	268.8	293.4	299.3	303.1

Source: Survey of Current Business.

19.74 Compare the wholesale price index of Problem 19.73 with the consumer price index given in Table 19.18 of Problem 19.39, and discuss the similarities and differences between these two indexes.

19.75 Table 19.26 shows the consumer price indexes for food, housing, and medical care in the United States for the years 1973–1983 with 1967 as the base.

(*a*) Obtain the price indexes with 1973 as the base.

(*b*) Would you have been able to obtain the results in part (*a*) if the base year 1967 had not been given? Explain.

Table 19.26

Year	1973	1974	1975	1976	1977	1978	1979	1980	1981	1982	1983
Food	141.4	161.7	175.4	180.8	192.2	211.2	234.7	255.3	274.9	285.8	291.8
Housing	133.7	148.8	164.5	174.6	186.5	202.8	227.6	263.3	293.5	314.7	323.1
Medical care	137.7	150.5	168.6	184.7	202.4	219.4	239.7	265.9	294.5	328.7	357.3

Source: U.S. Bureau of Labor Statistics.

19.76 Referring to Problem 19.74, determine (*a*) the percentage increase of housing costs over food costs, (*b*) the percentage increase of medical-care costs over food costs, (*c*) the percentage increase or decrease of medical-care costs over housing costs, and (*d*) the year when the housing-cost increases first began to exceed the food-cost increases.

DEFLATION OF TIME SERIES

19.77 (*a*) From the data in Table 19.25 of Problem 19.73, determine the wholesale purchasing power of a dollar in each of the years 1973–1983.

(*b*) Compare the results obtained in part (*a*) with the consumer purchasing power of a dollar obtained in Problem 19.40, and discuss reasons for the similarities or differences.

19.78 How much would the workers of Problem 19.39 have had to earn per week in 1983 just to maintain the same standard of living of 1973? Compare your answer with the actual earnings.

19.79 (*a*) A family purchased a house in 1975 for $45,000. Assuming that they made no addition to the house, use Table 19.17 of Problem 19.39 to determine a fair price for resale in 1982.

(*b*) What other factors should you take into account when estimating this resale price?

19.80 Work Problem 19.79 if the family made additions of $6000 and $4000 to the house in 1978 and 1980, respectively.

19.81 A given time series shows the total annual dollar value of a set of commodities.

(*a*) Describe how to adjust the time series so as to eliminate the effect of the dollar's changing value from year to year.

(*b*) Use an example to illustrate the method described in part (*a*).

19.82 Deflate the time series of Table 18.44, and explain the significance of the deflated data.

19.83 Prove that the method of deflating a time series (such as the method used in Problem 19.39) is strictly applicable only if the index numbers satisfy the factor-reversal test.

19.84 Table 19.27 shows the wholesale prices and quantities of various U.S. farm products for the years 1978 and 1985. All quantities are in millions of bushels except those of cotton, which are in millions of bales. Taking 1978 as the base year, calculate a wholesale price index number for 1985, using (*a*) the simple aggregate method, (*b*) a simple average (mean) of relatives, (*c*) Laspeyres' index, (*d*) Paasche's index, (*e*) Fisher's ideal index, (*f*) the Marshall–Edgeworth index, and (*g*) a weighted arithmetic mean with given-year value weights.

19.85 Taking 1978 as the base year, calculate a quantity index number for 1985 by using the data in Table 19.27 and each of the methods in Problem 19.84: (*a*) through (*g*).

Table 19.27

	1978		1985	
	Price (dollars)	Quantity	Price (dollars)	Quantity
Barley	2.32	454.8	2.00	589.2
Corn	2.53	7268	2.41	8865
Cotton	0.592	10.9	0.548	13.4
Oats	1.34	581.7	1.25	518.6
Soybeans	5.96	1869	5.16	2099
Wheat	3.71	1776	3.16	2425

Source: U.S. Department of Agriculture.

19.86 Prove that if the Laspeyres and Paasche index numbers are equal, then they are equal to the Marshall-Edgeworth and Fisher ideal index numbers.

19.87 Construct a table of the various types of index numbers, specifying in each case whether it does or does not satisfy the time-reversal, factor-reversal, and circular tests.

Answers to Supplementary Problems

CHAPTER 1

1.46 (*a*) Continuous; (*b*) continuous; (*c*) discrete; (*d*) discrete; (*e*) discrete.

1.47 (*a*) Zero upward; continuous. (*b*) 2, 3, . . . ; discrete.
(*c*) Single, married, divorced, separated, widowed; discrete. (*d*) Zero upward; continuous.
(*e*) 0, 1, 2, . . . ; discrete.

1.48 (*a*) 3300; (*b*) 5.8; (*c*) 0.004; (*d*) 46.74; (*e*) 126.00; (*f*) 4,000,000; (*g*) 148; (*h*) 0.000099; (*i*) 2180; (*j*) 43.88.

1.49 (*a*) 1,325,000; (*b*) 0.0041872; (*c*) 0.0000280; (*d*) 7,300,000,000; (*e*) 0.0003487; (*f*) 18.50.

1.50 (*a*) 3; (*b*) 4; (*c*) 7; (*d*) 3; (*e*) 8; (*f*) unlimited; (*g*) 3; (*h*) 3; (*i*) 4; (*j*) 5.

1.51 (*a*) 0.005 million bu, or 5000 bu; three. (*b*) 0.000000005 cm, or 5×10^{-9} cm; four. (*c*) 0.5 ft; four.
(*d*) 0.05×10^8 m, or 5×10^6 m; two. (*e*) 0.5 mi/sec; six. (*f*) 0.5 thousand mi/sec, or 500 mi/sec; three.

1.52 (*a*) 3.17×10^{-4}; (*b*) 4.280×10^8; (*c*) 2.160000×10^4; (*d*) 9.810×10^{-6}; (*e*) 7.32×10^5; (*f*) 1.80×10^{-3}.

1.53 (*a*) 374; (*b*) 14.0.

1.54 (*a*) 280 (two significant figures), 2.8 hundred, or 2.8×10^2; (*b*) 178.9;
(*c*) 250,000 (three significant figures), 250 thousand, or 2.50×10^5; (*d*) 53.0; (*e*) 5.461; (*f*) 9.05;
(*g*) 11.54; (*h*) 5,745,000 (four significant figures), 5745 thousand, 5.745 million, or 5.745×10^6; (*i*) 1.2;
(*j*) 4157.

1.55 (*a*) −11; (*b*) 2; (*c*) $\frac{35}{8}$, or 4.375; (*d*) 21; (*e*) 3; (*f*) −16; (*g*) $\sqrt{98}$, or 9.89961 approximately;
(*h*) $-7/\sqrt{34}$, or −1.20049 approximately; (*i*) 32; (*j*) $10/\sqrt{17}$, or 2.42536 approximately.

1.56 (*a*) 22, 18, 14, 10, 6, 2, −2, −6, and −10; (*b*) 19.6, 16.4, 13.2, 2.8, −0.8, −4, and −8.4;
(*c*) −1.2, 30, $10 - 4\sqrt{2} = 4.34$ approximately, and $10 + 4\pi = 22.57$ approximately;
(*d*) 3, 1, 5, 2.1, −1.5, 2.5, and 0; (*e*) $X = \frac{1}{4}(10 - Y)$.

1.57 (*a*) −5; (*b*) −24; (*c*) 8.

1.58 (*a*) −8; (*b*) 4; (*c*) −16.

1.76 (*a*) −4; (*b*) 2; (*c*) 5; (*d*) $\frac{3}{4}$; (*e*) 1; (*f*) −7.

1.77 (*a*) $a = 3$, $b = 4$; (*b*) $a = -2$, $b = 6$; (*c*) $X = -0.2$, $Y = -1.2$;
(*d*) $A = \frac{184}{7} = 26.28571$ approximately, $B = \frac{110}{7} = 15.71429$ approximately; (*e*) $a = 2$, $b = 3$, $c = 5$;
(*f*) $X = -1$, $Y = 3$, $Z = -2$; (*g*) $U = 0.4$, $V = -0.8$, $W = 0.3$.

1.78 (*b*) (2, −3); i.e., $X = 2$, $Y = -3$.

1.79 (*a*) 2, −2.5; (*b*) 2.1 and −0.8 approximately.

1.80 (*a*) $\dfrac{4 \pm \sqrt{76}}{6}$, or 2.12 and −0.79 approximately.

(*b*) 2 and −2.5.

(*c*) 0.549 and −2.549 approximately.

(*d*) $\dfrac{-8 \pm \sqrt{-36}}{2} = \dfrac{-8 \pm \sqrt{36}\sqrt{-1}}{2} = \dfrac{-8 \pm 6i}{2} = -4 \pm 3i$, where $i = \sqrt{-1}$.

These roots are *complex numbers* and will not show up when a graphic procedure is employed.

1.81 (*a*) $-6.15 < -4.3 < -1.5 < 1.52 < 2.37$; (*b*) $2.37 > 1.52 > -1.5 > -4.3 > -6.15$.

1.82 (*a*) $30 \leq N \leq 50$; (*b*) $S \geq 7$; (*c*) $-4 \leq X < 3$; (*d*) $P \leq 5$; (*e*) $X - Y > 2$.

1.83 (*a*) $X \geq 4$; (*b*) $X > 3$; (*c*) $N < 5$; (*d*) $Y \leq 1$; (*e*) $-8 \leq X \leq 7$; (*f*) $-1.8 \leq N < 3$; (*g*) $2 \leq a < 22$.

1.84 (*a*) 2.5877; (*b*) 9.5877 − 10; (*c*) 8.8987 − 10; (*d*) 4.1653; (*e*) 9.7812 − 10; (*f*) 7.4464 − 10; (*g*) 2.6779; (*h*) 0.0030; (*i*) 0.8541; (*j*) 1.8541; (*k*) 6.9912 − 10; (*l*) 7.9275.

1.85 (*a*) 3640; (*b*) 0.675; (*c*) 50.64; (*d*) 0.08445; (*e*) 295.1; (*f*) 0.0002951; (*g*) 0.06314; (*h*) 5096; (*i*) 1202; (*j*) 2,422,000, or 2.422×10^6.

1.86 (*a*) 1,296,000, or 1.296×10^6; (*b*) 0.05739, or 0.0574 to three significant figures; (*c*) 556.0; (*d*) 804.4; (*e*) 40,820; (*f*) 0.03438; (*g*) 15.51; (*h*) 45.67;
(*i*) $0.0004519 = 4.519 \times 10^{-4}$, or 4.52×10^{-4} to three significant figures; (*j*) 3096.

1.88 (*a*) $X^2 = 100Y^3$; (*b*) $Y = 3 \times 10^{-2X}$.

1.89 (*a*) 3; (*b*) $\frac{3}{2}$; (*c*) −2; (*d*) −5; (*e*) 0.

CHAPTER 2

2.19 (*b*) 62.

2.20 (*a*) 799; (*b*) 1000; (*c*) 949.5; (*d*) 1099.5 and 1199.5; (*e*) 100 (hours); (*f*) 76; (*g*) $\frac{62}{400} = 0.155$, or 15.5%; (*h*) 29.5%; (*i*) 19.0%; (*j*) 78.0%.

2.25 (*a*) 24%; (*b*) 11%; (*c*) 46%.

2.26 (*a*) 0.003 in; (*b*) 0.3195, 0.3225, 0.3255, . . . , 0.3375 in;
(*c*) 0.320–0.322, 0.323–0.325, 0.326–0.328, . . . , 0.335–0.337 in.

2.31 (*a*) \$2500 and \$150,000; (*b*) seven (although strictly speaking the last class has no specified size);
(*c*) one (although the first class appears to be an open class interval, it is actually a substitute for \$0–\$2499.9);
(*d*) \$0–\$2499;
(*e*) \$3749.50 and \$74,999.50 (for most practical purposes, these can be written \$3750 and \$75,000, respectively);
(*f*) \$9999.50 and \$19,999.50; (*g*) 36.3% and 52.1%; (*h*) 22.7%; (*i*) 8.6%;
(*j*) because of rounding errors in computing percentages.

2.33 (*a*) 492,100; (*b*) 1,455,000; (*c*) 153,700.

2.34 (*b*) 0.30; (*d*) 0.008 for 4 hours per day, and 0.52 for 8 hours per day.

CHAPTER 3

3.47 (*a*) $X_1+X_2+X_3+X_4+8$
(*b*) $f_1X_1^2+f_2X_2^2+f_3X_3^2+f_4X_4^2+f_5X_5^2$
(*c*) $U_1(U_1+6)+U_2(U_2+6)+U_3(U_3+6)$
(*d*) $Y_1^2+Y_2^2+\cdots+Y_N^2-4N$
(*e*) $4X_1Y_1+4X_2Y_2+4X_3Y_3+4X_4Y_4$

3.48 (*a*) $\sum_{j=1}^{3}(X_j+3)^3$; (*b*) $\sum_{j=1}^{15}f_j(Y_j-a)^2$; (*c*) $\sum_{j=1}^{N}(2X_j-3Y_j)$;

(*d*) $\sum_{j=1}^{8}\left(\frac{X_j}{Y_j}-1\right)^2$; (*e*) $\frac{\sum_{j=1}^{12}f_ja_j^2}{\sum_{j=1}^{12}f_j}$

3.51 (*a*) 20; (*b*) −37; (*c*) 53; (*d*) 6; (*e*) 226; (*f*) −62; (*g*) $\frac{25}{12}$.

3.52 (*a*) −1; (*b*) 23.

3.53 86

3.54 0.50 second

3.55 8.25

3.56 (*a*) 82; (*b*) 79.

3.57 78

3.58 80% males and 20% females

3.59 11.09 tons

3.60 501.0

3.61 0.72642 cm

3.62 26.2

3.63 715 hours

3.64 (*b*) 1.7349 cm

3.65 (*a*) Mean = 5.4, median = 5; (*b*) mean = 19.91, median = 19.85.

3.66 85

3.67 0.51 second

3.68 8

3.69 11.07 tons

3.70 490.6

3.71 0.72638 cm

3.72 25.4

3.73 (*a*) 33.1 for males, and 30.6 for females.

3.74 $9192

3.75 708.3 hours

3.76 (*a*) Mean = 8.9, median = 9, mode = 7.
(*b*) Mean = 6.4, median = 6. Since each of the numbers 4, 5, 6, 8, and 10 occurs twice, we can consider these to be the five modes; however, it is more reasonable to conclude in this case that no mode exists.

3.77 It does not exist.

3.78 0.53 second

3.79 10

3.80 11.06 tons

3.81 462

3.82 0.72632 cm

3.83 23.5

3.84 668.7 hours

3.88 (*a*) 8.4; (*b*) 4.23.

3.89 (*a*) $G = 8$; (*b*) $\bar{X} = 12.4$.

3.90 (*a*) 4.14; (*b*) 45.8.

3.91 (*a*) 11.07 tons; (*b*) 499.5.

3.92 18.9%

3.93 (*a*) 1.086%; (*b*) 212.3 million; (*c*) 252.3 million.

3.94 $1586.87

3.95 $1608.44

3.96 3.6 and 14.4

3.97 (*a*) 3.0; (*b*) 4.48.

3.98 (*a*) 3; (*b*) 0; (*c*) 0.

3.100 (*a*) 11.04; (*b*) 498.2.

3.101 38.3 mi/h

3.102 (*b*) 420 mi/h

3.104 (*a*) 25; (*b*) 3.55.

3.107 (*a*) Lower quartile = $Q_1 = 67$, middle quartile = Q_2 = median = 75, and upper quartile = $Q_3 = 83$.
(*b*) 25% scored 67 or lower (or 75% scored 67 or higher), 50% scored 75 or lower (or 50% scored 75 or higher), and 75% scored 83 or lower (or 25% scored 83 or higher).

3.108 (*a*) $Q_1 = 10.55$ tons, $Q_2 = 11.07$ tons, and $Q_3 = 11.57$ tons; (*b*) $Q_1 = 469.3$, $Q_2 = 490.6$, and $Q_3 = 523.3$.

3.109 (*a*) 31.1 and 29.1; (*b*) 39.7 and 36.9; (*c*) 68.8 and 66.2; (*d*) 54.7 and 51.2.

3.110 (*a*) 10.15 tons; (*b*) 11.78 tons; (*c*) 10.55 tons; (*d*) 11.57 tons.

3.112 (*a*) 83; (*b*) 64.

CHAPTER 4

4.33 (*a*) 9; (*b*) 4.273.

4.34 4.0 tons

4.35 0.0036 cm

4.36 7.88 kg

4.37 (*a*) 35; (*b*) indeterminate; (*c*) 900 hours.

4.38 (*a*) 18.2; (*b*) 3.58; (*c*) 6.21; (*d*) 0; (*e*) $\sqrt{2} = 1.414$ approximately; (*f*) 1.88.

4.39 (*a*) 2; (*b*) 0.85.

4.40 (*a*) 2.2; (*b*) 1.317.

4.41 0.576 ton

4.42 (*a*) 0.00437 cm; (*b*) 60.0%, 85.2%, and 96.4%.

4.43 (*a*) 3.0; (*b*) 2.8.

4.44 (*a*) 31.2; (*b*) 30.6.

4.45 (*a*) 6.0; (*b*) 6.0.

4.48 (*a*) 0.51 ton; (*b*) 27.0; (*c*) 12.

4.49 (*a*) $1801; (*b*) 10.8 years.

4.52 (*a*) 1.63 tons; (*b*) 33.6 or 34.

4.53 (*a*) \$136,650; (*b*) 42.4 years for males, and 41.2 years for females.

4.56 (*a*) 2.16; (*b*) 0.90; (*c*) 0.484.

4.58 45

4.59 (*a*) 0.733 ton; (*b*) 38.60; (*c*) 12.1.

4.61 (*a*) $\bar{X} = 2.47$; (*b*) $s = 1.11$.

4.63 (*a*) 0.00576 cm; (*b*) 72.1%, 93.3%, and 99.76%.

4.64 (*a*) 0.719 ton; (*b*) 38.24; (*c*) 11.8.

4.65 (*a*) 0.000569 cm; (*b*) 71.6%, 93.0%, and 99.68%.

4.66 (*a*) 146.8 lb and 12.9 lb

4.67 (*a*) 1.7349 cm and 0.00495 cm

4.74 (*a*) 15; (*b*) 12.

4.75 (*a*) Statistics; (*b*) algebra.

4.76 (*a*) 6.6%; (*b*) 19.0%.

4.77 51.9%

4.79 Algebra

4.80 0.19, −1.75, 1.17, 0.68, −0.29.

CHAPTER 5

5.15 (*a*) 6; (*b*) 40; (*c*) 288; (*d*) 2188.

5.16 (*a*) 0; (*b*) 4; (*c*) 0; (*d*) 25.86.

5.17 (*a*) −1; (*b*) 5; (*c*) −91; (*d*) 53.

5.19 0, 26.25, 0, 1193.1.

5.21 7

5.22 (*a*) 0, 6, 19, 42; (*b*) −4, 22, −117, 560; (*c*) 1, 7, 38, 155.

5.23 0, 0.2344, −0.0586, 0.0696.

5.25 (*a*) $m_1 = 0$; (*b*) $m_2 = pq$; (*c*) $m_3 = pq(q-p)$; (*d*) $m_4 = pq(p^2 - pq + q^2)$.

5.27 $m_1 = 0$, $m_2 = 5.97$, $m_3 = -0.397$, $m_4 = 89.22$.

5.29 m_1 (corrected) = 0, m_2 (corrected) = 5.440, m_3 (corrected) = −0.5920, m_4 (corrected) = 76.2332.

5.30 (*a*) $m_1 = 0$, $m_2 = 0.53743$, $m_3 = 0.36206$, $m_4 = 0.84914$;
(*b*) m_2 (corrected) $= 0.51660$, m_4 (corrected) $= 0.78378$.

5.31 (*a*) 0; (*b*) 52.95; (*c*) 92.35; (*d*) 7158.20; (*e*) 26.2; (*f*) 7.28; (*g*) 739.58; (*h*) 22,247; (*i*) 706,428; (*j*) 24,545.

5.32 (*a*) −0.2464; (*b*) −0.2464.

5.33 0.9190

5.34 First distribution

5.35 (*a*) 0.040; (*b*) 0.074.

5.36 (*a*) −0.02; (*b*) −0.13.

5.37 (*b*) −0.078

5.38 (*a*) 2.62; (*b*) 2.58.

5.39 (*a*) 2.94; (*b*) 2.94.

5.40 (*a*) Second; (*b*) first.

5.41 (*a*) Second; (*b*) neither; (*c*) first.

5.42 (*a*) Greater than 1875; (*b*) equal to 1875; (*c*) less than 1875.

5.43 (*a*) 0.313

CHAPTER 6

6.40 (*a*) $\frac{5}{26}$; (*b*) $\frac{5}{36}$; (*c*) 0.98; (*d*) $\frac{2}{9}$; (*e*) $\frac{7}{8}$.

6.41 (*a*) Probability of a king on the first draw and no king on the second draw.
(*b*) Probability of either a king on the first draw or a king on the second draw, or both.
(*c*) No king on the first draw or no king on the second draw, or both (i.e., no king on the first and second draws).
(*d*) Probability of a king on the third draw, given that a king was drawn on the first draw but not on the second draw.
(*e*) No king on the first, second, and third draws.
(*f*) Probability either of a king on the first draw and a king on the second draw or of no king on the second draw and a king on the third draw.

6.42 (*a*) $\frac{1}{3}$; (*b*) $\frac{3}{5}$; (*c*) $\frac{11}{15}$; (*d*) $\frac{2}{5}$; (*e*) $\frac{4}{5}$.

6.43 (*a*) $\frac{4}{25}$; (*b*) $\frac{4}{75}$; (*c*) $\frac{16}{25}$; (*d*) $\frac{64}{225}$; (*e*) $\frac{11}{15}$; (*f*) $\frac{1}{5}$; (*g*) $\frac{104}{225}$; (*h*) $\frac{221}{225}$; (*i*) $\frac{6}{25}$; (*j*) $\frac{52}{225}$.

6.44 (*a*) $\frac{29}{185}$; (*b*) $\frac{2}{37}$; (*c*) $\frac{118}{185}$; (*d*) $\frac{52}{185}$; (*e*) $\frac{11}{15}$; (*f*) $\frac{1}{5}$; (*g*) $\frac{86}{185}$; (*h*) $\frac{182}{185}$; (*i*) $\frac{9}{37}$; (*j*) $\frac{26}{111}$.

6.45 (*a*) $\frac{5}{18}$; (*b*) $\frac{11}{36}$; (*c*) $\frac{1}{36}$.

6.46 (*a*) $\frac{47}{52}$; (*b*) $\frac{16}{221}$; (*c*) $\frac{15}{34}$; (*d*) $\frac{13}{17}$; (*e*) $\frac{210}{221}$; (*f*) $\frac{10}{13}$; (*g*) $\frac{40}{51}$; (*h*) $\frac{77}{442}$.

6.47 $\frac{5}{18}$

6.48 (*a*) 81:44; (*b*) 21:4.

6.49 $\frac{19}{42}$

6.50 (*a*) $\frac{2}{5}$; (*b*) $\frac{1}{5}$; (*c*) $\frac{4}{15}$; (*d*) $\frac{13}{15}$.

6.51 (*a*) 37.5%; (*b*) 93.75%; (*c*) 6.25%; (*d*) 68.75%.

6.52 (*a*)

X	0	1	2	3	4
$p(X)$	$\frac{1}{16}$	$\frac{4}{16}$	$\frac{6}{16}$	$\frac{4}{16}$	$\frac{1}{16}$

6.53 (*a*) $\frac{1}{48}$; (*b*) $\frac{7}{24}$; (*c*) $\frac{3}{4}$; (*d*) $\frac{1}{6}$.

6.54 (*a*)

X	0	1	2	3
$p(X)$	$\frac{1}{6}$	$\frac{1}{2}$	$\frac{3}{10}$	$\frac{1}{30}$

6.55 (*a*) $\frac{3}{10}$; this is the probability of drawing a total of 2 red marbles.
(*b*) $\frac{5}{6}$; this is the probability of drawing 1, 2, or 3 red marbles (i.e., of drawing at least 1 red marble).

6.56 \$9

6.57 \$4.80 per day

6.58 *A* contributes \$12.50; *B* contributes \$7.50.

6.59 (*a*) 7; (*b*) 590; (*c*) 541; (*d*) 10,900.

6.60 (*a*) 1.2; (*b*) 0.56; (*c*) $\sqrt{0.56} = 0.75$ approximately.

6.64 (*a*) 12; (*b*) 2520; (*c*) 720.

6.65 $n = 5$

6.66 60

6.67 (*a*) 5040; (*b*) 720; (*c*) 240.

6.68 (*a*) 8400; (*b*) 2520.

6.69 (*a*) 32,805; (*b*) 11,664.

6.70 26

6.71 (*a*) 120; (*b*) 72; (*c*) 12.

6.72 (*a*) 35; (*b*) 70; (*c*) 45.

6.73 $n = 6$

6.74 210

6.75 840

6.76 (*a*) 42,000; (*b*) 7000.

6.77 (*a*) 120; (*b*) 12,600.

6.78 (*a*) 150; (*b*) 45; (*c*) 100.

6.79 (*a*) 17; (*b*) 163.

6.81 2.95×10^{25}

6.83 (*a*) $\frac{6}{5525}$; (*b*) $\frac{22}{425}$; (*c*) $\frac{169}{425}$; (*d*) $\frac{73}{5525}$.

6.84 $\frac{171}{1296}$

6.85 (*a*) 0.59049; (*b*) 0.32805; (*c*) 0.08866.

6.86 (*b*) $\frac{3}{4}$; (*c*) $\frac{7}{8}$.

6.87 (*a*) 8; (*b*) 78; (*c*) 86; (*d*) 102; (*e*) 20; (*f*) 142.

6.90 $\frac{1}{3}$

6.91 1/3,838,380 (i.e., the odds against winning are 3,838,379 to 1)

6.92 (*a*) 658,007 to 1; (*b*) 91,389 to 1; (*c*) 9879 to 1.

6.93 (*a*) 649,739 to 1; (*b*) 71,192 to 1; (*c*) 4164 to 1; (*d*) 693 to 1.

6.94 $\frac{11}{36}$

6.95 $\frac{1}{4}$

CHAPTER 7

7.35 (*a*) 5040; (*b*) 210; (*c*) 126; (*d*) 165; (*e*) 6.

7.36 (*a*) $q^7 + 7q^6p + 21q^5p^2 + 35q^4p^3 + 35q^3p^4 + 21q^2p^5 + 7qp^6 + p^7$
(*b*) $q^{10} + 10q^9p + 45q^8p^2 + 120q^7p^3 + 210q^6p^4 + 252q^5p^5 + 210q^4p^6 + 120q^3p^7 + 45q^2p^8 + 10qp^9 + p^{10}$

7.37 (*a*) $\frac{1}{64}$; (*b*) $\frac{3}{32}$; (*c*) $\frac{15}{64}$; (*d*) $\frac{5}{16}$; (*e*) $\frac{15}{64}$; (*f*) $\frac{3}{32}$; (*g*) $\frac{1}{64}$.

7.38 (*a*) $\frac{57}{64}$; (*b*) $\frac{21}{32}$.

7.39 (*a*) $\frac{1}{4}$; (*b*) $\frac{5}{16}$; (*c*) $\frac{11}{16}$; (*d*) $\frac{5}{8}$.

7.40 (*a*) 250; (*b*) 25; (*c*) 500.

7.41 (*a*) $\frac{17}{162}$; (*b*) $\frac{1}{324}$.

7.42 $\frac{64}{243}$

7.43 $\frac{193}{512}$

7.44 (*a*) $\frac{32}{243}$; (*b*) $\frac{192}{243}$; (*c*) $\frac{40}{243}$; (*d*) $\frac{242}{243}$.

7.45 (*a*) 42; (*b*) 3.550; (*c*) −0.1127; (*d*) 2.927.

7.47 (*a*) $Npq(q-p)$; (*b*) $Npq(1-6pq)+3N^2p^2q^2$.

7.49 (*a*) 1.5 and −1.6; (*b*) 72 and 90.

7.50 (*a*) 75.4; (*b*) 9.

7.51 (*a*) 0.8767; (*b*) 0.0786; (*c*) 0.2991.

7.52 (*a*) 0.0375; (*b*) 0.7123; (*c*) 0.9265; (*d*) 0.0154; (*e*) 0.7251; (*f*) 0.0395.

7.53 (*a*) 0.9495; (*b*) 0.9500; (*c*) 0.6826.

7.54 (*a*) 0.75; (*b*) −1.86; (*c*) 2.08; (*d*) 1.625 or 0.849; (*e*) ±1.645.

7.55 −0.995

7.56 (*a*) 0.0317; (*b*) 0.3790; (*c*) 0.1989.

7.57 (*a*) 20; (*b*) 36; (*c*) 227; (*d*) 40.

7.58 (*a*) 93%; (*b*) 8.1%; (*c*) 0.47%; (*d*) 15%.

7.59 84

7.60 (*a*) 61.7%; (*b*) 54.7%.

7.61 (*a*) 95.4%; (*b*) 23.0%; (*c*) 93.3%.

7.62 (*a*) 1.15; (*b*) 0.77

7.63 (*a*) 0.9962; (*b*) 0.0687; (*c*) 0.0286; (*d*) 0.0558.

7.64 (*a*) 0.2511; (*b*) 0.1342.

7.65 (*a*) 0.0567; (*b*) 0.9198; (*c*) 0.6404; (*d*) 0.0079.

7.66 0.0089

7.67 (*a*) 0.04979; (*b*) 0.1494; (*c*) 0.2241; (*d*) 0.2241; (*e*) 0.1680; (*f*) 0.1008.

7.68 (*a*) 0.0838; (*b*) 0.5976; (*c*) 0.4232.

7.69 (*a*) 0.05610; (*b*) 0.06131.

7.70 (*a*) 0.00248; (*b*) 0.04462; (*c*) 0.1607; (*d*) 0.1033; (*e*) 0.6964; (*f*) 0.0620.

7.71 (*a*) 0.08208; (*b*) 0.2052; (*c*) 0.2565; (*d*) 0.2138; (*e*) 0.8911; (*f*) 0.0142.

7.72 (*a*) $\frac{5}{3888}$; (*b*) $\frac{5}{324}$.

7.73 (*a*) 0.0348; (*b*) 0.000295.

7.74 $\frac{1}{16}$

7.75 $p(X) = \binom{4}{X}(0.32)^X(0.68)^{4-X}$. The expected frequencies are 32, 60, 43, 13, and 2, respectively.

7.77 The expected frequencies are 1.7, 5.5, 12.0, 15.9, 13.7, 7.6, 2.7, and 0.6, respectively.

7.78 The expected frequencies are 1.1, 4.0, 11.1, 23.9, 39.5, 50.2, 49.0, 36.6, 21.1, 9.4, 3.1, and 1.0, respectively.

7.79 The expected frequencies are 41.7, 53.4, 34.2, 14.6, and 4.7, respectively.

7.80 $p(X) = \dfrac{(0.61)^X e^{-0.61}}{X!}$. The expected frequencies are 108.7, 66.3, 20.2, 4.1, and 0.7, respectively.

CHAPTER 8

8.21 (*a*) 9.0; (*b*) 4.47; (*c*) 9.0; (*d*) 3.16.

8.22 (*a*) 9.0; (*b*) 4.47; (*c*) 9.0; (*d*) 2.58.

8.23 (*a*) $\mu_{\bar{X}} = 22.40$ g, $\sigma_{\bar{X}} = 0.008$ g; (*b*) $\mu_{\bar{X}} = 22.40$ g, $\sigma_{\bar{X}} =$ slightly less than 0.008 g.

8.24 (*a*) $\mu_{\bar{X}} = 22.40$ g, $\sigma_{\bar{X}} = 0.008$ g; (*b*) $\mu_{\bar{X}} = 22.40$ g, $\sigma_{\bar{X}} = 0.0057$ g.

8.25 (*a*) 237; (*b*) 2; (*c*) none; (*d*) 34.

8.26 (*a*) 0.4972; (*b*) 0.1587; (*c*) 0.0918; (*d*) 0.9544.

8.27 (*a*) 0.8164; (*b*) 0.0228; (*c*) 0.0038; (*d*) 1.0000.

8.28 0.0026

8.34 (*a*) 0.0029; (*b*) 0.9596; (*c*) 0.1446.

8.35 (*a*) 2; (*b*) 996; (*c*) 218.

8.36 (*a*) 0.0179; (*b*) 0.8664; (*c*) 0.1841.

8.37 (*a*) 6; (*b*) 9; (*c*) 2; (*d*) 12.

8.39 (*a*) 19; (*b*) 125.

8.40 (*a*) 0.0077; (*b*) 0.8869.

8.41 (*a*) 0.0028; (*b*) 0.9172.

8.42 (*a*) 0.2150; (*b*) 0.0064, 0.4504.

8.43 0.0482

8.44 0.0188

8.45 0.0410

8.47 (*a*) 118.79 g; (*b*) 0.74 g.

8.48 0.0228

8.49 (*a*) 7.2; (*b*) 8.4.

8.50 (*a*) 106; (*b*) 4.

8.51 159

8.52 (*a*) 78.7; (*b*) 0.0090.

CHAPTER 9

9.21 (*a*) 9.5 kg; (*b*) 0.74 kg^2; (*c*) 0.78 kg and 0.86 kg, respectively.

9.22 (*a*) 1200 h; (*b*) 105.4 h.

9.23 (*a*) Estimates of population standard deviations for sample sizes of 30, 50, and 100 tubes are 101.7 h, 101.0 h, and 100.5 h, respectively; estimates of population means are 1200 h in all cases.

9.24 (*a*) 11.09 ± 0.18 tons; (*b*) 11.09 ± 0.24 tons.

9.25 (*a*) 0.72642 ± 0.000095 in; (*b*) 0.72642 ± 0.000085 in; (*c*) 0.72642 ± 0.000072 in; (*d*) 0.72642 ± 0.000060 in.

9.26 (*a*) 0.72642 ± 0.000025 in; (*b*) 0.000025 in.

9.27 (*a*) At least 97; (*b*) at least 68; (*c*) at least 167; (*d*) at least 225.

9.28 (*a*) At least 385; (*b*) at least 271; (*c*) at least 666; (*d*) at least 900.

9.29 (*a*) 2400 ± 45 lb, 2400 ± 59 lb; (*b*) 87.6%.

9.30 (*a*) 0.70 ± 0.12, 0.69 ± 0.11; (*b*) 0.70 ± 0.15, 0.68 ± 0.15; (*c*) 0.70 ± 0.18, 0.67 ± 0.17.

9.31 (*a*) At least 323; (*b*) at least 560; (*c*) at least 756.

9.32 (*a*) 16,400; (*b*) 27,100; (*c*) 38,420; (*d*) 66,000.

9.33 (*a*) 1.07 ± 0.09 h; (*b*) 1.07 ± 0.12 h.

9.34 (*a*) 0.045 ± 0.073; (*b*) 0.045 ± 0.097; (*c*) 0.045 ± 0.112.

9.35 (*a*) 63.8 ± 0.24 lb; (*b*) 63.8 ± 0.31 lb.

9.36 (*a*) 180 ± 24.9 lb; (*b*) 180 ± 32.8 lb; (*c*) 180 ± 38.2 lb.

9.37 8.6 lb

9.38 (*a*) At least 4802; (*b*) at least 8321; (*c*) at least 11,250.

CHAPTER 10

10.29 (*a*) 0.2606

10.30 (*a*) Accept the hypothesis if between 22 and 42 red marbles are drawn, and reject it otherwise; (*b*) 0.99; (*c*) accept the hypothesis if between 24 and 40 red marbles are drawn, and reject it otherwise.

10.31 (*a*) $H_0: p = 0.5$, $H_1: p > 0.5$; (*b*) one-tailed test;
(*c*) reject H_0 if more than 39 red marbles are drawn, and accept it otherwise (or withhold decision);
(*d*) reject H_0 if more than 41 red marbles are drawn, and accept it otherwise (or withhold decision).

10.32 (*a*) We cannot reject the hypothesis at the 0.05 level; (*b*) we can reject the hypothesis at the 0.05 level.

10.33 Using either a two-tailed or a one-tailed test, we cannot reject the hypothesis at the 0.01 level.

10.34 Using a one-tailed test, we can reject the claim at both levels.

10.35 Using a one-tailed test, the result is significant at the 0.05 level, but not at the 0.01 level.

10.36 Yes, the result is significant at both levels, using a one-tailed test in each case.

10.37 Using either a one-tailed or a two-tailed test, the result is significant at the 0.05 level.

10.38 The result is significant at the 0.01 level by using a one-tailed test, but not by using a two-tailed test.

10.39 (*a*) 0.3112; (*b*) 0.0118; (*c*) 0; (*d*) 0; (*e*) 0.0118.

10.43 (*a*) 8.64 ± 0.96 oz; (*b*) 8.64 ± 0.83 oz; (*c*) 8.64 ± 0.63 oz.

10.44 The upper control limits are, respectively, (*a*) 6 and (*b*) 4 defective bolts.

10.45 (*a*) Yes; (*b*) no.

10.46 A one-tailed test at both levels of significance shows that brand *B* is superior to brand *A*.

10.47 A one-tailed test shows that the difference is significant at the 0.05 level, but not at the 0.01 level.

10.48 A one-tailed test shows that the new fertilizer is superior at both levels of significance.

10.49 (*a*) A two-tailed test shows no difference in the quality of performance at the 0.05 level.
(*b*) A one-tailed test shows that *B* is not performing better than *A* at the 0.05 level.

10.50 (*a*) A two-tailed test at the 0.05 level fails to reject the hypothesis of equal proportions.
(*b*) A one-tailed test at the 0.05 level shows that *A* has a greater proportion of red marbles than *B* does.

10.51 (*a*) 9; (*b*) 10; (*c*) 10; (*d*) 8.

10.54 (*a*) No; (*b*) yes; (c) no.

10.55 (*a*) Yes; (*b*) yes; (*c*) no.

10.56 (*a*) Yes; (*b*) yes; (*c*) yes.

10.57 (*a*) No; (*b*) no; (*c*) no.

CHAPTER 11

11.20 (*a*) 2.60; (*b*) 1.75; (*c*) 1.34; (*d*) 2.95; (*e*) 2.13.

11.21 (*a*) 3.75; (*b*) 2.68; (*c*) 2.48; (*d*) 2.39; (*e*) 2.33.

11.22 (*a*) 1.71; (*b*) 2.09; (*c*) 4.03; (*d*) −0.128.

11.23 (*a*) 1.81; (*b*) 2.76; (*c*) −0.879; (*d*) −1.37.

11.24 (*a*) ±4.60; (*b*) ±3.06; (*c*) ±2.79; (*d*) ±2.75; (*e*) ±2.70.

11.25 (*a*) 7.38 ± 0.82 g; (*b*) 7.38 ± 1.16 g.

11.26 (*a*) 7.38 ± 0.73 g; (*b*) 7.38 ± 0.96 g.

11.27 (*a*) 0.298 ± 0.030 second; (*b*) 0.298 ± 0.049 second.

11.28 A two-tailed test shows that there is no evidence at either the 0.05 or 0.01 level to indicate that the mean lifetime has changed.

11.29 A one-tailed test shows no decrease in the mean at either the 0.05 or 0.01 level.

11.30 A two-tailed test at both levels shows that the product does not meet the required specifications.

11.31 A one-tailed test at both levels shows that the mean copper content is higher than the specifications require.

11.32 A one-tailed test shows that the process should not be introduced if the significance level adopted is 0.01 but it should be introduced if the significance level adopted is 0.05.

11.33 A one-tailed test shows that brand *A* is better than brand *B* at the 0.05 significance level.

11.34 Using a two-tailed test at the 0.05 significance level, we would not conclude on the basis of the samples that there is a difference in acidity between the two types.

11.35 Using a one-tailed test at the 0.05 significance level, we would conclude that the first group is not superior to the second.

11.36 (*a*) 21.0; (*b*) 26.2; (*c*) 23.3.

11.37 (*a*) 15.5; (*b*) 30.1; (*c*) 41.3; (*d*) 55.8.

11.38 (*a*) 20.1; (*b*) 36.2; (*c*) 48.3; (*d*) 63.7.

11.39 (*a*) $\chi_1^2 = 9.59$, and $\chi_2^2 = 34.2$.

11.40 (*a*) 16.0; (*b*) 6.35; (*c*) assuming equal areas in the two tails, $\chi_1^2 = 2.17$ and $\chi_2^2 = 14.1$.

11.41 (*a*) 87.0 to 230.9 h; (*b*) 78.1 to 288.5 h.

11.42 (*a*) 95.6 to 170.4 h; (*b*) 88.9 to 190.8 h.

11.43 (*a*) 122.5; (*b*) 179.2.

11.44 (*a*) 207.7; (*b*) 295.2.

11.46 (*a*) 106.1 to 140.5 h; (*b*) 102.1 to 148.1 h.

11.47 105.5 to 139.6 h

11.48 On the basis of the given sample, the apparent increase in variability is not significant at either level.

11.49 The apparent decrease in variability is significant at the 0.05 level, but not at the 0.01 level.

11.50 (*a*) $F_{.95} = 3.07$; (*b*) $F_{.99} = 4.02$; (*c*) $F_{.95} = 2.11$; (*d*) $F_{.99} = 2.83$.

11.51 $F_{.95} = 1.95$, using interpolation.

11.52 The sample 1 variance is significantly greater at the 0.05 level, but not at the 0.01 level.

11.53 (*a*) Yes; (*b*) no.

CHAPTER 12

12.26 The hypothesis cannot be rejected at either level.

12.27 The conclusion is the same as before.

12.28 The new instructor is not following the grade pattern of the others. (The fact that the grades happen to be better than average *may* be due to better teaching ability or lower standards, or both.)

12.29 There is no reason to reject the hypothesis that the coins are fair.

12.30 There is no reason to reject the hypothesis at either level.

12.31 (*a*) 10, 60, and 50, respectively;
(*b*) the hypothesis that the results are the same as those expected cannot be rejected at the 0.05 level.

12.32 The difference is significant at the 0.05 level.

12.33 (*a*) The fit is good; (*b*) no.

12.34 (*a*) The fit is "too good"; (*b*) the fit is poor at the 0.05 level.

12.35 (*a*) The fit is very poor at the 0.05 level; since the binomial distribution gives a good fit of the data, this is consistent with Problem 12.33.
(*b*) The fit is good, but not "too good."

12.36 The hypothesis can be rejected at the 0.05 level, but not at the 0.01 level.

12.37 The conclusion is the same as before.

12.38 The hypothesis cannot be rejected at either level.

12.39 The hypothesis cannot be rejected at the 0.05 level.

12.40 The hypothesis can be rejected at both levels.

12.41 The hypothesis can be rejected at both levels.

12.42 The hypothesis cannot be rejected at either level.

12.49 (*a*) 0.3863 (uncorrected), and 0.3779 (with Yates' correction).

12.50 (*a*) 0.2205, 0.1985 (corrected); (*b*) 0.0872, 0.0738 (corrected).

12.51 0.4651

12.54 (*a*) 0.4188, 0.4082 (corrected).

12.55 (*a*) 0.2261, 0.2026 (corrected); (*b*) 0.0875, 0.0740 (corrected).

12.56 0.3715

CHAPTER 13

13.24 (*a*) 4; (*b*) 6; (*c*) $\frac{28}{3}$; (*d*) 10.5; (*e*) 6; (*f*) 9.

13.25 (2, 1)

13.26 (*a*) $2X+Y=4$; (*b*) X intercept $=2$, Y intercept $=4$; (*c*) -2, -6.

13.27 $Y=\frac{2}{3}X-3$, or $2X-3Y=9$.

13.28 (*a*) Slope $=\frac{3}{5}$, Y intercept $=-4$; (*b*) $3X-5Y=11$.

13.29 (*a*) $-\frac{4}{3}$; (*b*) $\frac{32}{3}$; (*c*) $4X+3Y=32$.

13.30 $X/3+Y/(-5)=1$, or $5X-3Y=15$.

13.31 (*a*) $°F=\frac{9}{5}°C+32$; (*b*) 176°F; (*c*) 20°C.

13.32 (*a*) $Y=-\frac{1}{3}+\frac{5}{7}X$, or $Y=-0.333+0.714X$; (*b*) $X=1+\frac{9}{7}Y$, or $X=1.00+1.29Y$.

13.33 (*a*) 3.24, 8.24; (*b*) 10.00.

13.35 (*b*) $Y=29.13+0.661X$; (*c*) $X=-14.39+1.15Y$; (*d*) 79; (*e*) 95.

13.38 $Y=5.51+3.20(X-3)+0.733(X-3)^2$, or $Y=2.51-1.20X+0.733X^2$.

13.39 (*b*) $D=41.77-1.096V+0.08786V^2$; (*c*) 170 ft, 516 ft.

13.43 (*b*) $Y=32.14(1.427)^X$, or $Y=32.14(10)^{0.1544X}$, or $Y=32.14\,e^{0.3556X}$, where $e=2.718\cdots$ is the natural logarithmic base;
(*d*) 387.

CHAPTER 14

14.40 (*b*) $Y = 4.000 + 0.500X$; (*c*) $X = 2.408 + 0.612Y$.

14.41 (*a*) 1.304; (*b*) 1.443.

14.42 (*a*) 24.50; (*b*) 17.00; (*c*) 7.50.

14.43 0.5533

14.45 1.5

14.46 (*a*) 0.8961; (*b*) $Y = 80.78 + 1.138X$; (*c*) 132.

14.47 (*a*) 0.958; (*b*) 0.872.

14.48 (*a*) $Y = 0.8X + 12$; (*b*) $X = 0.45Y + 1$.

14.49 (*a*) 1.60; (*b*) 1.20.

14.50 ± 0.80

14.51 75%

14.53 (*a*) -0.9203

14.54 (*a*) $Y = 18.04 - 1.34X$, $Y = 51.18 - 2.01X$.

14.58 0.5440

14.59 (*a*) $Y = 4.44X - 142.22$; (*b*) 141.9 lb and 177.5 lb, respectively.

14.60 (*a*) 16.92 lb; (*b*) 2.07 in.

14.62 0.754

14.63 0.22

14.64 (*a*) Yes; (*b*) no.

14.65 (*a*) No; (*b*) yes.

14.66 (*a*) 0.2923 and 0.7951; (*b*) 0.1763 and 0.8361.

14.67 (*a*) 0.3912 and 0.7500; (*b*) 0.3146 and 0.7861.

14.68 (*a*) 0.7096 and 0.9653; (*b*) 0.4961 and 0.7235.

14.69 (*a*) Yes; (*b*) no.

14.70 (*a*) 2.00 ± 0.21; (*b*) 2.00 ± 0.28.

14.71 (*a*) Using a one-tailed test, we can reject the hypothesis.
(*b*) Using a one-tailed test, we cannot reject the hypothesis.

14.72 (*a*) 37.0 ± 3.28; (*b*) 37.0 ± 4.45.

14.73 (*a*) 37.0 ± 0.69; (*b*) 37.0 ± 0.94.

14.74 (*a*) 1.138 ± 0.398; (*b*) 132.0 ± 16.6; (*c*) 132.0 ± 5.4.

CHAPTER 15

15.26 (*a*) $X_3 = b_{3.12} + b_{31.2}X_1 + b_{32.1}X_2$; (*b*) $X_4 = b_{4.1235} + b_{41.235}X_1 + b_{42.135}X_2 + b_{43.125}X_3$.

15.28 (*a*) $X_3 = 61.40 - 3.65X_1 + 2.54X_2$; (*b*) 40.

15.29 (*a*) $X_3 - 74 = 4.36(X_1 - 6.8) + 4.04(X_2 - 7.0)$, or $X_3 = 16.07 + 4.36X_1 + 4.04X_2$; (*b*) 84 and 66.

15.31 3.12

15.32 (*a*) 5.883; (*b*) 0.6882.

15.33 0.9927

15.34 (*a*) 0.7567; (*b*) 0.7255; (*c*) 0.6810.

15.37 (*a*) 0.5950; (*b*) −0.8995; (*c*) 0.8727.

15.38 (*a*) 0.2672; (*b*) 0.5099; (*c*) 0.4026.

15.42 (*a*) $X_4 = 6X_1 + 3X_2 - 4X_3 - 100$; (*b*) 54.

15.43 (*a*) 0.8710; (*b*) 0.8587; (*c*) −0.8426.

15.44 (*a*) 0.8947; (*b*) 2.680.

CHAPTER 16

16.21 There is a significant difference between the yields at both levels.

16.22 There is no significant difference between the tires at either level.

16.23 There is a significant difference between the teaching methods at the 0.05 level, but not at the 0.01 level.

16.24 There is a significant difference between the brands at the 0.05 level, but not at the 0.01 level.

16.25 There is a significant difference between the grades at both levels.

16.26 There is no significant difference between the operators or between the machines.

16.27 Same answer as for Problem 16.26.

16.28 At the 0.05 level there is a significant difference in terms of the type of corn, but not in terms of the soil.

16.29 At the 0.01 level there is no significant difference in terms of the type of corn or the soil.

16.30 At the 0.05 level there is a significant difference between both the tires and the automobiles.

16.31 At the 0.01 level there is no significant difference between either the tires or the automobiles.

16.32 At the 0.05 level there is a significant difference between the teaching methods, but not between the schools.

16.33 There is no significant difference in terms either of hair color or height.

16.34 Same answer as for Problem 16.33.

16.35 At the 0.05 level there is a significant difference due to the locations, but not due to the fertilizers.

16.36 At the 0.01 level there is no significant difference due to the locations or the fertilizers.

16.37 There is a significant difference between the operators, but not between the machines.

16.38 There is no significant difference between either the fertilizers or the soils.

16.39 Same answer as for Problem 16.38.

16.40 There is no significant difference in their scholastic achievement due to differences in height, hair color, or birthplace.

16.41 There are significant differences in terms of the species of chicken and the quantities of the first chemical, but not in terms of the second chemical or of the chicks' initial weights.

16.42 There are significant differences in cable strength due to the types of cable, but there are no significant differences due to the operators, machines, or companies.

16.43 There is no significant difference at either level.

16.44 There is no significant difference at either level.

16.46 At the 0.05 level there is a significant difference in examination scores due both to veteran status and to IQ.

16.47 At the 0.01 level the difference in examination scores due to veteran status is not significant, but the difference due to the IQ is significant.

16.48 There are no significant differences between the test scores in terms of the students' locations, but there are significant differences in terms of IQ.

16.49 Same answer as for Problem 16.48.

16.53 At the 0.05 level there is a significant difference due both to the chemicals and to the locations.

16.54 At the 0.05 level there are significant differences due to the locations, but not due to the fertilizers.

16.55 At the 0.01 level there are no significant differences due to the locations or the fertilizers.

16.56 There are no significant differences due to factor 1, factor 2, or treatments A, B, and C.

16.58 There are no significant differences due to the factors or the treatments.

CHAPTER 17

17.26 There is a difference at the 0.05 level, but not at the 0.01 level.

17.27 Yes.

17.28 The program is effective at the 0.05 level.

17.29 We can reject the hypothesis of increased sales at the 0.05 level.

17.30 No

17.31 (*a*) Reject; (*b*) accept; (*c*) accept; (*d*) reject.

17.34 There is no difference at the 0.05 level.

17.35 No.

17.36 (*a*) Yes; (*b*) yes.

17.37 Yes.

17.38 (*a*) Yes; (*b*) yes.

17.41 3

17.42 6

17.49 There is no significant difference at either level.

17.50 The difference is significant at the 0.05 level, but not at the 0.01 level.

17.51 The difference is significant at the 0.05 level, but not at the 0.01 level.

17.52 There is a significant difference between the grades at both levels.

17.55 (*a*) 8; (*b*) 10.

17.56 (*a*) 10; (*b*) the responses are random at the 0.05 level.

17.62 The sample is not random at the 0.05 level. There are *too many* runs, indicating a cyclic pattern.

17.63 The sample is not random at the 0.05 level. There are *too few* runs, indicating a trend pattern.

17.64 The digits are random at the 0.05 level.

17.65 (*a*) The digits are random at the 0.05 level; (*b*) the digits are random at the 0.05 level.

17.69 (*a*) 0.67; (*b*) the judges did not agree too well in their choices.

CHAPTER 18

18.22 (*a*) Cyclic; (*b*) seasonal; (*c*) long-term; (*d*) irregular; (*e*) long-term.

18.23 (*a*) 0.5, −0.5, −0.5, 0.5, 0.5, −0.5, −0.5, 0.5; (*b*) 0, $-\frac{1}{3}$, 0, $\frac{1}{3}$, 0, $-\frac{1}{3}$, 0; (*c*) 0, 0, 0, 0, 0, 0; (*d*) $\frac{1}{5}$, 0, $-\frac{1}{5}$, 0, $\frac{1}{5}$.

18.28 (*b*) 0, −0.5, 0, 0.5, 0, −0.5, 0; (*c*) $-\frac{1}{6}$, $-\frac{1}{6}$, $\frac{1}{6}$, $\frac{1}{6}$, $-\frac{1}{6}$, $-\frac{1}{6}$; (*d*) 0, 0, 0, 0, 0.

18.30 (*a*) 20; (*b*) 21; (*c*) 196.

CHAPTER 19

19.41 (*a*) 130.3; (*b*) 105.4, 91.9; (*c*) 95.6, 104.9, 99.5, 109.4, 105.9, 115.2, 124.6, 100.5.

19.45 (*a*) 100, 106, 93, 98, 108, 111; (*b*) 97, 102, 90, 95, 105, 108.

19.46 (*a*) 120; (*b*) 137.

19.47 (*a*) 200; (*b*) 150.

19.48 (*a*) 83.6, 88.8, 92.5, 96.1, 97.9, 99.6, 100.0, 97.6, 100.7, 105.3, 107.6, 109.5.
(*b*) 94.6, 100.6, 104.8, 108.8, 110.9, 112.8, 113.2, 110.6, 114.0, 119.2, 121.9, 123.9.

19.49 (*a*) 100, 140, 112, 96; (*b*) 104, 146, 117, 100; (*c*) 89.3, 125, 100, 85.7.

19.50 (*a*) 2.86; (*b*) 4.00; (*c*) 2.74 million short tons.

19.51 5% increase

19.52 (*a*) 100, 96, 92, 88, 84; (*b*) 104, 100, 96, 92, 98.

19.53 (*a*) 100; (*b*) 74.1, 66.7, 80.0, 100, and 80.0, corresponding to the years 1981-1985, respectively; (*c*) 101, 90.9, 109, 136, and 109, corresponding to the years 1981-1985, respectively.

19.78 $214.04

Appendix

Appendix I

Ordinates (*Y*) of the Standard Normal Curve at *z*

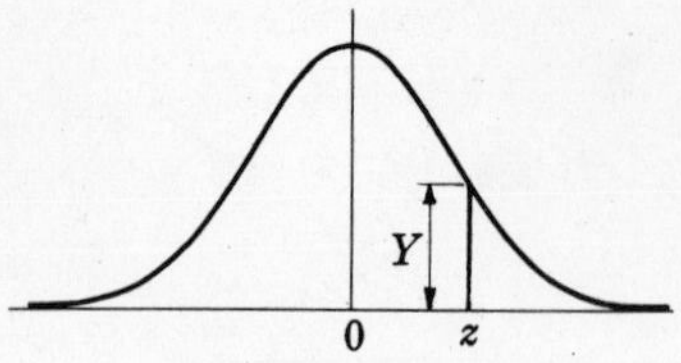

z	0	1	2	3	4	5	6	7	8	9
0.0	.3989	.3989	.3989	.3988	.3986	.3984	.3982	.3980	.3977	.3973
0.1	.3970	.3965	.3961	.3956	.3951	.3945	.3939	.3932	.3925	.3918
0.2	.3910	.3902	.3894	.3885	.3876	.3867	.3857	.3847	.3836	.3825
0.3	.3814	.3802	.3790	.3778	.3765	.3752	.3739	.3725	.3712	.3697
0.4	.3683	.3668	.3653	.3637	.3621	.3605	.3589	.3572	.3555	.3538
0.5	.3521	.3503	.3485	.3467	.3448	.3429	.3410	.3391	.3372	.3352
0.6	.3332	.3312	.3292	.3271	.3251	.3230	.3209	.3187	.3166	.3144
0.7	.3123	.3101	.3079	.3056	.3034	.3011	.2989	.2966	.2943	.2920
0.8	.2897	.2874	.2850	.2827	.2803	.2780	.2756	.2732	.2709	.2685
0.9	.2661	.2637	.2613	.2589	.2565	.2541	.2516	.2492	.2468	.2444
1.0	.2420	.2396	.2371	.2347	.2323	.2299	.2275	.2251	.2227	.2203
1.1	.2179	.2155	.2131	.2107	.2083	.2059	.2036	.2012	.1989	.1965
1.2	.1942	.1919	.1895	.1872	.1849	.1826	.1804	.1781	.1758	.1736
1.3	.1714	.1691	.1669	.1647	.1626	.1604	.1582	.1561	.1539	.1518
1.4	.1497	.1476	.1456	.1435	.1415	.1394	.1374	.1354	.1334	.1315
1.5	.1295	.1276	.1257	.1238	.1219	.1200	.1182	.1163	.1145	.1127
1.6	.1109	.1092	.1074	.1057	.1040	.1023	.1006	.0989	.0973	.0957
1.7	.0940	.0925	.0909	.0893	.0878	.0863	.0848	.0833	.0818	.0804
1.8	.0790	.0775	.0761	.0748	.0734	.0721	.0707	.0694	.0681	.0669
1.9	.0656	.0644	.0632	.0620	.0608	.0596	.0584	.0573	.0562	.0551
2.0	.0540	.0529	.0519	.0508	.0498	.0488	.0478	.0468	.0459	.0449
2.1	.0440	.0431	.0422	.0413	.0404	.0396	.0387	.0379	.0371	.0363
2.2	.0355	.0347	.0339	.0332	.0325	.0317	.0310	.0303	.0297	.0290
2.3	.0283	.0277	.0270	.0264	.0258	.0252	.0246	.0241	.0235	.0229
2.4	.0224	.0219	.0213	.0208	.0203	.0198	.0194	.0189	.0184	.0180
2.5	.0175	.0171	.0167	.0163	.0158	.0154	.0151	.0147	.0143	.0139
2.6	.0136	.0132	.0129	.0126	.0122	.0119	.0116	.0113	.0110	.0107
2.7	.0104	.0101	.0099	.0096	.0093	.0091	.0088	.0086	.0084	.0081
2.8	.0079	.0077	.0075	.0073	.0071	.0069	.0067	.0065	.0063	.0061
2.9	.0060	.0058	.0056	.0055	.0053	.0051	.0050	.0048	.0047	.0046
3.0	.0044	.0043	.0042	.0040	.0039	.0038	.0037	.0036	.0035	.0034
3.1	.0033	.0032	.0031	.0030	.0029	.0028	.0027	.0026	.0025	.0025
3.2	.0024	.0023	.0022	.0022	.0021	.0020	.0020	.0019	.0018	.0018
3.3	.0017	.0017	.0016	.0016	.0015	.0015	.0014	.0014	.0013	.0013
3.4	.0012	.0012	.0012	.0011	.0011	.0010	.0010	.0010	.0009	.0009
3.5	.0009	.0008	.0008	.0008	.0008	.0007	.0007	.0007	.0007	.0006
3.6	.0006	.0006	.0006	.0005	.0005	.0005	.0005	.0005	.0005	.0004
3.7	.0004	.0004	.0004	.0004	.0004	.0004	.0003	.0003	.0003	.0003
3.8	.0003	.0003	.0003	.0003	.0003	.0002	.0002	.0002	.0002	.0002
3.9	.0002	.0002	.0002	.0002	.0002	.0002	.0002	.0002	.0001	.0001

Appendix II

Areas Under the Standard Normal Curve from 0 to *z*

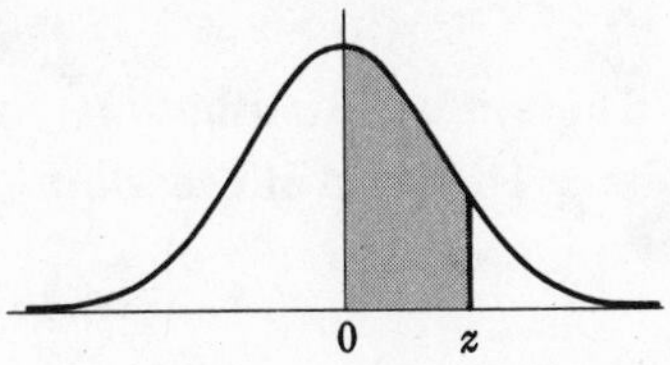

z	0	1	2	3	4	5	6	7	8	9
0.0	.0000	.0040	.0080	.0120	.0160	.0199	.0239	.0279	.0319	.0359
0.1	.0398	.0438	.0478	.0517	.0557	.0596	.0636	.0675	.0714	.0754
0.2	.0793	.0832	.0871	.0910	.0948	.0987	.1026	.1064	.1103	.1141
0.3	.1179	.1217	.1255	.1293	.1331	.1368	.1406	.1443	.1480	.1517
0.4	.1554	.1591	.1628	.1664	.1700	.1736	.1772	.1808	.1844	.1879
0.5	.1915	.1950	.1985	.2019	.2054	.2088	.2123	.2157	.2190	.2224
0.6	.2258	.2291	.2324	.2357	.2389	.2422	.2454	.2486	.2518	.2549
0.7	.2580	.2612	.2642	.2673	.2704	.2734	.2764	.2794	.2823	.2852
0.8	.2881	.2910	.2939	.2967	.2996	.3023	.3051	.3078	.3106	.3133
0.9	.3159	.3186	.3212	.3238	.3264	.3289	.3315	.3340	.3365	.3389
1.0	.3413	.3438	.3461	.3485	.3508	.3531	.3554	.3577	.3599	.3621
1.1	.3643	.3665	.3686	.3708	.3729	.3749	.3770	.3790	.3810	.3830
1.2	.3849	.3869	.3888	.3907	.3925	.3944	.3962	.3980	.3997	.4015
1.3	.4032	.4049	.4066	.4082	.4099	.4115	.4131	.4147	.4162	.4177
1.4	.4192	.4207	.4222	.4236	.4251	.4265	.4279	.4292	.4306	.4319
1.5	.4332	.4345	.4357	.4370	.4382	.4394	.4406	.4418	.4429	.4441
1.6	.4452	.4463	.4474	.4484	.4495	.4505	.4515	.4525	.4535	.4545
1.7	.4554	.4564	.4573	.4582	.4591	.4599	.4608	.4616	.4625	.4633
1.8	.4641	.4649	.4656	.4664	.4671	.4678	.4686	.4693	.4699	.4706
1.9	.4713	.4719	.4726	.4732	.4738	.4744	.4750	.4756	.4761	.4767
2.0	.4772	.4778	.4783	.4788	.4793	.4798	.4803	.4808	.4812	.4817
2.1	.4821	.4826	.4830	.4834	.4838	.4842	.4846	.4850	.4854	.4857
2.2	.4861	.4864	.4868	.4871	.4875	.4878	.4881	.4884	.4887	.4890
2.3	.4893	.4896	.4898	.4901	.4904	.4906	.4909	.4911	.4913	.4916
2.4	.4918	.4920	.4922	.4925	.4927	.4929	.4931	.4932	.4934	.4936
2.5	.4938	.4940	.4941	.4943	.4945	.4946	.4948	.4949	.4951	.4952
2.6	.4953	.4955	.4956	.4957	.4959	.4960	.4961	.4962	.4963	.4964
2.7	.4965	.4966	.4967	.4968	.4969	.4970	.4971	.4972	.4973	.4974
2.8	.4974	.4975	.4976	.4977	.4977	.4978	.4979	.4979	.4980	.4981
2.9	.4981	.4982	.4982	.4983	.4984	.4984	.4985	.4985	.4986	.4986
3.0	.4987	.4987	.4987	.4988	.4988	.4989	.4989	.4989	.4990	.4990
3.1	.4990	.4991	.4991	.4991	.4992	.4992	.4992	.4992	.4993	.4993
3.2	.4993	.4993	.4994	.4994	.4994	.4994	.4994	.4995	.4995	.4995
3.3	.4995	.4995	.4995	.4996	.4996	.4996	.4996	.4996	.4996	.4997
3.4	.4997	.4997	.4997	.4997	.4997	.4997	.4997	.4997	.4997	.4998
3.5	.4998	.4998	.4998	.4998	.4998	.4998	.4998	.4998	.4998	.4998
3.6	.4998	.4998	.4999	.4999	.4999	.4999	.4999	.4999	.4999	.4999
3.7	.4999	.4999	.4999	.4999	.4999	.4999	.4999	.4999	.4999	.4999
3.8	.4999	.4999	.4999	.4999	.4999	.4999	.4999	.4999	.4999	.4999
3.9	.5000	.5000	.5000	.5000	.5000	.5000	.5000	.5000	.5000	.5000

Appendix III

Percentile Values (t_p)
for
Student's t Distribution
with ν Degrees of Freedom
(shaded area = p)

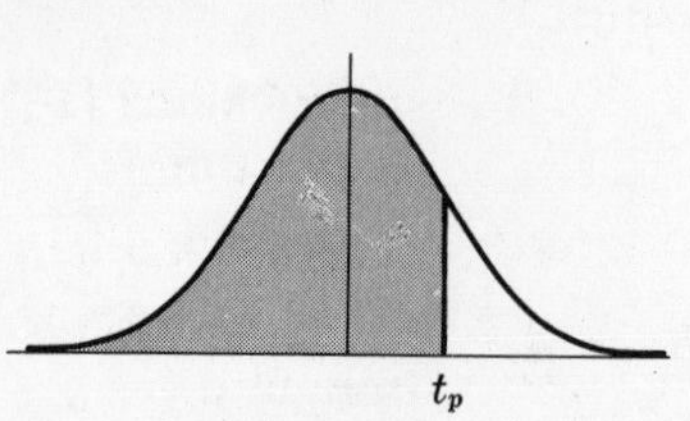

ν	$t_{.995}$	$t_{.99}$	$t_{.975}$	$t_{.95}$	$t_{.90}$	$t_{.80}$	$t_{.75}$	$t_{.70}$	$t_{.60}$	$t_{.55}$
1	63.66	31.82	12.71	6.31	3.08	1.376	1.000	.727	.325	.158
2	9.92	6.96	4.30	2.92	1.89	1.061	.816	.617	.289	.142
3	5.84	4.54	3.18	2.35	1.64	.978	.765	.584	.277	.137
4	4.60	3.75	2.78	2.13	1.53	.941	.741	.569	.271	.134
5	4.03	3.36	2.57	2.02	1.48	.920	.727	.559	.267	.132
6	3.71	3.14	2.45	1.94	1.44	.906	.718	.553	.265	.131
7	3.50	3.00	2.36	1.90	1.42	.896	.711	.549	.263	.130
8	3.36	2.90	2.31	1.86	1.40	.889	.706	.546	.262	.130
9	3.25	2.82	2.26	1.83	1.38	.883	.703	.543	.261	.129
10	3.17	2.76	2.23	1.81	1.37	.879	.700	.542	.260	.129
11	3.11	2.72	2.20	1.80	1.36	.876	.697	.540	.260	.129
12	3.06	2.68	2.18	1.78	1.36	.873	.695	.539	.259	.128
13	3.01	2.65	2.16	1.77	1.35	.870	.694	.538	.259	.128
14	2.98	2.62	2.14	1.76	1.34	.868	.692	.537	.258	.128
15	2.95	2.60	2.13	1.75	1.34	.866	.691	.536	.258	.128
16	2.92	2.58	2.12	1.75	1.34	.865	.690	.535	.258	.128
17	2.90	2.57	2.11	1.74	1.33	.863	.689	.534	.257	.128
18	2.88	2.55	2.10	1.73	1.33	.862	.688	.534	.257	.127
19	2.86	2.54	2.09	1.73	1.33	.861	.688	.533	.257	.127
20	2.84	2.53	2.09	1.72	1.32	.860	.687	.533	.257	.127
21	2.83	2.52	2.08	1.72	1.32	.859	.686	.532	.257	.127
22	2.82	2.51	2.07	1.72	1.32	.858	.686	.532	.256	.127
23	2.81	2.50	2.07	1.71	1.32	.858	.685	.532	.256	.127
24	2.80	2.49	2.06	1.71	1.32	.857	.685	.531	.256	.127
25	2.79	2.48	2.06	1.71	1.32	.856	.684	.531	.256	.127
26	2.78	2.48	2.06	1.71	1.32	.856	.684	.531	.256	.127
27	2.77	2.47	2.05	1.70	1.31	.855	.684	.531	.256	.127
28	2.76	2.47	2.05	1.70	1.31	.855	.683	.530	.256	.127
29	2.76	2.46	2.04	1.70	1.31	.854	.683	.530	.256	.127
30	2.75	2.46	2.04	1.70	1.31	.854	.683	.530	.256	.127
40	2.70	2.42	2.02	1.68	1.30	.851	.681	.529	.255	.126
60	2.66	2.39	2.00	1.67	1.30	.848	.679	.527	.254	.126
120	2.62	2.36	1.98	1.66	1.29	.845	.677	.526	.254	.126
∞	2.58	2.33	1.96	1.645	1.28	.842	.674	.524	.253	.126

Source: R. A. Fisher and F. Yates, *Statistical Tables for Biological, Agricultural and Medical Research* (5th edition), Table III, Oliver and Boyd Ltd., Edinburgh, by permission of the authors and publishers.

Appendix IV

Percentile Values (χ_p^2)
for
the Chi-Square Distribution
with ν Degrees of Freedom
(shaded area = p)

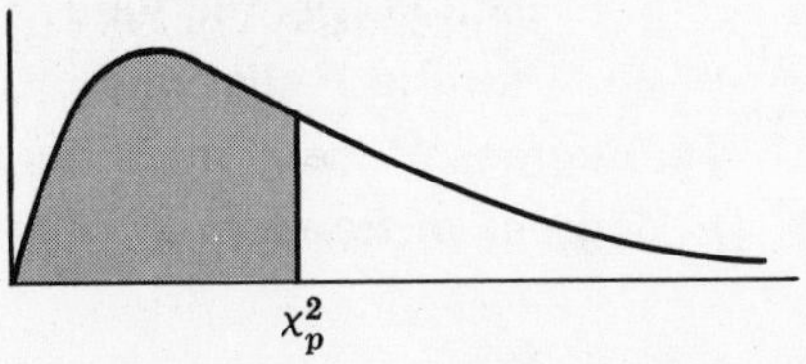

ν	$\chi^2_{.995}$	$\chi^2_{.99}$	$\chi^2_{.975}$	$\chi^2_{.95}$	$\chi^2_{.90}$	$\chi^2_{.75}$	$\chi^2_{.50}$	$\chi^2_{.25}$	$\chi^2_{.10}$	$\chi^2_{.05}$	$\chi^2_{.025}$	$\chi^2_{.01}$	$\chi^2_{.005}$
1	7.88	6.63	5.02	3.84	2.71	1.32	.455	.102	.0158	.0039	.0010	.0002	.0000
2	10.6	9.21	7.38	5.99	4.61	2.77	1.39	.575	.211	.103	.0506	.0201	.0100
3	12.8	11.3	9.35	7.81	6.25	4.11	2.37	1.21	.584	.352	.216	.115	.072
4	14.9	13.3	11.1	9.49	7.78	5.39	3.36	1.92	1.06	.711	.484	.297	.207
5	16.7	15.1	12.8	11.1	9.24	6.63	4.35	2.67	1.61	1.15	.831	.554	.412
6	18.5	16.8	14.4	12.6	10.6	7.84	5.35	3.45	2.20	1.64	1.24	.872	.676
7	20.3	18.5	16.0	14.1	12.0	9.04	6.35	4.25	2.83	2.17	1.69	1.24	.989
8	22.0	20.1	17.5	15.5	13.4	10.2	7.34	5.07	3.49	2.73	2.18	1.65	1.34
9	23.6	21.7	19.0	16.9	14.7	11.4	8.34	5.90	4.17	3.33	2.70	2.09	1.73
10	25.2	23.2	20.5	18.3	16.0	12.5	9.34	6.74	4.87	3.94	3.25	2.56	2.16
11	26.8	24.7	21.9	19.7	17.3	13.7	10.3	7.58	5.58	4.57	3.82	3.05	2.60
12	28.3	26.2	23.3	21.0	18.5	14.8	11.3	8.44	6.30	5.23	4.40	3.57	3.07
13	29.8	27.7	24.7	22.4	19.8	16.0	12.3	9.30	7.04	5.89	5.01	4.11	3.57
14	31.3	29.1	26.1	23.7	21.1	17.1	13.3	10.2	7.79	6.57	5.63	4.66	4.07
15	32.8	30.6	27.5	25.0	22.3	18.2	14.3	11.0	8.55	7.26	6.26	5.23	4.60
16	34.3	32.0	28.8	26.3	23.5	19.4	15.3	11.9	9.31	7.96	6.91	5.81	5.14
17	35.7	33.4	30.2	27.6	24.8	20.5	16.3	12.8	10.1	8.67	7.56	6.41	5.70
18	37.2	34.8	31.5	28.9	26.0	21.6	17.3	13.7	10.9	9.39	8.23	7.01	6.26
19	38.6	36.2	32.9	30.1	27.2	22.7	18.3	14.6	11.7	10.1	8.91	7.63	6.84
20	40.0	37.6	34.2	31.4	28.4	23.8	19.3	15.5	12.4	10.9	9.59	8.26	7.43
21	41.4	38.9	35.5	32.7	29.6	24.9	20.3	16.3	13.2	11.6	10.3	8.90	8.03
22	42.8	40.3	36.8	33.9	30.8	26.0	21.3	17.2	14.0	12.3	11.0	9.54	8.64
23	44.2	41.6	38.1	35.2	32.0	27.1	22.3	18.1	14.8	13.1	11.7	10.2	9.26
24	45.6	43.0	39.4	36.4	33.2	28.2	23.3	19.0	15.7	13.8	12.4	10.9	9.89
25	46.9	44.3	40.6	37.7	34.4	29.3	24.3	19.9	16.5	14.6	13.1	11.5	10.5
26	48.3	45.6	41.9	38.9	35.6	30.4	25.3	20.8	17.3	15.4	13.8	12.2	11.2
27	49.6	47.0	43.2	40.1	36.7	31.5	26.3	21.7	18.1	16.2	14.6	12.9	11.8
28	51.0	48.3	44.5	41.3	37.9	32.6	27.3	22.7	18.9	16.9	15.3	13.6	12.5
29	52.3	49.6	45.7	42.6	39.1	33.7	28.3	23.6	19.8	17.7	16.0	14.3	13.1
30	53.7	50.9	47.0	43.8	40.3	34.8	29.3	24.5	20.6	18.5	16.8	15.0	13.8
40	66.8	63.7	59.3	55.8	51.8	45.6	39.3	33.7	29.1	26.5	24.4	22.2	20.7
50	79.5	76.2	71.4	67.5	63.2	56.3	49.3	42.9	37.7	34.8	32.4	29.7	28.0
60	92.0	88.4	83.3	79.1	74.4	67.0	59.3	52.3	46.5	43.2	40.5	37.5	35.5
70	104.2	100.4	95.0	90.5	85.5	77.6	69.3	61.7	55.3	51.7	48.8	45.4	43.3
80	116.3	112.3	106.6	101.9	96.6	88.1	79.3	71.1	64.3	60.4	57.2	53.5	51.2
90	128.3	124.1	118.1	113.1	107.6	98.6	89.3	80.6	73.3	69.1	65.6	61.8	59.2
100	140.2	135.8	129.6	124.3	118.5	109.1	99.3	90.1	82.4	77.9	74.2	70.1	67.3

Source: Catherine M. Thompson, *Table of percentage points of the χ^2 distribution*, Biometrika, Vol. 32 (1941), by permission of the author and publisher.

Appendix V

95th Percentile Values
for the *F* Distribution
(ν_1 degrees of freedom in numerator)
(ν_2 degrees of freedom in denominator)

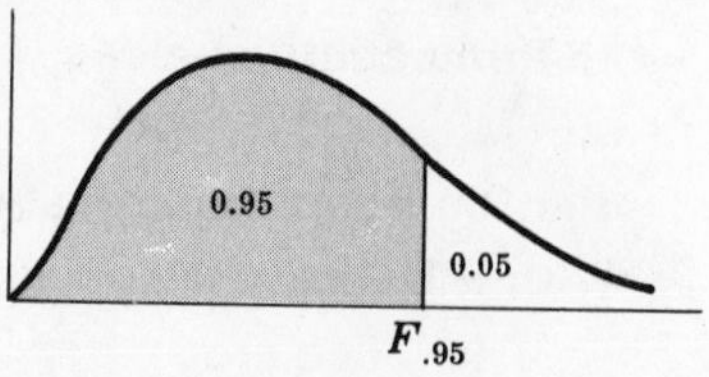

ν_2 \ ν_1	1	2	3	4	5	6	7	8	9	10	12	15	20	24	30	40	60	120	∞
1	161	200	216	225	230	234	237	239	241	242	244	246	248	249	250	251	252	253	254
2	18.5	19.0	19.2	19.2	19.3	19.3	19.4	19.4	19.4	19.4	19.4	19.4	19.4	19.5	19.5	19.5	19.5	19.5	19.5
3	10.1	9.55	9.28	9.12	9.01	8.94	8.89	8.85	8.81	8.79	8.74	8.70	8.66	8.64	8.62	8.59	8.57	8.55	8.53
4	7.71	6.94	6.59	6.39	6.26	6.16	6.09	6.04	6.00	5.96	5.91	5.86	5.80	5.77	5.75	5.72	5.69	5.66	5.63
5	6.61	5.79	5.41	5.19	5.05	4.95	4.88	4.82	4.77	4.74	4.68	4.62	4.56	4.53	4.50	4.46	4.43	4.40	4.37
6	5.99	5.14	4.76	4.53	4.39	4.28	4.21	4.15	4.10	4.06	4.00	3.94	3.87	3.84	3.81	3.77	3.74	3.70	3.67
7	5.59	4.74	4.35	4.12	3.97	3.87	3.79	3.73	3.68	3.64	3.57	3.51	3.44	3.41	3.38	3.34	3.30	3.27	3.23
8	5.32	4.46	4.07	3.84	3.69	3.58	3.50	3.44	3.39	3.35	3.28	3.22	3.15	3.12	3.08	3.04	3.01	2.97	2.93
9	5.12	4.26	3.86	3.63	3.48	3.37	3.29	3.23	3.18	3.14	3.07	3.01	2.94	2.90	2.86	2.83	2.79	2.75	2.71
10	4.96	4.10	3.71	3.48	3.33	3.22	3.14	3.07	3.02	2.98	2.91	2.85	2.77	2.74	2.70	2.66	2.62	2.58	2.54
11	4.84	3.98	3.59	3.36	3.20	3.09	3.01	2.95	2.90	2.85	2.79	2.72	2.65	2.61	2.57	2.53	2.49	2.45	2.40
12	4.75	3.89	3.49	3.26	3.11	3.00	2.91	2.85	2.80	2.75	2.69	2.62	2.54	2.51	2.47	2.43	2.38	2.34	2.30
13	4.67	3.81	3.41	3.18	3.03	2.92	2.83	2.77	2.71	2.67	2.60	2.53	2.46	2.42	2.38	2.34	2.30	2.25	2.21
14	4.60	3.74	3.34	3.11	2.96	2.85	2.76	2.70	2.65	2.60	2.53	2.46	2.39	2.35	2.31	2.27	2.22	2.18	2.13
15	4.54	3.68	3.29	3.06	2.90	2.79	2.71	2.64	2.59	2.54	2.48	2.40	2.33	2.29	2.25	2.20	2.16	2.11	2.07
16	4.49	3.63	3.24	3.01	2.85	2.74	2.66	2.59	2.54	2.49	2.42	2.35	2.28	2.24	2.19	2.15	2.11	2.06	2.01
17	4.45	3.59	3.20	2.96	2.81	2.70	2.61	2.55	2.49	2.45	2.38	2.31	2.23	2.19	2.15	2.10	2.06	2.01	1.96
18	4.41	3.55	3.16	2.93	2.77	2.66	2.58	2.51	2.46	2.41	2.34	2.27	2.19	2.15	2.11	2.06	2.02	1.97	1.92
19	4.38	3.52	3.13	2.90	2.74	2.63	2.54	2.48	2.42	2.38	2.31	2.23	2.16	2.11	2.07	2.03	1.98	1.93	1.88
20	4.35	3.49	3.10	2.87	2.71	2.60	2.51	2.45	2.39	2.35	2.28	2.20	2.12	2.08	2.04	1.99	1.95	1.90	1.84
21	4.32	3.47	3.07	2.84	2.68	2.57	2.49	2.42	2.37	2.32	2.25	2.18	2.10	2.05	2.01	1.96	1.92	1.87	1.81
22	4.30	3.44	3.05	2.82	2.66	2.55	2.46	2.40	2.34	2.30	2.23	2.15	2.07	2.03	1.98	1.94	1.89	1.84	1.78
23	4.28	3.42	3.03	2.80	2.64	2.53	2.44	2.37	2.32	2.27	2.20	2.13	2.05	2.01	1.96	1.91	1.86	1.81	1.76
24	4.26	3.40	3.01	2.78	2.62	2.51	2.42	2.36	2.30	2.25	2.18	2.11	2.03	1.98	1.94	1.89	1.84	1.79	1.73
25	4.24	3.39	2.99	2.76	2.60	2.49	2.40	2.34	2.28	2.24	2.16	2.09	2.01	1.96	1.92	1.87	1.82	1.77	1.71
26	4.23	3.37	2.98	2.74	2.59	2.47	2.39	2.32	2.27	2.22	2.15	2.07	1.99	1.95	1.90	1.85	1.80	1.75	1.69
27	4.21	3.35	2.96	2.73	2.57	2.46	2.37	2.31	2.25	2.20	2.13	2.06	1.97	1.93	1.88	1.84	1.79	1.73	1.67
28	4.20	3.34	2.95	2.71	2.56	2.45	2.36	2.29	2.24	2.19	2.12	2.04	1.96	1.91	1.87	1.82	1.77	1.71	1.65
29	4.18	3.33	2.93	2.70	2.55	2.43	2.35	2.28	2.22	2.18	2.10	2.03	1.94	1.90	1.85	1.81	1.75	1.70	1.64
30	4.17	3.32	2.92	2.69	2.53	2.42	2.33	2.27	2.21	2.16	2.09	2.01	1.93	1.89	1.84	1.79	1.74	1.68	1.62
40	4.08	3.23	2.84	2.61	2.45	2.34	2.25	2.18	2.12	2.08	2.00	1.92	1.84	1.79	1.74	1.69	1.64	1.58	1.51
60	4.00	3.15	2.76	2.53	2.37	2.25	2.17	2.10	2.04	1.99	1.92	1.84	1.75	1.70	1.65	1.59	1.53	1.47	1.39
120	3.92	3.07	2.68	2.45	2.29	2.18	2.09	2.02	1.96	1.91	1.83	1.75	1.66	1.61	1.55	1.50	1.43	1.35	1.25
∞	3.84	3.00	2.60	2.37	2.21	2.10	2.01	1.94	1.88	1.83	1.75	1.67	1.57	1.52	1.46	1.39	1.32	1.22	1.00

Source: E. S. Pearson and H. O. Hartley, *Biometrika Tables for Statisticians,* Vol. 2 (1972), Table 5, page 178, by permission.

Appendix VI

99th Percentile Values
for the *F* Distribution
(ν_1 degrees of freedom in numerator)
(ν_2 degrees of freedom in denominator)

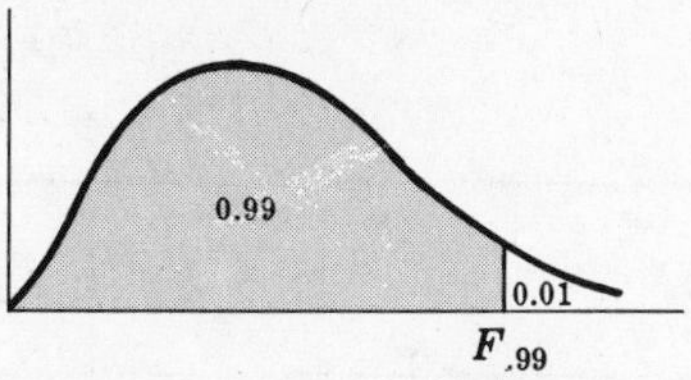

ν_2 \ ν_1	1	2	3	4	5	6	7	8	9	10	12	15	20	24	30	40	60	120	∞
1	4052	5000	5403	5625	5764	5859	5928	5981	6023	6056	6106	6157	6209	6235	6261	6287	6313	6339	6366
2	98.5	99.0	99.2	99.2	99.3	99.3	99.4	99.4	99.4	99.4	99.4	99.4	99.4	99.5	99.5	99.5	99.5	99.5	99.5
3	34.1	30.8	29.5	28.7	28.2	27.9	27.7	27.5	27.3	27.2	27.1	26.9	26.7	26.6	26.5	26.4	26.3	26.2	26.1
4	21.2	18.0	16.7	16.0	15.5	15.2	15.0	14.8	14.7	14.5	14.4	14.2	14.0	13.9	13.8	13.7	13.7	13.6	13.5
5	16.3	13.3	12.1	11.4	11.0	10.7	10.5	10.3	10.2	10.1	9.89	9.72	9.55	9.47	9.38	9.29	9.20	9.11	9.02
6	13.7	10.9	9.78	9.15	8.75	8.47	8.26	8.10	7.98	7.87	7.72	7.56	7.40	7.31	7.23	7.14	7.06	6.97	6.88
7	12.2	9.55	8.45	7.85	7.46	7.19	6.99	6.84	6.72	6.62	6.47	6.31	6.16	6.07	5.99	5.91	5.82	5.74	5.65
8	11.3	8.65	7.59	7.01	6.63	6.37	6.18	6.03	5.91	5.81	5.67	5.52	5.36	5.28	5.20	5.12	5.03	4.95	4.86
9	10.6	8.02	6.99	6.42	6.06	5.80	5.61	5.47	5.35	5.26	5.11	4.96	4.81	4.73	4.65	4.57	4.48	4.40	4.31
10	10.0	7.56	6.55	5.99	5.64	5.39	5.20	5.06	4.94	4.85	4.71	4.56	4.41	4.33	4.25	4.17	4.08	4.00	3.91
11	9.65	7.21	6.22	5.67	5.32	5.07	4.89	4.74	4.63	4.54	4.40	4.25	4.10	4.02	3.94	3.86	3.78	3.69	3.60
12	9.33	6.93	5.95	5.41	5.06	4.82	4.64	4.50	4.39	4.30	4.16	4.01	3.86	3.78	3.70	3.62	3.54	3.45	3.36
13	9.07	6.70	5.74	5.21	4.86	4.62	4.44	4.30	4.19	4.10	3.96	3.82	3.66	3.59	3.51	3.43	3.34	3.25	3.17
14	8.86	6.51	5.56	5.04	4.70	4.46	4.28	4.14	4.03	3.94	3.80	3.66	3.51	3.43	3.35	3.27	3.18	3.09	3.00
15	8.68	6.36	5.42	4.89	4.56	4.32	4.14	4.00	3.89	3.80	3.67	3.52	3.37	3.29	3.21	3.13	3.05	2.96	2.87
16	8.53	6.23	5.29	4.77	4.44	4.20	4.03	3.89	3.78	3.69	3.55	3.41	3.26	3.18	3.10	3.02	2.93	2.84	2.75
17	8.40	6.11	5.19	4.67	4.34	4.10	3.93	3.79	3.68	3.59	3.46	3.31	3.16	3.08	3.00	2.92	2.83	2.75	2.65
18	8.29	6.01	5.09	4.58	4.25	4.01	3.84	3.71	3.60	3.51	3.37	3.23	3.08	3.00	2.92	2.84	2.75	2.66	2.57
19	8.18	5.93	5.01	4.50	4.17	3.94	3.77	3.63	3.52	3.43	3.30	3.15	3.00	2.92	2.84	2.76	2.67	2.58	2.49
20	8.10	5.85	4.94	4.43	4.10	3.87	3.70	3.56	3.46	3.37	3.23	3.09	2.94	2.86	2.78	2.69	2.61	2.52	2.42
21	8.02	5.78	4.87	4.37	4.04	3.81	3.64	3.51	3.40	3.31	3.17	3.03	2.88	2.80	2.72	2.64	2.55	2.46	2.36
22	7.95	5.72	4.82	4.31	3.99	3.76	3.59	3.45	3.35	3.26	3.12	2.98	2.83	2.75	2.67	2.58	2.50	2.40	2.31
23	7.88	5.66	4.76	4.26	3.94	3.71	3.54	3.41	3.30	3.21	3.07	2.93	2.78	2.70	2.62	2.54	2.45	2.35	2.26
24	7.82	5.61	4.72	4.22	3.90	3.67	3.50	3.36	3.26	3.17	3.03	2.89	2.74	2.66	2.58	2.49	2.40	2.31	2.21
25	7.77	5.57	4.68	4.18	3.86	3.63	3.46	3.32	3.22	3.13	2.99	2.85	2.70	2.62	2.54	2.45	2.36	2.27	2.17
26	7.72	5.53	4.64	4.14	3.82	3.59	3.42	3.29	3.18	3.09	2.96	2.82	2.66	2.58	2.50	2.42	2.33	2.23	2.13
27	7.68	5.49	4.60	4.11	3.78	3.56	3.39	3.26	3.15	3.06	2.93	2.78	2.63	2.55	2.47	2.38	2.29	2.20	2.10
28	7.64	5.45	4.57	4.07	3.75	3.53	3.36	3.23	3.12	3.03	2.90	2.75	2.60	2.52	2.44	2.35	2.26	2.17	2.06
29	7.60	5.42	4.54	4.04	3.73	3.50	3.33	3.20	3.09	3.00	2.87	2.73	2.57	2.49	2.41	2.33	2.23	2.14	2.03
30	7.56	5.39	4.51	4.02	3.70	3.47	3.30	3.17	3.07	2.98	2.84	2.70	2.55	2.47	2.39	2.30	2.21	2.11	2.01
40	7.31	5.18	4.31	3.83	3.51	3.29	3.12	2.99	2.89	2.80	2.66	2.52	2.37	2.29	2.20	2.11	2.02	1.92	1.80
60	7.08	4.98	4.13	3.65	3.34	3.12	2.95	2.82	2.72	2.63	2.50	2.35	2.20	2.12	2.03	1.94	1.84	1.73	1.60
120	6.85	4.79	3.95	3.48	3.17	2.96	2.79	2.66	2.56	2.47	2.34	2.19	2.03	1.95	1.86	1.76	1.66	1.53	1.38
∞	6.63	4.61	3.78	3.32	3.02	2.80	2.64	2.51	2.41	2.32	2.18	2.04	1.88	1.79	1.70	1.59	1.47	1.32	1.00

Source: E. S. Pearson and H. O. Hartley, *Biometrika Tables for Statisticians*, Vol. 2 (1972), Table 5, page 180, by permission.

Appendix VII

Four-Place Common Logarithms

N	0	1	2	3	4	5	6	7	8	9	Proportional Parts 1	2	3	4	5	6	7	8	9
10	0000	0043	0086	0128	0170	0212	0253	0294	0334	0374	4	8	12	17	21	25	29	33	37
11	0414	0453	0492	0531	0569	0607	0645	0682	0719	0755	4	8	11	15	19	23	26	30	34
12	0792	0828	0864	0899	0934	0969	1004	1038	1072	1106	3	7	10	14	17	21	24	28	31
13	1139	1173	1206	1239	1271	1303	1335	1367	1399	1430	3	6	10	13	16	19	23	26	29
14	1461	1492	1523	1553	1584	1614	1644	1673	1703	1732	3	6	9	12	15	18	21	24	27
15	1761	1790	1818	1847	1875	1903	1931	1959	1987	2014	3	6	8	11	14	17	20	22	25
16	2041	2068	2095	2122	2148	2175	2201	2227	2253	2279	3	5	8	11	13	16	18	21	24
17	2304	2330	2355	2380	2405	2430	2455	2480	2504	2529	2	5	7	10	12	15	17	20	22
18	2553	2577	2601	2625	2648	2672	2695	2718	2742	2765	2	5	7	9	12	14	16	19	21
19	2788	2810	2833	2856	2878	2900	2923	2945	2967	2989	2	4	7	9	11	13	16	18	20
20	3010	3032	3054	3075	3096	3118	3139	3160	3181	3201	2	4	6	8	11	13	15	17	19
21	3222	3243	3263	3284	3304	3324	3345	3365	3385	3404	2	4	6	8	10	12	14	16	18
22	3424	3444	3464	3483	3502	3522	3541	3560	3579	3598	2	4	6	8	10	12	14	15	17
23	3617	3636	3655	3674	3692	3711	3729	3747	3766	3784	2	4	6	7	9	11	13	15	17
24	3802	3820	3838	3856	3874	3892	3909	3927	3945	3962	2	4	5	7	9	11	12	14	16
25	3979	3997	4014	4031	4048	4065	4082	4099	4116	4133	2	3	5	7	9	10	12	14	15
26	4150	4166	4183	4200	4216	4232	4249	4265	4281	4298	2	3	5	7	8	10	11	13	15
27	4314	4330	4346	4362	4378	4393	4409	4425	4440	4456	2	3	5	6	8	9	11	13	14
28	4472	4487	4502	4518	4533	4548	4564	4579	4594	4609	2	3	5	6	8	9	11	12	14
29	4624	4639	4654	4669	4683	4698	4713	4728	4742	4757	1	3	4	6	7	9	10	12	13
30	4771	4786	4800	4814	4829	4843	4857	4871	4886	4900	1	3	4	6	7	9	10	11	13
31	4914	4928	4942	4955	4969	4983	4997	5011	5024	5038	1	3	4	6	7	8	10	11	12
32	5051	5065	5079	5092	5105	5119	5132	5145	5159	5172	1	3	4	5	7	8	9	11	12
33	5185	5198	5211	5224	5237	5250	5263	5276	5289	5302	1	3	4	5	6	8	9	10	12
34	5315	5328	5340	5353	5366	5378	5391	5403	5416	5428	1	3	4	5	6	8	9	10	11
35	5441	5453	5465	5478	5490	5502	5514	5527	5539	5551	1	2	4	5	6	7	9	10	11
36	5563	5575	5587	5599	5611	5623	5635	5647	5658	5670	1	2	4	5	6	7	8	10	11
37	5682	5694	5705	5717	5729	5740	5752	5763	5775	5786	1	2	3	5	6	7	8	9	10
38	5798	5809	5821	5832	5843	5855	5866	5877	5888	5899	1	2	3	5	6	7	8	9	10
39	5911	5922	5933	5944	5955	5966	5977	5988	5999	6010	1	2	3	4	5	7	8	9	10
40	6021	6031	6042	6053	6064	6075	6085	6096	6107	6117	1	2	3	4	5	6	8	9	10
41	6128	6138	6149	6160	6170	6180	6191	6201	6212	6222	1	2	3	4	5	6	7	8	9
42	6232	6243	6253	6263	6274	6284	6294	6304	6314	6325	1	2	3	4	5	6	7	8	9
43	6335	6345	6355	6365	6375	6385	6395	6405	6415	6425	1	2	3	4	5	6	7	8	9
44	6435	6444	6454	6464	6474	6484	6493	6503	6513	6522	1	2	3	4	5	6	7	8	9
45	6532	6542	6551	6561	6571	6580	6590	6599	6609	6618	1	2	3	4	5	6	7	8	9
46	6628	6637	6646	6656	6665	6675	6684	6693	6702	6712	1	2	3	4	5	6	7	7	8
47	6721	6730	6739	6749	6758	6767	6776	6785	6794	6803	1	2	3	4	5	5	6	7	8
48	6812	6821	6830	6839	6848	6857	6866	6875	6884	6893	1	2	3	4	4	5	6	7	8
49	6902	6911	6920	6928	6937	6946	6955	6964	6972	6981	1	2	3	4	4	5	6	7	8
50	6990	6998	7007	7016	7024	7033	7042	7050	7059	7067	1	2	3	3	4	5	6	7	8
51	7076	7084	7093	7101	7110	7118	7126	7135	7143	7152	1	2	3	3	4	5	6	7	8
52	7160	7168	7177	7185	7193	7202	7210	7218	7226	7235	1	2	2	3	4	5	6	7	7
53	7243	7251	7259	7267	7275	7284	7292	7300	7308	7316	1	2	2	3	4	5	6	6	7
54	7324	7332	7340	7348	7356	7364	7372	7380	7388	7396	1	2	2	3	4	5	6	6	7
N	0	1	2	3	4	5	6	7	8	9	1	2	3	4	5	6	7	8	9

Four-Place Common Logarithms (continued)

N	0	1	2	3	4	5	6	7	8	9	Proportional Parts 1	2	3	4	5	6	7	8	9
55	7404	7412	7419	7427	7435	7443	7451	7459	7466	7474	1	2	2	3	4	5	5	6	7
56	7482	7490	7497	7505	7513	7520	7528	7536	7543	7551	1	2	2	3	4	5	5	6	7
57	7559	7566	7574	7582	7589	7597	7604	7612	7619	7627	1	2	2	3	4	5	5	6	7
58	7634	7642	7649	7657	7664	7672	7679	7686	7694	7701	1	1	2	3	4	4	5	6	7
59	7709	7716	7723	7731	7738	7745	7752	7760	7767	7774	1	1	2	3	4	4	5	6	7
60	7782	7789	7796	7803	7810	7818	7825	7832	7839	7846	1	1	2	3	4	4	5	6	6
61	7853	7860	7868	7875	7882	7889	7896	7903	7910	7917	1	1	2	3	4	4	5	6	6
62	7924	7931	7938	7945	7952	7959	7966	7973	7980	7987	1	1	2	3	3	4	5	6	6
63	7993	8000	8007	8014	8021	8028	8035	8041	8048	8055	1	1	2	3	3	4	5	5	6
64	8062	8069	8075	8082	8089	8096	8102	8109	8116	8122	1	1	2	3	3	4	5	5	6
65	8129	8136	8142	8149	8156	8162	8169	8176	8182	8189	1	1	2	3	3	4	5	5	6
66	8195	8202	8209	8215	8222	8228	8235	8241	8248	8254	1	1	2	3	3	4	5	5	6
67	8261	8267	8274	8280	8287	8293	8299	8306	8312	8319	1	1	2	3	3	4	5	5	6
68	8325	8331	8338	8344	8351	8357	8363	8370	8376	8382	1	1	2	3	3	4	4	5	6
69	8388	8395	8401	8407	8414	8420	8426	8432	8439	8445	1	1	2	2	3	4	4	5	6
70	8451	8457	8463	8470	8476	8482	8488	8494	8500	8506	1	1	2	2	3	4	4	5	6
71	8513	8519	8525	8531	8537	8543	8549	8555	8561	8567	1	1	2	2	3	4	4	5	5
72	8573	8579	8585	8591	8597	8603	8609	8615	8621	8627	1	1	2	2	3	4	4	5	5
73	8633	8639	8645	8651	8657	8663	8669	8675	8681	8686	1	1	2	2	3	4	4	5	5
74	8692	8698	8704	8710	8716	8722	8727	8733	8739	8745	1	1	2	2	3	4	4	5	5
75	8751	8756	8762	8768	8774	8779	8785	8791	8797	8802	1	1	2	2	3	3	4	5	5
76	8808	8814	8820	8825	8831	8837	8842	8848	8854	8859	1	1	2	2	3	3	4	5	5
77	8865	8871	8876	8882	8887	8893	8899	8904	8910	8915	1	1	2	2	3	3	4	4	5
78	8921	8927	8932	8938	8943	8949	8954	8960	8965	8971	1	1	2	2	3	3	4	4	5
79	8976	8982	8987	8993	8998	9004	9009	9015	9020	9025	1	1	2	2	3	3	4	4	5
80	9031	9036	9042	9047	9053	9058	9063	9069	9074	9079	1	1	2	2	3	3	4	4	5
81	9085	9090	9096	9101	9106	9112	9117	9122	9128	9133	1	1	2	2	3	3	4	4	5
82	9138	9143	9149	9154	9159	9165	9170	9175	9180	9186	1	1	2	2	3	3	4	4	5
83	9191	9196	9201	9206	9212	9217	9222	9227	9232	9238	1	1	2	2	3	3	4	4	5
84	9243	9248	9253	9258	9263	9269	9274	9279	9284	9289	1	1	2	2	3	3	4	4	5
85	9294	9299	9304	9309	9315	9320	9325	9330	9335	9340	1	1	2	2	3	3	4	4	5
86	9345	9350	9355	9360	9365	9370	9375	9380	9385	9390	1	1	2	2	3	3	4	4	5
87	9395	9400	9405	9410	9415	9420	9425	9430	9435	9440	0	1	1	2	2	3	3	4	4
88	9445	9450	9455	9460	9465	9469	9474	9479	9484	9489	0	1	1	2	2	3	3	4	4
89	9494	9499	9504	9509	9513	9518	9523	9528	9533	9538	0	1	1	2	2	3	3	4	4
90	9542	9547	9552	9557	9562	9566	9571	9576	9581	9586	0	1	1	2	2	3	3	4	4
91	9590	9595	9600	9605	9609	9614	9619	9624	9628	9633	0	1	1	2	2	3	3	4	4
92	9638	9643	9647	9652	9657	9661	9666	9671	9675	9680	0	1	1	2	2	3	3	4	4
93	9685	9689	9694	9699	9703	9708	9713	9717	9722	9727	0	1	1	2	2	3	3	4	4
94	9731	9736	9741	9745	9750	9754	9759	9763	9768	9773	0	1	1	2	2	3	3	4	4
95	9777	9782	9786	9791	9795	9800	9805	9809	9814	9818	0	1	1	2	2	3	3	4	4
96	9823	9827	9832	9836	9841	9845	9850	9854	9859	9863	0	1	1	2	2	3	3	4	4
97	9868	9872	9877	9881	9886	9890	9894	9899	9903	9908	0	1	1	2	2	3	3	4	4
98	9912	9917	9921	9926	9930	9934	9939	9943	9948	9952	0	1	1	2	2	3	3	4	4
99	9956	9961	9965	9969	9974	9978	9983	9987	9991	9996	0	1	1	2	2	3	3	3	4
N	0	1	2	3	4	5	6	7	8	9	1	2	3	4	5	6	7	8	9

Appendix VIII

Values of $e^{-\lambda}$

$(0 < \lambda < 1)$

λ	0	1	2	3	4	5	6	7	8	9
0.0	1.0000	.9900	.9802	.9704	.9608	.9512	.9418	.9324	.9231	.9139
0.1	.9048	.8958	.8869	.8781	.8694	.8607	.8521	.8437	.8353	.8270
0.2	.8187	.8106	.8025	.7945	.7866	.7788	.7711	.7634	.7558	.7483
0.3	.7408	.7334	.7261	.7189	.7118	.7047	.6977	.6907	.6839	.6771
0.4	.6703	.6636	.6570	.6505	.6440	.6376	.6313	.6250	.6188	.6126
0.5	.6065	.6005	.5945	.5886	.5827	.5770	.5712	.5655	.5599	.5543
0.6	.5488	.5434	.5379	.5326	.5273	.5220	.5169	.5117	.5066	.5016
0.7	.4966	.4916	.4868	.4819	.4771	.4724	.4677	.4630	.4584	.4538
0.8	.4493	.4449	.4404	.4360	.4317	.4274	.4232	.4190	.4148	.4107
0.9	.4066	.4025	.3985	.3946	.3906	.3867	.3829	.3791	.3753	.3716

$(\lambda = 1, 2, 3, \ldots, 10)$

λ	1	2	3	4	5	6	7	8	9	10
$e^{-\lambda}$	.36788	.13534	.04979	.01832	.006738	.002479	.000912	.000335	.000123	.000045

Note: To obtain values of $e^{-\lambda}$ for other values of λ, use the laws of exponents.

Example: $e^{-3.48} = (e^{-3.00})(e^{-0.48}) = (0.04979)(0.6188) = 0.03081$.

Appendix IX

Random Numbers

51772	74640	42331	29044	46621	62898	93582	04186	19640	87056
24033	23491	83587	06568	21960	21387	76105	10863	97453	90581
45939	60173	52078	25424	11645	55870	56974	37428	93507	94271
30586	02133	75797	45406	31041	86707	12973	17169	88116	42187
03585	79353	81938	82322	96799	85659	36081	50884	14070	74950
64937	03355	95863	20790	65304	55189	00745	65253	11822	15804
15630	64759	51135	98527	62586	41889	25439	88036	24034	67283
09448	56301	57683	30277	94623	85418	68829	06652	41982	49159
21631	91157	77331	60710	52290	16835	48653	71590	16159	14676
91097	17480	29414	06829	87843	28195	27279	47152	35683	47280
50532	25496	95652	42457	73547	76552	50020	24819	52984	76168
07136	40876	79971	54195	25708	51817	36732	72484	94923	75936
27989	64728	10744	08396	56242	90985	28868	99431	50995	20507
85184	73949	36601	46253	00477	25234	09908	36574	72139	70185
54398	21154	97810	36764	32869	11785	55261	59009	38714	38723
65544	34371	09591	07839	58892	92843	72828	91341	84821	63886
08263	65952	85762	64236	39238	18776	84303	99247	46149	03229
39817	67906	48236	16057	81812	15815	63700	85915	19219	45943
62257	04077	79443	95203	02479	30763	92486	54083	23631	05825
53298	90276	62545	21944	16530	03878	07516	95715	02526	33537

Appendix X

SAMPLE Screens From The Companion *Schaum's Electronic Tutor*

This book has a companion *Schaum's Electronic Tutor* which uses Mathcad® and is designed to help you learn the subject matter more readily. The *Electronic Tutor* uses the LIVE-MATH environment of Mathcad technical calculation software to give you on-screen access to approximately 100 representative solved problems from this book, together with summaries of key theoretical points and electronic cross-referencing and hyperlinking. The following pages reproduce a representative sample of screens from the *Electronic Tutor* and will help you understand the powerful capabilities of this electronic learning tool. Compare these screens with the associated solved problems from this book (the corresponding page numbers are listed at the start of each problem) to see how one complements the other.

In the companion *Schaum's Electronic Tutor*, you'll find all related text, diagrams, and equations for a particular solved problem together on your computer screen. As you can see on the following pages, all the math appears in familiar notation, including units. The format differences you may notice between the printed *Schaum's Outline* and the *Electronic Tutor* are designed to encourage your interaction with the material or show you alternate ways to solve challenging problems.

As you view the following pages, keep in mind that every number, formula, and graph shown ***is completely interactive when viewed on the computer screen.*** You can change the starting parameters of a problem and watch as new output graphs are calculated before your eyes; you can change any equation and immediately see the effect of the numerical calculations on the solution. Every equation, graph, and number you see is available for experimentation. Each adapted solved problem becomes a "live" worksheet you can modify to solve dozens of related problems. The companion *Electronic Tutor* thus will help you to learn and retain the material taught in this book and you can also use it as a working problem-solving tool.

The Mathcad icon shown on the right is printed throughout this *Schaum's Outline* to indicate which problems are found in the *Electronic Tutor.*

For more information about the companion *Electronic Tutor,* including system requirements, please see the back cover.

® Mathcad is a registered trademark of MathSoft, Inc.

Frequency Distributions, Histograms, and Frequency Polygons

(Schaum's Statistics, 2nd Ed., Solved Problems 2.8 and 2.9, pp. 45-46)

Problem 2.8

Also see Problems 2.4, 2.6, and 2.10 (all in print version)

In the following table the weights of 40 male students at State University are recorded to the nearest pound. Construct a frequency distribution.

$$\mathbf{WEIGHTS} := \begin{bmatrix} 138 & 164 & 150 & 132 & 144 & 125 & 149 & 157 \\ 146 & 158 & 140 & 147 & 136 & 148 & 152 & 144 \\ 168 & 126 & 138 & 176 & 163 & 119 & 154 & 165 \\ 146 & 173 & 142 & 147 & 135 & 153 & 140 & 135 \\ 161 & 145 & 135 & 142 & 150 & 156 & 145 & 128 \end{bmatrix}$$

Solution

Before we begin, to make things a bit easier, we'll pool the rows and columns of the data matrix into a single data vector w.

$r := \text{rows}(\mathbf{WEIGHTS})$ $\qquad c := \text{cols}(\mathbf{WEIGHTS})$

$k := 0 .. r \cdot c - 1$ where $r \cdot c = 40$

$$\mathbf{w}_k := \mathbf{WEIGHTS}_{\text{floor}\left(\frac{k}{c}\right), \text{mod}(k, c)}$$

To construct a frequency distribution, we'll need to form class intervals. The number of intervals,

$$\text{n\_intervals} = 12$$

is defined globally below in Problem 2.9. As we'll see there, changing this number can affect the shape of the distribution.

An approximate size for each interval can be obtained by dividing the range of the data

$\text{range} := \max(\mathbf{w}) - \min(\mathbf{w})$ $\qquad \text{range} = 57$

by the number of intervals,

$\text{approx\_class\_size} := \dfrac{\text{range}}{\text{n\_intervals}}$ $\qquad \text{approx\_class\_size} = 4.75$

Converting to an integer,

$class\_size := ceil(approx\_class\_size) \qquad class\_size = 5$

None of the interval boundaries should coincide with the actual data. Since the data are all integers, then, we can define the boundaries as noninteger values.

$lowest\_boundary := min(\mathbf{w}) - 1.5$

$\mathbf{boundaries}_0 := lowest\_boundary$

$i := 1 .. n\_intervals$

$\mathbf{boundaries}_i := \mathbf{boundaries}_{i-1} + class\_size$

$$\mathbf{boundaries} = \begin{bmatrix} 117.5 \\ 122.5 \\ 127.5 \\ 132.5 \\ 137.5 \\ 142.5 \\ 147.5 \\ 152.5 \\ 157.5 \\ 162.5 \\ 167.5 \\ 172.5 \\ 177.5 \end{bmatrix}$$

If both of the conditional expressions

$(min(\mathbf{boundaries}) < min(\mathbf{w})) = 1$

$(max(\mathbf{boundaries}) > max(\mathbf{w})) = 1$

where $min(\mathbf{w}) = 119 \quad max(\mathbf{w}) = 176$

return a value of 1, we'll know that all of the data are included within the boundaries.

The first two columns of our frequency distribution will contain the lower and upper class limits, respectively:

$j := 0 .. n\_intervals - 1$

$\mathbf{Freq\_dist}_{j,0} := ceil\left(\mathbf{boundaries}_j\right) \qquad \mathbf{Freq\_dist}_{j,1} := floor\left(\mathbf{boundaries}_{j+1}\right)$

From these we can calculate the class marks,

$$\mathbf{marks}_j := \frac{\mathbf{Freq\_dist}_{j,0} + \mathbf{Freq\_dist}_{j,1}}{2}$$

$$\mathbf{Freq\_dist} = \begin{bmatrix} 118 & 122 \\ 123 & 127 \\ 128 & 132 \\ 133 & 137 \\ 138 & 142 \\ 143 & 147 \\ 148 & 152 \\ 153 & 157 \\ 158 & 162 \\ 163 & 167 \\ 168 & 172 \\ 173 & 177 \end{bmatrix} \qquad \mathbf{marks} = \begin{bmatrix} 120 \\ 125 \\ 130 \\ 135 \\ 140 \\ 145 \\ 150 \\ 155 \\ 160 \\ 165 \\ 170 \\ 175 \end{bmatrix}$$

The last column of the frequency distribution will consist of a tally of scores falling between the corresponding class boundaries. Using Mathcad's histogram function,

$\mathbf{tally} := \text{hist}(\mathbf{boundaries}, \mathbf{w})$

$\mathbf{Freq\_dist}^{\langle 2 \rangle} := \mathbf{tally}$

If all of the data have been included, the sum of the tallies

$$\sum \mathbf{tally} = 40$$

should equal the sample size,

$$\text{rows}(\mathbf{w}) = 40$$

$$\mathbf{Freq\_dist} = \begin{bmatrix} 118 & 122 & 1 \\ 123 & 127 & 2 \\ 128 & 132 & 2 \\ 133 & 137 & 4 \\ 138 & 142 & 6 \\ 143 & 147 & 8 \\ 148 & 152 & 5 \\ 153 & 157 & 4 \\ 158 & 162 & 2 \\ 163 & 167 & 3 \\ 168 & 172 & 1 \\ 173 & 177 & 2 \end{bmatrix}$$

Extensions

For any given set of data, there are many different frequency distributions that will fit. Try changing the value of

lowest_boundary

defined above. Can you find values that will *not* include all of the data? Remember to watch both conditional statements. You can also experiment by increasing or decreasing the definition of

class_size

You can make a relative frequency distribution by a simple alteration of definitions:

$$\mathbf{Rel\_freq\_dist}^{\langle 0\rangle} := \mathbf{Freq\_dist}^{\langle 0\rangle}$$

$$\mathbf{Rel\_freq\_dist}^{\langle 1\rangle} := \mathbf{Freq\_dist}^{\langle 1\rangle}$$

$$\mathbf{Rel\_freq\_dist}^{\langle 2\rangle} := \frac{\mathbf{Freq\_dist}^{\langle 2\rangle}}{\sum \mathbf{tally}}$$

$$\mathbf{Freq\_dist} = \begin{bmatrix} 118 & 122 & 1 \\ 123 & 127 & 2 \\ 128 & 132 & 2 \\ 133 & 137 & 4 \\ 138 & 142 & 6 \\ 143 & 147 & 8 \\ 148 & 152 & 5 \\ 153 & 157 & 4 \\ 158 & 162 & 2 \\ 163 & 167 & 3 \\ 168 & 172 & 1 \\ 173 & 177 & 2 \end{bmatrix} \qquad \mathbf{Rel\_freq\_dist} = \begin{bmatrix} 118 & 122 & 0.025 \\ 123 & 127 & 0.05 \\ 128 & 132 & 0.05 \\ 133 & 137 & 0.1 \\ 138 & 142 & 0.15 \\ 143 & 147 & 0.2 \\ 148 & 152 & 0.125 \\ 153 & 157 & 0.1 \\ 158 & 162 & 0.05 \\ 163 & 167 & 0.075 \\ 168 & 172 & 0.025 \\ 173 & 177 & 0.05 \end{bmatrix}$$

What happens to the value of

$$\sum \mathbf{Rel\_freq\_dist}^{\langle 2\rangle} = 1$$

when all of the data are not included?

Problem 2.9

Also see Problem 2.10 (print version)

Construct (*a*) a histogram and (*b*) a frequency polygon for the weight distribution in Problem 2.8.

Solution

We can draw both the histogram and the frequency polygon on the same graph. So that the polygon will begin and end on the horizontal axis, as is customary, we'll need to add a value to the beginning and to the end of the tally vector:

$\mathbf{poly}_0 := 0$ $\mathbf{poly}_i := \mathbf{tally}_{i-1}$

$\mathbf{poly}_{n\_intervals+1} := 0$

The bars of the histogram will be centered on the class marks. To correspond with the polygon, we'll add a value to the beginning and to the end of the marks:

$\mathbf{m}_0 := \min(\mathbf{marks}) - \text{class\_size}$ $\mathbf{m}_i := \mathbf{marks}_{i-1}$

$\mathbf{m}_{n\_intervals+1} := \max(\mathbf{marks}) + \text{class\_size}$

$k := 0..\, n\_intervals + 1$

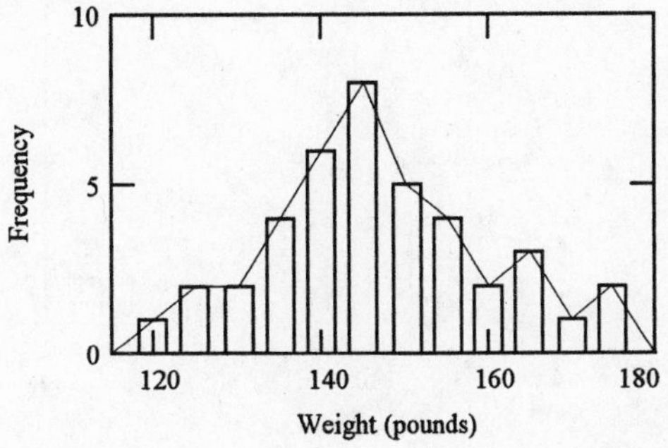

Extensions

How does changing the number of intervals affect the shape of a histogram? When you think of it, having too many intervals could very well defeat the purpose of grouping the data at all. On the other hand, having too few intervals could hide some prominent characteristics. You can explore these ideas by changing the value of

n_intervals

given below. For reference, the graph contains a histogram with 12 intervals. (Equations for this histogram appear on the screen to the right.) You'll want to notice whether the value of

$\sum$**tally**

equals 40. (For some small interval sizes, you may need to increase the value of

class_size

so that all of the data are included. See the **Extensions** to Problem 2.8 above.)

n_intervals ≡ 12 $\quad\quad$ $\sum$**tally** = 40

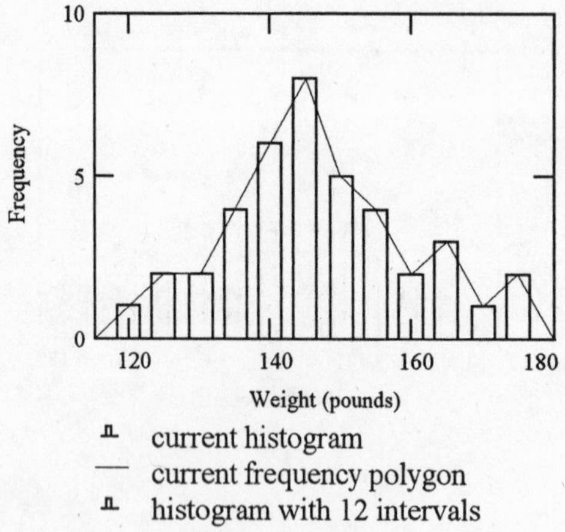

$$\textbf{Freq\_dist} = \begin{bmatrix} 118 & 122 & 1 \\ 123 & 127 & 2 \\ 128 & 132 & 2 \\ 133 & 137 & 4 \\ 138 & 142 & 6 \\ 143 & 147 & 8 \\ 148 & 152 & 5 \\ 153 & 157 & 4 \\ 158 & 162 & 2 \\ 163 & 167 & 3 \\ 168 & 172 & 1 \\ 173 & 177 & 2 \end{bmatrix}$$

Histograms, then, can sometimes be deceptive. Take a look at the following graph. The histogram with 12 intervals has been narrowed and stretched vertically so that the middle frequencies appear to be much larger than they are in relation to the others. What would happen if you used the cursor (in the form of an arrow) to flatten the graph and stretch it horizontally?

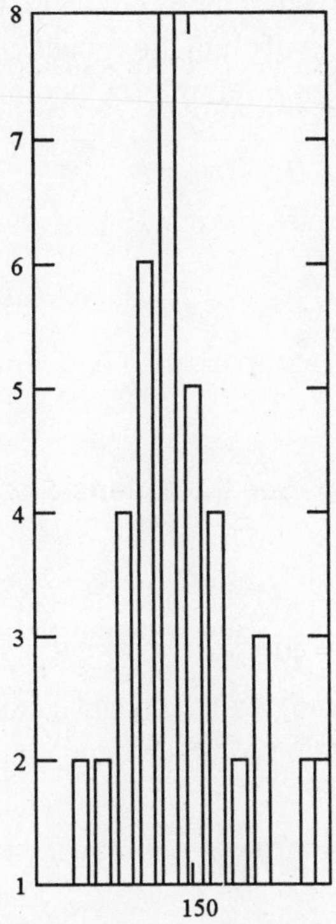

Sampling Distribution of Means

(Schaum's Statistics, 2nd Ed., Solved Problems 8.3 and 8.4 pp. 180-182)

Problem 8.3

Also see Problem 8.23 (print version)

Assume that the heights of 3000 male students at a university are normally distributed with mean 68.0 inches (in) and standard deviation 3.0 in. If 80 samples consisting of 25 students each are obtained, what would be the expected mean and standard deviation of the resulting sampling distribution of means if the sampling were done (*a*) with replacement and (*b*) without replacement?

Solution

The number of all possible samples of size 25 that could be taken from a group of 3000 students is

$3000^{25} = 8.473 \cdot 10^{86}$ when sampling with replacement, and

$$\frac{\left[\prod_{r=1}^{25} 3000 - r + 1\right]}{25!} = 4.941 \cdot 10^{61}$$ when sampling without replacement (See **Chapter 6**).

Since only 80 samples were taken, we have what's called an experimental distribution of the sample means.

(a) When sampling with replacement from a population with

$\mu := 68$ and $\sigma := 3$

the mean equals the population mean,

$$\mu = 68$$

and the standard error (or deviation) of the means equals

$$\frac{\sigma}{\sqrt{N}} \qquad \frac{\sigma}{\sqrt{25}} = 0.6$$

(b) When sampling without replacement, the mean remains the same,

$$\mu = 68$$

but the standard deviation equals

$$\frac{\sigma}{\sqrt{N}} \cdot \sqrt{\frac{Np - N}{Np - 1}} \qquad \frac{\sigma}{\sqrt{25}} \cdot \sqrt{\frac{3000 - 25}{3000 - 1}} = 0.598$$

Extensions

In the situation above, values for the standard deviation obtained from sampling both with and without replacement are very nearly the same. Of course this isn't always true. You can experiment by changing the sample size **N** and the population size **Np** given below. For instance, what happens when **N** gets smaller? Or when **Np** gets larger? Can you explain what happens when **N** equals **Np**, or when **N** equals 1?

$N := 25$

$Np := 3000$

with replacement: $\frac{\sigma}{\sqrt{N}} = 0.6$

without replacement: $\frac{\sigma}{\sqrt{N}} \cdot \sqrt{\frac{Np - N}{Np - 1}} = 0.598$

Notice that (for any given population size and value of σ), as the sample size increases, the standard deviations decrease. In the **Extensions** to Problem 8.4 below, we'll see how this fact affects the distribution of the sample means.

Problem 8.4

Also see Problem 8.25 (print version)

In how many samples of Problem 8.3 would you expect to find the mean (*a*) between 66.8 and 68.3 in and (*b*) less than 66.4 in?

Solution

(a)

We can solve this problem using basically the same techniques we learned in **Problem 7.23**. From Problem 8.3, we can take

$$\sigma\_xbar := 0.6$$

The desired proportion equals the area under the corresponding normal curve between the heights

$$H1 := 66.8 \quad \text{and} \quad H2 := 68.3$$

(indicated by vertical lines on the graph below. Equations for the graph appear on the screen to the right.).

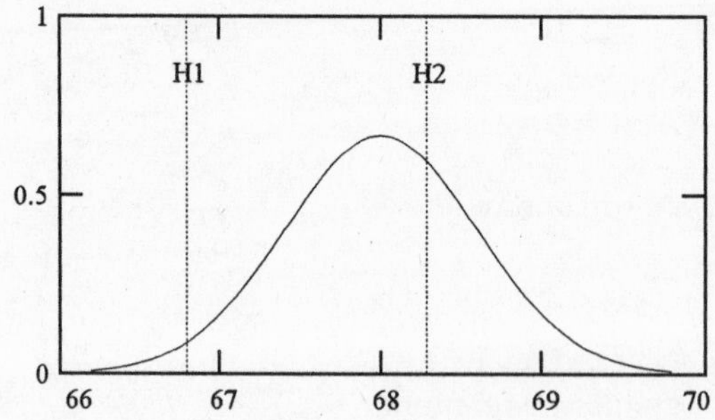

That is,

$$\text{Proportion} := \text{normal}(\mu, \sigma\_xbar, H2) - \text{normal}(\mu, \sigma\_xbar, H1)$$

$$\text{Proportion} = 0.6687$$

Note that here we used one of Mathcad's built-in functions rather than a table of standardized values. (You may want to review **Problem 7.23** to see why this is possible.)

The expected number of samples, then, can be found by

$$\text{floor}(80 \cdot \text{Proportion}) = 53$$

(b) The desired proportion equals the area under the corresponding normal curve to the left of the height

$$H := 66.4$$

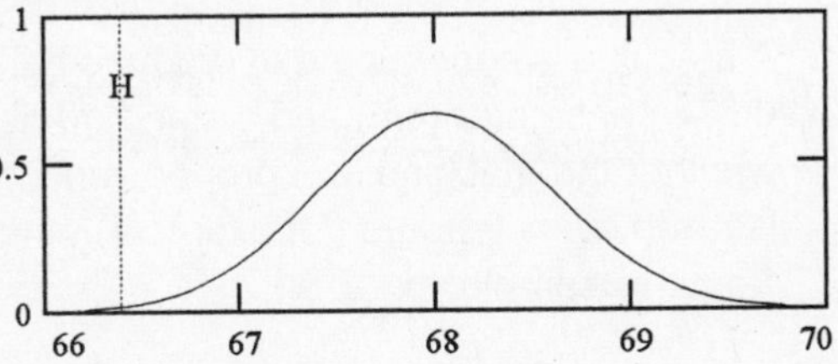

That is,

$$\text{Proportion\_b} := \text{normal}(\mu, \sigma\_\text{xbar}, H) \qquad \text{Proportion\_b} = 0.0038$$

so that the expected number of samples is

$$\text{floor}(80 \cdot \text{Proportion\_b}) = 0$$

Extensions Try changing the heights H1 H2 and H to obtain different expected values. In the Extension to Problem 8.3 above, we saw that an increase in the sample size (for a given population) causes a decrease in the standard deviation of the distribution of sample means. By increasing the value of **N** below, you can see how this affects both the graph of the corresponding sampling distribution and the corresponding proportion from part (*b*). For reference, a graph of the distribution for a sample of size 35 appears in blue.

$$N := 35 \qquad \sigma\_\text{xbar}(N) := \frac{\sigma}{\sqrt{N}} \cdot \sqrt{\frac{Np - N}{Np - 1}} \qquad \sigma\_\text{xbar}(N) = 0.504$$

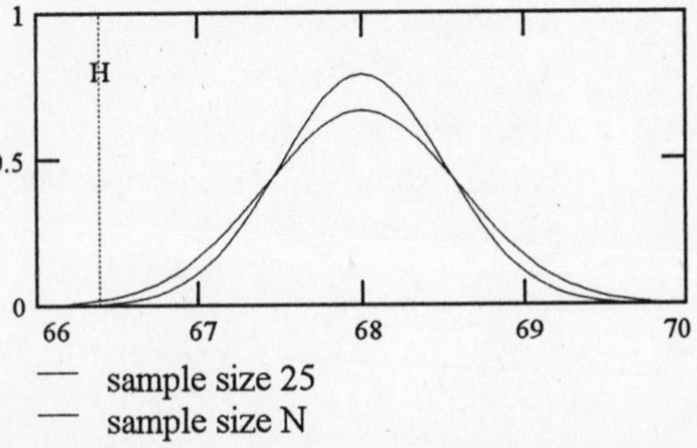

$$\text{Proportion\_b} := \text{normal}(\mu, \sigma\_\text{xbar}(N), H) \qquad \text{Proportion\_b} = 7.5363 \cdot 10^{-4}$$

Control Charts

(Schaum's Statistics, 2nd Ed., Solved Problem 10.16, pp. 221)

Problem 10.16

Also see Problem s 10.43 and 10.44 (both in print version)

A machine is constructed to produce ball bearings having a mean diameter of 0.574 centimeter (cm) and a standard deviation of 0.008 cm. To determine whether the machine is in proper working order, a sample of six ball bearings is taken every 2 hours (for example), and the mean diameter is computed from this sample.

(*a*) Design a decision rule whereby one can be fairly certain that the quality of the products is conforming to the required standards.
(*b*) Show how to graph the decision rule in part (a).

Solution

(a)

Assuming, for example, that the population of all ball bearing diameters being produced is infinite and normally distributed with

$$\mu := 0.574 \qquad \text{and} \qquad \sigma := 0.008$$

from the test statistic

$$z = \frac{\text{sample\_mean} - \mu}{\left(\frac{\sigma}{\sqrt{N}}\right)}$$

where $z = 3$ and $N = 6$ are defined globally below, we're

$$\text{cnorm}(z) - \text{cnorm}(-z) = 99.73 \cdot \%$$

confident that the sample mean must lie within the interval from

$$L := \mu - z \cdot \frac{\sigma}{\sqrt{N}} \qquad \text{to} \qquad U := \mu + z \cdot \frac{\sigma}{\sqrt{N}}$$

$$L = 0.564 \qquad U = 0.584$$

as shown on the graph,

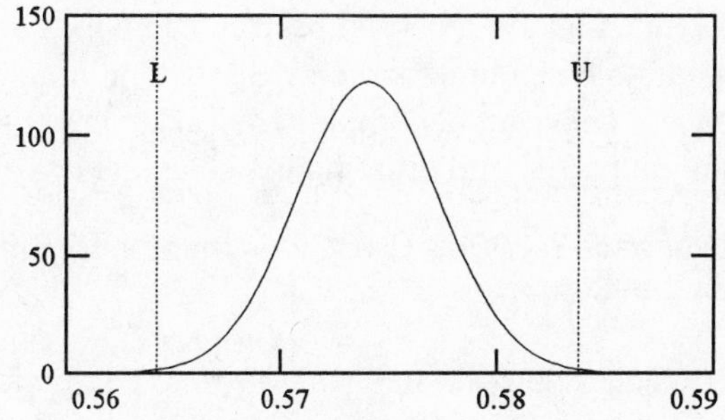

If, for any sample taken, the mean is outside this interval, we can be fairly certain that the machine is not in working order.

(b) We can keep track of the sampling process by creating a quality-control chart. An example of one appears in the **Extensions** to this problem. Each point on the chart represents the mean diameter of a sample of ball bearings. If a point appears outside the upper and lower confidence limits, we know that the machine should be inspected.

Extensions What would a trial run of this experiment look like? Should we increase the sample size? Or, perhaps, make the confidence range more narrow? Before answering these questions, let's actually simulate a few trials by creating several vectors of random numbers from the given normal distribution. (The number of samples, **num_samples**, and the sample size, **N**, are defined globally below.) Each vector will represent a random sample of ball bearing diameters. To generate the vectors, we'll use the built-in normal random number function, **gaussn**,

$i := 0 .. num\_samples - 1$

$\mathbf{random\_sample}^{\langle i \rangle} := \mu + \sigma \cdot gaussn(N)$

The sample means,

$$\mathbf{means}_i := \mathrm{mean}\left(\mathbf{random\_sample}^{\langle i \rangle}\right)$$

are plotted on the following graph. The upper and lower confidence limits appear as horizontal markers. Should the machine be inspected? Try creating a new set of samples by clicking in either the global definition of **N** or **num_samples**, and pressing the calculate key **F9**.

size of each sample: $N \equiv 6$ number of samples: $\mathrm{num\_samples} \equiv 25$

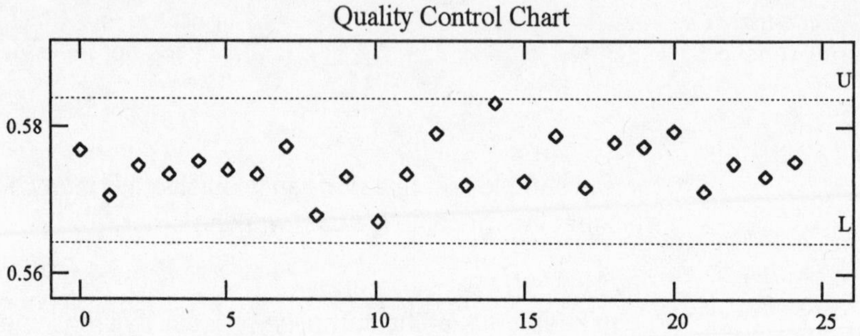

confidence limits: $L = 0.564$ $U = 0.584$

number of standard deviations from the mean: $z \equiv 3$

See if you can narrow the confidence range (by changing the value of **z**), so that at least one sample of ball bearings would be suspect. What happens when you change the sample size, or the number of samples?

Index

The following license agreement will apply if this Schaum's Outline contains a Schaum's Electronic Tutor.

The McGraw-Hill Companies, Inc. and MathSoft, Inc. - Schaum's Electronic Tutors; MathSoft, Inc--Mathcad Engine
License Agreement and Limited Warranty.

Both the program(s) (including all data and information contained therein) and the documentation are protected under applicable copyright laws. Your right to use the program(s) and the documentation are limited to the terms and conditions described herein.

Limited Non-Exclusive License
You May: (a) use the enclosed program(s) on a single computer; (b) physically transfer the program(s) from one computer to another provided that the program(s) are used on only one computer at a time, and that you remove any copies of the program(s) from the computer from which the program(s) are being transferred; (c) make copies of the program(s) solely for backup purposes. You must reproduce and include the copyright notice on a label on any back-up copy.

You May Not: (a) distribute copies of the program(s) or the documentation to others; (b) rent, lease or grant sublicenses or other rights to the program(s); (c) provide use of the program(s) in a computer service business, network, time-sharing, multiple CPU or multiple users arrangement without the prior written consent of MathSoft; (d) translate, decompile, reverse engineer or otherwise alter the program(s) or related documentation without the prior written consent of MathSoft.

Terms
Your license to use the program(s) and documentation will automatically terminate if you fail to comply with the terms of this Agreement. If this license is terminated you agree to destroy all copies of the program(s) and documentation.

Limited Warranty
MathSoft and McGraw-Hill warrant to the original licensee that the disk(s) on which the program(s) are recorded will be free from defects in materials and workmanship under normal use for a period of ninety (90) days from the date of purchase as evidenced by a copy of your receipt. If failure of the disk(s) has resulted from accident, abuse or misapplication of the product, then McGraw-Hill, MathSoft or third party Licensors shall have no responsibility to replace the disk(s) under this Limited Warranty.

This limited warranty and right of replacement is in lieu of, and you hereby waive, any and all other warranties both express and implied, including but not limited to warranties of merchantability and fitness for a particular purpose. The liability of McGraw-Hill, MathSoft or third party Licensors pursuant to this limited warranty shall be limited to the replacement of the defective disk(s), and in no event shall McGraw-Hill, MathSoft or third party Licensors be liable for incidental or consequential damages, including but not limited to loss of use, loss of profits, loss of data or data being rendered inaccurate, or losses sustained by third parties even if McGraw-Hill, MathSoft or third party Licensors have been advised of the possibility of such damages. McGraw-Hill and MathSoft make no representation or warranty that the results obtained will be successful or satisfy licensee's requirements, and McGraw-Hill and MathSoft shall have no liability for any errors or omissions in the programs or in the data and information contain therein. This warranty gives you specific legal rights which may vary from state to state. Some states do not allow the limitation or exclusion of liability for consequential damages, so the above limitation may not apply to you.

This License Agreement shall be governed by the laws of the Commonwealth of Massachusetts and shall inure to the benefit of McGraw-Hill, MathSoft, their respective successors, administrators, heirs and assigns of third party Licensors.